The Modern Coral Reef Aquarium

Svein A. Fosså · Alf Jacob Nilsen

———— Volume 3 ————

Harlequin Mantis Shrimp, *Odontodactylus scyllarus*
Photo: M. Kirschner

Credits:
All the photos, drawings, diagrams and tables are by the autors, except where otherwise stated in the captions.

Agents:

* Australia - ABS Technologies
              P. O. Box 697
              Stirling
              South Australia 5152
              Tel.: (61-8) 83 70 10 66
              Fax: (61-8) 83 70 10 68

* UK - Tropical Marine Centre Ltd.
         Solesbridge Lane
         Chorleywood
         Herforshire
         WD3 5SX England
         Tel.: 0 19 23 - 28 41 51
         Fax: 0 19 23 - 28 58 40

* Norway - NorZoo A/S
             Marken 4
             5017 Bergen
             Tel.: 55 31 11 21
             Fax: 55 96 07 28

* U.S.A. - CPR Aquatic, Inc.
             P.O. Box 1111
             3749 West End Road
             Arcata, CA 95521
             Tel.: (707) 826 - 96 36
             Fax: (707) 826 - 96 23
             Email: cpr@cprusa.com

          - Hollywood Import & Export, Inc.
             P.O. Box 220024 Hollywood
             FL 33022-0024
             Tel.: (954) 922 - 29 70
             Fax: (954) 926 - 54 76
             Email: aqualogusa@cs.com

The Modern Coral Reef Aquarium, Volume 3
First edition, 2000

Original title: "Korallrevsakvariet", © Svein A. Fosså/Alf Jacob Nilsen

Translation: U. E. Friese, St. Ives, NSW, Australia

Editors and layout: Dr. Dieter Brockmann, Mülheim, Germany, and
                    Werner Schmettkamp, Bornheim, Germany

Colour separations: Viscan Graphics, Singapore

Printed and bound by J.C.C. Bruns GmbH, Minden, Germany

ISBN 3-9288 19-28-3

Table of Contents

Chapter 5:
Comb Jellies, Entoprocts, Horseshoe Worms, Moss Animals, Lamp Shells, Water Bears, Sea Spiders, and Horseshoe Crabs . 161

A beautiful reefscape at Papua-New Guinea

Preface

The book series "The Modern Coral Reef Aquarium", and its forerunners in German and Swedish has engaged us now for more than 15 years since it was initiated during a study trip in the spring of 1984. During the span of this work we have been so lucky as to be allowed to visit and have discussions with aquarists and scientists in many countries, and we have studied coral reefs in their fantastic natural habitat. All in all these years have taught us a lot about aquarium keeping, coral reefs, reef science and people – for good and for bad. Generally it has been a great pleasure, however, and our enthusiasm for this project is – if possible – even larger now than it was when we started.

It is intriguing to note that several of those aquaria, which we held in high esteem back in 1984, would today possibly be regarded as complete disasters! If we go further back in time, even the majority of reef aquaria where nothing like the sort we see today. The progress in coral reef aquarium keeping has been tremendous, and unless you have been a part of development yourself, it will be very difficult to apprehend what really has happened in the incredibly short time span. Best of all, we have reason to believe that the future will bring even further progress. There are so many deeply involved aquarists, amateurs as well as professionals, who are striving to improve techniques in general husbandry, feeding, propagation, commercial scale breeding etc. that there is no reason whatsoever to believe that development has come to a halt. Quite on the contrary! We are eagerly looking forward to the next 15 years and expect that there will be the need for writing new aquarium books over and over again.

In this volume, an important section is our presentation of 43 selected international contemporary coral reef aquaria (chapter 7). We also look back in time and present some German tanks from the mid-eighties, where and when the modern concept of coral reef aquarium keeping was born. We would like to express our sincere thanks to all those aquarists that helped us with this presentation and we feel certain that our readers will get many ideas for their own tanks by studying this chapter.

This volume starts by looking back, not merely back in aquarium history, but way, way back in the earth's geological history to the time when the invertebrates arouse as a product of evolution. We continue with a closer look at the single-celled animals in chapter 2, a group of organisms that is really numerous in our aquaria. Many thanks to Robert Brons, deJong Marinelife B.V., Spijk, The Nederlands for proof-reading this chapter.

Chapter 3 deals with the most primitive of the invertebrate groups, the sponges of phylum Porifera. Many thanks to Dr. Rob van Soest, Instituut voor Systematiek en Populatiebiologie, Zoölogisch Museum, Universiteit van Amsterdam, Holland for identifying samples of sponges growing in reef aquaria and for proofreading the text.

Chapter 4 is a huge chapter dealing with many phyla grouped under the somewhat artificial title "Marine Worms". Here, more or less beautiful or horrifying worms are presented. Whether you like it or not, dear reader, it is a fact that worms are among the most common invertebrates in the reef aquarium. If you choose the open approach, you will probably also soon agree with us that they are very interesting aquarium inhabitants. The colourful and elegant Polyclad flatworms are presented with a unique photo-material and a few species of segmented worms, relatively new to science and not before presented to aquarists, are also shown in detail in this chapter. We would like to say "many thanks" to all those people that so kindly have helped us with this complex chapter either by looking at fixed worm-samples, studying photos or proofreading and correcting the manuscript. Without this help, the chapter would not nearly have become what it now is. Our good helpers include: Dr. Mary E. Petersen and Professor R. M. Kristensen, both of Zoologisk Museum, University of Copenhagen, Denmark; Dr. Greg Rouse, University of Sydney, Australia; Dr. Russell Hanley, Hanley Caswell and Associates, Kenmore, Australia; Dr. Lester Cannon, Queensland Museum, South Brisbane, Australia; Dr. Leslie Newman, University of Sunshine Coast, Maroochydore, Queensland, Australia; Dr. Phyllis

Knight-Jones, University College of Swansea, Dep. of Zoology, Swansea, UK; Professor Raymond Gibson; John Moores University, Liverpool, UK; Dr. Wolfgang Sterrer, Bermuda Aquarium Museum and Zoo, Bermuda and Dr. Harry ten Hove, Instituut voor Systematiek en Populatiebiologie, Zoölogisch Museum, Universiteit van Amsterdam, Holland.

Chapter 5 starts again with some retrospective looks at evolution. Here we present unique photos of fossil invertebrates from Ediacara, Australia. We continue by describing a series of minor phyla; amongst others the fascinating water bears of phylum Tardigrada. Professor R. M. Kristensen of the Zoological Museum, Copenhagen, Denmark – who has discovered no less than three new phyla – has kindly revised the text on this group and supplied indispensable drawings and photos. The sea spiders in the class Pycnogonida of phylum Arthropoda, is also dealt with in detail in chapter 5. This unique group is often overlooked, but appears quite frequently in marine aquaria. Many thanks to Dr. Frans Krapp of Museum Alexander Koenig, Bonn, Germany, who helped us with identification and revised the text. Also many thanks to Professor T. J. Hayward, University of Wales, Swansea, UK, who has identified photos of Bryozoa – another of the many groups discussed in chapter 5.

Chapter 6 is dedicated to an extensive discussion of the crustaceans. This large and important arthropod group, known scientifically as "Crustacea", is fairly well known and popular among aquarists. Despite the relative familiarity to aquarists, we hope that we have managed to incorporate some thought triggering ideas and new information here as well. We are sincerely thankful for assistance provided by Dr. L. B. Holthuis and Mr. Charles H. J. M. Fransen of Nationaal Natuurhistorisch Museum in Leiden, Netherlands for the Crustacea chapter. Furthermore, we are thankful to Dr. A. J. Bruce of Queensland Museum, South Brisbane, Australia, for making extensive comments on the section on shrimp.

The quality and variety of the photographic material is very important for a book such as this. As in previous volumes, many photographers have supplied us with excellent photos. It is utterly impossible to mention all photographers here, but some do deserve a special mention. We would like to express particular gratitude in this respect towards: Robert Brons, de Jong marinelife B.V., Spijk, The Nederlands, Scott W. Michael and Janine Cairns Michael, Lincoln, Nebraska, USA; Dr. Leslie Newman and Dr. Andrew Flowers, Queensland, Australia; Erling Svensen, Ocean Photo, Egersund, Norway – who all in principle has given us unlimited access to complete archives of incredible photos.

Many thanks for photos also to: Marj Awai, The Florida Aquarium, Tampa, Florida, USA; Professor David Bruton, Paleontological Museum, Oslo, Norway; Dr. Bruce Carlson, the Waikiki Aquarium, Honolulu, Hawaii, USA; Dr. Patrick L. Colin, Coral Reef Research Foundation, Koror, Palau; Michael Cufer, Oyster Bay, NSW, Australia; Dr. Peter Fenton, Royal Ontario Museum, Ontario Canada; Rolf Hansen, Nor Zoo, Bergen, Norway; Dr. I. Illich, Salzburg, Österreich; Ken Kates, Mollymook, NSW, Australia; Professor R. M. Kristensen, Zoological Museum, Copenhagen, Denmark; Torsten Luther, Rostock, Germany; Dr. Nevil S. Pledge, South Australian Museum, Adeleide, Australia; P. Schupp, Würzburg, Germany; Randle Robertson; Yoho-Burgess Shale Foundation, Field, Canada; Dr. Rob van Soest, Instituut voor Systematiek en Populatiebiologie, Zoölogisch Museum, Universiteit van Amsterdam, Holland; Joseph Yaiullo, Envirocon Coral Inc., New York, USA and Prof. Dr. Peter Wirtz; Universidade da Madeira, Funchal; Madeira, Portugal.

For various other help and support our thanks also go to: Dr. Peter Appel, GEUS, Copenhagen, Denmark; Dr. Phil Alderslade, N.T. Museums for Arts and Science, Darwin, Australia; Karl Ole Dahl, Bergen, Norway; Martin Moe Jr., Plantation, Florida, USA; Kjell Nagy, Flekkefjord, Norway; Christer Olsen, Stavanger Akvarieforretning, Stavanger, Norway; Jan Olsen, Aqua Design, Oldenburg, Germany; Julian Sprung and Daniel Ramirez, Two Little Fishies, Miami, Florida, USA and to Kenneth Olsen, Moss, Norway.

We would like to thank our translator Mr. U. E. Friese, St. Ives, NSW, Australia for a good hand with the hard work of translation. To our publisher, Birgit and Werner Schmettkamp and Dr. Dieter Brockmann in Birgit Schmettkamp Verlag (BSV), Bornheim, Germany, a most sincere thank for keeping up with us through several years. Without their efforts this project could never have been done.

Also warm thanks to our beloved wives, Kristin Hystad Fosså and Lise Nilsen who have watched us go on travels, taking photos, writing and discussing hour after hour on the phone. Strangely enough they still support us, but we are not quite sure whether they would want us to start on a new book series after this ...

Last, but certainly not least, many thanks to you, our readers! Without you there would certainly not have been neither books nor reef tanks!

Grimstad & Hidra in January 2000
Svein A. Fosså and Alf Jacob Nilsen

Chapter 1:

New Perspectives
for the
Modern Coral Reef Aquarium

The various phyla of invertebrate animals exhibit few mutual traits. Indeed, the only feature they do have in common, is the fact that they lack vertebrae. Many of the well known groups are closer related to vertebrate animals than to most of the other invertebrates. The designation "invertebrate" is, in effect, an artificial concept, which merely helps us to delineate animals, which are not closely related to us. It is rather easy for a marine aquarist to recognize the few vertebrates in his tank, because from among the large group of vertebrate animals, only the fishes are suited for a home aquarium. All other coral reef animals available from aquarium shops are invertebrates.

Although professional opinions vary among taxonomists, it can be realistically stated that invertebrates make up 36 animal phyla, containing at least 1 million known species (and beyond doubt, another large number of species which are yet to be discovered and/or described). More than 150,000 species are known from the sea, and there is no question that this number will increase, since our knowledge of the ocean, and especially about coral reefs, is continuously increasing.

In a book series, such as this, it is impossible to cover all groups of invertebrates to an equal extent. Because of their enormous significance as dominating animals on coral reefs, the phylum Cnidaria (corals, sea anemones, sea jellies, sea pens and related forms) has been described separately in Volume 2. In order to grant similar prominence to other important invertebrates, we have deemed it to be necessary to dedicate two Volumes (Volume 3 and Volume 4) to the remaining phyla.

Some aquarists may raise the question, why it is important for him or her, to deal with small, strange and obscure groups, such as the majority of exotic worm phyla, the sponges, the tunicates or sea spiders? Our answer is simple: the coral reef aquarium must also be an educational tool for gaining knowledge and for deepening the understanding and appreciation of coral reef biology in the broadest sense. This is the most significant potential of the coral reef aquarium and its greatest asset. In essence then, a coral reef aquarium is very much more than a portrait of exotic forms and colours.

For an aquarists to develop further, to better understand and to enjoy his hobby, as well as to appreciate the importance and value of the many forms of life on a reef and in a coral reef aquarium, he or she needs some relevant background knowledge. This is the main reason for us to discuss especially also those invertebrates at length, which - when viewed only superficially - appear to have little aquarium value. Consequently, certain topics are sometimes discussed at great length, well beyond what may be considered as important by some aquarists. On the other hand, we also provide detailed information summaries (species fact pages) of invertebrate species which are of particular importance or fascination to marine aquarists. The abbreviations used in these summaries (fact pages) are as follows:

GA: General aquarium suitability,
SE: Sensitivity,
CO: Compatibility with other animals.

The respective assessments for coral reef aquarium purposes are indicated by the following symbols:

+ = positive,
+/- = more or less positive,
- = negative,
0 = unknown.

Beyond that, there are numerous literature references listed to provide further reading.

To the left: A coral reef is inhabited by many colourful and fascinating animals; the majority are invertebrates. Corals are the dominant group, yet close examination also reveals the presence of many other organisms, such as sponges, marine worms, molluscs, sea stars, sea urchins, tunicates, as well as crabs, prawns and shrimps. This picture shows the nudibranch, *Halgerda carlsoni*.   Photo: L. Newman and A. Flower

Keeping coral reef aquaria is a dynamic avocation; much has changed in recent times and there are many changes in progress right now, some positive, others less so. We are certain, that the future development of the coral reef aquarium hobby, in continuation of the spirit dominant over the last two decades, will be positive. Yet, this depends primarily on the broadening of the biological knowledge and understanding of aquarists. Hopefully, our penetration in to the deepest fountain of reef biology will contribute to this process.

Evolution and genetic inheritance

No other scientific publication in biology has "stirred up" so much dust as the fundamental work "On the Origin of Species", by Charles Darwin. It appeared on 24th November, 1859, and is written in a perplexingly simple and straight forward style, which makes it easy to read. Indeed, the book became very popular, so that the first edition already sold out on the day of publication. It was this work alone, which sets it apart from other significant scientific theories ever published.

Darwin bases his theory of evolution on various pieces of factual evidence, which, at the time were intensely debated by biologist around the world. This factual evidence was based on fossil finds, the existence of rudimentary organs in numerous species, many similarities between different species during their embryonic development, etc. But the scientific world hesitated to discuss this theory publicly, since it clearly contradicted Christian teachings about the origin of life.

Today the principles of Darwin's Theory of Evolution are well known and they are widely ac-

cepted. Subsequent research into genetics has brought further advances. Some of Darwin's ideas have remained valid to this day; others have been adapted to our expanded knowledge, on the basis of new findings, which had been inaccessible to Darwin at the time. The most fascinating aspect in all this is the fact, that in order to support his theory of evolution, Darwin did not have access to the type of information commonly available to us now; the knowledge of the genes, chromosomes and DNA.

The first significant theories about the science of genetics appeared in 1865, in a book written by the Austrian monk Johann Gregor Mendel. But his work remained obscure and unknown until the 20th Century. Yet, as incredible, as it may seem, Darwin's library at Down House, where he lived for 40 years until his death in 1882, contained a presentation volume of Mendel's book, with its pages yet to be cut open!

It is important to note, that evolution is not a process which has taken place, but instead it is a process continuously going on all around us. Traditionally, it had been assumed that evolution is based on variation and natural selection. The expression "survival of the fittest" is also a central idea in the traditional theory of evolution. Here the concept of "survival" does not refer to the individual, but instead to an entire population of related individuals. Within the theory of evolution, an individual survives by passing on its genes to successive generations. The survival of an individual is not an example of survival in terms of evolution; on the other hand, reproduction is. Genes, the genetic material that is, are the real survivors.

"Variation" simply means, that a group of individuals is distinguished from other groups of individuals of the same species, on the basis of specific traits. These differences can indeed be very small and are frequently without apparent significance. Sometimes individuals display variati-

ons, which reduce their chances of survival and so effect their evolutionary success, but in other situations deviations from normal trends can turn out to be highly successful.

Most organisms produce more progeny than is necessary for maintaining a population, however, the mortality of juveniles is frequently immense. In the majority of species only a small fraction of progeny survives to adulthood. The survivors are those, in contrast to their siblings, which are better adapted to their environment. Their capabilities to react to a particular situation may also be slightly better than those of their parent generation. The survivors will then pass on their capabilities to the next generation. The less successful genes disappear - either by means of juvenile mortality or through an inability to reproduce. This is referred to as "natural selection". In the course of successive generations, minor variations become increasingly significant. The species concerned changes in appearance and behaviour, until it has finally developed in to a new species.

This theory of the development of new species through step-like transformations is the basis of the conservative philosophy of evolution. It is important to emphasise, however, that there are now several doctrines. Many scientists argue, that sometimes the separation in to new species occurs suddenly and a step-like transformation is impossible. In other words: they do not place any significance on natural selection in the development of new species (although they do not refute, that natural selection in respect to changes in particular traits of an existing species is of significance). This opinion is the reason for the discussions on whether "hopeful monsters" can indeed exist. This refers to individuals, which are in the process of changing in to a new species, but have so far developed only some of the characteristics of a new species. For instance, what advantage would there be for a reptile to have partially developed wings, while it waits to become a bird?

Thermodynamic theories have also been applied in experiments to explain evolution. The Second Theorem of Thermodynamics states, that the order of a system dissolves over time into maximum disorder or arbitrariness. A thermodynamic system is characterised in that it is constantly being supplied with new energy, and such a system undergoes changes. Simply stated, if the complexity of a species has sufficiently advanced, it starts to become de-organised (loss of cohesion). In this case, the possible result could be the development of a new species through separation or reorganisation of the gene pool (WILEY & BROOKS, 1982).

Fossil discoveries clearly document that during certain geological periods new species developed more frequently than during successive periods. This apparently gives more support to the theory of sudden species development, rather than to a species development which is slow, but ongoing. Yet, this is not a counter argument to the opinion, that in the course of evolution a species changes, to develop improved survival capabilities in its environment. To this day, Darwin's fundamental theory can still be considered as valid, more than 150 years after its proclamation.

Fossils and relationships

Evolution can be substantiated by studying fossils. Old sedimentary rocks contain imprints of life forms in existence millions of years ago. Although many (now) extinct organisms looked different than their current relatives, there are still many similarities. The degree of similarity depends on the geological age of fossils as well as on the rapidity of evolutionary change in the respective taxonomic group.

Trilobites are among the best known fossils. They were the first arthropods (phylum Arthropoda) to be discovered, and they became extinct during the Permian Period, 286 to 245 million years ago.

The Earth is about 4.6 billion years old (refer to Table: Geological Time Scale, on page 424). The earliest prokaryotes can be traced back about 3.7 billion years, while the first eukaryotes date back about 1.5 billion years. Single-celled organisms predominated about 700 million years ago. The evolution of multi-celled invertebrates commenced about 700 million years ago, while vertebrates (primitive fishes) appeared for the first time about 425 million years ago. Initially, the earth atmosphere did not contain oxygen, and offered no protection against the deadly ultra-violet rays. The environment was extremely hostile, especially on land.

The first bacterial life forms developed in water. These were heterotrophic forms, which lived on carbon dioxide containing compounds. It is general believed, that these bacteria developed in to immensely dense populations, which lead to enormous competition for limited food resources available. The bacteria, which were capable of utilising alternative energy sources, would have an advantage over the others; this was indeed what was happening. Some bacteria developed the capability to produce their own food inside cell walls by utilising the sun's radiation (light) as energy source. This process is referred to as "photosynthesis" (see Volume 1, pages 18-19).

Hydrogen is an essential element in photosynthesis. The first autotrophic organisms obtained the required hydrogen from sulfur springs, where there was a continuous supply of sulfuric acid (H_2SO_4). Sulfur springs often occur in areas of volcanic activities, and they must have been quite numerous during prehistoric ages. When the sulfur springs became rarer, some of the organisms developed the capability to obtain hydrogen from water (H_2O). This new opportunity must be considered as a revolutionary step in the future development of life on earth. Once hydrogen is removed from water, oxygen remains! The organisms, which presumably where the first to take this new step in evolution, were stromatolites, a primitive group of blue-green algae (Cyanobacteria). To this day, stromatolites have not yet become extinct. Representatives of these fascinating organisms can still be found in isolated oceanic bays with particularly high salinities. With the increasing production of oxygen, the earth's atmosphere became enriched with this gas. The lethal UV-rays were largely blocked out by the formation of ozone and new life forms could now develop in force. Parallel to the development of life, the face of the earth also changed: continents were displaced, the borders between land and sea, between fresh- and saltwater, changed. In conjunction with that, the climatic conditions alternated between ice ages and tropical periods. All of this must have certainly influenced the pathways of evolution.

We do not know exactly how multi-celled organisms came into being. It is possible that multi-celled life forms developed independently of each other and during different periods of evolutionary history. The first fossil finds of this nature came from rocks about 700 million years old. Some of the oldest fossils originated from Ediacara in Australia, while slightly younger fossils came from Tomotia in Russia and from Burgess Shale in Canada. The Australian and Russian fossils contained animals which have become altogether extinct, but fossils from the Burgess Shale show organisms related to species, which still exist to this day. Recently new and most exciting discoveries of Prekambrium and Kambrium fossils have been made in China.

The Burgess Shale fossils are about 550 million years old; among others, they contain trilobites, which became extinct about 250 million years ago, as well as crustaceans, spiders and primitive insects. In addition, 20 to 30 types of arthropods were found, which can not be related to any of the recent groups, and 15 to 20 species which are specialised to such a degree, that they represent distinct, separate animal phyla. It appears, as if evolution has "experimented" with different solutions, in order to find the correct path. Among the many papers and books available we recommend Gould (1991 and 1993) and Briggs et al. (1994) as a start to getting further information on these subjects.

Living beings have developed over millions of years. All organisms are related to each other,

some closer and others more remotely. In order to establish these relationships and to provide a proper overview, taxonomists have produced cladogrammes or phylogenetic trees. As already mentioned above, a species can not change spontaneously into another one. In other words, human have not developed from chimpanzees in the sense that chimpanzees have changed into humans. But somewhere in past, chimpanzees and humans have had a common ancestor, which is since long extinct. This close relationship becomes obvious in substantial similarities among respective genetic DNA sequences investigated. According to the modern cladistic theory of evolution (phylogenetic tree theory), the chimpanzee, *Pan trogodytes*, and the dwarf chimpanzee, *Pan paniscus*, are sibling species, which together represent the sibling group for humans, *Homo sapiens*. The gorilla, *Gorilla gorilla*, is a distant relative, which has had a mutual ancestor with the ancestor of both chimpanzee species and the human ancestor. The orangutan, *Pongo pygmaeus*, which is even more remotely related to us, has the gorilla, both chimpanzees and humans as sibling group.

The great apes, also referred to as primates, are a good example for explaining the theory of evolution, since they are well known and display characteristics which are readily identifiable by laymen. They may resemble us, yet they are sufficiently different, so that the dissimilarities can be recognised and understood without formal training. It becomes substantially more difficult, if we attempt to establish ancestral relationships among groups of invertebrates, as for instance among the tube worms of genus *Spirobranchus* (refer to page 12).

To determine this sort of relationship, requires detailed studies, using sophisticated equipment and an advanced knowledge of anatomy and morphology. This is the type of work which needs the cooperation of various resear-

chers and involves ongoing research over decades. The significance of such work can be enormous, since it may provide yet another piece, fitting in to the evolutionary puzzle of life on earth.

The five kingdoms

For a long time, all live organisms were placed taxonomically in to two kingdoms: the animal kingdom and the plant kingdom. Subsequently, scientists introduced a third kingdom for single-celled organisms. In most of the more recent taxonomic publications (e.g. MARGULIS & SCHWARTZ, 1998) it has become common practice, to place all living organisms in to the following five kingdoms:

- Procaryotae
Prokaryote organisms; these include all bacteria and blue-green algae (Cyanobacteria), with more than 5,000 known species.

- Protoctista
Eukaryote, single-celled organisms; these are Protozoans, aquatic- and mucoid fungi, as well as algae. The number of species is estimated to be somewhere between 65,000 and 200,000.

- Fungi
Fungi and lichens, with approximately 100,000 species.

- Plantae
All plants, which - following reproduction via spores (mosses and ferns) or seeds (all higher plants) - develop from embryos; approximately 400,000 species.

- Animalia
Multi-celled animals; from the unique *Trichoplax* (Placozoa) to all vertebrate animals; more than one million species.

All marine invertebrate phyla will be discussed in this and the following volume of this book series, with two exceptions. These are the phylum Cnidaria (animals with stinging cells), already described in considerable detail in Volume 2, and the only recently described Phylum Cycliophora (FUNCH & KRISTENSEN, 1996). The latter has been established specifically for the newly discovered species *Symbion pandora*. This phylum (and, of course, its single species) is too special to be discussed at length in this volume. Nevertheless, we can not resist the temptation to briefly introduce *Symbion pandora*: *S. pandora* is less than 1 mm long and occurs parasitic on the Norway Lobster, *Nephrops norvegicus*. The parasite attaches to the cilia-covered appendages of the lobster's mouth and feeds off left-over food from the lobster. In order to survive the moult process of the lobster, *S. pandora* breeds just prior to the lobster shedding its skin, producing free-swimming individuals, which leave the lobster undergoing its moult, and re-attach to the mouth of another lobster. Between moults, *S. pandora* reproduces by means of budding.

In order to provide the reader with an aid to understand the incredible diversity and the many fascinating life forms of marine invertebrates, some information about the taxonomic organisation and phylogenetic relationships will be useful.

Placing invertebrates in to higher taxa and classifying them, may be done primarily by looking for the following characteristics:

- structural organisation of cells,
- body symmetry,
- egg cleavage,
- larval form,
- digestive tract,
- abdominal cavity, and
- body structure (segmentation).

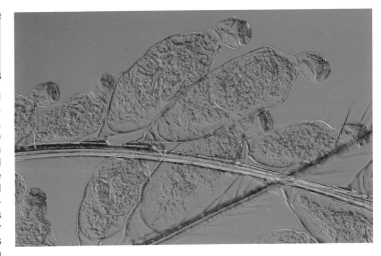

The latest phylum of the animal kingdom to be discovered is phylum Cycliophora. Its only species, *Symbion pandora*, reaches a length of only 1 mm and lives parasitically on the Norwegian Lobster, *Nephrops norvegicus*.

Photo: R. M. Kristensen

Structural organisation of cells

This refers to the condition of an animal being structured either from loosely inter-connected cells, or by cells, which develop into tissue and internal organs.

Body symmetry

Body symmetry is to be understood, whether (and to what degree) the body is symmetrically structured. Radial symmetry is present, when the body is built symmetrically around a central axis and each plane, which intersects the central axis, divides it into two identical halves. Bilateral symmetry is present, when the right half of the body is a mirror image of the left one. Pentaradial symmetry is a highly specialised symmetrical form and is found only in echinoderms (Echinodermata; spiny-skinned animals), whereby the body is (normally) arranged in five identical parts around a central axis.

Egg cleavage

Egg cleavage refers to the process of how an egg is dividing once it has been fertilised. There are two alternatives: spiral cleavage and radial cleavage. During spiral cleavage all parts appear as oblique planes relative to the main axis of the morula. In radial cleavage all parts are either parallel to or at right angle to the longitudinal axis of the morula. The morula is a mulberry-like, spherical cell aggregation, which develops from several cleavages of the fertilised egg cell.

Larval form

The larval form can not be explained with a simple definition, since there are many different types of larvae. Therefore, respective larval types are being described in detail during the discussion on individual phyla. There are, however, the following basic types of larval forms:

- Parenchymal larvae: These larvae have flagellated cells along their outside. The interior of the larvae consists of amoeboid cells.

- Planula larvae: This larvae has a dense outer cover of cilia, used for locomotion.

- Trochophore larvae: A larvae covered more or less with cilia, with a stomodeum (mouth-like opening), a simple digestive tract, a brain-like nerve nodule

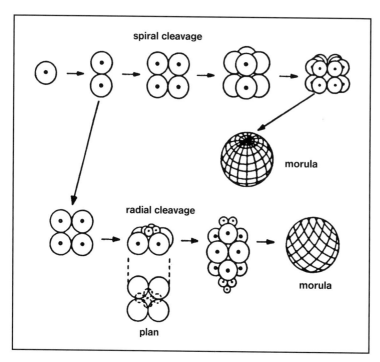

spiral cleavage

morula

radial cleavage

morula

plan

Radial and spiral cleavage.

transforms in to a mouth, while the anus develops later. In deuterostomal visceral development this process takes place in reverse. There are reasons to assume, that these two different processes, leading to the formation of mouth, anus and viscera, have occurred independent of each other and along two different evolutionary pathways. On this basis, the animal kingdom (Animalia) is divided into protostomal and deuterostomal phyla. Protostomal phyla are the bristle worms (Annelida), the "joint-footed" animals (Arthropoda), the "soft-bodied" animals (Mollusca) and the lophophorate phyla (Phoronida, Bryozoa and Brachiopoda). Deuterostomal phyla are spine-skinned animals (Echinodermata), vertebrates (Chordata) and tunicates (Urochordata). On page 425 there is a tabulated overview of all animal phyla with information in which volume the respective phyla are being described.

Abdominal cavity

There are four different alternatives: spongocoelom (artificial ab-

and glandular cells, which produce a shell.

- Nauplius larvae: A larvae with a single eye, two pairs of antenna and a pair of mandible (first mouth segment in Arthropoda).

- Dipleura larvae: Cilia covered, bilaterally-shaped larvae with oral and anal openings, skeleton and larval arms.

Digestive tract

A digestive tract is either absent or it can be present in a more or less developed form. The most primitive form of digestive tract is a stomach-like cavity (gastrovascular cavity), where food is stored and then digested by different enzymes. A more advanced digestive tract is the viscera. This can develop in two different ways: protostomal or deuterostomal. The basis for this is the embryonic development of a mouth and anus. Following fertilisation of the egg, it keeps dividing until the blastula stage - a spherical accumulation of cells - is reached. Du-

ring the following stages a gastrula and an inwardly directed canal is being formed, called a blastopore. In protostomal viscera development, the blastopore

Characteristics of Major Animal			
Phylum	**Level of Organization**	**Body Symmetry**	**Cleavage Pattern**
Porifera	Cellular	Radial	–
Coelenterata	Tissue organ	Radial	–
Platyhelminthes	Organ system	Bilateral	–
Nematoda	Organ system	Bilateral	Spiral cleavage
Annelida	Organ system	Bilateral	Spiral cleavage
Mollusca	Organ system	Bilateral	Spiral cleavage
Arthropoda	Organ system	Bilateral	Spiral cleavage
Echinodermata	Organ system	Pentaradial	Radial cleavage
Hemichordata	Organ system	Bilateral	Radial cleavage
Chordata	Organ system	Bilateral	Radial cleavage

dominal cavity in sponges), aco-elom (absence of an abdominal cavity) pseudocoelom (false abdominal cavity) and coelom (true abdominal cavity). The latter three alternatives are further discussed in detail in Chapter 4 (Marine Worms).

Body segmentation

There are organisms completely without body segmentation or with segmentation, which is only more or less visible. On the basis of this variable trait, invertebrates can be separated in to different phyla. The most important ones are listed in the table (see below). This review compares individual phyla in respect to their main distinguishing features. These are characteristics, which are particularly important for demonstrating the main pathways of evolution within the animal kingdom. On the basis of these comparisons, together with the subsequent classification, scientists investigating evolutionary trends are able to establish phylogenetic trees and discover possible points of origin of evolution. Eventually, as more and more details

are discovered and more precise knowledge of taxonomic evolution biology is being accumulated, a particular phylogenetic tree may well change its appearance.

Species identification and the diversity of life in a coral reef aquarium

In order to classify a particular organism, substantially more attention needs to be focussed on individual characteristics at the taxonomic levels of genus and species, than on the features of a particular phylum. It can often be rather difficult to find conspicuous characters which are valid and useful for diagnosing and identifying a species. For an aquarist, this means that it is often impossible to reach a decision in to what species or genus a particular specimen should be placed. Yet, most aquarists have an innate urge, to identify their

animals as precisely as possible. The simplest way to achieve this, is a comparison with illustrations in the popular aquarium literature. Of course, there is nothing wrong with this, provided there remains an awareness of the possible inaccuracies in such an approach. Exact species identification is frequently a lengthy and involved matter. Often even well-trained taxonomists, with experience in particular animal groups, will get in to significant difficulties, when they have to identify aquarium animals. This is especially true in cases where there is only limited information (or none at all!) about the geographical origin or habitat of a specimen. Identifying such specimen from photographs may be successful, but this is often a matter of luck. Preserved specimens or tissue samples are useful for some animal groups, yet a precise identification can still prove to be difficult.

A typical example of the difficulties involved in a correct identification from a photograph is the Black Elephant Snail, *Scutus unguis*, mentioned in Volume 1 (page 188), where we discuss animals commonly found on live rocks. We have sent out photographs of this snail to specialists, for identification. They concluded that this was a sea-hare of family Aplysidae, possibly a species belonging to the genus *Aplysia*. In due course, we examined some of the specimens more closely, and it turned out that this was not a sea-hare, but instead a false limpet of family Fissurellidae, order Docoglossa. Since the mantle of this animal normally covers its shell, as seen on the photograph, this snail did indeed look like a sea-hare. While it was an understandable mistake, this example clearly shows how easy it is to make a wrong decision by trying to identify a specimen on the basis of a photograph.

Beyond doubt, the coral reef aquarium reflects a wide diversity of organisms. For instance, in an aquarium of "Stavanger Akvarieforretning", Norway, we discovered some very extraordinary or-

Phyla. After WALLACE et al., 1986

Larval Type	Digestive Tract	Body Cavity	Segmentation
Flagellated	–	Primitive spongocoelom	–
Ciliated planula	Gastrovascular cavity	–	–
Similar to trocophore	Gastrovascular cavity	None	No
None	Complete gut (protostome)	Pseudocoelom	No
Trochophore	Complete gut (protostome)	Coelom (schizocoelom) greatly reduced in molluscs	Yes, but greatly reduced in many molluscs and arthropods
Trochophore	Complete gut (protostome)	Coelom (schizocoelom) greatly reduced in molluscs	Yes, but greatly reduced in many molluscs and arthropods
Nauplius in some crustaceas	Complete gut (protostome)	Coelom (schizocoelom) greatly reduced in molluscs	Yes, but greatly reduced in many molluscs and arthropods
Dipleurula or similar	Complete gut (deuterostome)	Coelom (enterocoelom)	No
Dipleurula or similar	Complete gut (deuterostome)	Coelom (enterocoelom)	No
Unique where occurring	Complete gut (deuterostome)	Coelom (enterocoelom)	Yes

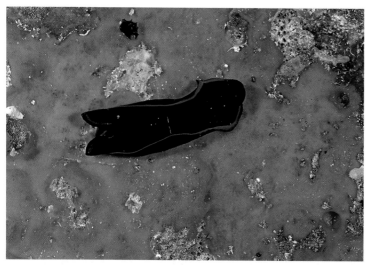

Aquarists have a tendency to identify animals on the basis of external characters, e.g. body shape and colouration. But this can lead to an unreliable identification and indeed it can even be totally incorrect, as shown in the example given here. The three sea slugs depicted on the left belong to the family Aglajidae, subclass Ophistobranchia. Species of genera *Chelidonura* and *Philinopsis* are fairly common and live on sandy bottoms. Both genera are represented in these photographs. Going by colouration alone, one could assume that the animals shown at the top and in the middle belong in to the same genus, while the one in the bottom photograph is a member of a different genus. But this is incorrect! The sea slug in the top photograph is *Chelidonura varians*, while the one in the centre photograph is *Philinopsis gardineri* (photo: L. Newman and A. Flowers), and the one at the bottom is *Philinopsis pilbryi* (photo: C. Bryce). Therefore, the two sea slugs, which are rather similar in colouration, belong in to two different genera. On the other hand, they can be distinguished as two different species on the basis of colouration: *Chelodonura varians* has light blue head bands, while these are absent in *Philinopsis gardineri*.

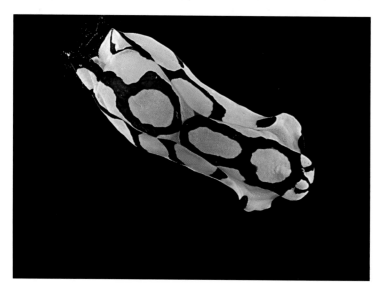

ganisms, which projected from the sediment. They resembled thin threads, moving with great rapidity in a circular motion in the open water. Observation under a binocular microscope (under low magnification) revealed, that these organisms were capable of dramatic contractions, and that they were growing out of a stolon. At first we assumed that they were gastrotrichs (phylum Gastrotricha). Some specimens were examined by Prof. R. M. Kristensen, Copenhagen, and he noted that these were hydrozoans of the genus *Coryne*, a fairly common genus in tropical seas. When one discovers a strange-looking organism in an aquarium, a superficial examination can easily lead to a wrong conclusion, and one can readily be under the impression to have discovered something spectacular or even a new species. Such an event, however, happens only very, very rarely.

Nowadays, the way a coral reef aquarium is being operated technically and biologically, it represents a valuable resource for acquiring knowledge and an appreciation of nature. Beyond doubt, it also is - and must be - a tool for scientific research. Unfortunately, in recent years we have noticed a tendency to place technology into the foreground and biology more into the background. While technology is certainly important, it is only an essential means for establishing a well-functioning, biological system!

Moreover, we are also under the impression, that lately there has been excessive emphasis on the care and maintenance of corals, especially stony corals. In view of recent maintenance and breeding successes of these corals, it is, however, understandable that interest is currently being focussed on them. In fact, we are also very interested in these animals! Stony corals play a key role in the ecology of coral reefs, and must therefore always be an integral part of any coral reef aquarium. Yet, they should not become an obstacle in the future development of the coral reef aquarium hobby.

Nowadays, we have mastered most aspects of the technology required for growing corals. We are maintaining corals in our aquaria to an extent undreamed of 10 or 15 years ago. But there are also other groups of animals, which are equally exciting and fascinating, and these animals still pose significant husbandry problems. We hope that in the future, aquarists will work on finding solutions for these problems. A coral reef is extremely diverse and the coral reef aquarium can be equally varied. It is the aquarist himself, who sets his own limits here.

Right: The coral reef is the most diverse marine ecosystem. On a reef flat like Omei Beach an enormous number of species live together in ecological balance.

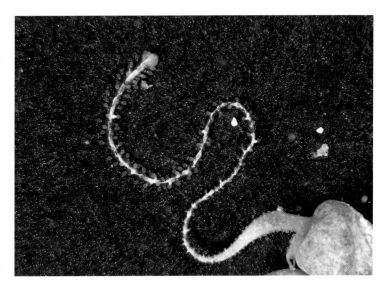

Coryne is a genus of Hydrozoa, common in tropical seas.

Under conditions currently prevailing in coral reef aquariums, nudibranchs are very difficult to keep. This is one of the problems, that needs to be resolved by aquarists in the future.

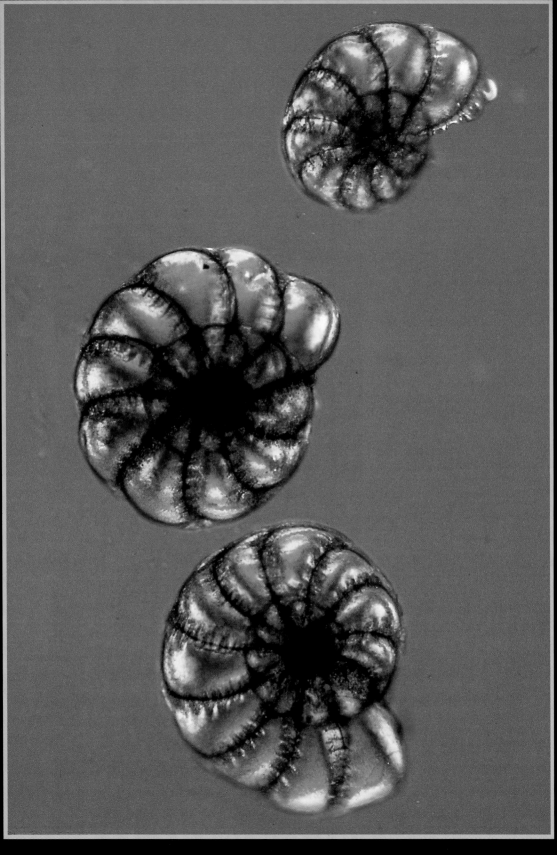

Chapter 2:

Single-celled Organisms

It is very easy to create a favourable environment for single-celled organisms. A glass container with a few litres of water and some nutrients, e.g. in the form of dried grass ("hay infusion") or a few small pieces of carrot that is all that is needed for such "infusoria culture". If this culture vessel is kept at room temperature and in a bright location, it will not take long for myriads of microscopic organisms to inhabit this environment. These resemble the simple life forms, that developed in water puddles, about 2 billion years ago, during the early age of the Earth. And so in many respects, the study of single-celled organisms leads us back to the origin of life.

Most of these single-celled organisms are not visible to the naked eye. However, with the aid of a microscope we can get an insight into a strange and unknown world, unfamiliar to most people. If we let some time go by, all along making sure that our micro-organism culture does not dry up, life in it will change. Some species disappear and are replaced by others. Just as life anywhere in nature, is a constant fight of life and death. Predatory microbes feed on smaller microbes, and only the strongest survive and pass on their genes to the next generations. One will quickly notice, that it is virtually impossible to gain a complete overview of the diversity of life, which develops in such a glass container.

Many single-celled organisms are parasites and can damage the inhabitants of a coral reef aquarium; however, the majority play a significant role in the ecosystem of an aquarium. Their individual shapes can be delicate and highly ornamental. Usually they are colourless; the colouration shown on these photographs are only optical effects. Top: Radiolarians from Barbados. Left: Foraminiferans; shown here is *Elphidium* spp. from a marine aquarium.

Photos: R. Brons

Subkingdom Protozoa
   Phylum Sarcomastigophora
      Subphylum Mastigophora Flagellates
         Class Phytomastigophorea
         Class Zoomastigophorea*
      Subphylum Sarcodina Amoebas
         Class Rhizopodea
            Order Amoebida
            Order Foraminiferida Foraminiferans
         Class Actinopodea
            Order Radiolaria Radiolarians
      Subphylum Opalinata*
   Phylum Ciliophora Ciliates
      Subphylum Holotricha*
      Subphylum Suctoria*
      Subphylum Peritrichia*
   Phylum Apicomplexa*
   Phylum Labyrinthomorha*
   Phylum Microspora*
   Phylum Ascetospora*
   Phylum Myxospora*

* = not dealt with in this book

Cell structure and habitat

The designation "unicellular or single-celled organism" is based on the fact that such organisms consists of a single cell only. Consequently, its size is nearly always in the microscopic realm, whereby the cells usually measure from 5 to 250 μm (1 μm = 0.001 mm). Only very few are visible to the unaided eye. Moreover, protozoans are nearly always tied to a wet environment. They occur in humid soil, in water virtually everywhere; in the smallest freshwater puddle as well as in the largest oceans. There are also many species, which live in the body fluid of other organisms, but only about 20 % live as commensals, symbionts or parasitically; the rest are free-living. Altogether, protozoans play a very important role in the food chain – in nature as well as in the aquarium.

Among the most dreaded protozoans are those causing malaria, *Plasmodium* spp. (phylum Apicomplexa). These parasites spend half of their life within the blood- and liver cells of mammals, birds and reptiles, and the other half in Malaria mosquitos.

Even among our aquarium organisms there are many examples of parasitic protozoans. In Volume 2 (page 314) we have already mentioned the ciliate *Helicostoma nonatum*, which attacks and destroys coral tissue (also refer to the fact page in this volume on page 31).

Also well-known from coral reef fish is the disease Oodinium. It is caused by the flagellate *Amyloodinium ocellatus*. The parasite alternates between a cyst stage - anchored within the skin of fishes - and a free-swimming daughter cell stage, which infest new fish host. The so-called "marine Ichthyophthirius" (white spot), is cau-

In some respects, our home aquaria can be compared to such an infusoria (microorganism) culture, but it is important not to misunderstand the term "microorganism". The topic of this Chapter is dedicated to the single-celled organisms; however, not all microorganisms are single-celled and of a simple structure. There are also groups, such as the rotifers (phylum Rotifera), which can readily be included in the concept "microorganism", although they have a complex body structure. Therefore also later on in this book we will return to microscopically small organisms. The microorganisms can be divided up further into two clearly distinguishable groups: **Prokaryota** and **Eukaryota**.

Prokaryotic organisms are characterized by the fact that they are structured rather simple. Their cells are usually smaller than 10 μm, and a nucleus is absent. The genetic material (DNA), which in other animals is located in the cell nucleus, is in these organisms distributed throughout the cell. The prokaryotes include primarily the bacteria and blue-green algae. The latter have also been di-

scussed in Volume 1 of this book series page 276 - 280. In Volume 1 page 50 we mentioned the role of bacteria on coral reefs and in the coral reef aquarium. In this particular volume we are not dealing with these groups again, but we would like to refer the reader to the publication by MARGULIS & SCHWARTZ (1998). It contains an excellent overview and detailed description of the phylum Prokaryota, as well as a thorough discussion of the Protozoa, whereby the microorganisms are compared systematically with all other living organisms.

The eukaryotes include all remaining organisms. Below we are dealing with those eukaryotes which consists of a single cell only; in other words, those single-celled organisms, which belong into the subkingdom Protozoa, kingdom Protista.

Nowadays there are different opinions on the classifications of the subkingdom Protozoa. Here we would like to present a simplified, systematic review (see Table above), which is based on publications by BARNES (1980), MARGULIS & SCHWARTZ (1998), as well as SEMB-JOHANSSON (1988).

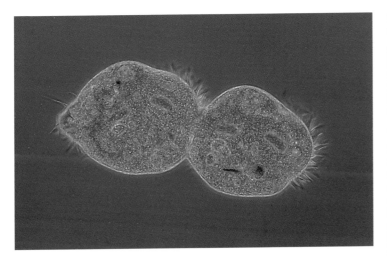

Asexual reproduction by cell division is common among protozoans. Shown here is a *Euplotes* species where cell division has nearly been completed.

Photo: R.Brons

sed by a ciliate, *Cryptocaryon irritans*. In addition, there are still many other single-celled parasites which attack freshwater as well as marine fishes (e. g. refer to BASSLEER, 1996, and MEHLHORN et al., 1992).

Protozoans must control their entire vital functions within a single cell. This is being accomplished by small units within the cell, the organelles (microtubuli). Each has specific functions, as for instance that of the cell mouth, the food vacuoles or the nucleus. In addition, many single-celled organisms e. g. many flagellates, also have pigments which can pick up and utilise solar energy. Such organisms present a transition between autotrophic and heterotrophic organisms or – stated simply – between plants and animals. However, most protozoans are clearly heterotrophic and feed on bacteria, algae, other protozoans, other microorganisms or the body- and tissue fluid of a possible host animal.

There are three principal alternatives in respect to locomotion among protozoans: some, like the flagellates, move about with the aid of a flagellum (whip-like appendage), or several flagella, as the case may be. Others, such as amoebas, develop pseudopodia ("false feet") by displacing the cell

content, for the purpose of locomotion. Yet, the most common means of transport is via the aid of tiny "hairs" (cilia), which are distributed over the outside of an organism, as in ciliates.

Protozoans usually reproduce by means of cell division, i.e. asexual reproduction. Occasionally, however, especially when environmental conditions become adverse, there is also sexual reproduction, whereby genetic ma-

terial is being exchanged between individuals.

There are also parasites among the flagellates, but for our purposes the free-living dinoflagellates are the most interesting. The order Dinoflagellata, class Phytomastigophora, includes several thousand species. Most of these are marine and they occur in all tropical seas. There are also some brackish- and freshwater species, as well as a few parasitic forms.

Many dinoflagellates carry pigments, which they can utilise to obtain energy with the aid of light; however, most still take in additional organic nutrients. Strangely enough, this group can therefore be described as being phytoplankton as well as zooplankton, depending upon the criteria applied to the definition of the distinguishing features between plant and animal. Therefore, there is no consensus among scientists on the precise taxonomic position of dinoflagellates. To be exact, they can neither be

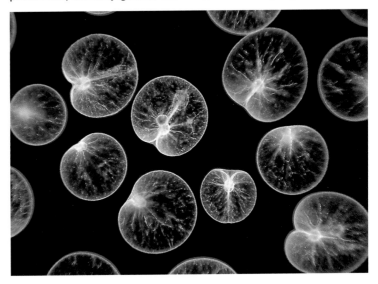

Dinoflagellates of genus *Noctiluca*. These tiny organisms, with a diameter of about 1,000 μm, are capable of producing bioluminescence, causing the well-known "Living Light of the Sea". Photo: R.Brons

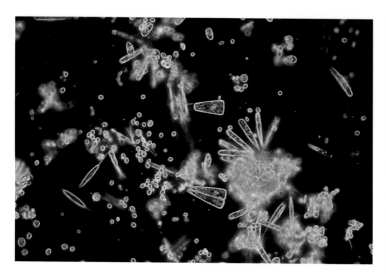

Examining the algae film from the front glass of a coral reef aquarium under a microscope, will reveal the presence of single-celled flagellates. Here they can be recognised as the small, round cells among the larger diatoms (app. 550X magnification).

considered as plants nor as animals. Combining all single-celled organisms in a single kingdom, that of the Protista, is an attempt to solve this problem. We conceded, however, that all this can be rather confusing to the reader, especially since this group also includes the zooxanthellae, those dinoflagellates so very well known to us aquarists. These have been discussed in Volume 1, pages 319-324.

Another reason, why flagellates give scientists a "taxonomic headache" is that, while they are commonly considered to be distinct eukaryotic organisms, their cell nucleus shows specific structures; consequently, some researchers consider dinoflagellates to be an intermediate form between prokaryotic and eukaryotic organisms, and so they refer to them as mesokaryotic organisms (MARGULIS & SCHWARTZ, 1998).

Flagellates move with the aid of flagella ("whip-like" appendages). Usually there are two flagella on each cell (zooxanthellae carry flagella only during the free-living stage). Many flagella form colonies, such as the well-known *Volvox* (order Volvocidae), which is a freshwater species.

Some flagellates are capable of producing very potent toxins. A population explosion of such species (= "red tide") can lead to mass mortalities among fishes living in the same area. Other flagellates have the ability to emit light energy, a phenomenon commonly known as bioluminescence. This "living light" can create fantastic nocturnal light effects, especially in temperate and tropical seas. The flagellates producing this bioluminescense belong into the genus *Noctiluca*.

In an aquarium dinoflagellates live among algae, for instance on the front glass. Flagellates can also be cultivated in the manner described at the beginning of this chapter. Setting up a culture with water from an aquarium, can – when samples are examined under a microscope – reveal which flagellates are present in the aquarium. We have rarely ever heard of a massive reproduction (algal bloom) of free-swimming dinoflagellates in a marine aquarium. Normally, flagellates do not present any problems for aquarists, but occasionally they grow as a slimy carpet rapidly covering the decoration causing a lot of frustration among the aquarists. Such growth is often confused with the slimy growth of blue-green algae.

Amoebas, foraminiferans and radiolarians

Amoebas

Amoebas of the order Amoebida move about by means pseudopodia. Some are naked and strongly reminiscent of a sliding lump of mucus. In others there is either a simple or intricately structured shell. These cells possess food vacuoles, which encapsulate organic particles, e.g. bacteria and algae which make up a large component in their food. When environmental conditions deteriorate (e. g. the habitat dries up), amoebas can form cysts, which then can endure extreme environmental conditions for prolonged periods of time. Using a micros-

Some single-celled organisms can grow to relatively large sizes, so that they can even be recognised by the naked eye, such as foraminiferan *Marginopora vertebralis*. It has a button-like shape, and is quite common on some coral reefs, such as those (shown here) in the Coral Sea.

cope we can occasionally discover amoebas in an aquarium; however, as a group they are of no significant concern to aquarists.

Foraminiferans

From an aquarist's point of view, the foraminiferans, order Foraminifera, are rather important animals. These organisms occur exclusively in the marine environment, where they in some habitats can be very numerous. We also find them commonly in a coral reef aquarium. Foraminiferans produce their shell from organic compounds and calcium carbonate. The simplest forms have only a single chamber, while other species develop shells with several chambers. The protoplasm of the cell is located in the interior of the shell. Through openings in the shell, foraminiferans can extend pseudopodia to the outside where, they can often be seen as slimy threads.

The size of foraminiferans can vary widely. In the smallest species, the shell has a diameter of only about 20 µm, but in the majority of species the shell diameter is between 0.1 and 2.0 mm. There are also "giants" among several benthic, deep water species, with maximum sizes of 4 to 5 cm. The largest of all species is *Neusina agazzi*, which can reach a shell size of 20 cm! The coral reef species *Marginopora vertebralis* (see page 26) reaches a size of 1-3 cm. On some coral reefs it is quite common and can quickly produce large populations.

In the ocean, foraminiferans play a significant role as sand producers. In some locations there are beaches where the sand consists almost exclusively of foraminiferan shells. It has been calculated, that about half of the carbonaceous deposits in the ocean are made up of foraminiferans (ALLEN & STEENE, 1994). The main contributor to these deposits are most notably *Globigerina* species. Another frequent genus is *Polystomella*. Its distribution extends from the Arctic Ocean in the north to the equator

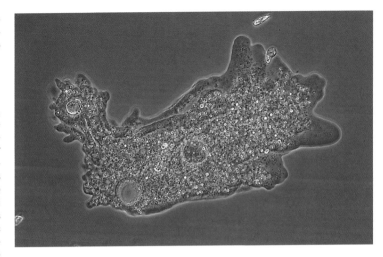

Amoeba in a marine aquarium.   Photo: R. Brons

in the south, where it occurs from the sea surface down to a depth of 300 m.

Foraminiferans are very common in a coral reef aquarium, especially when the tank was set up with "living rocks". Some of the species which can be found in an aquarium, have been described in Volume 1 (page 173).

While most foraminiferans are free-living, there are also some sessile species. The most conspicuous one among the latter, is the pink-coloured *Homotrema rubrum* (see fact-page 28). In an

aquarium, it often establishes large colonies in shaded areas, such as on the underside of corals and live rocks. *H. rubrum* can reach a maximum size of 1 cm. On the island of Bermuda this species is sometimes so numerous, that the beaches are virtually coloured pink.

Foraminiferans are omnivores and feed on algae, ciliates and even on small invertebrates, such as round worms and crustacean larvae. Moreover, many species living in shallow, tropical waters, also possess zooxanthellae. Numerous genera and species are

Foraminiferans developing inside their cell chamber. Shown here are the individual chambers of an *Elphidium*-species.   Photo: R. Brons

Homotrema rubrum

Distribution: Wide spread in tropical seas, details unknown.

Size: Normally smaller than 1 cm; pseudopods can reach sizes of several cm in length

Reproduction: Rapid asexual reproduction possible under optimum aquarium conditions.

Food: Feeds on organic particles suspended in water, are captured by means of pseudopodia.

Description: Red, knob-like, spiny shape. Sessile organism on living rocks. The pseudopodia are transparent and very thin.

Aquarium requirements: One of the few single-celled organisms in a coral reef aquarium, which is visible by the naked eye. Most frequently present in aquaria decorated with living rocks. Can grow rapidly and establish large populations. Does not tolerate high light levels, and therefore tends to live in more shaded areas.

GA: + ; **SE:** +/-; **CO:** +

Photos:
Top: Small populations in an aquarium.
Centre: Large population, established on living rocks.
Bottom: Close-up photograph of a single specimen; the pseudopods are clearly visible.

known from coral reefs, and the group is extremely abundant in the reef benthos. MATHER & BENNET (1993) provide a review of those species occurring in the southern region of the Great Barrier Reef; in addition, they also discuss this group in more general terms. DEVANEY & ELDREDGE (1977) give a detailed overview together with an identification key for the foraminiferans of Hawaii. For those aquarists, who would like to know more about foraminiferans, the above-mentioned articles provide useful starting points for further reading.

Radiolarians

The most exquisite shapes among protozoans are found in the radiolarians of the order Radiolaria. These are marine species, which usually live pelagically close to the sea surface. However, there are also species which migrate down to a depth of 4,500 m, as well as species which live exclusively at great depths.

Radiolarians develop an internal, central capsule from a chitinous substance. This capsule is surrounded by an external skeleton formed by symmetrically arranged spicules ("needles") made of silica or strontium sulfate. Long, thin pseudopodia can be extended from among the spicules. Several types of skeletal arrangements occur. One common type has a radiating structure in which the skeleton is composed of long spines that radiate out from the central capsule and extend beyond the outer surface of the body. Another type of skeleton is constructed as a lattice sphere. Depending upon the age of the animal there may be any number of spheres arranged concentrically outside and inside the body. Radiolarians accommodate zooxanthellae. Some radiolarians can growth to considerable size, where single individuals can reach a diameter of several millimetres, and others develop into 20 cm long colonies.

Just like the Foraminifera, radiolarians also contribute to the

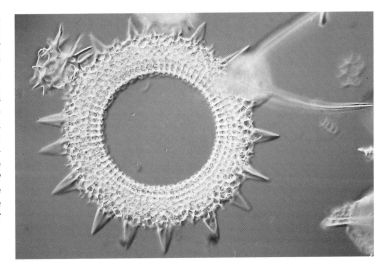

Radiolarian from Barbados.   Photo: R. Brons

bottom sediments in the ocean. Both groups are also well presented in fossils, since their calcareous shells become readily petrified. Fossil species of radiolarians can be dated back to the Pre-Cambrian Period.

Ciliates

Sometimes the term "Protozoans" is understood to apply only to the ciliates, although these organisms make up only a limited segment of the large sub-kingdom of Protozoa. This may well be due to the fact, that ciliates are well known to aquarists and that these organisms can be readily identified. Ciliates owe their name to the multitude of tiny hair-like processes (= cilia), which normally cover the entire cell; however, in some species only a certain section of the cell is covered by cilia. Cilia are sometimes confused with the longer cirri (filamentous appendages) as those which are

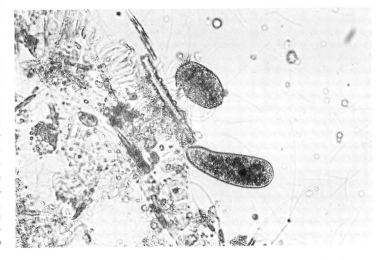

Two ciliates: *Euplotes* sp. above and an unknown species below, feeding on mucus from a *Sarcophyton* sp. (app. 550X magnification).

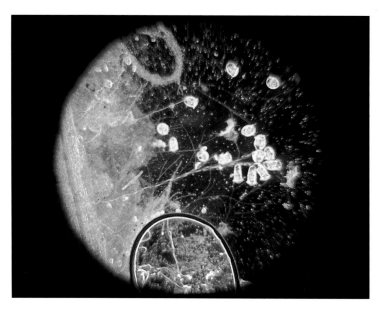

Sessile ciliates can produce colonies, such as this *Vorticella*-species (app. 100X magnification).

present in the genus *Euplotes*. Cilia provide locomotion for these organisms, but they can also be involved in more specific functions. In total, there are about 8,000 species of ciliates, and one would expect this number to increase substantially from as yet undiscovered species. They occur in freshwater as well as in brackish- and seawater.

Free-living ciliates have an opening in their cell wall, the mouth organ (oral opening of the cell), called cyclostomum. In many species this opening is easily recognizable, as for instance in the slipper animal of genus *Paramecium*, an organisms found in freshwater infusion cultures.

The main food of most ciliates are bacteria, which are virtually

"fanned" in to the cell mouth opening by the beating action of the cilia. But there are also predatory ciliates. An example of this is the large species *Didinium nasutum*, which feeds exclusively on *Paramecium* (slipper animals). In order to be able to do that, this species has developed specific capture organelles, which retain the prey and inject it with a venom. This paralyses the prey, which is then swallowed whole.

Most ciliates are free-swimming, but there are also a few sessile species, such as the bell-shaped members of genus *Vorticella*, which can form colonies or the trumpet-like *Stentor* spp., which live as a solitary animal. However, most of these sessile forms are able to leave their substrate, swim away and then re-attach themselves somewhere else. These are filter feeders, where the cilia create a tiny water current which supplies the food, e. g. bacteria.

Some ciliates, such as the members of family Folliculinidae, alternate between a sessile stage and a free-swimming stage. The free-swimming stage is for dispersion only, and food is not taken in. During the sessile stage, ciliates live in a transparent tube, the so-called loricum (pl. lorica). Normally, individuals which are

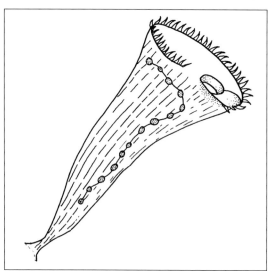

Lateral view of a trumpet animal, *Stentor* sp.
After PILLIPS in DEVANEY & ELDEGE (1977)

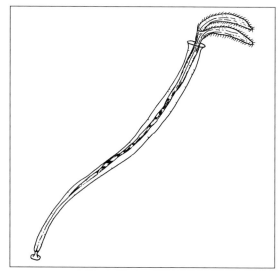

Lateral view of a sessile specimen of the family Folliculinidae.
After BARNES (1980)

Helicostoma nonatum

Distribution: Widely distributed; possibly in all tropical seas; no further details available.

Size: We have measured individual specimens with a length of 0.06 mm and a width of 0.015 mm.

Reproduction: Rapid asexual reproduction possible under optimum aquarium conditions.

Food: Feeds on the tissue of stony corals.

Description: Elongated ciliate, with cilia distributed over the entire cell. Excellent free-swimmer. Digested zooxanthellae, taken in as food, are clearly visible under a microscope (100X magnification).

Aquarium requirements: Can suddenly and without prior warning attack stony corals. Usually, this manifests itself first by the appearance of white spots on the coral, and these spots get larger as the organisms reproduces. Soon thereafter a slimy, brownish mass appears at the interface between dead and live tissue - this is the "trade mark" of this parasite. We do not know what causes such massive blooms, and if the disease is not treated the affected coral will die. *Helicostoma nonatum* infestations have been observed on many stony corals, including *Seriatopora* spp., *Acropora* spp., *Pocillopora damicornis* and *Euphyllia* spp. In order to kill the parasite, the affected colony must be submerged totally in freshwater for two minutes, which must be of the same temperature as the aquarium water. If possible, dead or severely affected branches should be removed. Normally this treatment eliminates the parasite, but there is a risk that the stony coral may not tolerate the exposure to freshwater.

GA: -; **SE:** +/-; **CO:** -

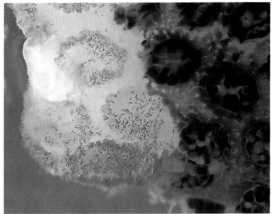

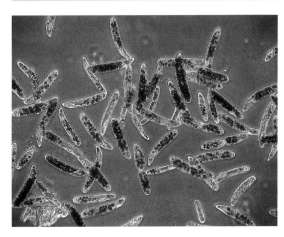

Photos:
Top: Infested colony of *Pocillopora damicornis.*
Centre: When viewed with a magnifying glass (20X magnification), the feeding marks caused by *Helicostoma nonatum* can clearly be seen.
Bottom: *Helicostoma nonatum*, viewed under a microscope (app. 250X magnification).

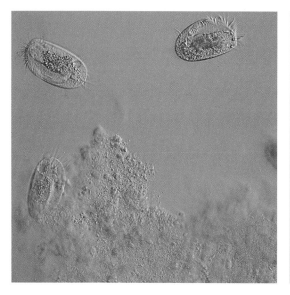

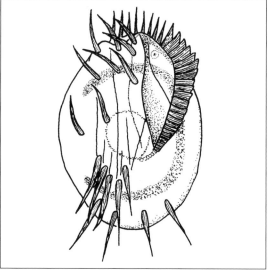

Euplotes vannus.   Photo: R. Brons   Ventral view of a ciliate of genus *Euplotes.* After Barnes (1980)

settling down build a new loricum, but they can also utilise previously used tubes. Devaney & Elridge (1977) describe several species from Hawaii, and they also provide an identification key.

In genus *Euplotes* the cirri are concentrated on some parts of the cell only. We have also observed ciliates in aquaria repeatedly, which closely resembled *Euplo-*

tes, but which probably belong to another genus.

The most fascinating ciliates are those of subphylum Suctoria. These are absolutely grotesque, as well as being highly effective predators of other microorganisms. As sessile organisms they live attached via a short stalk to the substrate. The cells are oval, with variably formed tentacles.

Each tentacle has a specific organelle for catching other ciliates - up to five or more at one time!

One could write an entire book about the microorganisms living in an aquarium. Although they are the most numerous, as well as being very important organisms, in the coral reef aquarium, little research as so far been done on them in this environment. With the aid of a suitable microscope, there are still a lot of interesting things to be discovered in this area by genuinely interested aquarists.

Placozoans

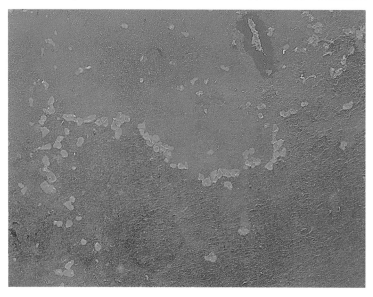

Placozoan *Trichoplax adhaerens*, on the front glass of a marine aquarium; feeding on the algae layer, where they can be recognised with the naked eye (app. 5x enlarged).   Photo: R. Brons

It sounds almost unbelievable, but the simplest multi-celled organism was discovered in an aquarium, in fact, by Franz Eilhard Schulze in 1883, in a marine aquarium of the Zoological Institute of the University of Graz. This organism was *Trichoplax adhaerens*, the only known species of the phylum Placozoa.

Trichoplax adhaerens is a tiny animal built up of many cells, and it has usually a diameter from 0.2 to 2.0 mm. It has characters in common with single-celled as well as with multi-celled organisms. In many respects it can be viewed as a connecting link between the kingdom Protista and the animal kingdom. And this is also the reason why it is being discussed in this chapter. *Trichoplax* shows many similarities with the planula larvae of cnidarian animals. In fact, initially it had been misidentified as such.

Trichoplax carries cilia, distributed over its entire head. Most of its cells contain surprisingly little genetic material (DNA), however, certain cells contain twice as much DNA than others, without any explanation for this being available. The chromosomes are also very short in *Trichoplax*, about the size as of a normal bacterium cell. *Trichoplax adhaerens* can reproduce asexually by means of simple division or through budding, whereby new individuals can develop from even the smallest fragments. Sexual reproduction is via the development of eggs and sperm. It has been observed that the formation of egg cells especially happened when a population had grown to a certain maximum of individuals or when a population was about to degenerate (MARGULIS & SCHWARTZ, 1998).

The occurrence of *Trichoplax adhaerens* has repeatedly been reported from the Mediterranean Sea, at the Plymouth Marine Biological Station in England and at the Rosenstiehl Marine Station in Miami (USA). This species also occurs relatively often in marine aquaria, where it was observed, for instance, at the Tempel University in Philadelphia (USA).

BRONS (personal communication) discovered *Trichoplax adhaerens* in an aquarium, which had been decorated with living rocks. These specimens were observed on the front glass, where they were feeding on algae and/or on organisms living among the algae. He also found *Trichoplax* in fish rearing tanks of the "Red Sea Fish pHarm" company, Eilat, Israel. The water in these rearing tanks contained many organic substances and a lot of algae on the glass. BRONS noticed substantial populations of *T. adhaerens* in thin algae

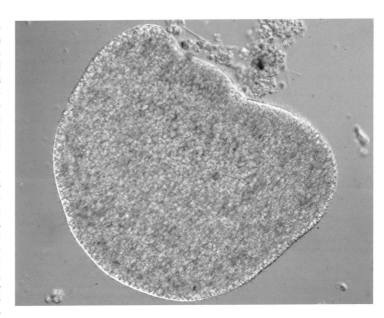

Placozoan *Trichoplax adhaerens.*
Photo: Institute for Zoology of the University Hohenheim

mats of red cyanobacteria. It is possible, that *T. adhaerens* was feeding on the algae and/or also on other organisms, such as copepods, nematodes and protozoans, which commonly develop among lush growth of cyanobacteria. In any event, this demonstrates that *T. adhaerens* tends to find optimum living conditions in aquarium water, which contains many organic substances. A second genus and species of Placozoa, *Treptoplax reptans* was described by MONTICELLI in 1897. Unfortunately, *Treptoplax reptans* has since then never again been observed and the true existence of the species is therefore uncertain.

Further information about this extraordinary animals can be found especially in ANKEN & KAPPEL (1992), JÄGERSTEIN (1955), RUTHMANN & TERWELP (1979), GRELL (1971 and 1972) and GRELL & BENWITZ (1971).

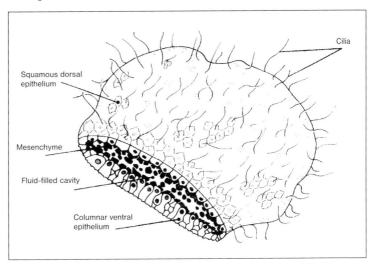

Sectional view of *Trichoplax.*

Chapter 3:

Sponges

Sponges represent the most primitive forms of multi-celled animals having much in common with single-celled animals. For a long time it was thought that they were plants. It was not until 1756, when it was found that they belong actually into the animal kingdom.

The evolutionary history of sponges goes far back. Sponge-like organisms were already in existence during the Pre-Cambrian Period, 640 to 700 million years ago. The recent sponges of class Demospongiae appeared to have arisen during the Cambrian Period, about 500 million years ago. The evolution of sponges reached its peak during the Ordovician Period, about 460 million years ago (MATHER & BENNETT, 1993). Many sponge families developed during this period, including the majority of the current ones. This Period also gave rise to a group of sponges with a strong skeleton, and over the following 100 million years or so, these particular sponges built significant reef structures, which were similar to our modern coral reefs. Fossil sponge reefs can still be found in many parts on earth.

Eventually, however, sponges had to give way to corals, which then took over the role as reef builders. At the end of the Devonian Period, about 350 million years ago, the reef-building sponges had finally disappeared. It was thought, that these sponges

After corals, sponges are the most numerous organisms in terms of the biomass of a coral reef. Many sponges have a highly ornamental shape together with a spectacular colour. Top: *Fasciospongia* sp., possibly *F. turgida* at the Fiji Islands. Left: *Aplysina archeri* at the U.S. Virgin Island in the Caribbean Sea. Photos: Scott W.Michael

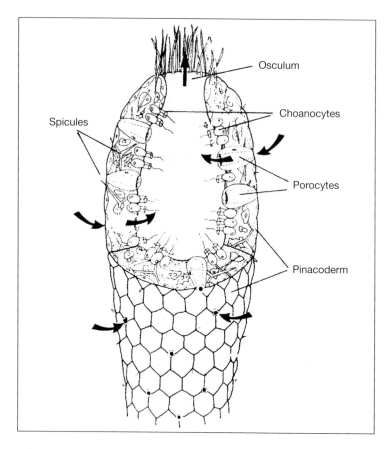

Osculum

Spicules

Choanocytes

Porocytes

Pinacoderm

Schematic structure of a sponge.

Drawing after BARNES (1980)

became totally extinct. However, recently their close relatives have been re-discovered in deep water, as for instance, on the Great Barrier Reef. These sponges, for instance *Acanthochaetes wellsi* and *Astrosclera willeyana* (order Agelasida, class Demospongia), have a sturdy calcareous skeleton, like that of reef-building corals (MATHER & BENNETT, 1993).

So far, about 6,000 to 7,000 species of sponges have been described, but this group is still insufficiently known, so that the actual number of species is likely to be much higher. The majority of sponges live in the sea, but there are also freshwater species. In general, sponges must be considered to be rather delicate aquarium inhabitants, yet, some of them will do well in captivity. These tend to develop gradually in most coral reef aquaria, where they establish themselves in pat-

ches of different sizes.

Sponges are not specifically tropical organisms. There are also many species which live in colder oceanic regions. Along the Norwegian coastline there are steep rock walls in areas with strong currents, and here are sponges which are larger than a football. Numerous sponges also inhabit the Mediterranean Sea and other subtropical seas. In tropical seas, sponges occur from shallow coral reef regions down to great oceanic depths. Moreover, there are species, which live associated with other organisms.

Structure and habitat

Internal organs are totally absent in sponges. Or simply: they con-

sist merely of interacting, individual cells. The various types of cells, however, have very specific functions. A sponge is perforated by a system of canals, where water flow in through **small** openings (porocytes) along the surface (pinacoderm). Special collar cells (Choanocytes), which are equipped with a flagellum, and are concentrated in discrete chambers (Choanocyte chambers), set off continuous water current throughout the colony. These collar cells are specialised cells in sponges. Finally, the water within the canal system leaves the colony again via **large** openings (pl. oscula; sing. osculum).

Sponges exhibit three different types of structural organisation. In the literature these three types are often referred to as "Ascon-", "Sycon-" and "Leucon-Type". It must be noted here, that the organisation of cells is not reflected in the external growth form (shape) of a sponge. Ascon- and Sycon types are rare, only occurring in Calcarea, while the overall majority of the sponges, including all demosponges are Leucon-types.

The water current generated by a sponge, is critical for its food intake. That is, sponges are filter feeders (suspension feeders). In fact, a fist-size sponge can filter 5,000 l of water a day! This in-flowing water carries detritus and many bacteria, which represent a significant part of the diet. In fact, up to 99% of the bacteria contained in the incoming current are being removed and utilised as food. The water current also supplies oxygen and important salts to sponges, and it also removed their metabolic waste products.

Inside a sponge there is a sort of "skeleton". It consists of tiny needles (= spicules from lat. spicula; singular spiculum) which are made of calcium carbonate or silica, or of a combination of these two substances. In a very few species the spicules are built from fragmented spongin fibres, structures that are not homologous or functional similar to the real spicules. The spicules make the sponges feel firm, although

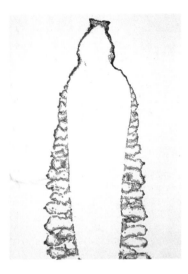

Above: Longitudinal section through a calcareous sponge of genus *Sycon*. In this low magnification the porocytes are not visible, however, the exhalant opening at the top is clearly visible. Below: Cross-section through the same sponge.

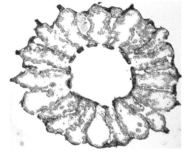

Callyspongia siphonella from the Red Sea. It is one of the most impressive looking sponges and it possesses only vestigial spicules. This sponge belongs to those species, which can tolerate very high light levels. It inhabits shallow water close to the edge of a reef.

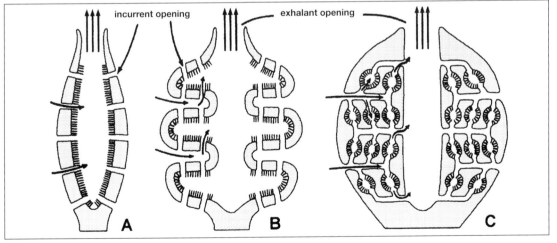

Organisational types of sponges: A – Ascon-type; B – Sycon-type; C – Leucon-type.

Drawing after BUCHSBAUM (1974)

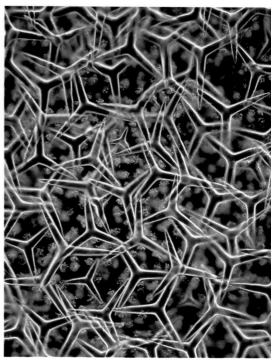

In most sponges the skeleton consists of spicules, which are developed from calcium carbonate or silica, in the latter case these may be cemented by a horny protein called spongin. The illustrations show the skeleton (left) and the spicules (right) of a calcareous sponge of genus *Leucosolenia.* Photos: R. Brons

they are actually made of a soft tissue. The needle (spiculum) skeleton is formed from ions dissolved in the ambient seawater. The cells create the right pH and use specific enzyme systems that cause the silica or calcium carbonate to precipitate along a predetermined axis or (in species forming siliceous spicules) along an organic thread. The spicules can vary substantially in size. Often they have delicate, intricate shapes, which are important systematic identification characters.

In addition, some sponges from tropical latitudes, also contain symbiotic algae, which contribute – more or less significantly – with their photosynthesis products to the nutrition of these sponges. In that respect, their form of life equals that of zooxanthellae. However, the symbiotic algae of these sponges are not dinoflagellates, as those in cnidarian animals, but they are blue-green algae (refer to Volume 1, page 324). Sponges with symbiotic algae are

most numerous at water depths from 10 to 30 m. In some cases, they can even occur in very shallow water.

Sponges can have highly ornamental shapes, ranging from rather straight tubes, to large sacks and on to more or less indeterminable shapes. They can also occur as layers or mats, creeping over some substrate. The variable shape is presumably related to an enlargement of the surface area and to an optimum light utilization. But the overall shape of a sponge is also of importance for effective water circulation within the colony. Finally, the habitat in which a sponge lives, may also influence its shape. This then means, that one and the same species can have a different appearance from one habitat to the next.

Research suggests, that the amount of organic nutrients in water, as well as the degree of water turbulence, have a substantial influence on species composition and the distribution

of sponges. Some species can tolerate a high turbulence, but then on the other hand require nutrient-poor and clear water. Most species live on oceanic reefs. Those species which tolerate being periodically covered by sediments, are found on inshore, coastal (littoral) reefs, where there is less water exchange and the amount of organic material is higher (WILKINSON & CHESHIRE, 1989).

Many sponges contain toxins, so that they represent a danger to other organisms. They use this to protect themselves against becoming overgrown by algae and hydroids. Moreover, such sponges are not eaten by fish or other animals. This characteristic can be of significance under aquarium conditions (refer to *Haliclona* sp., in fact sheet on page 61). In some cases, sponge toxins can even cause a severe burning pain in humans.

Sponges can not move and are so principally defenseless and exposed to possible predators, such as fishes, snails and worms. Yet, being eaten is far less common among sponges, than one would expect. This may well be due to their toxicity. Sponges are probably not always directly toxic to fish, but instead they are an undesirable taste, so that fish do not like to feed on them. Yet, there are certain fishes, which are food specialists and which are immune to sponge toxins. These include several marine angelfish, e.g. *Holacanthus*- and *Pomacanthus*-species (RANDALL & HARTMAN, 1968).

There are also some cnidarian animals which are immune to sponge toxins. Man encrusting anemones live symbiotically with sponges and even penetrate completely into sponge tissue. VAN SOEST & VERSEVELDT (1987) report on a unique symbiotic relationship between the sponge *Mycale* sp. and the coral *Tubipora* sp. from the shallow water reefs around the Indonesian island of Komodo. Moreover, there are crabs, which carry sponges on their carapace as perfect camouflage. A rather unusual symbiosis has recently been discovered in Australia, between a sponge and the holaxonian coral *Alertigorgia orientalis*. The cylindrically-shaped sponge grows on the bottom. The larvae of the coral settle on the sponge and start to grow there. Gradually, a holaxonian coral colony grows around the sponge, which eventually lives in the basal section of the coral, and so becomes overgrown by it. Externally, the structure looks like a single, solitary, branched holaxonian coral. It is uncertain, for how long the sponge can survive in this overgrown condition, and which advantages or disadvantages each "partner" derives from this symbiotic relationship (ALDERSLADE, personal communication).

It is unclear, which toxins are produced by the sponge and which toxins have been derived from food filtered out of the water, as – for instance – single-celled algae, which often contain toxins. If such algae are filtered out by a

The growth of sponges is incredibly variable in terms of shape and size. This gigantic *Xestospongia muta* is as large as a human, but it grows only a few centimetres each year. Therefore, the specimen shown here may be in excess of 100 years old.

Photo taken at Grand Cayman Island, Caribbean Sea: Scott W. Michael

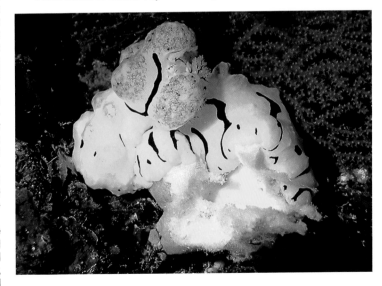

Some organisms feed on sponges, such as this nudibranch seen here on the Great Barrier Reef.   Photo: M. Cufer

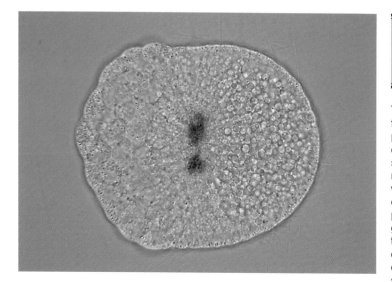

Larvae of a calcareous sponge, genus *Sycon.*   Photo: R. Brons

sponge, the algal toxins can accumulate in the sponge. Many sponges live symbiotically with bacteria, whereby the latter can make up 40% of the sponge tissue (WILKINSON, 1984). Bacteria are responsible for the production of many sponge toxins.

Sponges can reproduce sexually as well as asexually. The latter takes place by means of fragmentation, where by individual parts are cut off the body and then develop in to new sponges. During sexual reproduction eggs and sperms are produced by modified collar cells or amo-

ebocytes. In viviparous sponges sperm is given off into the water, while the egg cells remain in the sponge where they are then fertilized and develop into larvae.

Sexual reproduction is often oviparous. These Sponges release sperm and eggs simultaneously into the surrounding water. Within a few days the larvae develops into a small sessile sponge. We have observed this kind of reproduction repeatedly in a coral reef aquarium. Suddenly massive numbers of tiny sponges appear everywhere on the tank decoration.

The systematics of phylum Porifera (see page 42) is rather complicated and is based on (among other characters) the shape of the spicules and the structure of the needle (spicule) skeleton. Only very few sponge species from coral reefs are easy to identify, provide they have a characteristic growth form or a specific colouration. For aquarists it is generally easier to identify Caribbean species. These are also better known scientifically than those from the Indo-Pacific region. The most readily understood review of the Caribbean sponges is that by HUMANN (1992) and the book by GAMILL (1997), which identifies and illustrates 120 species. Many species have been described from the Indo-Pacific region, but the descriptions are very often inadequate and revisions are badly needed. ALLEN & STEENE (1994), COLIN & ANDERSEN (1995) as well as GOSLINER et al. (1996) all provide a photographic overview of the most frequently occurring sponges of the Indo-Pacific, however, without any detailed discussion. HOOPER (in MATHER & BENNETT, 1998), gives a systematic summary of the sponges of the Great Barrier Reef. This publication also contains a general description of sponge structure and -ecology, together with illustrations of spicule structures.

As mentioned above, a sponge can change its shape depending upon location and exposure. For that reason it is usually impossible to identify sponges on the basis of photographs or by merely looking at an individual on the reef or in an aquarium. Even determining the genus by appearance alone can be rather unreliable, or it may even be outright impossible. The order of a particular specimen can usually be established, but in many cases even that can encounter difficul-

The Philippine Calcareous sponge *Leucetta philippinensis*, photographed at the Fiji Islands.   Photo: Scott W. Michael

ties. More than 100 families of sponges have been established so far.

Useful identification keys down to order or even family level can be found, for instance in LEVI (1973), BERGQUIST (1978) or HARTMAN (1982). Overall, the systematics of sponges is currently still rather inconclusive (MATHER & BENNETT, 1998).

We do not believe it is sensible to attempt to identify uncertain species. Pages 48 and 49 depict a selection of sponges from the Indo-Pacific. As far as it is possible, details about a species- or genus name are being provided, however, with an additional reference number; this can facilitate a subsequent identification. Page 50 shows some sponges from the Red Sea, and on page 51 there are sponges from the Caribbean Sea.

The phylum Porifera is divided into three classes:

• **Class Calcarea,**

• **Class Demospongiae,**

• **Class Hexactinellida.**

The class Sclerospongiae (coral sponges), which has long been viewed as a separate, small class, is now considered to be polyphyletic, and its (former) species are now placed either in the Calcarea or the Demospongiae.

Class Calcarea

Calcareous sponges of class Calcarea have spicules of calcium carbonate without axial filaments. Their larvae are blastulate (hollow). Usually their growth form is weakly defined or it is unbranched. The club-like small *Sycon* spp. often appear in a coral reef aquarium, especially in the filter chamber or in the sump where the light intensity is low and the flow of water is steady. Similarly, the genera *Leucosolenia* and *Leucetta* are rather common on the reef. *Leucetta* species can be very colourful, but we have yet to see this genus in the coral reef aquarium.

We observed this calcareous sponge of genus *Clathrina* in a shallow lagoon on the underside of a rock, in the Maldives. The genus *Clathrina* incorporates a complex of species, which all look very similar and have a world-wide distribution.

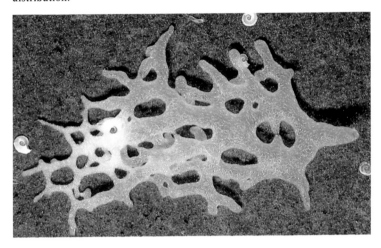

Calcareous sponge of genus *Leucosolenia* (?).   Photo: R. Brons

Calcareous sponges of genus *Sycon.*   Photo: R. Brons

Phylum Porifera
  Class Calcarea
    Subclass Calcinea
      Order Clathrinida
        Clathrinida, Leucaltis, Pericharax, Leucetta
      Order Murrayonida
    Subclass Calcaronea
      Order Leucosolenida
        Leucosolenia, Leucilla, Sycon
      Order Lithonida

  Class Demospongiae
    Order Astrophorida
      Jaspis, Disyringia
    Order Lithistida
      Suborder Rhabdosina
      Suborder Anoplina
      Suborder Triaenosina
      Theonella
    Order Spirophorida
      Cinachyra, Paphidotethya
    Order Hadromerida
      Spirastrella, Axos, Acanthochaetetes, Tethya
    Order Angelasida
      Agelas, Astrosclera
    Order Homosclerophorida
      Oscarella, Corticium
    Order Halichondrida
      Ciocalypta, Halichondria, Phakellia, Auletta,
      Raniochalina
    Order Poecilosclerida
      Amphinomia, Echinodictyum, Raspailia,
      Hemectyonilla, Clathria, Biemna, Crella, Crambe,
      Monanchora, Aka, Mycale
    Order Haplosclerida
      Gelliodes, Callyspongia, Amphimedon,
      Xestospongia, Haliclona
    Order Dictyoceratida
      Fascaplysinopsis, Carteriospongia, Collospongia,
      Luffariella, Spongia, Phyllospongia, Dysidea, Ircinia
    Order Dendrceratida
      Aplysilla, Dendrilla
    Order Verongida
      Ianthella, Pseudoceratina, Aplysina

  Class Hexactinellida
    Subclass Amphidiscophora
      Order Amphidiscosida
        Hyalonema, Monorhaphis
    Subclass Hexasterophora
      Order Hexactinosida
      Order Lyssaacinosida
        Holascus
      Order Lychniscosida

Class Demospongiae

With more than 85% of all sponge species (about 6,000), the horny sponges (keratosa) (with a skeleton made up of fibers of a protein-like, substance called "spongin") and silica sponges make up the class Demospongiae. The siliceous spicules have a hollow interior, in which lies an axial filament. Most larvae are parenchymella (solid). These sponges are usually colourful, since their cells contain pigments. They occur at all depths and have highly variable shapes. The Calcarea as well as the Demospongiae have a pinacoderm lining the outside and the canals, and a choanoderm lining the choanocyte cambers. In between there is a acellular matrix (mesohyl) which contains the skeleton, collagen fibers and various free moving cells. There are also many collar cells, each carrying a central flagellum, which is surrounded by numerous micro-villi (tiny, bristle-like outgrowths). The surface is covered by large, flat cells (pinacocytes).

Class Hexactinellida

In the glass sponges of class Hexactinellida the cells are not separated from each other, but instead have developed into syncytia. These are groups of cells which share one or more cell nuclei. The cells along the surface of these sponges, as well as the choanocytes, form such syncytia. However, this must not be viewed as a "non-cellular matrix" or as "non-cellular protoplasm". The cells and all organelles are present, only the cell walls have not been developed or have been lost.

    Glass sponges live at depths from 13 to 9,000 m and often have a cup-like shape. Their spicules are made of silica and have a basic hexaradiat shape. They reach their greatest species diversity between 50 and 1,000 m depth. The Venus Basket, *Euplectella* sp. It is a well-known representative of this class.

Dysidea herbacea is one of the few photo synthetically-active sponges, which can be kept in a well-illuminated coral reef aquarium. This photo shows a well-growing specimen in a tank at the Löbbecke Museum, Düsseldorf.

Although sponges represent an important ecological component on coral reefs, the sponge fauna as such has been only insufficiently been investigated so far. Only corals represent a larger biomass on coral reefs than sponges (WILKINSON, 1983a and 1983b). This is particularly conspicuous on reefs in the Caribbean Sea, where sponges represent a biomass five to six times that of the Great Barrier Reef. This is probably due to the availability of a larger food supply and reduced predation by fish in the Caribbean Sea than on the Great Barrier Reef (WILKIINSON, 1987a). Moreover, there are fewer sponges with symbiotic blue-green algae in the Caribbean Sea than there are throughout the Indo-Pacific region.

With sponges – just like corals – it had been a puzzle for a long time, how such a large biomass could thrive in such a relatively nutrient-poor environment. The answer lies in their symbiotic relationship with blue-green algae.

From an ecological perspective, one can categorize the development of sponges into four groups.

❶ Sponges with symbiotic blue-green algae

Within this group we have to distinguish between sponges where blue-green algae play a significant role in nutrition (autotrophic sponges), and those where algae make only a minor contribution to the energy supply (myxotrophic sponges).

Sponges with symbiotic blue-green algae are commonly found at water depth from 10 to 30 m. Occasionally, however, individual specimens may also occur in shallow water areas of a reef where there are high light levels. Investigations on such populations on Flinders Reef (Coral Sea) revealed that nine out of ten species of sponges rather common in that region, carried symbiotic blue-green algae. In fact, depen-

ding upon the season, the blue-green algae in these sponges provided 48 to 80 % of the food requirements, by transferring organic products derived from their photo-synthetic activities into the cells of sponges (WILKINSON, 1983a, 1983b, 1987a, 1987b).

Although one can consider many of these sponges as being almost autotrophic organisms, they contribute – according to WILKINSON (1987a and 1987b) – only to a limited extent to the gross primary production (GPP, refer to Volume 1, pages 25-31) of a reef. And this in an area where sponges represent a large biomass and where up to 60 specimens have been counted per square metre (= 1.2 kg of sponges/m^2).

Autotrophic sponges contain

The colouration of *Dysidea herbacea* can range from yellow to green. We have observed this sponge a few times in the Maldives, where we found it in the slightly turbid water of a lagoon (left), as well as in crystal clear water at the edge of a reef (right).

Xestospongia exigua is known to occur in very shallow water, exposed to very high light levels; however, it has never been reported that it is a photo synthetic species. We discovered this particular specimen on a reef flat at Siladen, North Sulawesi.

the same protective pigments against ultra-violet radiation as corals, which they can use to adapt to a life under extremely high light levels. They include *Carteriospongia flabellifera, C. foliascens* (refer to fact page on page 57), *C. vermifera, Phyllospongia lamellosa, Neofibularia irata, Dysidea herbacea* and *Pseudaxinyssa* spp., and others (WILKINSON & EVANS, 1989).

A combination of food intake occurs in some myxotrophic sponges; that is, either by means of filtration as well as a nutrient supply from their symbiotic blue-green algae. This group includes many rather colourful sponges found on coral reefs, where they usually grow in shaded areas. Blue-green algae are still capable of normal photo-synthetic activities even at substantially reduced light levels. However, in all probability many species within this group depend only to a rather limited degree on any food supplied by their blue-green algae symbionts.

The group of auto-heterotrophic sponges is non-uniform, which is reflected in the composition of its fauna. There is a distinct relationship between that and the amount of nutrients available. In northern Sulawesi we have observed large differences in the number of sponges on littoral reefs, in comparison to neritic reefs in the Coral Sea and in the Maldives.

On a coral reef, sponges with blue-green algae are the dominant animal group underneath rocks, in caves and crevices. They are often very numerous along drop offs, at depths of 15 m and below. If such drop offs are very steep, so that there are projections, small caves and ledges, sponges can be rather numerous right up to the edge of the reef.

The magnificent colours of these sponges range from intensive red, shades of blue or yellow, right up to the less attractive colours of grey or brownish-black. The colours are based on chemical compounds within sponge cells. Just as in the diversity of colouration, there is a similar variety of shapes among sponges, ranging from tube-like species to those which grow in creeping fashion, along a substrate.

In sponges of the order Halichondrida (which now incorporates the former order Axinellida), the numerous spicules are not branched, but slightly curved. This order includes leaf-like and branched sponges which are orange- or yellow-coloured, as

This sponge was photographed in the Red Sea, at a depth of only 3 m and exposed to full sunlight.

Photo: T. Luther

Sponge of order Haplosclerida, possibly a *Callyspongia* species, at 15 m depth on a reef slope at Kanifinolhu, Maldives.

The yellow sponge is an unknown *Crella* species; the red sponge is *Crella cyathophora* and the dark red one is possibly a *Monanchora* species.

for instance in genera *Phakellia, Acanthella* or *Reniochalina*.

The family Chalinidae (order Haplosclerida) includes genus *Haliclona*, which contains many colourful, encrusting or branching sponges. The Blue Reef Sponge, *Haliclona*, is frequently imported, as two different species, belonging to two different genera (refer to fact sheet on page 61). Some *Haliclona* species, such as *H. frascigera*, produce highly attractive tube-like colonies.

In family Tetillidae (with a single genus only) we find the round *Cinachyrella* species, which are easy to recognise (see fact sheet on page 58). These sponges have the size of a tennis ball and are covered with large craters-like pits.

The family Ianthellidae (order Verongida) includes the genus

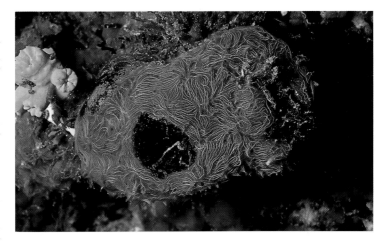

This is a rather frequently found sponge on Indo-Pacific reefs, as seen here in the Maldives. The popular literature describes it generally as *Spirastrella* sp.; however, this is incorrect. The correct taxon is *Haliclona nematifera* (De Laubenfels, 1954). A characteristic trait of this species are the white lines, which appear to be due to a symbiotic fungus (Van Soest, personal communication).

Agelas mauritania at the Great Barrier Reef.

Jaspis serpentina, Coral Sea.

Agelas cf. *conifera* at the U.S.Virgin Islands, Caribbean Sea. Photo: Scott W. Michael

Haliclona fascigera develops attractive tubes. It is one of the most common species of this genus in the central Indo-Pacific region (photo taken at Bunaken, North Sulawesi).

Aplysina fistularia at the U.S. Virgin Islands, Caribbean Sea. Photo: Scott W. Michael

Large individuals of *Ianthella* species at Exmouth, Western Australia, together with other species. The red specimen in the foreground of the photo on the right is *Ianthella basta*.

Ianthella, with several species. Some of them (e. g. *Ianthella basta*) can produce large slab-like or conical structures. The genus *Aplysina*, which occurs in the Caribbean Sea, belongs to the family Aplysinidae in the same order. Its species produce slender, branched structures along reef walls in deep water.

The variability within the group of sponges with symbiotic blue-green algae is so enormous, that identification in most instances is extremely difficult, if not outright impossible. The photos shown on pages 48 to 51 give some idea of the diversity within this group of sponges.

❷ Sponges without symbiotic blue-green algae, which live in nutrient-rich water

The sponges in this group are often numerous in mangrove areas close to river estuaries, on littoral reefs, on sand flats and among algae between and around coral reefs, which are all areas with nutrient-rich water. These sponges are also able to tolerate variable salinities and water with some turbidity.

Collecting activities on the Great Barrier Reef have revealed more than 200 species, which live in such nutrient-rich locations (MATHER & BENNETT, 1993). The sponges in this region are exclusively heterotrophic. They can survive only by filtering food particles out of the water, and so they are hardly of interest to aquarists.

❸ Deep water sponges

As already indicated by their popular name, sponges in this group live near the bottom of coral reefs, at depths of several hundred metres. They are, of course, heterotrophic, and so they too are of no interest to aquarists. In this group we also find relicts from the sponge fauna of the Tethys Sea.

❹ Boring sponges

Boring sponges can penetrate into the calcareous skeletons of corals, by dissolving them with small amounts of acid. Once we observed a boring sponge in a *Porites* species, which had been imported from the Caribbean. When this happens, the sponge must be removed from the coral, before it is placed into an aquarium.

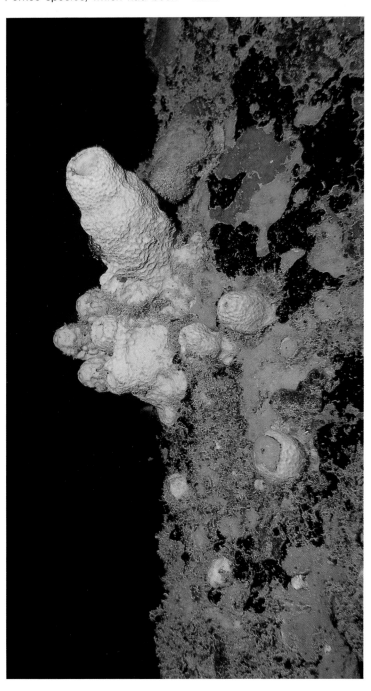

The beauty of sponges lies in their colouration as well as in their shape. This photo shows a diversity of creeper-like sponges and the tube-like, yellow *Verongula rigida* in the U.S. Virgin Islands, Caribbean Sea. Photo: Scott W. Michael

Auletta constricta in an aquarium.

Axinyssa sp. "KA5-POR-01".

Callyspongia sp. "KA5-POR-02".

Callyspongia sp. "KA5-POR-03".

Chelonaplysilla sp. "KA5-POR-04".

Fascispongia costifera. Photo: Scott W. Michael

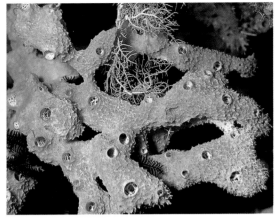

Ircinia sp. "KA5-POR-05".

Mycale cf. *laxissima*.

Oceanapia amboinensis in an aquarium.

Spirastrella inconstans.

Torectandra choanoides.

Two photos: Scott W. Michael

Xestospongia testudinaria.

Callyspongia sp. "KA5-POR-06". Photo: P. Wirtz

Cliona sp. Photo: Scott W. Michael

Grayella cyatophora. Photo: J. Cairns-Michael

Haliclona fascigera. Photo: Scott W. Michael

Hymedismia lancifera.

Two photos: Scott W. Michael

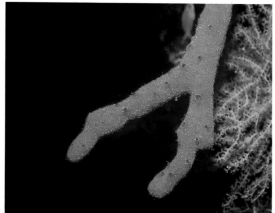

Latrunculia corticata.

Agelas clathrodes. Photo: Scott W. Michael

Agelas widenmayeri.

Aplysina cauliformis. Photo: Scott W. Michael

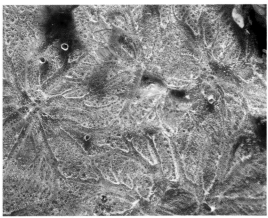

Callyspongia vaginalis. Photo: P. Wirtz

Ircinia sp. "KA5-POR-07". Photo: P. Wirtz

Monanchora arbuscula. Photo: J. Cairns-Michael

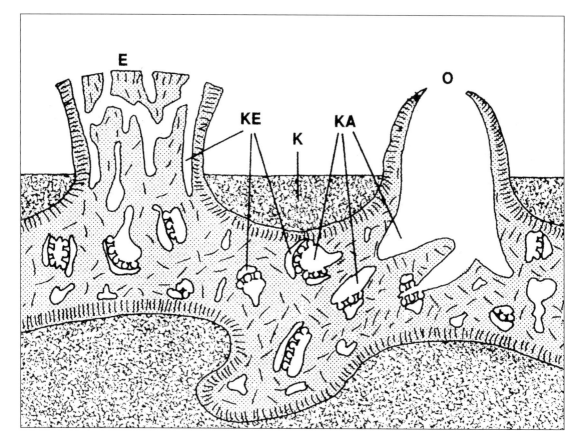

Schematic cross-section through a Boring Sponge of genus *Cliona*, living inside the skeleton of a stony coral. E = Incurrent opening; O = Osculum (exhalant opening); KE = canals for incurrent water; KA = canals for exhalant water; K = calcareous material.

Drawing after SCHUMACHER (1982)

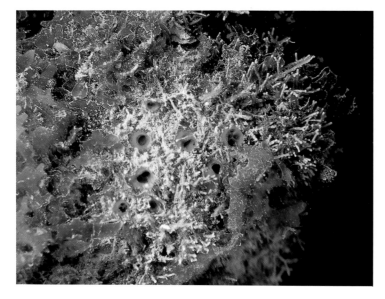

Boring sponge inside a coral at Caja de Muerto, in the vicinity of Puerto Rico, Caribbean Sea.

The genus *Cliona* (family Clionidae, order Hadromerida) contains more than 165 species, which are capable of drilling into – not only coral skeletons – but also into rocks and the shells of molluscs. The colours vary from green to yellow and on to bright red. The first species ever to be described was *Cliona celata*, which had attacked the shells of oysters on an oyster farm. It is also reported, that members of *Cliona* live on many clams, especially those producing pearls.

Cliona orientalis spread out over the surface of coral colonies, but never grows beyond them. In fact, this sponge can produce massive structures and cover more than 2 square metres of coral substrate. Its surface is dark brown and the interior is of a pale yellow colour. This species is easy to identify. *C. viridis* is light yellow and drills into coral rocks with its small, hard papillae. *C. vastifica* is widely distributed in the Red Sea and its surface is bright red.

The genus *Aka* (incorporating the former well-known genus *Siphonodictyon*) includes an unknown number of species. *Aka coralliphaga* is well-known and quite common in the Caribbean Sea. This sponge extends its exhalant opening (osculum) only for a relatively short distance beyond the coral; however, it bores large internal cavities inside the coral, causing considerable damage to the coral skeleton. In the Maldives, we have seen the black *Aka mucosa* repeatedly. It bores into large *Porites* colonies, and it extends some of its tissue to such a degree that the exhalant openings extend well above the coral, like pipes in to the open water. This coral tolerates the sponge and gradually grows around the pipe.

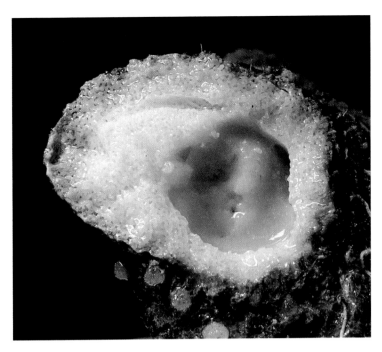

We discovered a Boring Sponge of genus *Cliona* inside this *Porites* hard coral, but only after breaking the coral apart.

The Black Boring Sponge, *Aka mucosa*, is easy to identify. The photograph shows how this sponge has attacked a *Porites* colony, near Kuredo in the Maldives.

Sponges in the coral reef aquarium

It is difficult to provide clear guidelines for keeping sponges in a coral reef aquarium, since the experiences of aquarists have not been uniform and the husbandry results have varied significantly from one aquarium to the next. Generally, sponges must be considered as being rather delicate aquarium animals. Although the majority of imported sponges may well be very colourful, yet most of these organisms do not do well in an aquarium.

In those cases, where sponges have developed on their own in an aquarium, this has usually been from sponge fragments attached to living rocks or to the underside of corals. As such a tank gradually "matures" one can often observe an increase in the sponge population. At the same time we can see that some species are indeed quite hardy and find their particular niches in the aquarium. In fact pages on pages 56 to 64 we have presented a few species, which are typical for well-established aquaria and where they have developed on living rocks.

The purely auto-trophic sponges of genera *Cateriospongia* and *Phyllospongia* also represent an exception to the rule. They have proven to be rather easy to keep, which may be related to their intra-cellular blue-green algae. In addition, we have had good results with the yellow *Pseudosuberites andrewsi* (see fact sheet on page 62).

Large sponge specimens, like the frequently imported, blue *Haliclona* sp. and *Xestospongia* sp. (fact sheets on page 61) and other colourful sponges are often exposed to air while being collected or in shipped in transit. The consequence of this is, that their water canal system is being destroyed. When this happens the canals fill up with air, and we have seen sponges offered for sale actually floating in the shop aquarium. The result of such treatment is inevitably a dead sponge. In general it can be said, that sponges are difficult to transport, and they

Pseudaxinella reticulata from the Caribbean Sea, in an aquarium.

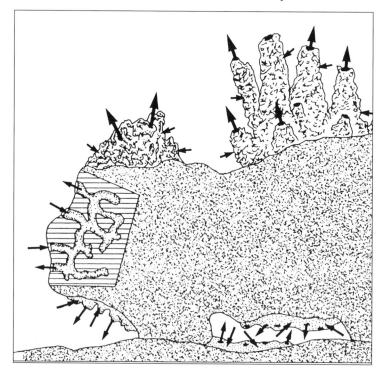

This illustration shows how sponges can establish themselves on rocks. The arrows indicate the direction of incurrent and exhalant water flow.

Drawing after BARNES, 1980

also require special treatment during collecting and subsequent transport. On the other hand, small sponge fragments appear to survive far better than large individuals.

The Caribbean Sea is the origin of the branched, red, orange or yellow *Higginsia* sp., which is relatively often imported for the aquarium trade. This marine sponge grows in shallow water on hard substrate or in water with a strong currents on the exposed side of steep reef walls. Occasionally it is also found on the reef roof or plateau in bright sun light. However, more commonly this sponge occurs at depths of greater than 5 m and it is most numerous at about 25 m. In our experience, it is very difficult to keep this species alive in an aquarium for any length of time. The totally red *Pseudaxinella* sp. is also being imported from the same area. This species is found in very shallow water under very intense light. Here too we have observed that this is another species which is very difficult to keep alive in an aquarium for an extended period of time. Possibly though, small fragments will more readily adapt to life in a coral reef aquarium, than large individual specimens.

If sponges are to be kept in an aquarium, it is important they are placed so that they receive rather dim lighting; or better yet, they should be kept in a dedicated sponge aquarium with low levels of illumination. In addition, most sponges require such heavy supplementary feeding, that it appears fundamentally impossible to keep them together with hermatypic corals. The intensive feeding regimen required for that, creates such bio-load of organic waste products that eventually there will be massive, uncontrollable algae growth. Instead, in a dedicated sponge aquarium, one can alternate between a period of heavy feeding (e. g. drop-feeding for four hours) and twelve hours of strong filtration (followed by an immediate cleaning of the filter). This is deemed to be a sound starting point for operating a sponge aquarium effectively. Water circulation should be very strong, possibly with changing directions. The pumps must be installed in such a way, that they also create ade-

Higginsia sp. "KA5-POR-08" from the Caribbean Sea (in an aquarium).

quate water movement underneath overhanging ledges and in caves.

Another way to explore sponges in the coral reef aquarium is to decorate a small tank with fresh live rocks that one can observe having colonies of sponges on them. Try to collect several pieces with many different species of sponges and arrange them so that they are exposed to a steady water flow. Let the light be weak and add liquid organic food regularly, but without over-feeding the tank. Do not use a skimmer and do not add any organisms that can feed from the sponges, and let the number of fishes and mobile invertebrates be low. Just let the tank be, maintain it normally and observe which sponges that grow and which ones that declines. It may sounds boring to have such a tank, but believe us - it is very interesting to follow how the sponges and other organisms develop from the rocks. In any event, it is important to remember, that sponges are difficult to keep. A dedicated sponge aquarium is a task best left to advanced and very experienced aquarists.

The photo synthetic Worm Sponge, *Carteriospongia vermifera* thrives in a coral reef aquarium, as seen here at "Biotop Aquaristik", St. Augustin-Hangelar, Germany.

Acanthella cavernosa
Spiny Sponge

Distribution: Widely distributed throughout the Indo-Pacific region; generally rather common.

Size and growth form: Massive sponge with many rough, blunt protuberances, with parchment-like membranes in between which occasionally block some exhalant openings. The base of this sponge often develops into a sturdy column.

Reproduction: Unknown under aquarium conditions.

Food: Filter feeder. Requires suspended organic particles as food.

Description: First described by DENDY (1922). All species within the genus *Acanthella* are very difficult to identify.

Aquarium requirements: A rather frequently imported species. Easy to keep, however, strong water current and moderate light intensity are required.

GA: +/-; **SE:** +/-; **CO:** +

Photo:

Spiny Sponge in a coral reef aquarium.   Photo: J. Olsen

Acanthodendrilla sp. "KA5-POR-09"
Fibre Sponge

Distribution: Indo-Pacific; no further details available.

Size and growth form: In our aquarium, this sponge has developed into a round, fist-size sponge specimen.

Reproduction: Unknown under aquarium conditions.

Food: Filter feeder. Requires suspended organic particles as food.

Description: This genus was established by BERGQUIST (1995), which includes so far only a single (*Acanthodendrilla*) species. The Fibre Sponge "KA5-POR-09" presented here is still an undescribed species of this genus. The skeleton consists of a thread-like (fibrous) material, arranged in an irregular, reticulated pattern, which also contains some detritus. The primary fibres protrude beyond the sponge's surface. The hard fibre skeleton and its irregular structure is typical for this genus (VAN SOEST, personal communication), and this feature distinguishes it from the other genera (*Dictyodendrilla* and *Igernella*) of family Dictyodendrillidae.

Aquarium requirements: The sponge shown here grew in a shaded area, from a living rock. Some detritus had accumulated at that site. "KA5-POR-09" appears to be rather hardy.

GA: +; **SE:** +/-; **CO:** +

Photo:

Fibre Sponge "KA5-POR-09" in a coral reef aquarium.

Carteriospongia foliascens

Distribution: Widely distributed throughout the Indo-Pacific.

Reproduction: Easy to culture in an aquarium, by fragmentation. No details available about sexual reproduction.

Size and growth form: Develops into cup-like or laminar shapes, with a diameter of 10 to 20 cm.

Food: Feeds on organic compounds provided by its symbiotic blue-green algae; also a filter feeder.

Description: First described by PALLAS (1766). Surface covered by small nodules. Can produce mono-specific stands in certain locations, covering large areas. Inhabits very shallow reef areas with high light intensity and down reef slopes to levels with medium light intensities.

Aquarium requirements: Very well suited for a coral reef aquarium, but requires a high light intensity. Unfortunately, only rarely available in the aquarium trade.

GA: +; **SE:** 0; **CO:** +

Photo:
Cup-shaped specimen in shallow water of a reef flat, at Green Island, Great Barrier Reef.

Chondrilla sp. "KA5-POR-10"
Chicken Liver Sponge

Distribution: Widely distributed in tropical seas. Details unknown.

Size and growth form: Develops thick, round — but distinctly encrusting – individuals. Remains small under aquarium conditions, where dead coral often become overgrown by this sponge.

Reproduction: Can be reproduced in an aquarium by fragmentation. No information available about sexual reproduction.

Food: Filter feeder.

Description: The taxon *Chondrilla nucula* SCHMIDT (1862) used world-wide for the Chicken Liver Sponge; however, according to VAN SOEST (personal communication) this may involve a species complex, which includes *C. nucula*. In the absence of a revision, it remains uncertain whether the sponge discussed here is actually *C. nucula*. The surface is shiny smooth, of a liver-brown to yellow-brown colour, rather reminiscent of fresh chicken liver. For the most part the tissue does not contain any spicules.

Aquarium requirements: As often as the Chicken Liver sponge is being established on dead coral fragments, it is equally common as small specimens on living rocks. Should be kept in semi-shaded areas (total shade must be avoided). A hardy species, which grows well in an aquarium.

GA: +; **SE:** +/-; **CO:** +

Photo:
Typical growth form of a Chicken Liver Sponge in our aquarium. In this case the sponge grows around a tube of a vermetid snail.

Cinachyrella **spp.**
Ball Sponges

Distribution: Widely distributed throughout the Indo-Pacific and Western Atlantic.

Size and growth form: These are normally small to medium-sized, ball-like sponges.

Reproduction: Unknown under aquarium conditions.

Food: Filter feeder.

Description: This genus has so far been insufficiently investigated in the Indo-Pacific, and a revision is clearly required. RUETZLER & SMITH (1992) provide a revision of the species of the Western Atlantic. These sponges have large oscula craters, and live generally in shaded areas of a reef, e.g. in caves.

Aquarium requirements: We have found small specimens (1 to 3 cm diameter) a few times, underneath or behind living rocks, where they were apparently thriving.

GA: +; **SE:** +/-; **CO:** +

Photos:

Top: *Cinachyrella* sp. "KA5-POR-11" in an aquarium.

Centre: Two small specimens of *Cinachyrella* cf. *malaccensis* on the back of a living rock, which has been part of the tank decoration for some years.

Bottom left: *Cinachyrella* sp. "KA5-POR-12", possibly *C. kuekenthali*.

Bottom right: *Cinachyrella* sp. "KA5-POR-13", together with a shrimp of genus *Leandrites* in a cave at the Maldives.

Collospongia auris
Ear Sponge

Distribution: Widely distributed throughout the Indo-Pacific.

Size and growth form: Grows as a "creeper" and develops plate-like (ear-shaped: auris, lat. = ear) specimens with upright lobes.

Reproduction: Can easily be reproduced in an aquarium by fragmentation. No information available about sexual reproduction.

Food: Filter feeder; also utilises products created by the metabolic activities of its symbiotic blue-green algae.

Description: First described by BERGQUIST et al. (1990). Occurs in shallow reef areas under high light intensity. The colour of this sponge is bluish-grey.

Aquarium requirements: Easy to keep in a coral reef aquarium. Rapidly growing; under optimum conditions this sponge will overgrow large parts of the aquarium's interior. Very well suited for a coral reef aquarium, but will require very bright lighting.

GA: +; **SE:** +; **CO:** +

Photo:
Ear Sponge in a sales tank at "Aqua Weber", Hennef, Germany.

Dendrilla sp. "KA5-POR-14"
Rubber Sponge

Distribution: Known from Australia and Indonesia; no further details available.

Size and growth form: Strongly branched, sometimes finger-like. Rather large with a maximum height of 65 cm. The branches are thick, roundish and appear rubbery.

Reproduction: Presumably produces larvae, since this is the rule in order Dendroceratida, which includes "KA5-POR-14". Nothing known about captive breeding.

Food: Filter feeder. Requires suspended organic particles as food.

Description: The genus *Dendrilla* (family Darwinellidae) was established by LENDENFELD (1883). The fibres do not contain any support material. Presumably, "KA5-POR-14" has not yet been described scientifically. Common name derived from the thick fibres of elastic consistency and the rubbery skin. Oscula rather tiny, with diameters of only 0.2 to 0.8 mm. *Dendrilla rosea* is a related species from Australia, New Zealand and New Caledonia (refer to BERGQUIST, 1980 and 1995). "KA5-POR-14" can be mistaken for the rather similar *Axos cliftoni*, order Axinellida (see HOOPER, 1986).

Aquarium requirements: Occasionally available in the aquarium trade, however, must be categorized as being very difficult to keep in an aquarium. Requires a dedicated sponge aquarium with strong water movement, medium to weak lighting and large amounts of tiny food organisms. Suitable only for experienced aquarists.

GA: -; SE: -; CO: +

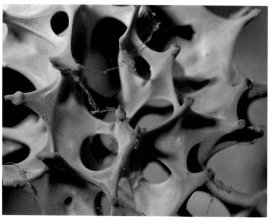

Photos:
Top: Rubber Sponge seen here in a coral reef aquarium at the dealership "Preis-Aquaristik", Bayerfeld, Germany.
Bottom: Close-up view of sponge surface.

Haliclona sp. "KA5-POR-15"
Soft Blue Sponge

Distribution: Indo-Pacific; apparently Central Pacific, around Indonesia; however, further details are not known.

Size and growth form: Usually imported as small to medium-sized specimens of irregular growth form.

Reproduction: Asexual reproduction via fragmentation possible under aquarium conditions. No information available about sexual reproduction in captivity.

Food: Filter feeder.

Description: With an intensive blue colour. Generally imported as *H. madrepora*, a species described in 1889 by DENDY as *Reniera madrepora*. *H. amboinensis* is also blue, but has a different skeletal structure. However, according to VAN SOEST (personal communication) "KA5-POR-15" is a different species. In a comparison to "KA5-POR-16" (below) the tissue feels soft.

Aquarium requirements: Frequently available in the aquarium trade. Presumably the most commonly imported sponge from the central Indo-Pacific region. Requires proper water movement and some light. It is advisable to break up a large specimen into smaller pieces, which will – although growing only slowly – establish themselves. The diet must consist of dissolved organic material and tiny zooplankton.

Photo:
"KA5-POR-15" specimen, which was raised from a tiny fragment in a coral reef aquarium.

GA: +/-; **SE:** +/- ; **CO:** +/-

Xestospongia sp. "KA5-POR-16"
Hard Blue Sponge

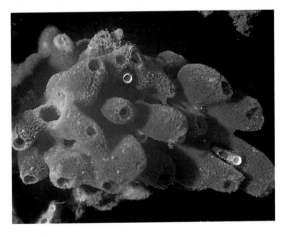

Distribution: Indo-Pacific; apparently in the Central Pacific around Indonesia; however, further details are not known.

Size and growth form: Usually imported as small to medium-sized specimens of irregular growth form.

Reproduction: Asexual reproduction via fragmentation possible under aquarium conditions. No information available about sexual reproduction in captivity.

Food: Filter feeder.

Description: With an intensive blue colour. Looks rather similar to "KA5-POR-15", however, because of smaller mesh, the tissue feels harder and firmer. This is a species which has not yet been described scientifically.

Aquarium requirements: Very frequently available in the aquarium trade. More difficult to keep than "KA5-POR-15". It is advisable to cut a large specimen into small or medium-size pieces, which are then placed at sites with medium light intensity and a moderately strong current. Growth is generally slow. Dead specimens can give off sponge toxins, which may be harmful to soft corals and other invertebrates.

Photo:
Typical growth form of "KA5-POR-16", as commonly available in the aquarium trade.

GA: +/-; **SE:** /-; **CO:** +/-

Pseudosuberites andrewsi

Distribution: Widely distributed throughout the Indo-Pacific.

Size and growth form: Normally encrusting, but can also produce upright shapes.

Reproduction: Asexual reproduction by fragmentation easily possible under aquarium conditions. No information available about sexual reproduction.

Food: Filter feeder.

Description: Originally described from Christmas Island, by KIRKPATRIC (1900). Sponge with light yellow colour.

Aquarium requirements: Very hardy. Slow but steady growth under low lighting only, but with a moderate current present. In our aquarium, we have kept a specimen for several years living inside a cave, with very low light intensity. Frequently available in the aquarium trade.

GA: +; **SE:** +/-; **CO:** +

Photo:
Aquarium specimen, as available in the aquarium trade.

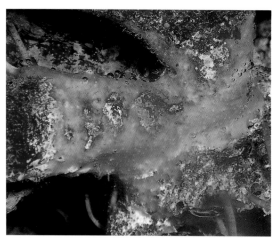

Pleraplysilla cf. australis

Distribution: Indo-Pacific; no further details available.

Size and growth form: Encrusting, forming a thin mat (80-120 µm thick) as a reticulated structure. With a slimy appearance, coloured grey or brownish.

Reproduction: Asexual reproduction by fragmentation possible under aquarium conditions. No information available about sexual reproduction.

Food: Filter feeder.

Description: *P. australis* was first described by HENTSCHEEL (1913) as *Spongelia spinifera* var. *australis*. Half a dozen species are described world-wide, but a revision of this genus is urgently required. The growth is encrusting and the colours of the species most often seen in the aquaria are greyish or pale whitish.

Aquarium requirements: Occurs most frequently in coral reef aquaria, but the thin grey mats in shaded areas of the tank are usually overlooked. Appears to be able to tolerate only low light intensities.

GA:: +; **SE::** +/-; **CO:** +

Photo:
Pleraplysilla mat at the base of a *Euphyllia* sp. in an aquarium.

Stylissa carteri
Cork Bark- or Cork Sponge

Distribution: Widely distributed in tropical seas; fairly frequent in some areas.

Size and growth form: Irregular, upright shapes, reminiscent of a piece of cork bark. Usually less than 20 cm in diameter.

Reproduction: Asexual reproduction by fragmentation possible under aquarium conditions. No information available about sexual reproduction.

Food: Filter feeder.

Description: First described by DENDY (1889), also known as *Acanthella cateri* or *Axinella carteri*. The outward-growing sections are thin, laminar, and of irregular shape. The edges are arch-like. Growth is rapid. The skeleton consists of a very irregular network of pointed spicules, which can be extremely dense in some parts of the sponge.

Aquarium requirements: Frequently imported, and easy to keep. Requires a moderate current and medium to low light intensities.

GA: +; **SE:** +/-; **CO:** +/-

Photos:
Top: Specimen in a sales tank of "Aqua Design", Oldenburg, Germany.
Bottom: Specimen in a coral reef aquarium.

Tethya spp.
Balloon sponges

Distribution: Widely distributed in tropical seas; well known from the Caribbean.

Size and growth form: Usually balloon-shaped, small to medium size.

Reproduction: Asexual reproduction by fragmentation possible under aquarium conditions. No information available about sexual reproduction.

Food: Filter feeder.

Description: The genus *Tethya* contains several species which look all very similar, and which can only be identified by a specialist. Individual specimens usually grow into a helmet- or balloon shape, which is either yellow, orange or red, often overgrown by algae.

Aquarium requirements: Hardy and well suited for coral reef aquaria, but must be provided with a moderately strong current. *Tethya* sp. "KA5-POR-17" (top photo) grew only slowly in our aquarium, but thrived under weak illumination at the bottom of a cave, where some detritus had accumulated.

GA: +; **SE:** +/-; **CO:** +

Photos:
Top: *Tethya* sp. "KA5-POR-17", which is possibly identical with *T. maza*.
Bottom left: *Tethya* sp. "KA5-POR-18" in a tank owned by P. Chlupaty (†).
Bottom right: *Tethya* sp. "KA5-POR-19" near Puerto Rico, Caribbean.

Impressive and attractive sponge formation at Exmouth, Western Australia.   Photo: Scott W. Michael

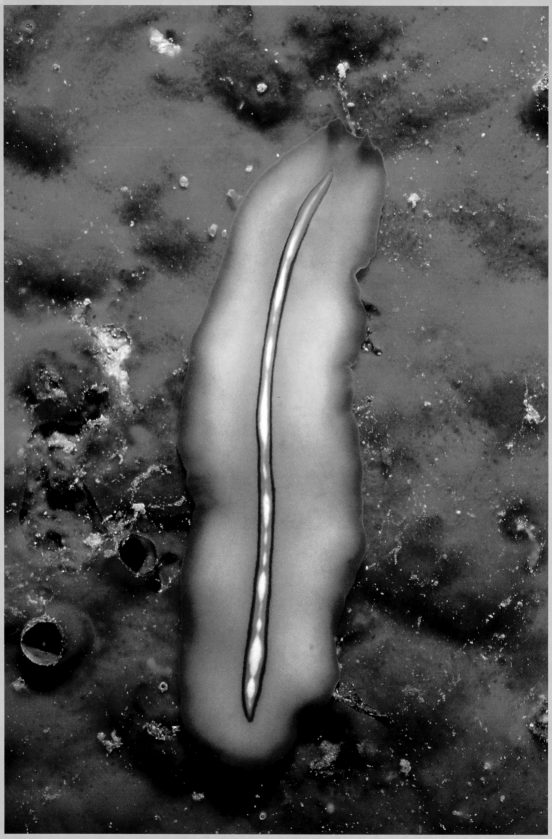

Chapter 4:

Marine Worms

Whenever worms are discussed, most people instinctively conjure up images in their mind of eel-like animals creeping along; animals, which either have no legs at all or only very small ones, and which are simply repulsive. Very broadly speaking, marine worms encompass at least 17 phyla with about 100,000 known species. However, for some of these phyla the collective name "worms" is misleading, and refers largely to the external appearance of the organism, than to any mutual characters in structure and natural history that are being shared with other phyla. For lack of a more suitable name, we would like to select the term "marine worms" for this chapter.

The most primitive worms are distinguished from cnidarians and ctenophores (comb jellies) in that they possess three cell layers: the innermost endoderm, followed by the mesoderm and then outermost ectoderm. In addition, worms have well-developed internal organs, such as strong muscles, a digestive tract and a nervous system. Moreover, worms can be split up into three clearly

Marine worms are an extraordinarily diverse group of animals. They contain delicate, crawling species with a soft and fragile body, such as the common *Pseudoceros bifurcus*, shown here on the left (photo: L. Newman and A. Flowers), and the very colourful Christmas Tree worms of genus *Spirobranchus*, shown above (photo: Scott W. Michael). This photograph shows two species: the brownish specimen (bottom right) is *S. gardineri*, and the other specimens are *S. corniculatus* (see page 142 for further information).

Division of Marine Worm Phyla

1. **Acoelomate Phyla**
   Platyhelminthes · Flatworms
   Gnathostomulida · Jaw Worms
   Nemertea · Ribbon Worms

2. **Pseudocoelomate Phyla**
   Nematoda · Round Worms
   Nematomorpha*
   Gastrotricha · Gastrotrichs
   Rotifera · Rotifers
   Acanthocephala*
   Kinorhyncha · Mud Dragons
   Priapulida · Proboscis Worms
   Loricifera · Girdle Wearers

3. **Coelomate Phyla**
   Annelida · Segmented Worms
   Echiurida · Sausages Worms
   Sipunculida · Peanut Worms
   Pogonophora · Beard Worms
   Chaetognatha · Arrow Worms
   Hemichordata · Acorn Worms

   *not dealt with in this book

distinguishable groups, depending upon the structure and formation of the abdominal cavity (coelom). In order to better understand the structure, biology and phylogenetic history of worms,

the concept "coelom" needs to be discussed in greater detail. See LANZAVECCHIA et al. (1995) for an extensive discussion on body cavities.

In many invertebrates and in all vertebrates, the coelom is the internal cavity, which has developed between the gut and the outer body wall. It provides space for the internal organs and it is internally lined - in part or totally - with epithelium. The body cavity can be either totally absent, or be only incompletely developed from an earlier embryonic stage (blastula stage). Complete development of this cavity is initiated by the middle (mesodermal) cell layer.

Development of the coelom is among the most decisive steps in the evolution of the animal kingdom. In worms we can distinguish between the various developmental stages of the coelom. On that basis we can roughly group marine worms into the following none-phylogenetic assemblages:

❶ **acoelomate** phyla, where the coelom is absent,

❷ **pseudocoelomate** phyla, where a "false" (pseudo) coelom (only partially lined on the inside with epithelium) has been developed from the blastula stage, and

❸ **coelomate** phyla, which have a "genuine" abdominal cavity, developed from mesodermal tissue, and which is totally lined on the inside with epithelium. However, new investigations with the use of electron microscopy have shown that animals in some of the phyla can be both acoelomate (as juveniles) and pseudocoelomate (as adults).

From an aquarist's point of view, only the phylum Annelida (segmented worms) is of great significance. Some of the other phyla could be considered as being important, principally as food organisms for fishes. Others should be mentioned because occasionally they may appear in aquaria, and again others catch our attention because of their colours or interesting natural history. Beyond that, aquarists will have only sporadic contact with the majority of organisms in the 17 phyla listed. Moreover, the worms are often so small that their presence can only be detected with a

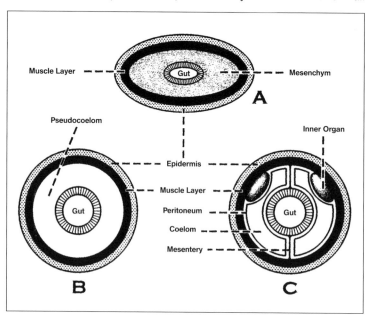

Structure of the abdominal cavity of marine worms: A – acoelomate, B – pseudocoelomate, and C – coelomate phyla.

Drawing after BARNES (1980)

microscope. Yet, others may be buried in the substrate, where they play a very important role as organisms involved in the break down or organic materials. As decomposers these tiny worms play an important role also in the modern coral reef aquarium. Without them it would simply not function.

Acoelomate Phyla

The acoelomate phyla do not possess a coelom, either because it has never been developed or because it has been secondary lost (thus, this has to be regarded as a poly- or paraphyletic group). They are the most primitive of the 15 phyla, discussed in this chapter, but nevertheless, they play a significant role in coral reef ecology. There are many large, extraordinarily marked, colourful species among the flatworms (phylum Platyhelminthes) and the ribbon worms (phylum Nemertea), while for instant the jawed worms of phylum Gnathostomulida are less colourful and they are also microscopically small.

Phylum Platyhelminthes – Flatworms

Anyone snorkelling around a coral reef, will sooner or later come across some leafy-thin, completely flattened, colourful organisms which crawl among the corals or float around in the water with graceful movements. These are flatworms of the order Polycladida (belonging to the former class Turbellaria, see pages 76-86 for details), which are among the most colourful inhabitants of coral reefs. Yet, most turbellarians are very small, with relatively inconspicuous markings. In that respect, the large, colourful polyclad flatworms are unique representative of this group. In terms of aquarium husbandry, flatworms are rarely ever available since they are rather difficult to keep. In part this is due to the fact that they have special food requirements. On the other hand, small parasitic turbellarians occur often in a coral reef aquarium, and can pose potentially significant problems to the aquarist.

As a whole the phylum shows a great diversity in morphology, habitat, biogeography and life-history strategies (LITTLEWOOD et al., 1999). Flatworms are the most primitive invertebrates with three cell layers (triploblastic metazoans), and they have been widely regarded - together with the phylum Gnatostomulida (page 87) - as the earliest divergent bilaterian group and sister-group to all other triploblasts. They are therefore subject of intensive phylogenetic research to resolve the question of the development of primitive invertebrate animals. This applies particularly to the turbellarians.

Systematic overview on the phylum Platyhelminthes
(only down to the rank of order)

"Turbellaria"
    Clade Acoelomorpha
        Order Nemertodermatida
        Order Acoela*
    Clade Catenulida
        Order Catenulida
    Clade Rhabditophora
        Subclade „Lecithoepitheliata"
        Order Gnosonesimida
        Order Prorhynchida
        Subclade Prolecithophora
        Subclade Macrostommorpha
        Order Haplopharyngida
        Order Macrostomida
        Subclade Polycladida
        Order Polycladida*
        Subclade Seriata
        Order Proseriata
        Order Tricladida
        Subclade Rhabdocoelida
        Order Rhabdocoela
        Order Temnocephalida
"Monogena"
Trematoda
    Clade Aspidogastrea
    Clade Digenea
Cestoda
    Clade Amphilinidea
    Clade Gyrocotylidea
    Clade Eucestoda

Only the taxa marked with * are treated in detail in this chapter

Systematics

Phylum Platyhelminthes has traditionally been divided into the three classes Turbellaria, Trematoda (flukes) and Cestoda (tape worms). Turbellaria has traditionally included the free-living species and contained at least nine orders including Acoela (small marine flatworms, often commensal) and Polycladida (the big colourful forms). Trematoda has included the order Monogena (probably about 20,000 species of flukes with a single host in the life cycle and usually ectoparasitic) and Digena (with over 6,000 species all having 4-6 hosts in their life cycle, and almost entirely endoparasitic). Cestoda is the most highly specialized taxa including only internal parasitic species commonly known as tapeworms, in the subclasses Eucestoda and Cestodaria.

Our views have, however, changed greatly lately as new phylogenetic research has taken place. Today there is a basic agreement that the taxa Trematoda and Cestoda are clearly monophyletic; that is all species in Trematoda (or Cestoda respectively) have a common ancestor. The former class of Turbellaria is clearly polyphyletic, i. e. species in this group have not evolved from a common ancestor. The traditionally well established order Acoela as well as other taxa in Turbellaria do probably not even belong to the phylum Platyhelminthes (RUIZ-TRILLO et al., 1999). The monophyly of Monogena is doubtful and in general the phylogeny in the phylum remains to a large extent unresolved. See EHLERS (1985), LITTLEWOOD *et al. (1999), LITVAITIS & ROHDE (1999) and RIEGER et al. (1991) for further informations. The systematic overview on page 69 is based on these sources and gives an overview of the taxa in Platyhelminthes down to the rank of order.

Flatworms also belong to those

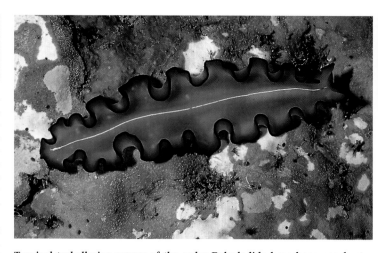

Tropical turbellarian worms of the order Polycladida have been poorly studied for a long period of time. Because of recent taxonomic work by Dr. Leslie Newman and Dr. Lester Cannon, many new genera and species have been described. The beautifully coloured turbellarian worm shown above belongs into the newly established genus *Maiazoon*. It is *M. osaki*.

Photo: L. Newman and A. Flowers

animals, which were the first to develop a posterior and an anterior orientation of the body. Many of the more than 15,000 known flatworms are marine, but there are also several freshwater species and some, which occur in moist terrestrial habitats. Platyhelminthes also includes perhaps the largest clade of obligate parasites, grouped in the taxon Neodermata incorporating the monogeneans, cestodes, digeneans and aspidogastreans. Neodermatans are characterized by their "new skin" which replaces the plesiomorphous ciliated epidermis on transitions from larva to adult. They parasitize an enormous number of vertebrates and invertebrates and have become significantly modified in terms of their appearance and mode of life. An example of this is the longest worm in this group, the tape worm *Taenia solium*, which can reach a length in excess of 30 m. The group also includes some of the most medically and economically important parasites known (LITTLEWOOD et al., 1999).

Turbellaria is the most important taxon in the phylum Platyhelminthes seen from an aquarist's point of view. In Trematoda (flukes) and Cestoda (tape worms)

we only find parasitic species. Although we can find parasitic tape worms in coral reef fishes, generally, however, the latter two taxa are of little significance to the marine aquarium hobby. However problems with flukes and tapeworms occur frequently in the freshwater realm. We are not going to discuss flukes and tape worms further in this chapter.

"Turbellaria" – Flatworms

In older literature, the separation of tubellarians was based on the development of the gut. According to that system, there are four orders (Acoela, Rhabdocoela, Tricladida and Polycladida); but this is outdated. Today many different anatomical details are used as a basis for the classification of these worms, and it would go beyond the scope of this book to discuss these in detail. To obtain further information the reader is referred to CANNON (1986), which contains an excellent review of all families and orders, together with illustrations and appropriate commentaries. In addition, there is also an identification key, leading up to orders and families, as well as a chronological literature overview of old and new publications about these animals. In FAUBEL (1983, 1984) and PRUDHOE (1985) there is a thorough systemstic review of the Polycladida, while NEWMAN & CANNON (1994b, 1997, 1998) provide an excellent overview over the genera *Pseudoceros* and *Pseudobiceros*.

In fact, the tropical tubellarians are not the ones that have been intensively studied, but instead the species of Acoela from northern European coastal waters have been examined in great detail (e. g. for further details see DÖRJES, 1968).

Anatomy

Flatworms are unsegmented worms with three cell layers, a distinct anterior and posterior section, as well as with a dorsal and abdominal region. They are strongly compressed dorso-ventrally, bilaterally symmetrical and they move about crawling on their cilia. Body shapes vary among flatworms, from typical oval shapes (found among many species of the superfamily Planoceroidea) to elongated species (found among many species of the superfamily Cestoplanoidea). The size is also highly variable, from the smallest known species, *Stylostomum notula*, which is less than 1 mm long, to the largest species *Discoplana gigas*, which can reach a length in excess of 15 cm. But most species stay within a length from 10 to 60 mm.

The ventral abdominal region, moving over a substrate below, is smooth and often without pigmentation, while the dorsal surface is often slightly convex with a brown or grey colour; however, there are also some families of turbelllarians with very attractive markings. Although the dorsal region is often smooth, it can also be covered with papillae, tubercles or elongated protruberances. At the anterior end of the body there are usually two tentacles over the brain or along

Pseudoceros imperatus during copulation, near Madang, Papua-New Guinea.
Photo: L. Newman and A. Flowers

the anterior margin, which can normally not be retracted into the body. Below the outer skin (epidermis) there are light-sensitive cells (photo-receptors), usually anteriorly, but they can also extend along the body towards the posterior end. The photo-receptors react to light and are often referred to as "eyes". However, they are certainly not eyes in the sense that they can reflect an image of the surroundings onto a retina.

The mouth is located along the midline of the body, often anteri-

Pseudoceros lindae during copulation, at Heron Island, Great Barrier Reef.
Photo: L. Newman and A. Flowers

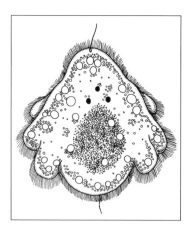

"Müller's Larvae" of a *Pseudoceros* species. Drawing from NEWMAN & CANNON (1994b)

orly, e. g. in *Pseudoceros* spp. In other species it can also be located far posterior, e. g. in *Stylochus* spp.

The cross-section of a turbellarian shows the epidermis (outer skin layer) on the outside with protuberances (microvilli), which increase the surface area of the outer skin. Below the epidermis is a muscle layer, which consists of longitudinal as well as transverse muscle cells.

A characteristic feature of flatworms is the presence of many glandular cells, which are located inside the muscle layer or sometimes even in the epidermis. These glandular cells produce a mucus, which helps the worm to glide along the substrate. If necessary, tubellarians can also execute graceful swimming movements, by ruffling the margins in an undulating motion. The mucous excretion also serves to encapsulate prey organisms. There are many types of mucus-secreting cells, and all appear to be externally very similar, but they have variable physiological functions which have not yet been fully investigated (PRUDHOE, 1985).

One special type of cell occurs in the order Polycladida; these are the rhabdites. Their function is still unclear, however, it assumed that they are of a protective nature, whereby they excrete a mucus which protects the worm. The ultra-structures of these cells suggest that there is an evolutionary connection between these cells and the stinging cells of cnidarian animals (REISINGER & KELBETZ, 1964). Unfortunately, the Polycladida have not yet been studied in detail for very long and the latest research shows that this order is far more diverse than had originally been thought. Consequently, a series of new genera and species have been recently described by NEWMAN & CANNON (1994a, 1996a, 1996b, 1997, 1998). A major problem in the past was the lack of any way to properly fix and preserve these animals since they tend to autolyse when stressed. It was not until NEWMAN & CANNON (1995) solved this problem that the door to the study of these flatworms was opened.

Flatworms have neither a respiratory system nor do they have a blood circulatory system. Gas exchange takes place directly across the epidermis. The continuous movement of cilia along the epidermis assures a smooth water flow along the surface of the worm, and so facilitates an even oxygen uptake and carbon dioxide discharge. Peristaltic movements of the gut and the active internal cilia effect the transport of gases in the interior of the worm. Of course, any gas exchange based on diffusion also limits the size of the animal. They also have no anus and waste material is reguritated out through the mouth.

Reproduction

Flatworms have well developed sex organs, which are located ventrally along the abdomen, behind the pharynx, and often appear as a whitish area. The reproductive structures are extremely complex, and it is also the definitive systematic characteristic in many flatworms. Therefore, in publications with keys to the genera and species there are always detailed drawings of the genitalia. Only in a few genera is colour pattern a reliable systematic characteristic. With the exception of *Discoplana gigas* and a few other species, polyclad flatworms are hermaphrodites, possessing both male and female reproductive organs but they do not seem to fertilize themselves. Also, there is nothing known about asexual reproduction in polyclads.

Copulation and reproduction in flatworms are apparently not tied to a specific time of the year. Sperm is deposited into females

The majority of turbellarian worms from genus *Pseudoceros* feed on colonial tunicates. This makes them food specialists, and are therefore difficult to keep alive in an aquarium. Drawing from NEWMAN & CANNON (1994b)

by reciprocal copulation or hypodermic insemination where it migrates to the oviducts to fertilise the ova (MICHIELS & NEWMAN, 1998). In copulation females normally have strictly control over the process. By hypodermic insemination the sperm is injected directly under the partner's skin a feature that is well known in hermaphrodites, but rare among animals having separate sexes. Insemination gives the male direct access to the eggs, while the females are left with the costs of healing of wounds and lose control over fertilization. MICHIELS & NEWMAN (1998) observe the mating behaviour among a population of *Pseudoceros bifurcus* and found that the animals indeed attempted to increase sperm donation over sperm receipt. A small coral reef aquarium should be perfect for studying this interesting behaviour further.

The number of eggs is highly variable, from 7,000 up to 21,000 in *Stylochus inimicus*, and in *S. ijimai* even up to 132,000 eggs (PRUDHOE, 1985). The eggs are deposited in thin mats or in spiral- or sawtooth-shaped bands. They are enclosed by a gelatinous substance and are usually one cell thick. It has not yet been determined whether the maternal animals die after spawning or whether

Unknown species of the familiy Pseudocerotidae, which lives on the photosynthetic, colonial tunicate *Didemnum molle*.
Photo: L. Newman and A. Flowers

they stay alive.

Hatching time is dependent upon temperature, salinity and size of the egg yolk. The larvae, called "Müller's larvae", or "Gottes larvae" are reminiscent of a trochophore larvae, as found in many other invertebrates. It can develop either into an adult (direct development), or undergo metamorphosis (indirect development) through a planktonic stage.

The sucker (adhesive organ) is

found ventrally close to the opening of the reproductive structures. It is believed that the sucker helps the worm to attach itself to the substrate. It might also be used in copulation.

Colouration

As mentioned above, some flatworms are exquisitely coloured, especially Polyclads, which belong into the suborder Cotylea. Only very few invertebrates on a coral reef display such colour and splendour. The colours are formed by pigment granules in the epidermis or in the muscle layers; however, colouration in flatworms can also be dependent upon the type of prey consumed.

CROZIER (1917) observed that specimens of *Pseudoceros* fed on tunicates with different colours would take on the colour of their respective prey. In addition, CROZIER also found that the dyes would accumulate not only in the digestive system of the worm, but also appeared in its epidermal cells. LEVETZOW (1943) noted that *Thysanozoon brochii*, which occurs in the Gulf of Naples and feeds on the common ascidian tunicate *Ciona intestinalis*, normally takes on the light brown colour shade which corresponds

The imitator flatworm, *Pseudoceros imitatus* (right), mimics the nudibranch, *Phyllidiela pustulosa* (left).
Photo: L. Newman and A. Flowers

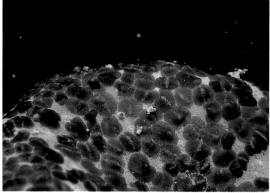

Acoel flatworms live on the surface of soft corals of genus *Sarcophyton* in Papua-New Guinea. Although many of these turbellarian worms carry symbiotic algae, they probably also take in supplementary food from the microorganisms caught in the mucous secretion of the corals.   Photo: L. Newman and A. Flowers

to that of the tunicate. However, some specimens were coloured lilac, a type of colouration found in a colonial tunicate, that of *Botryllus* sp., often occuring as a "creepers", growing over *Ciona intestinalis*.

The conclusion is that colouration is not solely based on the presence of pigments in the epidermis but that it is also sequestered from prey animals.

Food

What do flatworms feed on? Many of the small platyhelminthes of order Tricladida, no doubt, feed on dead organisms and other organic detritus. Species of the order Acoela, which possess symbiotic

algae are commonly found on cnidarians may also feed on mucus excreted by their cnidarian host. Similarly, acoels, which occur sporadically on the substrate of an aquarium, probably feed on diatoms.

NEWMAN & CANNON (1994b) report that colonial tunicates are the most important food for *Pseudoceros*. Many species of *Pseudobiceros* feed on a variety of small invertebrates. Consequently these flatworms are clearly not suited for an aquarium. The diet of polyclads has not been researched in detail but it is not simple to find suitable food for specimens being maintained in captivity. Therefore, we must regard turbellarian flat-

worms as very delicate aquarium organisms.

Regeneration

Many people associate flatworms with considerable regenerative capabilities, that is, the ability to develop new body sections after an injury. This applies, for instance, to the regeneration in small tricladids, especially freshwater species. In these animals new body sections can develop from merely a torn off piece of a worm. Among the large colourful Polycladida the knowledge on their capability to regenerate tissue is lacking at present, but scientists are working on the subject.

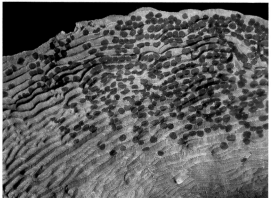

Acoel flatworms on branches of a scleraxonian coral from family Melithaeidae, at Papua-New Guinea.
Photo: L. Newman and A. Flowers

Small acoel flatworms on the surface of a stony coral of genus *Leptoseris* on a reef at Bunaken, North Sulawesi, Indonesia.

A new body can develope if a damage area contains some brain ganglia (nerve center) from the head section. Other anatomical parts can be regenerated only partially or not at all. However, tubellarians can repair relatively large injuries rapidly through the formation of new tissue.

Although the regenerative capability is well developed, many species, especially polyclads, can easily autolyse if they are handled carelessly or when they are exposed stress. We have observed this phenomenon ourselves, when we transported three *"Pseudoceros pardalis"* (see photo on page 84) from the Caribbean in the same plastic bag. Two specimens had been exposed to slight physical pressure and this lead to their immediate degeneration.

Habitat

The order Polycladida is almost exclusively marine. Only species of *Limnostylochus* are found in fresh- or brackish water. Sporadically members of other genera also migrate into water with low salinities or even semi-terrestrial habitats (NEWMAN & CANNON, 1997b). Flatworms occur to great oceanic depths, however, most species are found in the intertidal zone. A few species lead a pelagic existence.

Flatworms live in a wide range of habitats on a coral reef. They occur underneath rocks, among algae, in empty clam and mussel shells, or associated with ascidians, sponges and corals. Some species live in close association with other animals without inflicting any direct damage on them. *Cateroplana colobocentroti*, which lives on the sea urchin *Colobocentrus* sp., is such an example. This turbellarian is very closely tied to its host, and does not occur without it. This symbiotic relationship has been observed in Indonesia and in Hawaii – two areas in the Indo-Pacific which are more than 8000 km apart (PRUDHOE, 1985).

Another example of symbiosis

between a flatworm and another organism is *Stylochoplana parasitica*, which lives parasitically underneath the operculum of the beetle snail *Liolophura japonica*. When the worm and the snail are separated, the worm dies within a short period of time. So far it has remained unclear why the worm cannot survive even for a short period time without its host. Possibly it has adapted to the abundant, oxygen-rich water which flows continuously over the gills of the snail.

An as of yet undescribed species of pseudocerotid lives symbiotically with the photo-synthetic, colonial tunicate *Didemnum molle*. Some flatworms are predators of other invertebrates especially commercially important bivalve species and they can inflict severe damage to oyster farms.

There are many examples of mimicry of coral reefs inhabitants and flatworms are no exception. The Imitator Flatworm, *Pseudoceros imitatus*, is an exceptionally effective mimic of the Pustule Night Snail, *Phyllidela pustulosa*, which provides the turbellarian with effective protection against predators (see NEWMAN et al., 1994). Many other species mimic nudibranch colour patterns yet it is unclear whether one or both animals are toxic. Several other animals are known to mimic polyclads. For example juvenile batfish are black with a bright orange margin and have been observed swimming on their side undulating their fins in the same sensual movement as some Pseudocerotids (see NEWMAN & CANNON, 1994a).

Clade Acoelomorpha
Order Acoela

The flatworms of cold waters have been relatively well studied, however little is known regarding tropical species. On the other hand, Acoels are well known within aquarium circles since they tend to establish themselves as commensals on cnidarians, a type of behaviour which can also be commonly observed on coral

reefs. Aquarists often apply the erroneous term "planarians" to this group of worms, a designation which applies only to the flatworms of order Tricladida.

As mentioned on page 70 the phylogenetic position of Acoela is far from clear. Traditionally the group has been placed as an order in the class Turbellaria, but according to LITTLEWOOD et al. (1999) and RHODE (pers. comm.), it can very well be that Acoela does not even belong to the phylum Platyhelminthes. Until their true position is established, we find it best to include them here.

The members of Acolea are small, marine flatworms usually only a few mm in length. Traditionally they are considered more primitive than polyclads with respect to body structure. They differ from the large polyclads among others by not having a gut or any other digestive system. The mouth opens directly into the parenchyma (body tissue). They also lack the ventral sucker, protonephridia (excretory organs) and eyes. Unlike most of the bigger flatworms acoels reproduce frequently by asexual reproduction, often by fission. The best known genus in the Acoela is *Convoluta*.

Volume 2 (chapter 16, pages 314-315) provides a brief discussion of parasitic flatworms which attack cnidarians. There are many species which live with cnidarians in a commensal relationship where the host is not detrimentally affected by the turbellarian, while the worm in turn gets food from its host. Many commensal flatworms live together with symbiotic algae. *Convoluta convoluta* accommodates the diatom *Licmophora* sp. (APLET, 1969), while *C. roscoffensis* lives symbiotically with the green algae *Tetraselmis convolutae* (PARKE & MANTON, 1967; SMITH & DOUGLAS, 1987). The symbiotic relationship between algae and two turbellarian worms *Amphiscolops* cf. *australis* and *Haplodiscus* sp. has been investigated by TRENCH & WINSOR (1987). Both turbellarian worms live together with corals. It is also known that *A.* cf. *australis* occurs in large aggregations on the bottom of the Sea of Belau. While *A.* cf. *australis* is specialised to live only on a certain type of algae of genus *Amphidinium*. *Haplodiscus* sp. lives symbiotically with another, very large *Amphidinium* sp., as well as with a *Symbiodinium* sp. Both of these belong into the family Gymnodiniidae.

In tropical seas we have been able to observe commensal flatworms on hermatypic corals of the genera *Montipora* and *Leptoseris*, as well as on ahermatypic corals of the genus *Tubastraea* (see Volume 2, page 314-315). These worms also occur frequently on soft corals especially on those of the genus *Sarcophyton* and on holaxonian corals of the family Melithaeidae.

In the aquarium we find acoels often on disc anemones of genus *Discosoma*, as well as on soft corals. Under aquarium conditions we have never observed these worms inflicting damage to their host. However, they can multiply to such an extent that they cause an adverse aesthetic impact on the entire tank. It has been our experience that the population level of flatworms in an aquarium will eventually regulate itself. The identification of these commensals flatworms is unreliable, however, it stands to reason that they belong into the genus *Waminoa* (WINSOR, pers. comm.).

A somewhat objectionable representative of the Acoela, which often occurs often in an aquarium, is the small *Convolutrilobia* (?) sp. This worm does not live on cnidarians, instead it spreads out along the bottom of the aquarium, where it presumably feeds on algae. These flatworms, coloured yellow-red, are smaller than those commonly found on cnidarians. Under certain circumstances there can, due to asexual reproduction, be a virtual population explosion, so that the worms cover the entire bottom and all tank decoration in plague proportions. According to PIKA (pers. comm.), such an outbreak can be effectively combatted by the wrasse *Halichoeres marginatus*.

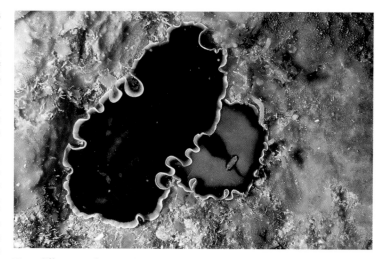

Two different colour variations of the acotylean *Callioplana marginata* at Heron Island, Great Barrier Reef.   Photo: L. Newman and A. Flowers

Clade Rhabditophora
Order Polycladida

The order Polycladida contains the two suborders Acotylea and Cotylea.

- Suborder Acotylea

In this suborder the sucker (adhesive organ), normally found just behind the female's genital pore is absent. This characteristic distinguishes Acotyleans from the suborder Cotylea which possesses a sucker. However, based on CANNON (1986) we present the systematics of this group on page 77, which includes all families, however, only a small selection of some of the most common genera is listed.

The Acotylea is an enormously diverse group and a full coverage is not possible here. Species of superfamily Cestoplanoidea have eyespots in the head region of the body. Some species are narrow and long, some are free living, while others occur as symbionts on hermit crabs.

Eyespots along the sides of the body are absent in the superfamily Planoceroidea. *Apidioplana* spp. (family Apidioplanidae) live symbiotically on holaxonian corals. One of the most frequently encountered genera is *Callioplana*, and *C. marginata* with its ty-

pical oval shape, two tentacles and eyespots is strongly reminiscent of species of family Pseudoceratidae. They are active predators feeding on other small invertebrates.

In coral reefs most of the members of superfamily Planoceroidea live under rocks in low light habitats. Here they are well-protected against predators and so there is no need for protective colouration. For the most part these worms are inconspicuously coloured and are often almost transparent, an example is *Paraplanocera oligoglena* (family Planoceridae). These worms are rounded oval. Among other forms, this family also contains many planktonic species.

The family Leptoplaniidae contains species which commonly occur on coral reefs. In the superfamily Stylochoidae species display distinct eyespots along the sides of the body. From among this group, species like *Stylochus* sp. and *Imogine matatasi* (family Stylochidae) are known predators of rock- and pearl oyster, as well as giant clams. These worms have caused considerable damage to oyster farms in Australia and throughout the Pacific Region (NEWMAN et al., 1993; JENNINGS & NEWMAN, 1996a, b).

Flatworms of family Stylochidae have, like the rest of the flat-

Two unknown planocerid acotyleans from One Tree Island, Great Barrier Reef. Both species are transparent, which is typical for species which live in darkness. Photos: L. Newman and A. Flowers

worms, not been studied very well, but are one of the largest and most widely distributed groups represented by many genera and species in tropical seas. There are also brackish- and freshwater species in this family. The species have a reticulated dark colour on a solid background, and tentacles pointing forward, (CANNON, 1986). *Stylochus* is the type genus, but the family also contains the genus *Imogine*. The two genera are separated based on differences in the structure of the seminal vesicle (JENNINGS & NEWMAN, 1996a). Even though stylochid flatworms are known to be pests of cultured bivalves around the world, very little is known about their biology. Many species are found associated with oysters, but it is unclear if whether or not all species actually prey on the bivalves.

Suborder Acotylea

Superfamily Cestoplanoidea
   Family Cestoplanidae
      Cestoplana
   Family Diplopharyngeatidae
   Family Emprosthophanyngidae
Superfamily Planoceroidea
   Family Apidioplanidae
      Apidioplana
   Family Callioplanidae
      Callioplana
   Family Enantiidae
   Family Gnesiocerotidae
   Family Hoploplanidae
   Family Leptoplaniidae
      Leptoplana, Discoplana,
      Dignyopora
   Family Planoceridae
      Planocera, Paraplanocera
   Family Stylochocestidae
   Family Themathidae
Superfamily Stylochoidea
   Family Cryptocelididae
   Family Discocelididae
   Family Latocestidae
   Family Plehniidae
   Family Polyposthiidae
   Family Stylochidae
      Stylochus, Indistylochus,
      Enterogonia, Leptostylochus,
      Mexistylochus

Paraplanoceros oligoglena at Madang, Papua-New Guinea. Photo: L. Newman and A. Flowers

Imogine mcgrathi is notorious for causing massive damage to oyster farms, here at Stradbroke Island, Moreton Bay, Australia. Photo: L. Newman and A. Flowers

- Suborder Cotylea

Cotyleans can be distinguished from those in suborder Acotyleans by the presence of a ventral sucker, immediately behind the female genital pore although this character may be difficult to see. Cotyleans contain many families and genera with large, free-living species, easily noticed on a coral reef. It is conceivable that some of these will eventually appear in the aquarium trade, especially those of family Pseudoceratidae. The systematic overview of suborder Cotylea (see to the right), which includes all families as well as the most important genera, gives an idea of the complexity of the group where a revision is much needed. See FAUBEL, 1984; PRUD-HOE, 1985; NEWMAN & CANNON (1994a and b, 1996a and b, 1997, 1998) for further information.

In family Prosthiostomidae the worms are extremely long and narrow with a smooth surface without tentacles, however, there is a well-developed ventral sucker. The family contains mainly tropical species of the genus *Prosthiostonum*.

Members of family Euryleptidae tend to be small, oval-shaped and are either covered by papillae or smooth-bodied. One *Cycloporus* sp. occurs commonly on soft corals such as *Sarcophyton*. However, *Cycloporus* is also found under rocks and commensually with sponges and ascidians. These flatworms can be quite attractively coloured. Eyespots may occur along the anterior margin or in two elongated clusters over the brain. Eyespots also contained in this family is the genus *Eurylepta* where species are – in terms of body shape – more elongated than those of *Cycloporus*. They also have longer tentacles with eyespots along the sides. *Eurylepta* occur in tropical as well as in temperate and colder seas and are easily confused with Pseudocerotids. The main difference is that Euleptrids possess marginal tentacles and two cerebral eyespots wheras Pseudocerotids have pseudotentacles

formed from the anterior margin and only one cerebral eyespot.

Members of the monogeneric family Pericelididae (genus *Pericelis*) commonly occur in tropical seas. They are also known from the reef aquarium. These worms are relatively thick, wide and extensively ruffled along the margin. They also possess two small pseudotentacles with eyespots. This genus contain several species yet the majority of them has not yet been described.

The best studied and most conspicuously coloured polyclads are those in the family Pseudocerotidae. Only recently has this family been studied in detail. NEWMAN & CANNON (1994b, 1997, 1998) describe and redescribe many species of the genera *Pseudoceros* and *Pseudobiceros*, the two most diverse genera in

Prosthiostomum sp., possibly *P. trilineatum* at Madang, Papua-New Guinea.
Photo: L. Newman and A. Flowers

Pericelis spp.

Distribution: Indo-Pacific and Caribbean; no further details available.
Size: From less than 1 cm up to several centimetres.
Reproduction: Details unknown.
Food: Since *Pericelis* sp. "KA5-PER-02" survived well under aquarium conditions, it appears to have taken various kinds of food, probably small invertebrates by engulfing them.
Description: *Pericelis* (LADILOW, 1902) is the only genus of family Pericelididae. PRUDHOE (1985) describes the genus as (translated): "... elongated to widely oval with small anterior, widely separated marginal pairs of tentacles. Ventral sucker (adhersive organ) disc located posteriorly. Marginal eyes in continuous rows surrounding the head, cerebral eyes in two elongated bunches, frontal eyes present ..." Fundamentally, the body of *Pericelis* is fleshy and wide, the pseudotentacles are small and folded. "KA5-PER-02" has been found in aquaria. It is dorsally ruffled, with a brownish background and numerous oval, light-brown spots, which increased in numbers towards the margin; the ventral surface is whitish (see photos upper right and centre). We found *Pericelis* sp. "KA5-PER-02" under rocks among algae on an exposed (at low tide) reef flat along the Daintree coast, Northern Queensland, Australia.
Aquarium requirements: Very little is known about this worm. "KA5-PER-02" has been found among live rocks when a coral reef aquarium was emptied after several years of operation. It can be presumed that this specimen in question had been introduced into the aquarium together with live rocks. The specimen was transferred to one of our tanks, but was never seen again. It stands to reason, that this turbellarian worm lives in crevices and hollows of rocks and is therefore rarely ever seen.

GA: +; **SE:** +; **CO:** 0

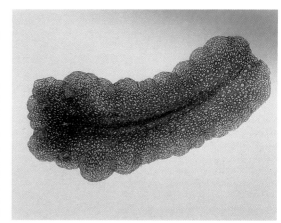

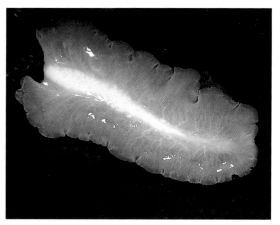

Photos:
Top: Dorsal side of *Pericelis* sp. "KA5-PER-02".
Centre: Ventral side of *Pericelis* sp. "KA5-PER-02".
Bottom: *Pericelis* sp. "KA5-PER-02", as found below a rock in Northern Queensland, Australia.

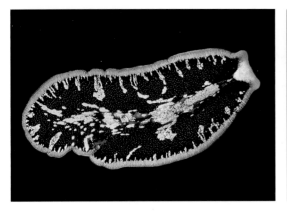
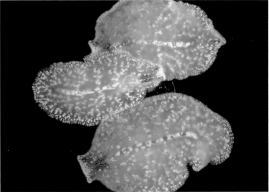

Tiny, magnificently coloured and extremely delicate turbellarians of genus *Cycloporus* at Heron Island, Great Barrier Reef.
Photos: L. Newman and A. Flowers

Pericelis sp. "KA5-PER-01". Turbellarian worms of genus *Pericelis* occur sometimes in a coral reef aquarium. Apparently they may be introduced together with live rocks (also see fact sheet on page 79).
Photo: L. Newman and A. Flowers

this family. Yet, there are still many species which have not yet been formally described as the family Pseudocerotidae probably contains more than 500 species (NEWMAN, pers. comm.). Over 90 % of the polyclad specimens that were collected at Heron Islands and One Tree Island in the southern Great Barrier Reef, Australia were undescribed species (NEWMAN & CANNON, 1994b).

Pseudoceros and *Pseudobiceros* can be readily identified on the basis of their colour patterns. *Pseudobiceros* generally display the more colourful patterns, often involving a combination of spots, stripes and dots against a unicoloured background. This makes the various species highly attractive to us humans, but the spectacular colours are warnings to predators about their distastefullness. NEWMAN & CANNON

Two euryleptids of the new genus *Margitirella*, to the left *M. marygarsonae*, to the right *M. fuscopunctata*, at Heron Island, Great Barrier Reef.
Photos: L. Newman and A. Flowers

(1994a, 1997, 1998) have published a review of colour patterns of *Pseudoceros* as well as of *Pseudobiceros*. In *Pseudoceros* the body is pliable (soft), extremely delicate, oval-shaped, and it often narrows posteriorly. The anterior margin has simple folded pseudotentacles with a horsehoe-shaped eyespots, containing about 100 eyes.

The members of *Pseudobiceros* are the biggest and most conspicious flatworms found on the coral reefs, but are even more fragile than *Pseudoceros*. Their margin is strongly folded into ear-shaped and pointed pseudotentacles. The cerebral eyespots is small and contain about 200 eyes. Colour patterns in *Pseudobiceros* are often more flambyouant than in *Pseudoceros*.

The most distinguishing character – as already indicated by the genera names – lies in the fact that in *Pseudoceros* possess only a **single** male genital pore and apparatus behind the mouth opening, while there are **two** male systems in *Pseudobiceros*. There are also differences between the two genera shown in their copulatory behaviour. Beyond that, there are anatomical differences, which involve complex techniques for examination. Also *Pseudoceros* are much more specific in their food selection than *Pseudobiceros*. Further information can be obtained by referring to the work of NEWMAN & CANNON (1994b).

One of the most common *Pseudoceros* species is *P. bifurcus*. With its lilac-coloured margin, a lilac-white centre section and a white and orange median stripe, it is an extraordinarily colourful species. Yet, this colour pattern can vary within the species. Like the majority of species within this family, this species feeds on colonial tunicates, especially on *Eudistoma laysani*. This clearly indicates, that the *Pseudoceros* spp. are highly developed food specialists.

An equally magnificent-looking species is *Pseudoceros sapphirinus* with its velvet black body

This small, rather colourful turbellarian, *Pseudoceros susanae*, occurs frequently in the Maldives (see NEWMAN & ANDERSON, 1997 for description). The species has frequently been misidentified as *Pseudoceros dimidiatus* in popular literature.

completely enclosed by a deep blue band. This species can be frequently encountered on the Great Barrier Reef where it often is found gliding across live coral. If this worm is being disturbed, it will give off a dark-red mucus.

Among those species with a mottled colour pattern is *Pseudoceros felis* with markings resembling those of a wild cat (felis, lat. = cat). This species is smaller than most other ones of this genus, measuring only a few centimetres in length.

If one visits the Maldives and dives some of the magnificient reefs of these remote islands, one should not be surprised to come across *Pseudoceros susanae*, a recently described flatworm, (NEWMAN & ANDERSON, 1997). In

several older popular books *P. susanae* has been misidentified as *P. dimidiatus*. The species is perhaps the most abundant species of polyclads in the Maldives and is also known from the Seychelles and from Indonesia. The body is elongated-oval with shallow marginal ruffles. The pseudotentacles are simply folds and the cerebral eyespot is horshoe shaped with about 40 eyes. There are three or four rows of dorsal pseudobranchial eyes along the anterior margins and ventral pseudobranchial eyes in two clusters. The background color is light to brilliant blue being darker towards the margins. Medially the colour is orange with a longitudinal white stripe. Between the orange and blue areas there is a

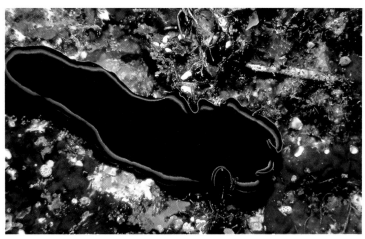

Pseudoceros sapphirinus seen here at Lizard Island, Great Barrier Reef, shows the typical shape of one of the larger turbellarian worms of genus *Pseudoceros*.

Photo: L. Newman and A. Flowers

Pseudoceros bimarginatus

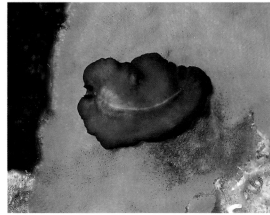

Pseudoceros bolool

Pseudoceros concinnus

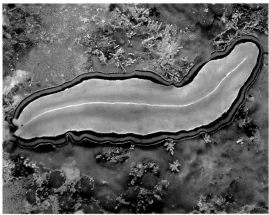

Pseudoceros confusus

Pseudoceros dimidiatus

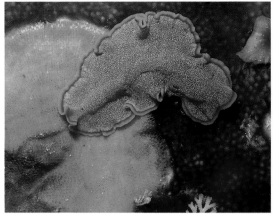

Pseudoceros ferrugineus

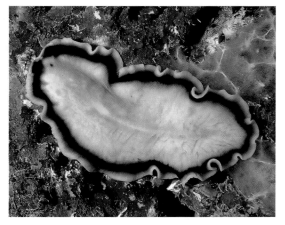

Pseudoceros jebborum

Pseudoceros leptostichus

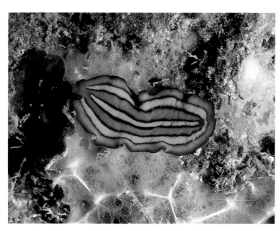

Pseudoceros tristriatus

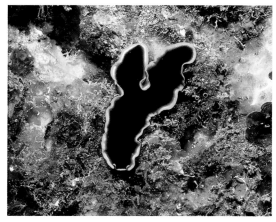

Pseudoceros sp. "KA5-PSE-02"

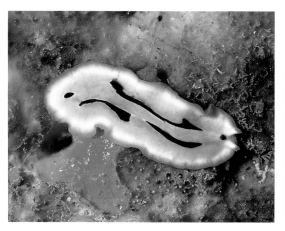

Pseudoceros scriptus

Pseudoceros sp. "KA5-PSE-04"

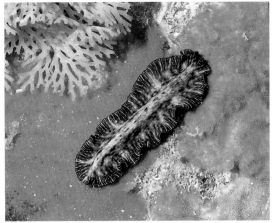

Pseudoceros felis at Heron Island, Great Barrier Reef. This is a recently described species. The species name refers to the colouration of a wild cat.

Photo: L. Newman and A. Flowers

This turbellarian is generally named as *Pseudoceros pardalis*, but it is a *Pseudobiceros* or *Phrikoceros* species. Julian Sprung collected this specimen near Puerto Rico and kept it for several weeks in a coral reef aquarium.

variable band of white. The colouration makes this species just spectacular.

On pages 82-83 we present presenting some additional *Pseudoceros* species.

Pseudobiceros are possibly even more impressive and beautiful than *Pseudoceros*. On the other hand, they are distinctly more sensitive and can quickly degenerate as soon as they are stressed. The best-known species are *Pseudobiceros hancockanus* and *P. bedfordi* (commonly known as the Persian Carpet Worm), which had originally been included in genus Pseudoceros. On page 85 there are six *Pseudobiceros* species which are common in the Indo-Pacific region.

Pseudocerotids also occur in the Caribbeans, but they are less common here than in the indo-Pacific. For instance, the species depicted above. HUMAN (1994b) described it as *Pseudoceros pardalis*, however, according to NEWMAN (pers. comm.) it is a species of *Pseudobiceros* or *Phrikoceros*.

Flatworms were collected at Puerto Rico and kept experimentally in an aquarium. They lived for

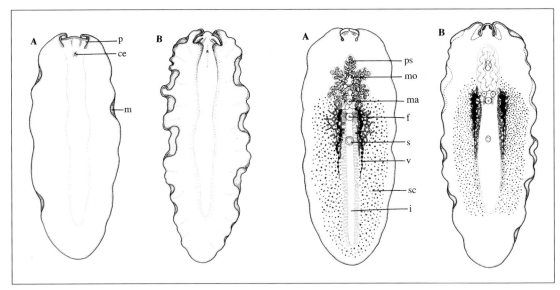

Morphological differences between genera *Pseudoceros* (A) and *Pseudobiceros* (B). The drawing on the left depicts the dorsal side, the drawing on the right the ventral side: p – pseudotentacle; ce – cerebral eyes; m – marginal fold, i – intestine, s – suction cup; ma – male sex pore, f – female sex pore; mo – mouth; ps – pharynx; sc – scattered ovaries and testis; v – vascularised soft tissue.
Drawings from NEWMAN & CANNON (1994b)

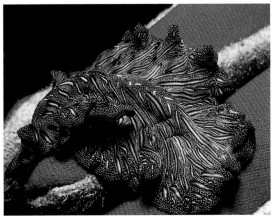

Pseudobiceros bedfordi

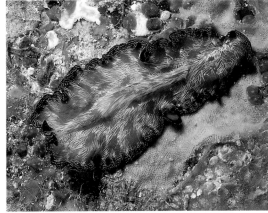

Pseudobiceros fulgor

Pseudobiceros gloriosus

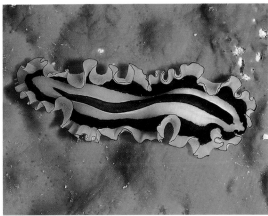

Pseudobiceros gratus

Pseudobiceros hancockanus

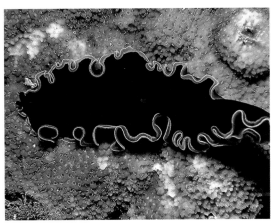

Pseudobiceros uniarborensis

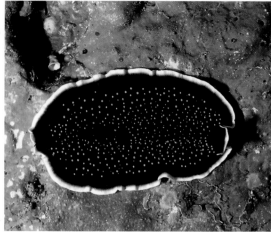

Thysanozoon nigropapillosus (left), seen here at night on the Great Barrier Reef, is a common member of the genus (photo: E. Svensen). *Thysanozoon* sp. "KA5-PSE-05" (right) at Madang, Papua-New Guinea (photo: L. Newman and A. Flowers).

a relatively long time but eventually died by accident as they were sucked into the inlet of a circulating pump. Consequently, circulating pumps with strong suction are not suitable for keeping flatworms.

Among the most impressive Pseudocerotids are the *Thysanozoon* species. The most common form is *T. nigropapillosus*, but this genus includes many species, which all possess distinct papillae or tubercles on their back. Even their gut can branch into numerous protruberances expanding its surface area. *Acanthozoon* species strongly resemble those of the genus *Thysanozoon*, however, the latter have only one male pore, rather than the two in *Thysanozoon*.

To keep polyclad flatworms alive in an aquarium, they must be given a dedicated tank with live rocks and biological filtration. But the question remains as how to obtain and maintain food for them; the probability that this is successful is slim indeed. Dr. Leslie Newman told us that she has been able to keep Polyclads alive in captivity by regulary feeding them with fresh ascidians that were changed once a week. This might be possible only for those aquarists living close to the sea. Also many flatworms are active predators that also contain toxins so that their mucus may harm or even kill other animals in the aquarium. With few exceptions we would therefore in general advise not to import flatworms.

Flatworms are among the most attractive organisms of a coral reef and rival nudibranchs in their brilliant colour patterns. Although they are not suitable for aquarium maintenance, it seemed relevant to us to discuss this group of worms in some detail.

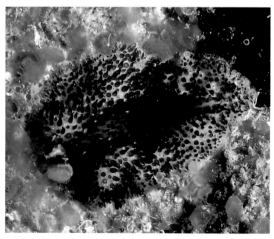
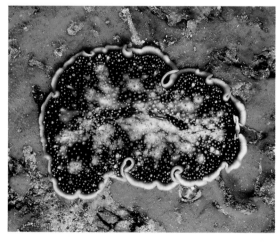

Thysanozoon sp. "KA5-PSE-06" (left) and *Acanthozoon* sp. "KA5-PSE-07" at One Tree Island, Great Barrier Reef.
Photos: L. Newman and A. Flowers.

These are small marine worms, which live buried in sand in shallow water. The phylum was discovered in the 1920's by REMANE and his students, however, because of World War II the collected animal was not described until 1956 by AX.

Originally Ax described the gnathostomulids as an order of flatworms in the class Turbellaria, and is was not until 1969, when RIEDL, recognised that this was indeed a new phylum. Since then about 100 species have been found, but these worms are still rarely ever mentioned in text books. This is even more extraordinary, since their discovery is very important from a phylogenetic point of view, and in terms of significance for the concept of evolution this far exceeds other "missing links", e. g. the coelacanth, *Latimeria chalumnae*.

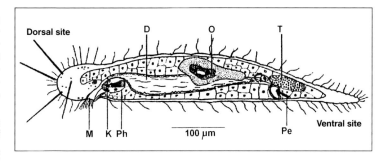

Longitudinal cross-section (lateral view) through gnathostomulid specimen: M – mouth; K – jaw; Ph – pharynx; Pe – penis; D – intestine (gut); O – ovaries; T – testis.   **Drawing after KRISTENSEN & NÖRREVANG (1978)**

In some cases, gnathostomulid worms can occur in enormous numbers. One peculiarity of these worms is their ability to tolerate a very oxygen-deficient environment. Many species can live even under totally anaerobic conditions, and are therefore capable of anaerobic respiration. In other words, they can obtain oxygen from other sources – possibly from sulfide molecules.

These worms are not large; most will not exceed 0.5 to 1.0 mm in length. They are longish, occasionally thread-like. The body surface is covered by cilia. An anal pore is absent or present

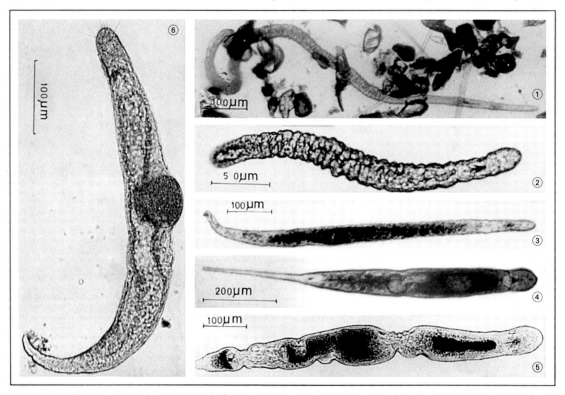

Five species of Gnathostomulida, commonly found in coral sand: 1 – *Haplognathia simplex*; 2 – *Gnathostomaria lutheri*; 3 – *Mesognatharia remanei*; 4 – *Gnathostomula paradoxa*; 5 – *Austragnathia riedli*; 6 – *Gnathostomula paradoxa*, lateral view.   Photos: W. E. Sterrer

only temporarily. The metabolic waste products created by food (principally bacteria and fungi) are discharged directly by diffusion via the body surface. Most

gnathostomulids are hermaphrodites.

Normally we do not see these worms in a coral reef aquarium, but this is probably due to a

lack of appropriate research. In fact, we have seen gnathostomulids only once in our own research tank (see Volume 1, page 180).

Phylum Nemertea - Ribbon Worms

Ribbon worms are elongated, moderately flattened worms, which were once considered to be a further development of flatworms. They show a more advanced development in body structure. Ribbon worms are predominantly marine, but there are also some freshwater forms and a few terrestrial species.

Although ribbon worms are often very abundant, they are rarely seen since they bury in sand or mud, hide under rocks or occur among colonial invertebrates or among algae. They are mostly nocturnal animals, shying away from light. Ribbon worms can be found from the intertidal zone down to depths of 2,500 m or more. Several species are pelagic, while a small number of species lives commensally with sponges, clams, mussels or tunicates. Only one species is known to be endoparasitic, living in echiuroids. According to GIBSON (1995) there are currently 1149 species in 250 genera.

Ribbon worms can be very colourful, as seen here in this unidentified specimen at the Bahamas. Photo: P. Humann

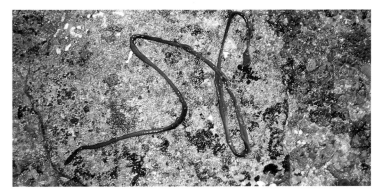

This unidentified ribbon worm, possibly a *Baseodiscus* species, was removed from a bore hole in a live rock and photographed at Suva Reef, Fiji Islands. The viewer's attention is drawn to the enlarged head region.

Anatomy and reproduction

The most conspicuous character of ribbon worms is a tubular muscular organ (proboscis) which is everted at the anterior end. In some cases the proboscis can be twice as long as the actual body of the worm. It is everted for defence and to capture prey. Ribbon worms, therefore, are sometimes also referred to as proboscis worms.

In *Gorgonorhynchus* species (family Lineidae) the proboscis has 32 branches. In other species

it is equipped with needle-like stylets, which makes it an excellent defensive and offensive weapon. *Gorgonorhynchus repens* is a common species, widely distributed in the Indo-Pacific region, and on the Great Barrier Reef at Heron Island it is the most common species (GIBSON, 1981a). In *Baseodiscus delineatus*, probably the best-known ribbon worm on coral reefs (see page 94) the proboscis is long and flexible,

and easily wound around a prey organism.

Many ribbon worms are capable of extending their body to an incredible length. Some nemerteans are only a few centimetres long, but they can readily double that length. On the other hand, some species grow to an enormous length, such as *Lineus longissimus*. Specimens of this worm are commonly found with a length of about 1-5 m, but there have

Gorgonorhynchus repens, is one of the most common ribbon worms throughout the Indo-Pacific. It is especially common in the Great Barrier Reef, as seen here at Lizard Island.   Photo: L. Newman and A. Flowers

This *Lineus longissimus* specimen was "only" a few metres long.

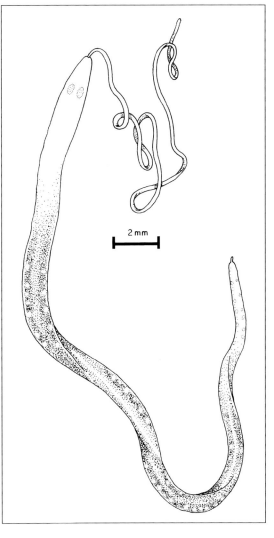

Bennettiella insularis with partially extended proboscis.
Drawing after GIBSON (1981a)

been individual reports of lengths in excess of 30 m. In fact, the "world record" is supposed to be 55 m! We have talked to divers, who have pulled *L. longissimus* for several metres out of rocky crevices, without reaching the end of the worm! Moreover, many ribbon worms can retract their head into the body and so hide it completely.

Ribbon worms are almost exclusively carnivorous, and feed on small, live or dead, invertebrates such as polychaete worms, clams, mussels and crustaceans. Many nemerteans capture their prey alive with their proboscis, swallow it whole and then digest it in a well-developed gut. Other species first kill or paralyse their prey by secretions from their proboscis, then everting their stomach to discharge acids and enzymes which soften the prey tissues so that they can be sucked up by the worm.

Ribbon worms are the only acoelomate worms which have a well-developed circulatory system, where colourless blood flows through a blood vessel extending along both sides of the intestine. They also possess an excretory system which resembles that of flatworms, but it can sometimes, particularly in terrestrial and freshwater species, be substantially modified. Nemerteans also have eyespots similar to those found in flatworms.

Ribbon worms have an intestine (gut), which extends throughout the length of the body and terminates via an anal pore. These animals are thus the simplest in the animal kingdom to possess a straight-through gut.

Most of the marine ribbon worms possess separate sexes, but some freshwater species, and a small number of commensal forms, are hermaphroditic. Their reproductive system is simple. Usually the eggs are shed directly into the water during mating, where they are then fertilized. Internal fertilization is found in a few species, however, and some of these give birth to live young.

Most ribbon worms develop directly into an adult specimen, but a number of species undergo a pelagic larval stage, which concludes with an extraordinary metamorphosis: the adult specimen develops inside the larva.

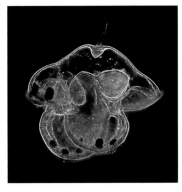

Planktonic larval stage of a ribbon worm (magnification 150x).
Photo: R. Brons

Systematics

The phylum Nemertea is separated into the classes Anopla and Enopla (see the systematic overview on the right).

The Class Anopla is characterized by the fact that the mouth is located underneath or behind the brain, and the proboscis is not armed with one or more stylets (in a recently discovered exception to this rule, from Texas, the proboscis is armed with two longitudinal rows of spines which give it the appearance of a chain-saw). The class contains two orders, the Palaeonemertea and Heteronemertea, both of which are known from coral reefs.

Conspicuous for the class Enopla is the fact that the mouth

Phylum Nemertea

Class Anopla

Order		Palaeonemertea
	Family	Hubrechtidae *Hubrechtella*
Order		Heteronemertea
	Family	Cerebratulidae *Cerebratulina, Quasilineus* *Bennettiella , Cerebratulus, Dushia,* *Valencinia, Parborlasia*
	Family	Gorgonorhynchidae *Gorgonorhynchus*
	Family	Lineidae *Lineopselloides, Lineus* *Micrura, Notospermus*
	Family	Mixolineidae *Aetheorhynchus*
	Family	Valenciniidae *Baseodiscus*

Class Enopla

Order		Hoplonemertea
	Suborder	Monostilifera
	Family	Amphiporidae *Amphiporus, Paramphiporus,* *Poseidonemertes*
	Family	Cratenemertidae *Nipponnemertes*
	Family	Emplectonematidae *Tetranemertes*
	Family	Prosorhochmidae *Pantinonemertes, Friedrichia*
	Family	Tetrastemmatidae *Tetrastemma, Africanemertes,* *Nemertellina*
	Suborder	Polystilifera
	Family	Drepanobandidae *Drepanobanda*
	Family	Drepanophorellidae *Drepanophorella, Drepanophoresta,* *Drepanophoria*
	Family	Drepanophoridae *Curranemertes, Drepanophorina,* *Polychista, Punnettia,* *Urichonemertes, Xenonemertes*
	Suborder	Bdellonemertea

is located in front of the brain, usually sharing the same opening as the proboscis. This class contains two orders, of which only the Hoplonemertea is known from coral reefs.

Ribbon worms on coral reefs

Class Anopla

- Order Palaeonemertea

The genus *Hubrechtella* (order Palaeonemertea) occurs in tropical as well as in temperate seas. *H. queenslandica* is an example and known from the Great Barrier Reef. It is only about 5 cm long and less than 1 mm thick, and is coloured white or yellowish. It lives underneath coral rocks, in mud and sand, in the close proximity of coral fragments (GIBSON, 1979a).

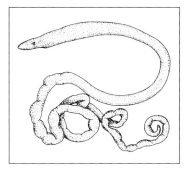

Hubrechtella queenslandica
Drawing from GIBSON (1981a)

- Order Heteronemertea

The family Lineidae depicts in a fascinating fashion what a remarkable group of animals the ribbon worms are. *Lineus binigrilinearis* is known from the central Indo-Pacific, while *L. hancocki* is a species from the Indian Ocean. This family is distinguished from other families by a series of anatomical characters which, however, are beyond the scope of this book

Parborlasia sp. at Heron Island, Great Barrier Reef.
Photo: L. Newman and A. Flowers

(for details see GIBSON, 1981a).

Among the tropical species of the family Lineidae there are many which reach our aquaria together with rocks covered by living organisms. These include *Notospermus* species, of which *N. tricuspidatus* can readily be recognized by the white W-shaped colour marking near the back of its head, while the rest of the body is a dark green. This species occurs along East Africa and the Maldives, eastward to the Ryukyu Islands, and on to Guam and the Great Barrier Reef. *N. geniculata* has a similarly wide geographic distribution and characteristic colour markings consisting of transverse white bands, and it cannot easily be mistaken for other species.

The genus *Micrura* encompasses more than 40 species, which make it one of the most species-rich genera within the family Lineidae. It should be noted that comparatively little systematic work has been done on this family; moreover, *Micrura* species appear to have considerable variability (GIBSON, 1981a). *M. trigonocephala* is known to occur on coral reefs around Sri Lanka.

The small *Aetheorhynchus actites* is chocolate-brown in colour with small white markings far an-

teriorly. It belongs in the family Mixolineidae, which contains only a few tropical species.

The situation is somewhat different with the family Cerebratulidae, where some of the species are very colourful and attractive. There we find many genera and species occurring on coral reefs. One of these is *Bennettiella insularis*, only a few centimetres long with a rounded cross-section for much of its body length but with a dorsoventrally compressed tail. Anteriorly and posteriorly this worm is cream-coloured, with a lilac-brown middle section, but with a light-coloured longitudinal line along its abdomen. The proboscis is twice as long as its body (GIBSON, 1981a). *B. insularis* is known from the Great Barrier Reef, where it often occurs in pure coral sand or underneath coral boulders.

In the genus *Cerebratulus* there are more than 100 valid species (GIBSON, 1995). *C. bicornis* is known to occur around New Caledonia, *C. ischurus* from the Maldives, and *C. krempfi* from Djibouti in the Gulf od Tadjoura.

The genus *Dushia* contains only one species, *D. atra*, which is found in the Caribbean Sea and along the coastline of Florida.

The genus *Quasilineus* con-

Notospermus geniculatus (left) is widely distributed throughout the Indo-Pacific. *N. tricuspidata* (right) at Madang, Papua-New Guinea.
Photo: L. Newman and A. Flowers

tains some rather beautifully-coloured species, such as *Q. pulcherrimus*, where the body is dorsally a bright yellow with a conspicuous, longitudinal median dorsal black band. There is a white spot on the tip of its head and a slender, vivid orange stripe extends along each side of the body. This species grows quite large and probably reaches a length of 30-50 centimetres, but it is still no challenge for many extremely long *Baseodiscus* sp.

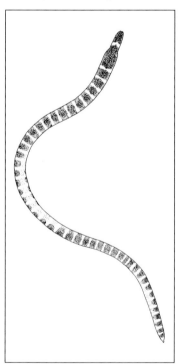

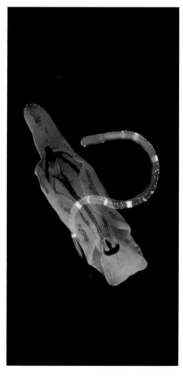

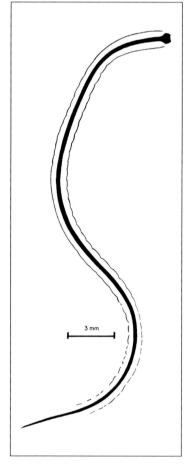

Notospermus geniculatus.
Drawing from Gibson (1981a)

Micrura callima off Western Australia.
Photo: C. Bryce

Quasilineus pulcherrimus.
Drawing from Gibson (1981a)

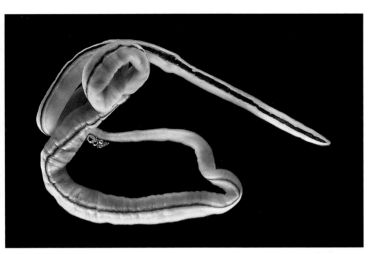

Quasilineus lucidoculatus off Western Australia.   Photo: C. Bryce

Q. pulcherrimus is known from the Great Barrier Reef.

In Western Australia we find *Q. lucidoculatus*. This species has a flat, compressed body, with a salmon-red or lilac-white background colour, marked with several longitudinal stripes arranged as a reddish-brown median band bordered by thinner orange or yellow-white stripes.

The best-known ribbon worms from coral reefs are found in the family Valenciniidae. *Baseodiscus* is the only genus which occurs in tropical regions. It can be said of some *Baseodiscus* species that they are very conspicuous and can thus often be easily found on a coral reef. Consequently, there is every possibility that these worms may also become introduced into our aquaria via live rocks. *Baseodiscus* species live among algae, in the substrate or in cavities or crevices in rocks covered by other living organisms.

Baseodiscus delineatus has a light yellowish background colour with many longitudinal reddish-brown stripes, which extend along the entire body. At the anterior end the body is dorsoventrally compressed, but becomes increasingly rounder farther back. The maximum length of these worms is unknown. Preserved specimens have been reported with lengths from 24 to 66 centimetres (GIBSON, 1979b). When one takes into account that most ribbon worms tend to shrink substantially when preserved, it stands to reason that some of the worms may reach a length of several metres when alive.

Baseodiscus delineatus has a strong mouth, visible as a median cleft on the underside of the body just behind the head. As with all species of this genus, the proboscis is only slender. No other known ribbon worm has such a wide distribution as *B. delineatus*. It has been found to occur in the northern as well as the southern hemisphere, circum-globally in all tropical, subtropical and temperate seas. This alone is already an indication that *B. delineatus* has enormous capabilities to adapt to new environmental conditions, so that it may also be very suitable for an aquarium.

On the reef, this ribbon worm lives under rocks, in sand or in mud, as well as among mangrove roots, sea grasses and algae, and on other colonial invertebrates in the intertidal zone down to depths of more than 50 m.

Baseodiscus hemprichii has a dark longitudinal band against a white or cream-coloured background. It has an elegant appearance. In its natural habitat, maximum lengths in excess of 1 metre have been often observed. According to IWATA, 1954 (in GIBSON, 1979b), the "record length" for this species is 8 m. The head is

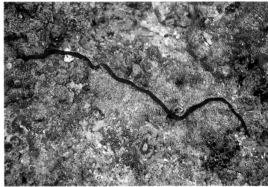

The genus *Baseodiscus* is the best-known genus of tropical ribbon worms. The species are usually closely associated with coral rubble or coral boulders. On Suva Reef (Fiji Islands) we observed several specimens of a so far unidentified red species. The worms protruded from holes in live rocks (left) and actually left the hole in search of food (right).

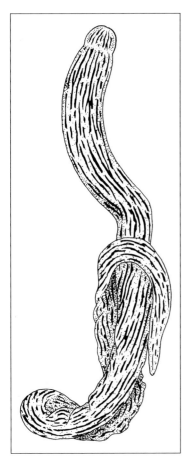

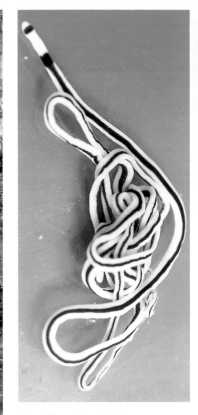

Baseodiscus hemprichii.
Photo: I. Bennett

Baseodiscus delineatus is a very frequently occurring ribbon worm and can easily be identified by its uninterrupted, thin light brown longitudinal stripes. Drawing from Gibson (1981a); Photo at Madang, Papua-New Guinea:
L. Newman and A. Flowers

compressed and can be round or heart-shaped, depending upon how far the worm has extended itself. The longitudinal band, commencing on the back just behind the head, is the most reliable species character, although at its front end it may be very variable in shape. It can also be coloured black, lilac-black, dark brown or reddish-brown. There is another longitudinal band on the underside of the body but this is generally narrower than the dorsal. *B. hemprichii* occurs in shallow water areas of reef flats and down to depths of 10 m, where it may occur among coral rocks or be buried in coarse sand. It is widely distributed throughout the Indo-Pacific: from the Red Sea and East Africa, eastward to Western Samoa and Hawaii.

Baseodiscus quinquelineatus is easily recognisable by the white to lilac-white background colouration, and the five to seven thin, black or dark-brown longitudinal stripes. The stripes commence at the head and extend along the entire body. Usually there are three stripes along the dorsal region and two along the abdomen, but there may be up to seven stripes arranged as five dorsally and two ventrally. Occasionally, these stripes may meet in different areas along the body, in other cases some of the stripes may end before they reach the tail. So far no other species in this genus is known with such conspicuous

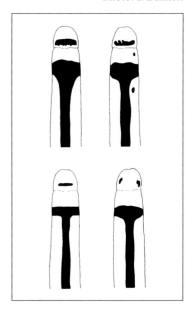

Four different markings of head and the anterior end of the dorsal stripe in *Baseodiscus hemprichii.*
Drawings from Gibson (1981a)

colour markings. Even in cases where the number and development of the stripes vary, the species can always be easily identified. *B. quinquelineatus* grows to considerable lengths, and observations of individuals in their natural habitat have shown lengths of 6 m. This species is slightly wider than *B. delineatus*, and it has been reported from the Central Indo-Pacific and the Great Barrier Reef (GIBSON, 1979b).

Beyond these common *Baseodiscus* species, there are others which have been described, such as: *B. edmondsoni*, known only from coral reefs of the Hawaiian Islands, *B. indicus* found in the Maldives, and *B. mexicanus* living inside a firm mucous tube under rocks and among sea shells and corals from the intertidal region down to a depth of 100 m. It occurs in the Gulf of California and along the west coast of Mexico, Panama and the coasts of Colombia and Chile, as well as in the Galàpagos Islands. *B. punnetti* is also distributed along the coast of California, as well as in the Gulf of California. This worm buries in sand or lives among algae, from the intertidal zone down to depths of 380 m. *B. sordidus* and *B. unistriatus* are both known from the Indian Ocean, but the latter also occurs in the Red Sea.

Class Enopla

- Order Hoplonemertea

This order is divided into two suborders. In the suborder Monostilifera the head is often distinctly rounded off and bears four large eyes or many small eyes. The proboscis is armed with a single central stylet mounted on a cylindrical basis.

Tetranemertes hermaphroditicus may serve as an example for a species in the Monostilifera. This worm is extremely thin and has a flattened head, which carries about 20 small eyes on each side, arranged in two longitudinal rows. The body is a pale lilac colour, with almost transparent sides. It is commonly found on reef

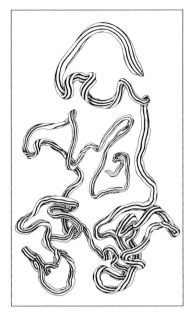

Baseodiscus quinquelineatus.
Drawings from GIBSON (1981a)

flats living in pure coral sand and among coral rubble.

Species from other genera of Monostilifera, such as *Poseidonemertes caribensis*, occur in shallow reef areas and among sea grasses in the Caribbean Sea; *Amphiporus albicans* is found

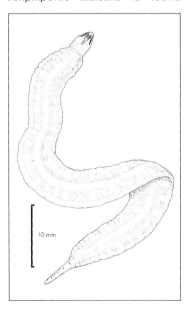

Urichonemertes pilorhynchus.
Drawings from GIBSON (1981a)

among corals in the Red Sea (GIBSON, 1982).

In the suborder Polystilifera, the head is often triangular, with many large eyes, and the proboscis is armed with several small stylets carried on a shield-like basis. *Drepanobanda* spp. are well known from coral reefs of the Indo-Pacific. *Curranemertes natans* from Venezuela is characterized by the fact that it can swim over short distances by sinusoidal body undulations. The unusual *Urichonemertes* sp. grows to a length of about 10 cm and has a distinctly triangular head, with a deep fold which continues posteriorly, and gives the anterior part of the body a triangular cross-sectional shape. The numerous large eyes are arranged in three rows. The colour of this species is a plain grey.

Ribbon worms in the coral reef aquarium

We have observed slender, dark red ribbon worms in the bottom substrate of a flow-through chamber yet, quite fundamentally, ribbon worms do not generally occur in a coral reef aquarium. In general these animals are rather fragile and may break easily, so they do not survive transportation very well. On the other hand, on the basis of their food preferences (small invertebrates), they could possibly be suitable animals for an aquarium. We would indeed be very appreciative for any reader input about experiences with these animals under aquarium conditions. In addition to the text references indicated, we also recommend the following publications: GIBSON (1973), GIBSON (1974), GIBSON (1981b), GIBSON (1986), GIBSON (1993), GIBSON & SUNDBERG (1992), SUNDBERG & GIBSON (1995) and GIBSON et al. (1982).

Pseudocoelomate phyla

The worms of pseudocoelomate phyla possess a "false abdominal cavity". So far none of these phyla has achieved any significance for the aquarium hobby. Yet, they are of importance from an ecological perspective, since they make up an important part of the bottom fauna, and they are an essential component in the animal diversity of coral reefs. Moreover, many of them have an interesting natural history. In this section we would like to discuss briefly, six of the eight phyla (see "Division of Marine Worm Phyla" on page 68). The animals in the seventh phylum, the Acanthocephala, are exclusively parasitic; the larvae is found in invertebrates and the adult on vertebrate animals. Species of the eighth phylum, the Nematomorpha, occur mostly in freshwater, however, it also includes the class Nectonematoidea, which is exclusively marine. Some of the larvae of *Nectonema* species live parasitically on hermit crabs and on other crustaceans.

The meiofauna in the bottom of a coral reef aquarium can be rather diverse and contain a large number of interesting organisms. One of the limiting factors for the development within a closed aquarium system is the level of oxygen. Shown here is an approximately 6 cm thick bottom layer in the first chamber (60 l volume) of our mechanical filtration system. This chamber contains crushed rocks, crushed coral, etc. Organic material from dead algae and food remains sink to the bottom of the chamber which has a continuous and steady water flow. The result is a substratum with a top layer rich in oxygen and organic nutrients and an anaerobic- or nearly anaerobic lower layer, which can be seen as a yellowish area. The upper half of the substratum contains a multitude of various organisms, such as sponges, crustaceans, a population of an unidentified ribbon worm, bristle worms of family Amphinomidae and *Phyllochaetopterus* sp., various burrowing snails and of course many single-celled organisms.

Meiofauna and interstitial animal communities

In the discussion of the following phyla we will repeatedly encounter organisms, which belong to the meiofauna, a term which needs to be explained briefly. The meiofauna includes organisms of a size less than 500 µm (0.5 mm) which falls in between those in the macrofauna (i. e. those visible with the naked eye) and those in the microfauna (e. g. animals visible only with the aid of a microscope). In essence then, the term meiofauna applies principally to the size of organisms. Animals of the meiofauna are of a size that permits them to easily bury themselves in bottom substrate, without encountering substantial physical resistence. But these animals can also occur on the bottom and in the open water. The majority, however, normally lives buried in the upper bottom layers. Those organisms of the meiofauna which live buried between sand grains, are referred to as the interstitial fauna, a fauna which is often overlooked. It is of a rather nonuniform composition, but still it is extremely important for the biological equilibrium, on a coral reef as well as in the coral reef aquarium.

Studies on the interstitial fauna have been made by GUZMAN et al. (1987), ANZARI & IINGOLE (1983), COULL (1970), RAO & MISRA (1983), SALVAR & RENAUD-MORNANT (1969), RENAUD-MORNANT et al. (1971), and others. In the majority of these studies, round worms made up the predominant group of animals. Other important groups are the shrimp-like animals (ostracods and copepods) of subphylum Crustacea, bristle worms (class Polychaeta), various snails of phylum Mollusca, kinorhynchs (phylum Kinorhyncha), and shelled amoebas (kingdom Protista). Here we can also encounter organisms which we tend to associated primarily with the terrestrial environment, such as saltmites (order Acarian, phylum Arthropoda). According to KRISTENSEN (pers. comm.) these are rather

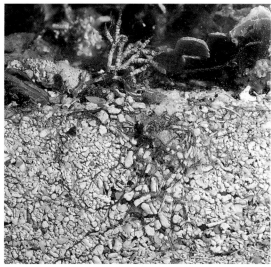

Normally we do not want anaerobic zones to build up in the substratum of an aquarium, and therefore we use thin bottom layers. However, in recent years a different aquarium system has been developed by Prof. Jaubert, Director of Aquarium Monaco. This system utilises a thick bottom layer placed over a mesh; below this mesh the water is strongly enriched with dissolved organic substances and nitrate. The bottom layer contains a diversified meiofauna throughout, since it has access to sufficient oxygen (JAUBERT, 1989). The photograph on the left shows the Jaubert System set up in an aquarium by Julian Sprung, Miami (USA). The Jaubert System has been tested on coral reef tanks by various aquarists, mainly in the United States. It is certainly an alternative for operating a coral reef aquarium successfully. The photograph on the right gives a close-up view of the upper parts of the substrate.

common among coral sand fragments. Then there are also numerous larvae from different organisms. Together with nematodes and copepods, they are often rather abundantly represented in the substrate layers of a coral reef.

The vertical and horizontal distribution of the interstitial fauna depends on the grain size of the sediment, the oxygen content, the composition of the fauna as such and the availability of food. In an aquarium the meiofauna lives among the algae as well as buried in the bottom. We have not investigated this quantitatively or qualitatively, but we have found repeatedly among the bottom substrate of aquariums, large numbers of polychaetes and sizable copepod population, which could be recognised with the naked eye. Using a microscope will then reveal a large number of roundworms.

In a well-conditioned coral reef aquarium there is an interstitial fauna hidden in the bottom. We assume that its composition depends, on one hand, on how much food in the form of waste products given off by fish and invertebrates is accessible to these organisms, and on the other hand on the water circulation and thickness of the substrate. We have no doubt that this fauna plays a decisive role in the overall stability of a coral reef aquarium. These small organisms feed on the organic material of plants and animals, and so they are involved in the recycling of substances within the food chain.

Phylum Nematoda – Round Worms

Round worms are found just about everywhere and often in enormous numbers. In fact, these are the most numerous organisms on earth. If we removed everything from our planet, except the round worms, we would still continue to see the contours of the continents. So far, more than 80,000 species of round worms have been described, which are probably only about 10 % of the free-living species that actually exist. Free-living species are found in terrestrial soils and marine sediments where they decompose plant and animal material. Most round worms are free-living, but there are also infamous predators with a world-wide distribution, and parasitic species seem to live in almost all animals and plants (NILSEN, 1998). The *Onchocera* species can cause river blindness (onchocercosis), hair worms, *Wucheria* species can lead to elephantiasis (filariasis) in humans, by blocking the lymphatic system. In the maw (or eel-) worm we are dealing with the round worm *Ascaris lumbricoides*, a notorious parasite, which attacks internal organs in humans. While free-living round worms are distinctly round, with an elongated shape, many of the parasitic species are sac-like. Fortunately, we do not have to deal with such organisms in our coral reef aquarium.

Round worms are extremely robust animals. In the first instance, this applies to the strong outer skin (cuticula) present in all nematodes. This gives them adequate protection and it also assures that this animal group can survive even the most extreme environmental conditions. With a length of little more than 1mm, the majority of round worms species is rather small, but there are some species which attain a length of up to 1 m. The longest known species is the up to 8.4 m long and 2.5 cm wide *Placentanema gigantissima* living in the placenta of whales.

Round worms are worms in the truest sense of the word. Although there are thousands of species and a multitude of life forms and adaptations, the body in the majority of round worms tapers evenly to a point at both ends. The outer body is smooth and does not carry any bristles or protruberances. The mouth is located anteriorly, and the anal opening is in a posterior location. Internally, there is a gut which extends through the entire length of the worm. In cross-section the body is almost round.

As mentioned above, the body is enclosed by a thick cuticula as a protective skin layer. The cuticula, which consists of several intermediate layers of variable structure and chemical composition, is the main reason for the remarkable survival success of round worms. But there are also species with an atypical development; especially in the bottom substrate of a coral reef aquarium can we find such species. *Epsilonema* and *Desmoscolex* are two genera, which demonstrate this point. These genera lack their pseudocoel and move around very different from other nematodes.

There is hardly any inhabitable environment on earth, which is not occupied by round worms,

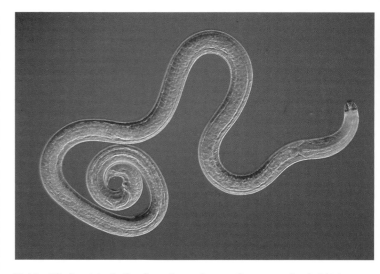

Unidentified, yet typically shaped round worm from a marine habitat.
Photo: R. Brons

Marine round worm among detritus.
Photos: R. Brons

and we find billions of them on a coral reef. There, round worms occur primarily in the sediment, where they are part of the meiofauna of a coral reef; a fauna so far only insufficiently studied. Just as elsewhere, round worms play an important role on a coral reef in the decomposition of organic substances, however, the details involved have so far not yet been resolved.

In an aquarium we find round worms among algal growth, on live rocks or in the bottom substrate. For detailed investigations a microscope is required. Round worms feed on tiny invertebrates,

algae, detritus or bacteria, and they do an excellent job "cleaners". Although the round worm fauna of a coral reef aquarium has not yet been studied in detail, we are of the opinion that they play a significant role in the stability of an aquarium system.

Food remains and dead organic material, among them dead algae, must be decomposed and their compounds recycled in a closed aquarium system. Here is where the round worms do an important job. Place a bit of detritus under a microscope, and you will discover numerous round worms feeding on the organic material.

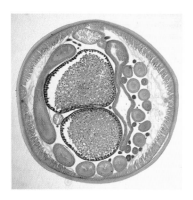

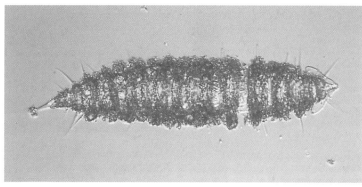

Histological cross-section through female round worm: the outer, bright red layer is the strong cuticula, which protects the animal against mechanical damage and which enables it to crawl through sediments and similar materials. On the inside of the cuticula is the dark red epidermis with its "fringe curtain" of muscles. Four nerve strands can be seen as tiny projections in the upper right, left and at the bottom. The many small red dots and the large red, elongated structure on the left are the ovaries. The white space is the pseudocoelom. The large chambers with the dark red walls are the uterus with egg cells. On the right is the intestine as a whitish elongated structure with a red margin.

Photo: R. Brons

Demoscolex sp. (magnification 500x) from a reef at Heron Island, Great Barrier Reef.   Photo: R. M. Kristensen

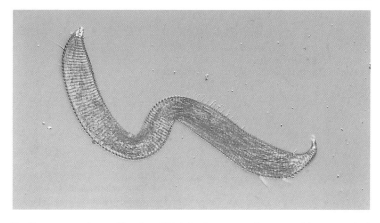

Epsilomena sp. (magnification 500x) is also a round worm with an atypical shape, from a reef of the Great Barrier Reef.   Photo: R. M. Kristensen

Phylum Gastrotricha – Gastrotrichs

The gastrotrichs make up a small phylum of only about 200 species. They are all small worms, which live in the bottom substrate or in mud, both in the marine and in the freshwater environment. They are numerous on coral reefs.

Gastrotricha means "abdominal hairs", a very appropriate designation, since large ventral areas on the body of these worms, especially the abdominal region, are covered by cilia. On the back there are dorsal scales or spines. The body is elongated. The anterior section, off set from the remainder of the body by a constriction, is rounded off. The

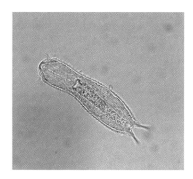

Unidentified gastrotrich from the Red Sea.   Photo: R. Brons

posterior end is often split in two, but it can also terminate in a single point. Nearly all gastrot-

richs have adhesive glands at their terminal end. Although gastrotrichs are microscopically small, they are well-developed. They have a powerful esophagus and a simple gut, which extends through the animal over its entire length. In this respect, they resemble round worms. The esophagus of gastrotrichs works by means of suction, so that prey organisms are actually sucked into the mouth. The food consists of single-celled algae, single-celled organisms and bacteria. In their mode of life they are reminiscent of rotifers. In fact, both groups are often found together in the same habitat.

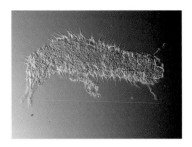  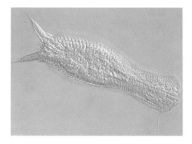

Left: An undescribed gastrotrich of genus *Xenodasys* (magnification 270x). Centre: Antenna gastrotrich, *Chordodasys antennatus* (magnification 270x). Right: Gastrotrich of genus *Xenotrichula* (magnification 800x) from Stradbroke Island, Queensland, Australia.   Photos: R. M. Kristensen

The phylum is divided into two classes: Chaetonotida and Macodasyida. The former occurs mainly in freshwater. It is characterized by the fact, that so far only female or hermaphrodite specimens have been found. The females produce two types of eggs. In one type the young will hatch in the course of two days as new females (SEMB-JOHANSSON, 1986). The other type is laid during a resting period, to facilitate the survival of a species at times of unfavourable environmental condition.

Class Macrodasyida contains mainly marine species, which are all hermaphrodites. In connection with an experimental aquarium (NILSEN, 1998) we for the first time discovered gastrotrichs among detritus and dead algae in a coral reef aquarium.

Phylum Rotifera – Rotifers

Unidentified rotifer from brackish water in Holland.   Photo: R. Brons

From an aquarist's point of view rotifers are important organisms, since they are being cultured in large amounts as food for fish larvae. Rotifers occur worldwide, principally in freshwater and in damp terrestrial environments, but there are also a considerable number of marine species. Overall, there are about 1800 known species.

The popular term for rotifers being "wheel-like" animals (rota, lat. = wheel; -fer = bearing) refers to the presence of a crown of cilia

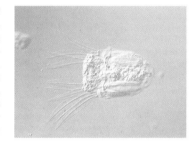

Large rotifer, *Polyarthra major* (magnification 270x), from Kings Beach, Queensland, Australia.
Photo: R. M. Kristensen

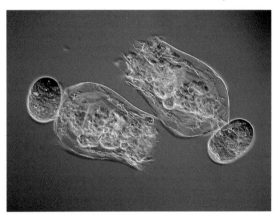 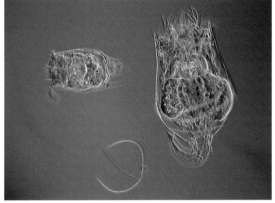

Brachionus sp.: Left – two females with eggs sacs at the end of the body. Right – fully grown female, a juvenile and the empty shells of an egg sac (both illustrations 130x magnification).   Photos: R. Brons

at the anterior end of the organisms. When these cilia are moving, it creates an impression of a moving wheel.

Roughly speaking, the body of rotifers can be divided into three sections: head, middle section, and adhesive toe section. Although rotifers are very small (normally 0.04 to 2.0 mm), they exhibit an advanced structure. They have internal organs, such as a stomach, a light sensitive eye spot and genital glands. The reproductive biology of rotifers is particularly interesting.

Food intake takes place by ciliary action at the anterior end of the organism. The food, which consists largely of small organic particles and single-celled algae is transported into a muscle pharynx equipped with powerful jaws and teeth. These macerate the food with a grinding motion and pass the food through the esophagus top the stomach. In

some predatory rotifers the diet consists solely of other rotifers. In these predator species the jaws and teeth of the pharynx can be extruded through the mouth to actually capture the prey.

Rotifers occur as pelagic and as sessile organisms, but some also alternate between a sessile and a pelagic mode of life. Among the pelagic rotifers, that is, those which spend their entire life in open water, it is not uncommon for their appearance to change in the course of a year. This phenomenon is generally referred to as cyclomorphosis. Most pelagic rotifers live a solitary life, but there are also some colonial species.

Among the sessile rotifers are some rather selective species. Not only do they select *where* to settle, suchas on a specific species of algae, but they even specifically select with spot on the algae to attach to. Finally, there are also species, which have become

adapted to a life in the substrate, although this type of adaptation is relatively rare on a coral reef. These rotifers posses modified cilia, used for moving.

Finally there are many rotifers which live parasitically on other organisms, especially sessile forms which live on the gills of crustaceans. Some rotifers lead a life as endoparasites, and can so be found inside snail eggs.

Rotifers appear to possess a number of remarkable biological modes of life. Ecologically, they play a significant role, since they can develop into very large populations under favourable conditions. For other organisms they represent an important food source and rotifers are also of considerable use in nutrient recycling. Finally, it would not be possible to rear marine fishes under captive conditions to the extent it is being done to day, without the use of rotifers.

Phylum Kinorhyncha - Mud Dragons

The kinorynchs form only a small, relatively insignificant phylum, but from a biological point of view they are very interesting animals, which occur in the bottom substrate along continental coastlines. They are particularly common in mud bottom. There are about 150 species that have been

described, but so far little research has been done on this phylum, and it stands to reason that there is still a large number of species yet to be discovered.

On the average, kinorhynchs are slightly larger than rotifers, with a length of about 1 mm. The body is elongated and somewhat

reminiscent of a type of gastrotrich. There is an outer cuticula, but it is separated into 13 clearly distinguishable segments. This is the most conspicuous feature of kinorhynchs.

It only appears as if the body is split up into segments, because only the outer skin layer, muscles

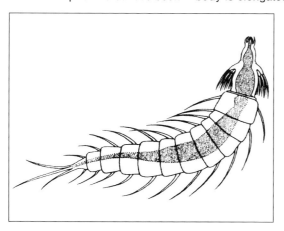

Typical shape of a kinorhynch.
Drawing after SEMB-JOHANNSSON (1988)

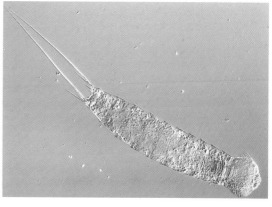

Female of a kinorhynch of genus *Echinoderes* from Stradbroke Island, Australia (magnification 200x).
Photo: R. M. Kristensen

and nerve cords are segmented, and there is no true segmentation as in annelid worms. The first two segments (the head and the neck) carry strong bristles. These are hollow and movable and are used for locomotion in substrate. Posteriorly the body can termi- nate in two or several long termi- nal spines, pointing posteriorly. Most species feed on diatoms, bacteria or dead organic material.

Phylum Priapulida – Proboscis Worms

The proboscis worms form a small animal group which are exclusively marine resembling the kinorynchs. So far only 12 species have been described, all of highly variable lengths. The small, sand-dwelling *Tubiluchus corallicola* measures less than 2 mm. This worm is very fre- quently found in coral sand in the Caribbean. In contrast, *Priapulus caudatus* reaches a length in ex- cess of 20 cm.

Proboscis worms spend their entire life buried in sand or in some other soft substrate. They can dig into the bottom using pumping body movements. Along the outside of the body these worms have serrations and there are distinct rings around the body, however, this is not a sign of segmentation. Some species possess a tail, which consist of one or two outgrowths. In *Priapu- lus* species the posterior end car- ries caudal appendages, which consist of a hollow stalk with many spherical vesicles. In *Acan- thopriapulus* sp. The tail has many outgrowths and probably serves as attachment organ.

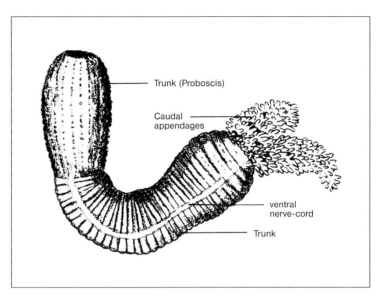

Priapulus bicaudatus.

Some proboscis worms, parti- cularly the large *Priapulus* spe- cies feed on other invertebrates, specially on bristle worms. The small species probably feed on detritus. Proboscis worms have separate sexes. The free-living larval stage can last for a long time. A larvae can live for more than two years in bottom sub- strate, where it feeds until it has developed into an adult animal.

To the best of our knowledge, proboscis worms have not yet been observed to occur coral reef aquaria.

Drawing after Barnes (1980)

Phylum Loricifera – Girdle Wearers

If some of the animal groups dis- cussed in this book can be de- scribed as being peculiar, it cer- tainly applies to the loriciferans. This phylum was discovered by Kristensen in 1983. So far 89 dif- ferent kinds of loriciferans have been found, yet only 10 of these have been fully described as dis- tinct species.

Girdle wearers are part of the interstitial fauna and live in narrow crevices and other hollow spa- ces, which develop between sedi- ment particles. Many species are cosmopolitan, and they are quite small, usually only about 0.3 mm long. Their size corresponds to that of many rotifers. The popular designation "girdle wearer" is a li- teral translation of the scientific name, which refers to the six ar- moured plates (lorica, lat. = shield, and fero lat. = to carry) which run parallel with the longi- tudinal axis of the organism. The posterior half of the body is co- vered with these plates.

In adults there are three clearly distinguishable body regions: head region, chest region, and posterior region. Up front is the head region with a telescope- like or funnel-shaped mouth, at the end of an oral (mouth) canal, which leads down to a muscular pharynx. The head region in adults has nine rows of appenda- ges. Males have a total of 247 ap- pendages, while there are only 235 in females. Most of these ap- pendages are tactile hairs, but there are also individual cilia co- vered with a thin layer of cuticle.

The neck region is equipped

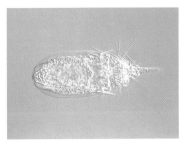

Undescribed girdle wearer (magnification 400x) of genus *Nanaloricus* from Fort Pierce, Florida, USA.
Photo: R. M. Kristensen

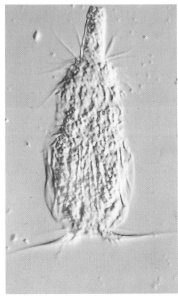

The first girdle wearer ever to be discovered and described, was *Nanaloricus mysticus* (magnification 1050x). The illustration shows a Higgins-Larvae of this species, collected at Roscoff, France, the original site where this species was discovered.
Photo: R. M. Kristensen

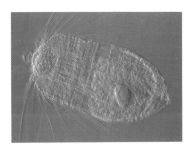

Female of a yet undescribed girdle wearer (magnification 540x), of genus *Rugiloricus* from Mozambique.
Photo: R. M. Kristensen

with about 15 stiff, serrated bristles, the so-called trichoscalides. They protrude and form a ring around the organisms. The head and chest region can be retracted into the posterior part of the body, where both are protected by the gridle-like lorica. Adult specimens have (far posteriorly) a flower-like sense chemoreseptor (flosculi), with a large opening in its centre. Girdle wearers have a very characteristic external shape, which can reflect light in all shades of the rainbow. A gut extends throughout the entire organism, and it terminates in an anus, far posteriorly.

The adult forms of most species feed on bacteria, however, some are ecto-parasites. A characteristic feature of the internal anatomy is a large brain, which occupies most of the head, where

it surrounds the pharynx on all sides. Similarly, the larvae of Loricifera, the so-called "Higgins" larvae (named after the American biologist Higgins, a leading scientist researching the meiofauna) display many peculiarities. They

are very small (80 to 285 μm), and detailed studies on them requires the use of a scanning electron microscope.

The best-known species is *Nanaloricus mysticus*, which was also the first one to be described (KRISTENSEN, 1983). Some species occur at extreme oceanic depths, such as *Pliciloricus hadalis*, which was found at a depth of 8260 m in red deep sea mud (KRISTENSEN & SHIRAYAMA, 1988).

So far representatives for this fascinating phylum have as far as we know not be observed in a coral reef aquarium. It would, however, not surprise us at all if Girdle Wearers one day appear in a sample collected from an aquarium, as the modern coral reef aquarium seems to contain most of the known animal phyla.

Girdle wearer can reflect light in all colours of the rainbow; shown here is an adult male of *Rugiloricus carolensis* (magnification 400x).
Photo and drawing to the right: R. M. Kristensen

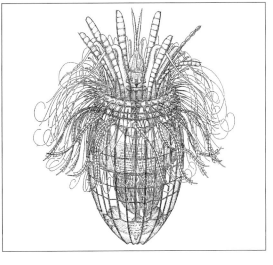

Typical shape of a girdle wearer.

Coelomate phyla

The coelomate phyla possess a true abdominal cavity (coelom). It is formed by mesodermal tissue (peritoneum), which also completely lines the inside of the coelom. This same tissue also encloses the internal organs. A still unresolved question among biologists is, whether this true abdominal cavity has developed only once, or twice (independently of each other), during the evolution of the organisms. Most likely in animals with a true abdominal cavity there are two different lines of development. One of these terminates with vertebrate animals, and the other comes to an end with segmented worms (Annelida) and insects. From among the seven coelomate phyla, the phylum Annelida (segmented worms) is clearly the most important one from an aquarist's point of view.

Phylum Annelida - Segmented Worms

The phylum Annelida (segmented worms) incorporates at least 18,000 species (WESTHEIDE & RIEGER, 1996). The relationships of the phylum has been under much discussion recently (for example, ROUSE & FAUCHALD, 1995, 1997; EIBYE-JACOBSEN & NIELSEN, 1997; McHUGH, 1997; NIELSEN, 1997; FAUCHALD & ROUSE, 1997; ROUSE, 1997). As many groups are still poorly known, agreement is unlikely to be reached in the near future. Moreover, the "Polychaeta" and "Oligochaeta" are now generally considered to be polyphyletic groups rather than monophyletic ones that have each evolved from a common ancestor, and also to include several groups earlier regarded as distinct phyla (for example, Pogonophora and Echiura are now usually placed in the "Polychaeta". For simplicity, the three groups traditionally referred to Annelida are herein treated as follows (number of species based on WESTHEIDE & RIEGER, 1996):

❶ Class "Polychaeta" - marine bristle worms: about 10,000 species, in about 80 families.

❷ Class Clitellata - worms with a clitellum, over 8000 species.

❸ - Order "Oligochaeta" - terrestrial and freshwater bristle worms; earthworms with about 3000 species in about 280 genera.

This marine leech, a *Pontobdella* species, had attached itself to a ray.
Photo: L. Newman and A. Flowers

❹ - Order Hirudinea - leeches; about 300 species in 40 genera.

In all annelid worms the body is separated into segments. Those in "Polychaeta" are the only annelids of interest to the marine aquarium hobby. However, it must also be noted here that over the last few years more and more "Oligochaeta" have been shown to be present in the marine environment. Although *Grania macrochaeta* (family Enchytraeidae) and although *Heronidrilus* spp., as well as other genera of family Tubificidae, have been found relatively frequent on coral reefs (MATHER & BENNETT, 1993), we will not discuss these groups any further. Leeches (order Hirudinea) are essentially freshwater animals, although there are a few marine species, which attach themselves to pelagic fishes. Yet, they are not particularly relevant to the marine aquarium hobby, and so we will not discuss them in this book.

Marine bristle worms are common on coral reefs and they are of considerable importance to the marine aquarist keeping a coral reef tank. There are many attractive species, which can easily be seen on a coral reef. All coral reef aquaria accommodate marine bristle worms, either unintentionally after an inadvertent introduction via live rocks, or as an intentional purchase from an aquarium shop.

The designation "marine bristle worms" is highly appropriate for this class, since most of the 10,000 species occur in the sea. There they live in shallow intertidal regions down to vast depths. Recently several new species were discovered, which live close to volcanic springs at Galápagos Islands at a depth of 2500 m, where the water is hot and contains sulfur. There is also a calcareous tube worm, *Marifugia cavatica*, which lives in the freshwater of caves in Bosnia-Herzegovina. It is probably a relict from a Period, when these areas where actually below sea level (TEN HOVE, 1988). Also, on Sumatra there are several terrestrial bristle worms of family Nereididae. From all that, it is obvious that bristle worms occupy many ecological niches.

As the scientific name of the class "Polychaeta" (polys, gr. =

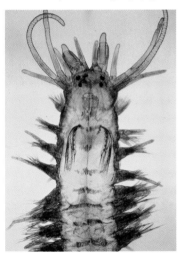

Bristle worms have various appendages along their body. In the species shown here (family Nereidae) the antenna, the peristomial cirri and the palps around the mouth are all well visible, as are the eyes and the head lobes. The thorax region commences below the head with the pharynx and the jaws. Body segments are well-developed. Each segment carries stump feet with various bristles.   Photo: G. Rouse

many; chaeta, lat. = bristle) already suggests, these worms carry "many bristles". Each body segment has two or more, small or large (bristle-like) parapodia. These appendages, together with the strongly defined segmentation, enable the worms to move about with sinusoidal body movements. This may look fearsome or intimidating, and create the impression as if marine bristle worms are dangerous creatures. Fortunately, this is not true. With the exception of a few large, free-living species which can inflict a painful bite, and some species with venomous spines, marine bristle worms are generally peaceful and harmless to humans.

General biology

Marine bristle worms, or simply referred to as "bristle worms", have two fundamentally different forms of life, errant (usually free living) or sedentary (e. g. tubicolous, boring, nestling or burrowing). Within these two forms there are numerous variations and adaptations. Many of the free-living forms move around a lot, but some, like species in the family Eunicidae, spend much of their time in tubes although they are typical free-living forms. Some of the sedentary forms, like the species in the family Sabellidae, spend all their life in a tube which they build themselves, while others - like members of the families Cirratulidae or Capitellidae - either burrow in the sediment or rest in crevices or burrows.

Errant bristle worm

Most errant bristle worms crawl along the bottom, bury themselves in the substrate, remain hidden under rocks, are pelagic or

live as parasites on other organisms. A few, however, are active predators that live in tubes partly buried in the substrate. Anterior appendages such as antennae are well developed, and many species have complex eyes with lenses. The segmental appendages (tentacular cirri) surrounding the mouth can be strongly modified and particularly large. Moreover, errant bristle worms usually have a large, eversible pharynx; in most carnivorous species the pharynx has strong jaws. Many species are purely carnivorous, feeding on other invertebrate animals. Some errant species are herbivores (see fact sheet on page 121), but there are also omnivorous species, which will eat nearly anything they can handle.

Segmentation is usually quite conspicuous. Each segment, at its origin, is separated from the next one by internal cross walls (septa). In highly mobile species, however, this separation can be substantially reduced. Each segment has a pair of parapodia which are usually divided into an upper part (notopodium) and a lower part (neuropodium). Each of these parts has chitinous bristles (setae) and a cirrus, with one or more internal supporting bristles (aciculae). Cirri have a sensory function, but they can also be modified to perform other functions (e. g. respiration). The parapodia are used principally for locomotion.

Small species take up oxygen across the body surface, while larger species may have well-developed gills (branchiae). In the latter, however, some oxygen exchange also takes place by diffusion along the body surface. The gills of errant species are often developed as modified sections of the parapodia, but there is strong variability among species on this.

Sedentary bristle worms

Sedentary bristle worms live in tu-

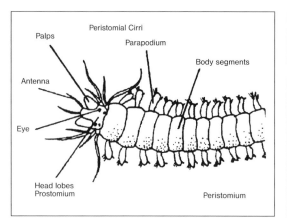

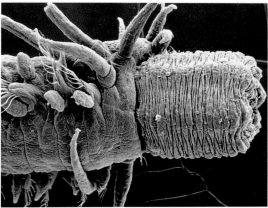

Left: Drawing of dorsal region of an errant bristle worm (after VINE, 1986). Right: Scanning electron microscope (SEM) photo of an errant bristle worm of family Phyllodocidae. Clearly visible are prostomium, peristomial cirri and the body segments with their bristles; the pharynx is everted.   Photo: G. Rouse

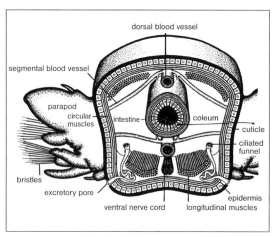

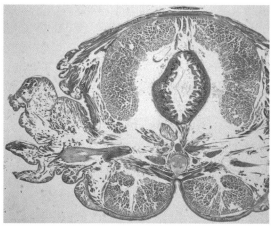

Drawing (after BUCHSBAUM, 1976) and histological cross-section (photo: R. Brons) of an errant bristle worm.

Many errant bristle worms have gills, which are shown here at a *Eurythoe* sp. as reddish outgrowths along the basis of the bristles (magnification 40x).

bes or burrows, so many of them are also referred to as "tube worms". In contrast to most errant species, the heads of sedentary bristle worms do not have antennae, and if eyes are present on the head, they are as pigmented spots without lenses. Some species (e. g. *Cirratulus* spp., family Cirratulidae) have rows of eyespots and some of the tube-dwelling Sabellidae have relatively well-developed eyes on the tentacle crown (TEN HOVE, 1988). Tentacular cirri of the type found in errant families are absent, but many species have grooved tentacles. Parapodia are often absent or small, and there are no in-

 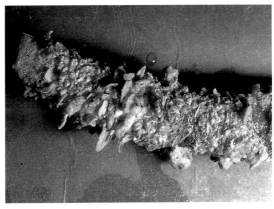

Left: Three different tube worms of family Sabellidae side by side in an aquarium: *Sabellastarte spectabilis* (left), *Megalomma* sp. (centre) and *Bispira tricyclia* (right). The tubes are about the same size, two have been built from mud particles, while one also contains larger sand grains. Right: Many tubes, like the one shown here of *Megalomma* sp., are made from coral fragments and sand grains, held together by mucus produced by the worm.

ternal supporting bristles (present in errant species).

Tubes of sedentary bristle worms can have most peculiar shapes. For example, they can be straight, twisted or U-shaped; with or without attached mud particles, sand grains or coral fragments, held in place by mucus secreted by the worm. The tubes can be mostly buried in the bottom sediment (infaunal) or attached to a hard substrate (epifaunal); they can also be of mud, sand grains, parchment-like or calcareous. The most advanced tube worms (family Serpulidae) construct their tubes out of calcium carbonate material.

Tubes can be partially or totally resting on the bottom, be buried in substrate or bored into coral rocks. Some tube worms have tubes that stand like columns rising from the bottom, while yet others have tubes that form densely matted colonies. Fossil reefs dating back to the Jurassic- or Creta- ceous Periods (about 135 million years ago), which consist of colonial calcareous tube worms, are known from many parts of the world, such as the north-western region of Germany, for instance (TEN HOVE & VAN DER HURK, 1993).

Tubes protect the worms, and most worms will not leave their tubes evoluntarily. Such a permanent life inside the tube is, however, at the expense of an ability to flee from enemies. Instead of fleeing, many tube worms are capa-

 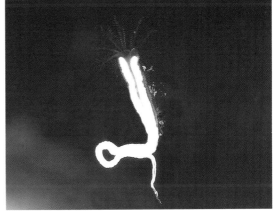

Left: The tube of the small *Phyllochaetopterus* sp. is parchment-like and fortified with coral fragments. In this particular case here, the tube is attached directly on to the aquarium glass, so one could look inside. In the nature the anterior part of the tube usually protrudes above the substratum. Behind that, an errant *Eurythoe* sp. is hiding in a dead coral fragment. Right: The most refined tubes are those made of out of calcium carbonate. This one belongs to a *Vermiliopsis* species which has settle on aquarium glass. The viewer's attention is also drawn to the small errant bristle worm (family Syllidae) crawling on the outside (on the right) of the tube. These bristle worms often attach themselves to the tubes of other worms.

The tentacular crowns of tube worms look beautiful; here a *Bispira* species at Mabouja Island in the Caribbean Sea. The mouth opening and palps are clearly visible on the worm in the centre of the photograph.   Photo: G. Berthold

ble of retracting lightning-fast back into their tube.

The nervous system of bristle worms shows generally sluggish reactions. Yet in some species a few specific giant nerve fibres which extend throughout the entire body can react in a fraction of a second to sudden changes in light intensity, leading to a sudden contraction of the segments and withdrawal into the tube as soon as the eyes perceive a shadow or something that could be an enemy. This is an important adaptation to a permanent life in a tube. Some sabellids (e. g. *Fabricia* spp.) have developed a "back door" by having an opening at each end of the tube, but most tubes have but a single opening.

Tube worms have adapted over millions of years to a life in hiding, either in a tube buried in the substrate, or inside a tube which extends into the open water; yet, at the same time their body structure has sometimes been substantially modified. Tube worms do not burrow in the substrate, and in some species the anterior

appendages have become substantially modified into a crown of tentacles, an apparatus which effectively removes food from water flowing past. This is of profound importance, since the worms are no longer able to chase after prey. These tentacles consist of pri-

mary or main branches (radioles), which carry small lateral branches. The latter are covered by cilia, which create a current flowing along the main branch and then continue on upward and beyond. Food particles are captured by the lateral branches and then

Part of the tentacular crown of *Sabellastarte spectabilis*: The main radioles carry secondary (lateral) branches, which are covered with cilia and used for capturing food which is in turn transported to the mouth.

transported in a longitudinal groove in the middle of each main branch towards the bottom, where they are sorted into different size groups. Only the smallest particles are passed on to the mouth to be eaten, while large particles are ejected. This kind of sorting mechanism is particularly well developed in the family Sabellidae. There are no less than three grooves on each main branch, where food particles of different sizes can be sorted out (TEN HOVE, 1988). In some species the crown of tentacles consists of two or more clusters which can search along the bottom for food.

In species which remain in the tubes (e. g. family Chaetopteridae) there are often segments which have become modified into a simple pumping mechanism that provides a continuous water flow through the tube. An accumulation of waste products in the tube would most certainly cause the death of the worm, and with chaetopterids, a water current also brings with it food. In Sabellidae there is a ciliated groove along the abdomen of the worm, where waste products are collected and transported by the water current towards the opening of the tube, to be discharged into the open water. Species which can extend out of the tube usually have well-developed branchiae, and gas exchange takes place in the open water.

Altogether there is considerable variability in structure and mode of life among tube worms. We will return to some of these aspects when discussing individual families later on in this chapter.

The general biology of the class "Polychaeta" is complicated as well as variable. Within the limited space available here it is impossible for us to go into much detail in some of these areas. Again, we have to refer the reader to the relevant literature, such as RUPPERT & BARNES (1994). In TEN HOVE (1988) there is an easy to comprehend, interesting depiction of the biology of marine bristle worms. In PETERSEN & KIR-

Pileolaria sp. stores larvae in its brood chamber.

Photo: R. Brons

KEGAARD (1991) there is a scientific overview of many families as well as general ecological and biological information.

Reproduction

The reproductive biology of bristle worms is particularly interesting. Asexual reproduction is known from several families of bristle worms, such as Spionidae, Chaetopteridae, Cirratulidae, Sabellidae, Sybillidae, and others. This explains how some bristle worms (e. g. family Spionidae) are able to develop large populations in coral reef aquaria. Asexual reproduction takes place by the body splitting into two or more parts, after which each part generates the missing regions and develops into a new worm.

Just like all other organisms, bristle worms periodically also undergo sexual reproduction. Often this is tied to certain times of the year, controlled by temperature and light. Most species have separate sexes, but some species change sex in the course of their life, and a few are hermaphrodites.

Most bristle worms do not have specific sex organs, and in the

more primitive species sex cells develop in most segments. This can be seen in many "scaleworm" species of the families Polynoidae and Sigalionidae and in all members of family Eunicidae.

More advanced species produces gametes in specific segments, something which is usually related to a specialisation of the body, visible by the division of the body into different sections. The gametes are usually given off into the abdominal cavity of the segments producing sex cells, where they mature. Once maturation has been completed, the gametes are shed into the surrounding water. We have been able to observe this ourselves in an aquarium. This is the most common way that bristle worms to disseminate gametes. The fertilized eggs develop into trochophore larvae, which possess cilia for locomotion and sometimes also for food capture (TEN HOVE, 1988). After a variable period of time, from a few hours to a few weeks or more, depending on the species, the larvae sink to the bottom, undergo a metamorphosis and develop into adult worms.

There are, however, large variations in the mode of release of gametes. This is particularly dramatic in some species of the families Nereididae, Eunicidae and Syllidae, where the segments contai-

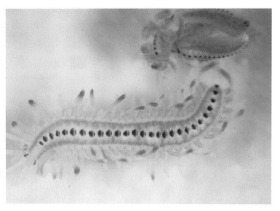
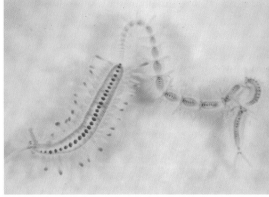

Asexual reproduction is known to occur in many bristle worms. In *Myrianida* species (family Syllidae) clones are being budded off from the posterior end of the body.   Photos: G. Rouse

ning gametes burst, liberating the sex cells. The mature individuals virtually "explode", and then immediately suffer a dramatic death after the gametes have been released.

In some tube-building species, mating and fertilisation take place within the tubes. The fertilized eggs are either deposited outside the tube in a gelatinous egg mass, or are kept inside the tube and cared for by the parent, or they are deposited on the back of a male worm, where they develop into juvenile worms.

In some Sabellidae, for instance in *Augeneriella* sp. from the Great Barrier Reef and in *Fabricia stellaris* from European seas, the maternal worm guards the larvae inside the tube, where they are well protected. Once the larvae are fully developed they crawl out of the tube and construct their own tube close to the maternal one, sometimes on the maternal tube itself. In this way, colonies of a nearly unimaginable density can develop, with up to 1.5 million individuals per square metre. But individual colony member are very small, with a length of 1-3 mm (ROUSE, pers. comm.).

There are also a few species, e. g. *Salmacina implexa* (family Serpulidae), where the larvae hatch inside the tube, so that fully developed larvae are given off. Some *Spirorbis* species encapsulate their larvae inside special brood

chambers, either within the small calcareous tube or in the operculum, where development takes place. This reduces the duration of the planktonic stage and with it the danger of being eaten.

Also some errant species protect their eggs, such as *Autolytus* spp. (family Syllidae). Here the female carries the eggs underneath the abdomen and contributes to

This specimen of *Autolytus* sp. (family Syllidae) was collected on the Great Barrier Reef during mass breeding. The eggs are attached to the ventral body side.   Photo: G. Rouse

We found this epitoke of a Nereidae species in our coral reef aquarium in April 1991. It was swimming through the aquarium at great speed at night (magnification 2x).

the massive reproduction of this worm on the Great Barrier Reef and other locations. In the syllid genera *Exogone* and *Sphaerosyllis*, the fertilized eggs remain attached to the surface of the female, where they remain until the developing juveniles have about six segments, after which the juveniles wiggle free and start a life of their own.

The most fascinating and extraordinary mode of reproduction in marine bristle worms is associated with the formation of "epitokes". An epitoke is a specific reproductive individual which is modified to such an extent that it gives up the crawling, burrowing or tube-building mode on the bottom and leads a pelagic life for a brief period, usually less than a day. After the gametes are released, the epitoke dies. Such modification involves changes in the head, eyes, bristles, appendages, segment size and musculature. The eyes become enlarged, special bristles may develop and segments in the sexual part of the body become filled with gametes. Both males and females produce such epitokes, the male epitokes being filled with sperm cells and female ones with eggs. Often the segments with sex cells are the most strongly modified and filled with gametes to such an extent that it looks as if the worm body is divided into two parts. This happens in some species of the family Nereididae, where the entire

Class Polychaeta

Order Spionida
  Family Spionidae
        Laonice, Spiophanes, Microspio, Prionospio
  Family Chaetopteridae
        Chaetopterus, Phyllochaetopterus,
        Mesochaetopterus, Spiochaetopterus
  Family Cirratulidae
        Aphelochaeta, Cirriformia, Cirratulus,
        Caulleriella, Chaetozone, Tharyx;
        Dodecaceria, Timarete

Order Capitellida
  Family Capitellidae
        Capitella

Order Phyllodocida
  Family Phyllodocidae
        Phyllodoce, Eulalia
  Family Polynoidae
        Harmothoe, Lepidonotus, Gastrolepidia,
        Hermenia, Iphione
  Family Acoetidae
  Family Pholoidae
  Family Hesionidae
        Hesione, Leocrates
  Family Nereididae
        Nereis, Leptonereis, Platynereis,
        Perinereis, Leonnates
  Family Syllidae
        Syllis, Haplosyllis, Autolytus,
        Myrianida

Order Amphinomida
  Family Amphinomidae
        Hermodice, Eurythoe, Cloenia

Order Eunicida
  Family Eunicidae
        Eunice, Palola, Euniphysa, Marphysa,
        Paramarphysa, Nematonereis, Lysidice

  Family Dorvilleidae
        Dorvillea, Ophryotrocha

Order Terebellida
  Family Terebellidae
        Terebella, Reteterebella, Loimia

Order Sabellida
  Family Sabellidae
        Sabella, Bispira, Sabellastarte, Anamobaea,
        Megalomma, Myxicola, Fabricia
  Family Serpulidae
    Subfamily Serpulinae
        Serpula, Hydroides, Spirobranchus,
        Filogranella, Vermiliopsis, Crucigera, Pomatoceros,
        Floriprotes, Pseudovermilia
    Subfamily Filograninae
        Protula, Salmacina
    Subfamily Spirorbinae
        Spirorbis, Janua

specimen becomes an epitoke. In species of the Eunicidae and Syllidae only the most posterior segments form epitokes, which are constricted off when the sex cells have matured. In *Myrianida* species, also of the family Syllidae, such epitokes are budded off the posterior end of the worm as long chains, with the oldest epitoke (the one to be freed first) at the end of the chain.

We have observed epitokes of family Nereididae in an aquarium. At night we saw 2-3 cm long bristle worms swimming very rapidly through the open water area in the tank. At first we thought that this was a new species, but gradually it became clear that these were epitokes of nereididids. In nature, epitokes are often released synchronously and so produce a mass spawning. This phenomenon is related to the mass spawning of corals (see Vol. 2, page 51-52). Such synchronous mass spawning assures fertilization and thus the survival of a species. As in corals, such mass simultaneous breeding is triggered by temperature and the lunar cycle. In the Pacific region, epitokes of *Palola* spp. are considered to be delicacies and are highly prized as food.

Family Spionidae

The species in this family are largely small, sedentary tube worms, but there are also some free-living species. *Polydora*- and *Boccardia* species occur in soft-bottom substrates, world-wide in all seas, and also bore in calcareous objects, while *Aonides* spp. are common along the sandy bottoms of temperate and tropical seas (FAUCHALD, 1977). All spionids have two grooved palps (tactile sensors) which have been adapted to take up food and few or many pairs of variously shaped dorsal branchiae. The most recent review of the family is that of BLAKE (1996a), who gives a detailed and higly readable acount of the morphology, taxonomy, biology, ecology (including feeding, tube building and boring), reproduction and speciation of spionids. The family is one of the largest and most important among polychaetes. Occasionally there can be a massive development of spionids in an aquarium, whereby large areas of the bottom or live rocks become covered with these worms.

Family Chaetopteridae

In the Chaetopteridae the body is divided into three regions of rather variable appearance. The anterior region has nine or more segments, the middle region has two or more, and there are a variable number of segments in the posterior region. All species have two grooved tentacles or palps and one or more large, modified setae on each side of segment 4 of the anterior region. Neuropodia (the ventral or lower part of the parapodia) of the middle and posterior regions are unique among polychaetes in having two lobes rather than one. Each lobe has a row of tiny, flat, oval setae (uncini) with a row of teeth along one side.

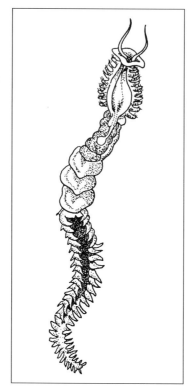

Chaetopterus variopedatus.
Drawing from VINE (1986)

Under low magnification each row of uncini looks like the teeth of one side of a zipper. The dorsal bristles (notosetae) are simple (not jointed) and consist of the modified setae on segment 4,

lance-shaped setae and slender bristles.

All members of the Chaetopteridae live in tubes. When removed from their tubes, they are usually unable to build new ones, but if put in a glass tube, they can add new tube material to the openings. The tubes of *Chaetopterus* species are U-shaped, with a small opening at each end and the largest diameter at about the halfway point. They are either buried in the sediment so that only the two ends of the tube (the chimneys) are visible, or are attached to solid objects. As indicated by the species name of *C. pergamentaceus* (from the Antilles), its tube is parchment-like. In other species, sand grains, mud, shell fragments or other debris may be attached to the tube. The shape of the tubes in other genera is basically straight and slender, of similar width throughout and open at one end only, but in aquaria tubes may assume shapes not usually found in the field. In some species the tubes have side branches. Chaetopterids may be solitary or form colonies. For example, *Mesochaetopterus saggittarius* is a colonial species, and *Spiochaetopterus costarum* is solitary, but one which can build branched tubes. *Phyllochaetopterus* sp. "KA5-POL-01" (see fact sheet 113),

Chaetopterus sp. (possibly *C. luteus*) at Dunwich, Stradbroke Island, Great Barrier Reef. Left: An opening of the U-shaped tube protrudes a few centimetres above the bottom. Right: The tube and the worm have been removed from the sediment and opened for research purposes. The flattened segments of the thorax and the green-coloured digestive glands are well visible.

Photos: L. Newman and A. Flowers

Phyllochaetopterus sp. "KA5-POL-01"

Distribution: The species depicted here probably occurs in the Indo-Pacific. Details about the distribution are unknown. This genus was originally described from the Adriatic Sea (Mediterranean Sea).

Size and appearance: Under aquarium conditions normally about 3 cm, sometimes up to 5 cm long and 1-2 mm wide. Lives buried in coral sand and builds a parchment-like tube, which is covered with sand grains. Usually the tube is mostly buried in sand, with only the anterior end protruding on occasion. Two palps are nearly always visible at the end of the tube. Tube length normally about 5 to 6 times as long as the worm occupying it.

Reproduction: Under aquarium conditions asexual reproduction by fragmentation and regeneration, which can lead to the establishment of large populations.

Food: Captures food with secreted mucous sacs. The two rod-like palps, which can be as long as the entire worm body, protrude from the tube and probably collects detritus and plankton as supplementary food from the surrounding water. the main function of the palps is removal of excrements from the tube.

Description: *Phyllochaetopterus* spp. have a pair of short, antenna-like structures near the basis of the palps. At least 17 species have so far been described (FAUCHALD, 1977), but some of these probably belong into other genera. Our aquarium specimens have nine anterior, two middle and a variable number of posterior segments. The fourth segment has four or five blunt bristles on either side. Anterior and central part of the body cream-coloured or whitish, posterior body black or dark blue-green. Tubes narrow, with sand grains attached, but always distinctly separated from each other. *Phyllochaetopterus* sp. "KA5-POL-01" is similar to *P. verrilli*, but is 8 cm longer (NISHI & ARAI, 1996).

Aquarium requirements: *Phyllochaetopterus* sp. "KA5-POL-01" can be categorized as a hardy aquarium species which is easy to keep. Water current to supply and keep food particles suspended in the water column is essential. This is an interesting aquarium animal, which can produce large populations. It is ideal for biological observations. For instance, we have observed that this worm builds a curved tube, inside which it can turn around.

GA: +; SE: +; CO : +

Photos:
Top: Tube partially protruding from the bottom. The worm's palps are extended.
Centre: Transparent, curved tube totally buried, but placed directly against the aquarium glass.
Bottom: Specimen removed from its tube.

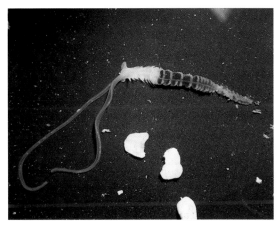

which sometimes occurs in a coral reef aquarium, has straight tubes, often with fragments of mollusc shells or sand grains attached to it. Tubes of other species may be twisted or ringed. Sometimes one or more small crabs or polychaetes live as commensals together with a worm inside the tube; this is most common with species of *Chaetopterus* but also occurs in other genera (PETERSEN & BRITAYEV, 1997). The commensals do not harm the worm, however, they do tend to "steal" some of its food.

Chaetopterus species are known for their ability to luminesce, but no one knew why they did so. MARTIN & ANCTIL (1984) placed worms in glass tubes so they could be observed; the worms added a chimney to each end of the tube. When the chimney closest to the worm was shaken, as by a curious fish, a blob of luminescent mucus was immediately sent out through the chimney and the worm retreated to the other end of the tube, suggesting that the mucus serves to distract the fish and enable the worm to survive.

Chaetopterids are filter feeders. They collect plankton with fine-meshed mucous sacs or bags secreted by the wing-shaped notopodia of the first middle segment (*Chaetopterus* spp.) or by slightly different arrangements in the other genera. After a short period of time, e. g. 15 minutes, the bag is rolled up and transported in a ciliated groove on the back to the mouth. Details of feeding in *Chaetopterus* were first described by MACGINITIE (1939). BARNES (1964, 1965) and NISHI & ARAI (1996) observed similar mechanisms in other genera.

All members of family Chaetopteridae are capable of regenerating lost anterior and posterior body sections. Some species also reproduce asexually by fragmentation. When this happens, the worms break into two or more sections and then regenerate the missing body parts. Asexual reproduction in chaetopterids was first reported by POTTS (1914) for

several species from the northeast Pacific. It appears to be especially common in species of *Phyllochaetopterus* (POTTS, 1914; see also pages 109-111) and also occurs in some *Spiochaetopterus* (BHAUD et al., 1994; BHAUD, 1998).

Sexual reproduction takes place by discharging eggs and sperm into the open water, where fertilization occurs. Fertilized eggs develop into barrel-shaped trochophore larvae, and some of these can remain in the plankton for many months.

The genus *Chaetopterus* was established in 1830 for *C. pergamentaceus* from the "Sea of the Antilles". About 25-30 species have been described, but not all are distinct. The genus is presently under revision by NISHI (mainly species in Japanese waters; 1996) and PETERSEN (various areas; pers. comm.). For a long time most workers considered all species to be varieties of *C. variopedatus* (RENIER, 1804) from the Adriatic Sea, which was incorrectly thought to occur worldwide. Re-examination of old and new material from type localities or nearby has now shown that the name *C. variopedatus* has been used for several species (PETERSEN, 1984a, b, and in preparation). *Chaetopterus* species vary in size from 10-15 mm for *C. longipes* (NISHI, 1996) to 25-40 cm for *C. cautus* (PETERSEN, 1997).

Our research tank includes a chamber which receives the water before it flows on into the protein skimmer. This chamber (volume about 60 l) has a 5-10 cm thick bottom layer of fine coral sand, mixed with crushed live rocks and coral fragments. Among other purposes, this chamber also functions as a "settling tank", where detritus and coarse particles accumulate. This small tank contains a rich fauna of interstitial organisms (see page 96). Among other organisms, there, on the bottom, lives a very interesting and decorative bristle worm of the genus *Phyllochaetopterus*.

Phyllochaetopterus sp. "KA5-POL-01" builds small tubes on the

bottom and can develop into a large colony. We were able to observe how the worms built their tubes. When one of these tubes was built against a glass side of the chamber, this gave us a close-up view of this worm. There we noted that the worm can turn around inside its chamber (see fact sheet on page 113). In essence then, its anterior section can extend out of either of the two openings. Together with the population of *Phyllochaetopterus* sp., there are also several specimens of *Eurythoe* sp. "KA5-POL-02" of the family Amphinomidae (see page 124), as well as some *Timarete filigera* (family Cirratulidae) (see fact sheet page 115), all in the same tank. And so over the years, the small inflow chamber has become a convincing example of the fact that interesting organisms can be kept in a small tank.

Family Cirratulidae

In our opinion species of the family Cirratulidae are among the most fascinating bristle worms that can be observed in a coral reef aquarium. Even though many species are not particularly large, their shape and colour will attract attention. Cirratulids burrow in the substrate or live in small cavities, such as holes and crevices in live rocks or dead coral fragments. These worms have a substantial ability for asexual reproduction. This is most certainly the reason why they can establish themselves in relatively large numbers in our aquaria. During asexual reproduction the body breaks into two or more fragments, each of which then regenerates the missing regions: head, tail, or both. Regenerated body parts can be recognised by their smaller diameter and paler colour than the original segments. In some species of *Cirratulus* and *Dodecaceria*, asexual reproduction is a nor-

Timarete filigera
Ball-of-Yarn Bristle Worm

Distribution: Widely distributed throughout the Indo-Pacific, perhaps circumtropical, details are unknown.

Size and appearance: Up to 250 mm long and 6 mm in diameter, but aquarium specimens are usually smaller than this. Lives in narrow crevices of coral or live rocks, but also buried in sand or on the tubes of other bristle worms. When disturbed will immediately retract its filamentous tentacles and branchia into a dense mass.

Reproduction: Reproduces asexually by fragmentation and regeneration, PETERSEN (1991, 1999 in press).

Feeding: Deposit feeder that uses its grooved tentacles to obtain particles from the sediment. They can also use the eversible pharynx to feed directly on food particles, (FAUCHALD & JUMARS, 1979).

Description: Belongs to the family Cirratulidae. The genus *Timarete* is characterized by a flattened, wedge-shaped prostomium, two groups of grooved dorsal tentacles arising from several anterior segments after the first branchiae, branchiae displaced dorsally on middle segments, and setae including acicular hooks. Three species (*T. filigera, T. punctata* and *T. caribous*) often coexist in the same habitat, but only *T. filigera* has been reported from aquaria. None of the species have eyespots as adults and the branchiae are stout. *T. filigera* is orange to brownish with branchiae and tentacles blood red and frosted with whitish or yellowish pigment. Dorsal tentacles arising above segments 3-5 or 4-6. Acicular hooks are slender, pale to straw coloured; ventral hooks similar throughout, not single and darker in posterior segments.

Aquarium requirements: Very robust bristle worm, which is frequently overlooked because of its small size. We have seen a few larger specimens crawl along the bottom during darkness. Beautiful if seen through a stereomicroscope. Belongs to the important cryptofauna of an aquarium, that is, animals that hide in crevices and burrows.

GA: +; SE: +; CO: +

Photos:
Top: Ball-of-yarn bristle worm, *Timarete filigera*, among turf algae and detritus in an aquarium.
Centre: Close-up view of the anterior segments with tentacles and branchiae (25x magnification).
Bottom: *T. filigera* from Lizard Island, Great Barrier Reef.
Photo: M. E. Petersen

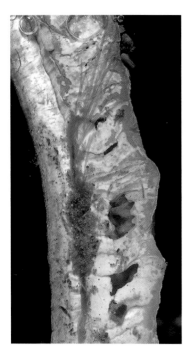

This abandoned tube of a vermetid snail has been attached to the front glass of our aquarium. Between the glass and the tube, lives the Ball-of-Yarn bristle worm *Timarete filigera*, which uses its long filaments to collect food particles. Through the holes in the snail tube one can see a few glistening bristles and segments of another bristle worm of genus *Eurythoe* (family Amphionomidae) which has occupied the empty "house" for protection.

mal part of the life cycle; the cycle ends when, after one or more years, some of the asexually reproduced individuals become sexually mature epitokes (see section on reproduction), swim up to the surface, shed their eggs or sperm, and die. In some species of *Caulleriella*, the epitokes are bioluminescent and can produce a bluish light. Most cirratulids are either male or female, but a few species are hermaphrodites (having male and female gametes in the same individual) and brood their young (PETERSEN, 1994 and 1999). In some European species of *Dodecaceria*, males are usually absent, and eggs start to divide inside the female without being fertilized by a male (parthenoge-

nesis). Much of this is still incompletely understood, and in some cases more than one species may be involved. A brief review of reproduction in the Cirratulidae, including references to the above, is given in Petersen (1999).

Cirratulids occur in cold as well as in warm seas and at all depths. BLAKE (1996b) reviewed the taxonomy and biology of the family and recognised 10 genera. The exact number of distinct species is uncertain; FAUCHALD (1977) recognized about 130, but some of these have since been moved to other families and many new species have been described. The true number is probably at least twice that. All cirratulids have a body that is more or less pointed at both ends, two or many grooved tentacles on one or more anterior segments, and few (*Dodecaceria* spp.) to numerous (all other species) filamentous (thread-like) branchiae, usually mostly on anterior and middle segments; bristles are all simple (unjointed), but differ in size, shape and arrangement. They usually emerge directly from the body.

In, e. g. *Cirriformia*, *Cirratulus*, and *Timarete*, the tentacles and branchiae appear as spectacular filamentous outgrowths on one or more segments close to the head, in some instances nearly equal to the length of the body. Seeing a cirratulid for the very first time, one could get the impression that it is bundle of matted worms. Yet, in reality it is only a single individual with numerous branchiae and grooved tentacles, which latter are used for capturing food. The tentacles collect sediment particles, and manipulate these into the mouth where they are swallowed. Food particles can also be swallowed directly by means of an eversible saclike pharynx. It is quite an impressive sight to see a cirratulid in full activity and with all tentacles extended. Other genera, e. g. *Tharyx*, *Chaetozone*, and *Dodecaceria*, have only two grooved tentacles (palps) for capturing food. Like *Timarete filigera*, many species of *Dodecaceria* are able to repro-

duce asexually as well as sexually, whereas sexual reproduction (presence of individuals with gametes) has not yet been reported for any *Timarete*, although it almost certainly occurs.

Family Capitellidae

The family Capitellidae has a large number of species. According to FAUCHALD (1977) there are at least 38 genera. There are many small species, each only a few centimetres long, with a cylindrical and slender body. The body is often clearly delineated into an anterior region (thorax) and a hind body (abdomen). Bristles of the anterior thoracic segments are slender and pointed; they are referred to as "capillary bristles". Farther back there may also be hooded hook-shaped bristles, which are the only kind present on the abdomen.

Capitellids can be very numerous in certain types of habitat. *Capitella* spp. have been used as pollution indicators, since they thrive on substrates which are heavily polluted (FAUCHALD, 1977; GRASSLE & GRASSLE, 1974), but the belief that most specimens are *C. capitata* has been shown to be incorrect; GRASSLE & GRASSLE (1976) found six different species in a small test area in Falmouth, Massachusetts after an oil spill.

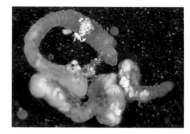

A tiny, unknown bristle worm of family Capitellidae, which we found in our aquarium. Coral grains are visible inside the intestine, they must have swallowed to remove food particles subsequently (magnification 15x).

Genus and species identification requires a microscopic examination of the thoracic segments, in order to determine the number of segments and to examine the location of capillary bristles. In general, this is rather difficult and is best left to specialists. We have found capitellids in our experimental aquarium, so that it is not impossible that these bristle worms also occur frequently in coral reef aquaria.

Family Phyllodocidae

The family Phyllodocidae belongs to the order Phyllodocida, the largest in the class Polychaeta. The most recent revision of the family is that of PLEIJEL (1991), who recognised 18 distinct genera. Phyllodocids occur principally in shallow water and are more common on firm substrate than on sand or

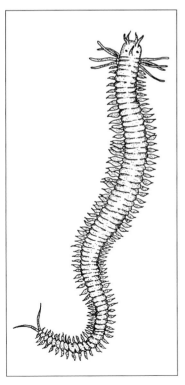

Eulalia viridis.
Drawing after VINE (1986)

mud. There are a few very colourful species.

Bristle worms in this family produce a lot of mucus when they are disturbed. This can also happen when they are introduced into an aquarium together with live rocks. *Phyllodoce* and *Eulalia* are the genera most commonly encountered on coral reefs. All species in these two genera have four (*Phyllodoce*) or five (*Eulalia*) antennae on the head lobe and four pairs of tentacular cirri on the first three segments. The pharynx is eversible (see scanning electron microscope photo page 106), but there are no jaws. Many species have paddle-shaped parapodia.

Phyllodocids can be rather common on live rocks introduced into an aquarium. The basic diet for these bristle worms is dead or dying organisms (VINE, 1986), which can create some concern among aquarists. Although some species look very dangerous, they are quite harmless.

Family Polynoidae

The species in the family have large, shingle-like scales, which originate on specific segments and cover most or all of the dorsal surface. This has also given them the name "scaleworms". In some tropical species the scales can be very colourful, but most commonly they are brown.

Polynoid scaleworms have one, two or (most commonly) three antennae on their head and a powerful, eversible pharynx with four jaws. The parapodia on segments not bearing scales have a dorsal cirrus as well as a ventral cirrus. These worms are frequently found on live rocks or on the underside of coral colonies. Usually they are only a few centimetres long. FAUCHALD (1977) lists more than 100 genera, and PETTIBONE (1982) mentions 120; according to RUFF (1995), who provides a brief review of the fa-

mily, there are about 700 species.

Lepidonotus carinulatus seems to be particularly frequent on live rocks. It is distributed throughout the entire western Indo-Pacific, where it occurs most commonly on litoral (coastal) reefs, and even in mangrove areas. There are several colour varieties of this species.

Another species found very frequently on litoral reefs is *Iphione muricata*. This is a carnivorous worm, feeding on small crustaceans and on other bristle worms. The dorsal scales are coarse and strong. They protect the worm against mechanical damage. A particularly important function here is the protection of the respiratory surface on dorsal side of the worm. When the worm is being attacked or frightened, it rolls itself into a small ball, and so protects itself against enemies.

Underneath coral boulders and rocks we find one of the most common scaleworms of the coral reef: *Hermenia acantholepis*. As in some of the other scaleworms, the scales have been reduced in size, except those located in the head region. When scales are reduced, their protective capacity is also lessened. Scaleworms with reduced scales either live inside the tube of a host organism (e. g. another bristle worm), where the water coming into the tube is clean and nearly particle-free, or in habitats where the water carries little particulate matter, such as in neritic (off-shore) coral reefs.

Some scaleworms live in a commensal association with other invertebrates. One example of this is *Gastrolepidia clavigera*, a worm found together with 30 sea cucumber species. The worm can mimic the colours of the host animal, but nobody knows how this is done. Most likely the mimic takes place due to a selection among the populations of young worms. Worms which settle on a host animal without matching the host's colours will be discovered and eaten by fish because of their inadequate camouflage. The colour mimicry can be rather highly de-

Left: *Lepidonotus carinulatus* is one of the most common polynoids on litoral reefs and in mangrove areas; it is often imported into aquaria together with live rocks. Right: *Iphione muricata* (family Polynoidae) at Heron Island, Great Barrier Reef (photo: L. Newman and A. Flowers).

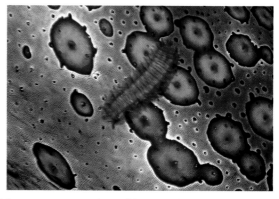

Hermenia acantholepis (left) and *Gastrolepidia clavigera* (right, on a sea cucumber) of family Polynoidae at Madang, Papua-New Guinea.   Photos: L. Newman and A. Flowers

veloped. The sea cucumber *Holothuria atra* is nearly black, and the entire body is covered with sand grains. Individual *Gastrolepidia clavigera* which live in association with this sea cucumber are black, with small, creamy white spots on their scales.

Family Hesionidae

In the family Hesionidae most species are small and flattened dorso-ventrally. They are common in very shallow water, where they are usually found on a sandy bottom. The family has recently been reviewed and revised by PLEIJEL (1998), who recognized 22 distinct genera.

The small *Hesione genetta* is

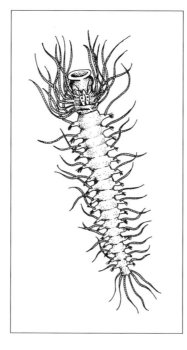

Above: Hesione genetta at Heron Island, Great Barrier Reef.
Photo: L. Newman and A. Flowers
To the left: *Leocrates claparedii*.
Drawing after Vine (1986)

among the most common species of this genus, and can serve as a general example of this group of bristle worms. It is frequently found on coral reefs throughout the western Indo-Pacific, and displays many traits which are characteristic of this family. The worm is soft and fragile, has well-developed eyes, and can move rapidly along the bottom pursuing food, which probably consists of small invertebrates, such as crustaceans and other bristle worms.

In the Red Sea, *Hesione pantherina* occurs on sandy bottoms, while the somewhat fearsome-looking *Leocrates claparedii* lives on live rocks and corals.

Family Nereididae

In the family Nereididae there are errant bristle worms which somewhat resemble the eunicids (see further below); however, the Nereididae have a more compressed body. Most species are marine, but there are also a few brackish water – and some (very few) freshwater species. In Sumatra, some species of the genera *Lycastis*, *Lycastopsis* and *Nereis* are terrestrial. These species have been described by PFLUG-FELDER (1933). They are only a millimetre wide and up to 10 cm long. In contrast, most marine species are rather large, with marked segmentation, well-developed parapodia on each segment and sturdy jaws with an eversible pharynx. They belong to the most

Nereis sp. with small antennae and long cirri and a distinctly segmented body.

common errant bristle worms on coral reefs, where they burrow in sand or mud. The most frequently occurring genera are *Perinereis*, *Leonnates*, *Ceratonereis*, *Nereis* and *Neanthes*.

Reproduction in nereididids is often through the development of heteronereids or epitokes where the entire worm is transformed. The eyes enlarge, special bristles are formed, the gut degenerates, and the segments are essentially reduced to sacs with mature sex cells and transformed parapodia. On a special day, at dusk, when water temperature and moonlight are coordinated, the worms swim to the surface and perform a spectacular mating dance in the open water. The males give off pheromones, which stimulate rapid movements of both males and females, during which the weake-

ned body wall tears or breaks, releasing the sex cells. The worms literally seem to explode, and die shortly after spawning. This is in contrast to the families Eunicidae and Syllidae, where the stolons that will become epitokes are formed from (usually) the posterior part of the worm and the anterior part continues to live and regenerates a new posterior end after the epitoke has been released.

Family Syllidae

In comparison to the Nereididae and Eunicidae, the species in this family are relatively small. Many are distinctly compressed dorsoventrally, and they occur very frequently on coral rocks. The family is large, with about 70 genera and well over 600 species. A brief review of the family, including its biology and a key to major groups, is given by KUDENOV & HARRIS (1995).

Reproduction in Syllidae is extremely varied. Some species, e. g. *Syllis gracilis* and *Proceraea halleziana*, reproduce asexually by fragmentation, where constrictions form between segments, the fragments separate and regenerate the missing region(s) after separation. This appears to be the same type as seen in Cirratulidae and Chaetopteridae and is not related to sexual reproduction.

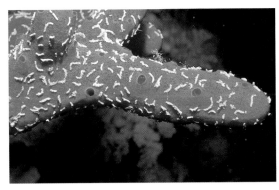

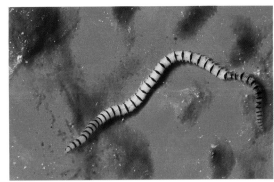

Left: *Haplosyllis spongicola*, seen here in the Red Sea (photo; J. Cairns-Michael), lives in association with sponges and feeds off their cells. Right: Unknown species of family Syllidae, seen here at Heron Island, Great Barrier Reef, in association with a sponge (photo: L. Newman and A. Flowers).

During sexual reproduction of the above and other species, the nonsexual adult (an atoke, also called the stock) may bud off individuals singly at the posterior end (*Syllis gracilis*), in clusters (*Trypanosyllis* spp.) or chains (*Myrianida* sp.) from the end or sides (*Syllis ramosus*) of the body. The individuals budded off in this way (stolons) are the sexual individuals that will develop into epitokes filled with gametes, with the modifications mentioned earlier: enlarged eyes, special swimming setae, gut reduced or absent, etc. In Syllidae the male and female epitokes not only differ from the atoke, but may also differ structurally from one another, e. g. males may have forked antennae, females non-forked ones and a sac in which the eggs are brooded, which caused earlier workers to think they belonged to three different genera (see also under reproduction).

Syllids are mostly considered carnivorous. Some species are food specialists and feed on hydroids. They have a pharynx with a strong tooth that can pierce the stiff covering (theca) of the hydroid, enabling the worm to suck up the soft hydroid tissue inside (MATHER & BENNETT, 1993). Other species may be selective deposit feeders (FAUCHALD & JUMARS, 1979).

Other species live symbiotically, such as the small *Haplosyllis spongicola*, which occurs in large aggregations on sponge colonies. However, it can also be found as single individuals on the bottom of a reef. *H. spongicola* feeds on sponge cells, locating them with a special designed proboscis (ERHARD & MOOSLEITNER, 1995) and has a circumtropical distribution. There are also many other syllids which live together with sponges.

Occasionally, we have found individuals of this family in a coral reef aquarium. These had been imported hidden among live rocks (see Vol. 1, page 180). The bristle worms in the family are among the most numerous inhabitants of a coral reef, and most

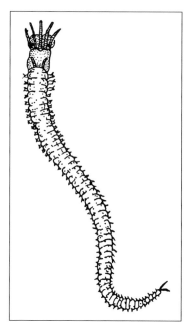

Eunice antennata.
Drawing after Vine (1986)

certainly occur very frequently on live rocks. They are, however, difficult to detect.

Family Eunicidae

The bristle worms in the family Eunicidae are rather large, with an errant or sedentary mode of life. Some can reach a maximum length of up to 3 m, and have a diameter of up to 2-3 cm. Although many of these worm have a fearsome appearance, they are fairly harmless in reality. This family contains at least 300 species, of which many seem to be rather similar. There are herbivorous species and detritus feeders, as well as carnivores. All species have several jaws, located in an eversible pharynx. Alone the genus *Eunice* is huge, with over 200 species (FAUCHALD, 1992a).

Errant species are common on reefs, but they usually live cryptically under rocks or in the hollow spaces of coral rocks. Because of

Head and thorax of *Eunice* sp.
Photo: G. Rouse

this, they are unintentionally introduced into coral reef aquaria. The most extraordinary example known to us of such a worm having been introduced inadvertently into a coral reef aquarium comes from Günter Gross at Speyer, Germany. When he emptied his tank, he discovered a 1.5-2 m long eunicid worm, which was identified as *Palola* cf. *siciliensis* (GROSS, 1995; NILSEN, 1996, see fact sheet on page 121).

Palolo worms and their mass reproduction are well known from the central Indo-Pacific. There, during certain nights, many thousands of epitokes swarm about, distributing eggs and sperm. According to FAUCHALD (1992b) the genus *Palola* contains about 20 species, several of which are incompletely known. The "well known" *P. siciliensis* has been misidentified as several other species, so its true distribution is presently unknown. It may be limited to the Mediterranean and perhaps the Indian Ocean (HANLEY, pers. comm.).

The most frequently encountered genus of the family is *Eunice*. Similar to the *Palola* species and

Palola spp., *Palola* cf. *siciliensis*
Palolo worms

Distribution: Mainly tropical or subtropical, with a few species (*P. siciliensis* and *P. paloloides*) in temperate to warm-temperate waters. A review of the types (FAUCHALD, 1992b) revealed at least 12 distinct species, perhaps up to 20; because of taxonomic confusion and misidentifications, distribution of the different species is uncertain.

Size and appearance: Some species up to a length of 2.5-3.0 m and a width of about 3 cm, but most are about 1 m long and slender, 0.5 cm wide.

Reproduction: *Palolo* worms are famous for their mass annual spawning on the Pacific coral reefs, which is timed to coincide with the large spring tides in October and November, although some species breed in the spring. During the mass spawning each of the adult worms sheds the rear 2/3 of the body, which during the preceding months has undergone a metamorphosis into a reproductive "epitoke" filled with either female or male gametes, and capable of swimming to the surface where the gametes are spread. The epitokes contain high concentrations of proteins and oils and are highly prized as food. After the release of the epitoke, the anterior part of the adult worm (the atoke) withdraws and continues burrowing, feeding and growing in the reef in preparation for the next mass spawning in 12 months time.

Food: Normally feeding on algae, such as *Padina* spp., dead corals, sponges, sea anemones, etc. on the reef, but has been observed to eat soft corals in the aquarium (GROSS, 1995).

Description: Belong to the family Eunicidae. Very common species. Commonly seen on reefs in the Indo-Pacific, specially on platform reefs in north-western Australia where they hide in crevices and only emerge from the shelter when feeding. The body is clearly divided into segments with each segment bearing large bristles. The mouth contains several strong pairs of jaws. Colour greenish brown.

Aquarium requirements: The specimen shown in the photograph on this page and on page 122 was found in a reef aquarium where it had been introduced with live rocks (GROSS, 1995; NILSEN, 1996). The specimen measured 1.5-2.0 m in length. This is the only time we have heard that such a big worm has been found in the reef aquarium and it clearly illustrates how diverse and interesting the fauna of the reef aquarium can be. This worm did, however, badly damage the coral population and the aquarium had to be emptied to cope with the situation. Nonetheless, we do not at all recommend that worms be removed from live rocks. Most of the polychaetes introduced with live rocks are rather harmless.

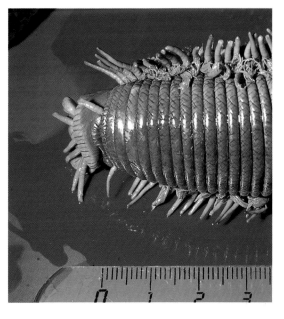

Photo:
Close-up view of the head of *P.* cf. *siciliensis* (see also photo on page 122).

Notes on identity: The large species from the Indo West Pacific found in Mr. Gross' aquarium has the characters used by FAUCHALD (1992b) to define *P. siciliensis*, except for being much larger in width (25 mm to FAUCHALD's maximum 4 mm). FAUCHALD also reports *P. siciliensis* to be found in the Mediterrenian Sea and possible in the Indian Ocean, but not widespread in the Indo Pacific. In the German edition of this chapter (FOSSÁ & NILSEN, 1996) we used the name *P. siciliensis* for this specimen. We now believe that further examination and comparisons with FAUCHALD's type material must be done to make a final conclusion on the identity of this magnificient creature.

GA: +; **SE:** +; **CO:** +/-

Palola cf. *siciliensis* (half of total lenght) in the aquarium of G. Gross.   Photo: G. Linnert

some Nereididae, these bristle worms can also engage in mass reproduction. Moreover, in some Pacific regions, these worms are considered to be real delicacies by the local population. Among the most common coral reef inhabitants are *Eunice antennata, E. australia*, and *E. indica* (see VINE, 1986). These worms live among coral fragments and rocks. Most are predators with strong jaws and an eversible pharynx. *Eunice* spp. are also common on live rocks, and must generally be considered as some of the errant bristle worms which most frequently enter our aquaria hidden in live rocks.

Along the coast of northern Australia and in the central Indo-Pacific, there are a few species of *Eunice* that build conspicuous, branched tubes. These include *E. tubifex* and *E. metatropos* (HANLEY, 1986).

In *Eunice tubifex* the tube consists of polysaccharides, and it is tough and parchment-like. The polysaccharides are secreted by the worm and harden when coming into contact with seawater. The tubes, which have several openings in a serrated pattern, lead down into a hollow space within a rock or piece of coral. About 10-15 cm down into the rock or coral there is an oval cavity lined with a parchment-like substance, where the worm spends most of its life. When feeding, the worm extends the ante-

rior part out of the tube and search the substrat surounding their tube for food. In essence, this species combines and errant mode of life with a life in seclusion. *E. tubifex* reach a length of up to 1.5 m, but the average length is "only" 0.8-1.0 m.

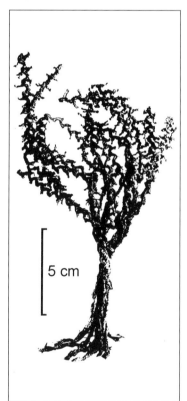

5 cm

Left: The upper part of a tube of *Eunice tubifex*, here at East Arm Wharf, near Darwin, Australia, protrudes above the bottom and is covered by encrusting anemones of genus *Acrozoanthus* (photo: P. Alderslade). Right (top): Worm removed from tube. Right (bottom): Close-up (ventral view) of head region. (photo: P. Alderslade).

Eunice metatropos lives in colonies where the individual worm build tubes that at first appear close together and then separates resulting in a tree-like shaped worm colony.

Drawing from a photograph in HANLEY (1986)

One particular characteristic of *Eunice tubifex* is not its mode of life, but the fact that the part of the tube emerging from the substrate is often overgrown by zoanthid anemones of genus *Acrozoanthus*. These zoanthid anemones often attract the attention of aquarium collectors, who cut off the tubes in order to sell them as aquarium animals. For a long time aquarists (including ourselves; see Vol. 2, page 276) believed that these were zoanthid anemones living symbiotically with a sponge. But in reality they are zoanthid anemones which live on the upper part of a tube of the bristle worm *Eunice tubifex*. Not all tubes are covered by zoanthid anemones, and so this is probably a commensal symbiotic relationship, where the worm – in contrast to the zoanthid anemones – re-ceives little benefit from this rela-tionship.

Eunice metatropos lives in dee-per water than *E. tubifex*. The spe-cies was described by HANLEY (1986). The type material was bro-ught up from 80 m in an otter trawl off the northwest coast of Austra-lia. *E. metatropos* builds tubes just like those of *E. tubifex*, but there are no symbiotic anemones. Moreover, the tubes are more in-tertwined, so that several tubes make up a branched structure, and a number of worms live to-gether in a colony (see drawing on page 122). Such association in groups is rare among bristle worms. There are possible bene-fits in this in terms of food gathe-ring. It appears as if *E. metatropos* looks for food on the bottom aro-und the colony. The accumulation of several tubes in a branched and flexible structure can also re-present an adaptation to (prevai-ling) water currents.

Family Dorvilleidae

The family Dorvilleidae encom-passes relatively small bristle worms, which are most numerous in shallow water; however, re-cently they have also been found at considerable depths in the nor-thern Pacific. JUMARS (1974) revi-sed the family, designating 8 ge-nera, of which *Dorvillea*, *Ophryotrocha* and *Schistomerin-gos* with 15, 11 and 10 species, respectively, were the largest (FAUCHALD, 1977). Since then nu-merous new genera and species

Left: The tentacles of *Eupolymnia* sp. look similar to spaghetti (seen here in the Jaubert-System-Aquarium of J. Sprung, Miami). Right: Typical appearance of *Reteterebella queenslandia* in a reef slope in the Maldives.

When we carefully turned over a rock in shallow water on Flinders Reef, we found this tube of *Loimia medusa*, made of coral fragments (left). After carefully opening the tube, the purple-coloured tentacles became visible (right).

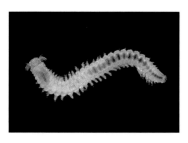

Ophryotrocha sp. (?) from Shark Bay, Australia.   Photo: G. Rouse

have been erected and there are now well over 100 species; the most recent review, including taxonomy, biology and a key to 20 of the 22 known genera is given by HILBIG (1995).

Dorvilleids are related to the Eunicidae, and like them have antennae, palps and strong jaws. However, they differ in having two antennae rather than one or three, and in having jaws with several rows of small teeth instead of 4-6 pairs of larger pieces (HILBIG, 1995). So far we have not yet encountered this family in a coral reef aquarium; however, it stands to reason, that some species can become established in our aquaria via imports with live rocks.

Family Terebellidae

Species of the family Terebellidae are sedentary bristle worms, which often live buried in cylindrical hollows. The body is made up of two sections. At the anterior end these worms have notopodia as well as neuropodia, while the posterior body has only neuropodia (see pages 105 and 106). These worms have very long grooved tentacles, which normally can not be retracted into the body. They are adhesive and are used for selective food intake off the bottom. Some species, however, also feed on plankton and extend the tentacles out into open water. Because of the appearance of these feeding tentacles, these worms have been given the rather suitable, popular name

"spaghetti worms". FAUCHALD (1977) lists about 90 genera; HOLTHE (1986) reviewed the family and considered 56 valid.

To visitors of the the Indo-Pacific coral reefs, the best-known spaghetti worm is *Reteterebella queenslandia*, with a tube buried deeply among coral rocks. The worm extends its more than 1 m long tentacles over the substrate in search of food. This species is widely distributed throughout the Indo-Pacific. According to HOLTHE (1986) it is the only species in the genus. There are several species of spaghetti worms of the genus *Eupolymnia* in the Caribbean which are rather similar to their relatives in the Indo-Pacific.

The genus *Loimia* contains several species, some of which occur in certain coral reef habitats throughout the entire Indo-Pacific. This worm builds a tube of coral fragments and sand, gathered together by the sensitive tentacles. For a long time, *L. medusa* was thought to have a circumtropical distribution; however, HUTCHINGS & GLASBY (1988, 1995) have shown that there are actually several species involved with a variable distribution (HANLEY, pers. comm.).

We have observed terebellid species several times in a coral reef aquarium, as they extended their long, thread-like tentacles from live rocks in search of food.

Family Amphinomidae

The bristle worms in the family Amphinomidae are called "fireworms". They have needle-sharp bristles, which can easily cause injuries. Moreover, in some genera the bristles have venom glands at their bases. A sting can cause a severe burning pain and lead to inflammation. **Therefore, it is imperative NOT to touch fireworms!**

Fireworms are dorso-ventrally compressed. A characteristic feature of fireworms is the presence

The characteristic feature of fire worms of family Amphinonidae is a sensory organ called the caruncle. It extends from the head lobe to the first body segment. It does not occur in any other family. This photo (magnification 15x) depicts the Blue-striped Fire Worm, *Eurythoe* sp. "KA5-POL-02", which often appears in coral reef aquaria. The caruncle is clearly visible starting between the light pink eyes and extends at least to the third body segment. The thin, spiny bristles at the stumped legs contain a venom. Therefore, it is not advisable to touch this worm.

of a sensory organ, the caruncle (a dermal ridge of highly vascularized connective tissue) at the back of the head and extending over the first few body segments. The shape and extent of the caruncle is a distinguishing characteristic between different genera. Fireworms are often beautifully coloured. Most occur in shallow water, but there are also a few deep-sea species. FAUCHALD (1977) lists 17 genera; KUDENOV (1995) lists 19, and indicates that only a few genera have been revised.

One of the best known species is the Caribbean fireworm *Hermodice carunculata*, which is widely distributed in the Caribbean Sea. It feeds on coral polyps. The normal length of this worm is 10-15 cm, but specimens up to 30 cm long have been recorded. The caruncle is large, about wide as long, and lacks a distinct central elevation (which is typical for genus *Eurythoe*), but instead it has two perpendicular folds. The

each segment. The body is greenish, and the bristles are transparent to opaque white.

While the food requirements of the Caribbean and Indo-Pacific fireworms make them unsuitable for a coral reef aquarium, the blue-striped fireworm, *Eurythoe* sp. "KA5-POL-02" does not appear to cause any damage, since it feeds on detritus and dead organic material. The largest specimen we have ever found in our aquarium was 8 cm long and 1-2 cm wide. Normally the specimens are smaller and narrower. The body colour is bright orange to

Caribbean fire worm, *Hermodice carunculata*, on stony corals ar Puerto Rico.

bristles are hair-like thin and have venom glands at their bases. The bushy external gills are clearly visible on either side of each segment. Body colour ranges from greenish and brownish up to reddish. The bristles vary from transparent to white. During the day, *H. carunculata* often hides underneath rocks, but it can also be found on stony corals and in sea grass beds. According to FAUCH-ALD (1977), the genus *Hermodice* contains four species.

The Indo-Pacific fireworm *Eurythoe complanata* looks rather similar to *Hermodice carunculata*. However, it has an elongated caruncle which is raised along the midline and extends over at least three segments. This type of caruncle is typical for the genus *Eurythoe*. *E. complanata* is widely distributed in the Indo-Pacific region. It also feeds on coral polyps. The bristles in this species are also hair-like thin and have venom glands at their bases. The bushy external gills are also clearly visible on either side of

Typical appearance of Blue-striped Fire Worm, *Eurythoe* sp. "KA5-POL-02".

reddish yellow. There is a blue longitudinal stripe on the back. The other body characters are the same as described for *E. complanata*. Usually the blue-striped fireworm hides under rocks or in crevices, but it can also bury itself in sand. It searches for food along the bottom, primarily at night. It has been observed that this species sometimes enters a giant clam through its incurrent opening. We have kept a large population of blue-striped fireworms in our aquarium, but we were never able to observe any damage caused to giant clams.

Eurythoe complanata at Heron island, Great Barrier Reef.
Photo: L. Newman and A. Flowers

The gold-bristle fireworm, *Chloeia flava*, grows to a length of 10 cm, with a width of 4 cm. Each segment is equipped with gold-coloured bristles. On its head there are clearly visible black spots. This species is widely distributed in the Indo-Pacific. It is omnivorous and can be found in many different types of habitat.

Family Sabellidae

All, but one member of this family (*Calcisabella piloseta*, described by PERKINS, 1991) live in soft and pliable tubes. These tubes are made of different materials, but frequently they are polysaccharides excreted by the worm, and strengthened with mud particles. Occasionally, the tubes are also covered on the outside with sand grains and other fragments. They are either buried in sand or are anchored firmly in small crevices or among corals. Large sabellids, such as the well-known *Sabellastarte* species always remain within the tube and never leave it voluntarily. Therefore, the branchial crown with the mouth at its centre, are usually the only thing visible of the worm. Some of the smaller species, e.g. *Fabricia* species, however, are capable of crawling around on the outside.

As with all bristle worms, the body in sabellids is divided into distinct, bristle-carrying segments. But in comparison to errant bristle worms, the bristles in sabellids are relatively small, which can give the tapered body a fairly smooth appearance. Also, the body is divided into two sections: the thorax (chest region) and the abdomen (posterior body). Both sections have different types of bristles. The longer slim bristles are in compact groups one each side of each body segment. The smaller hooked bristles (uncini) and their companion bristles (if present), form glistening transverse rows

The tentacular crown is usually the only thing one can see of tube worms. In family Sabellidae, specifically in genus *Sabellastarte*, the tentacular crowns are large and very colourful. However, an identification to species often require that the worm is removed from its tube and studied in detail through a binocular lens. The photograph shows a very beautiful *Sabellastarte* species on a shallow reef flat at Manado Tua, North Sulawesi.

(tori). These are long and ventral to the bristle bundles in the anterior segments (regarded as the thorax) and shorter and dorsal to such bundles in the rest of the body (abdomen). This arrangement and structure of the bristles are only one of many important systematic characters in family Sabellidae.

FAUCHALD (1977) places 34 genera into family Sabellidae. Most are not concerned with the aquarium hobby, but some are quite frequently available in the aquarium trade. *Sabellastarte* species are particularly well known. These are large sedentary bristle worms, which bury their tubes in sand or coral rubble and crevices and were amongst the first of the invertebrates frequently kept in aquaria.

Typical for large *Sabellastarte* species as well as for most of the other genera in this family, are the presence of the paired ventral collar lobes (see photo on page 128), which assist in the spread of mucoslit to the anterior margin of the tube (NICOL, 1931). In the aquarium literature we find the names *Sabellastarte indica*, *S. japonica*, *S. magnifica*, *S. sanctijosephi* and *S. spectabilis* in a colourful array. Although these names refer to scientific descriptions more than a hundred years old, most are still valid, but for a correct species identification it is necessary to remove the worm from its tube, which can be fatal.

The aquarium literature erroneously refers to the most common cork-screw sabellids as *Sabellastarte indica* and *S. sanc-*

This small tube worm often forms dense populations as a result of asexual reproduction. Although the worm has been kept for decades in reef aquaria, its true identity remained unknown to aquarists until recently. We now know that this beautiful and easily kept species is *Bispira viola* (see fact sheet on page 135).

Anamobaea orstedii at Puerto Rico.

Sabellastarte spectabilis in an aquarium, often erroneously referred to as *S. sanctijosephi.*

tijosephi. There has been much confusion in the literature with regard to the status of *S. indica,* due to the fact that the name was already preoccupied in 1820 when SAVIGNY described the species. Research by KNIGHT-JONES (pers. comm.) shows that the best replacement name for that Indian Ocean species is *S. spectabilis* and that *S. spectabilis* is distinct from the older, but very similar *S. magnifica* from the Caribbean re-

gion. *S. spectabilis* differs from *S. sanctijosephi* by the irregular arrangement of its radioles arising from the base of the crown like the head of a mop, wheras the crown of *S. sanctijosephi* is more like a cup. Both species live on reefs in hollows among corals, but they can also be found on level bottom. Both species can be kept easily in a coral reef aquarium, but they do require supplementary food in the form of very

small plankton or suspended organic particles (see fact sheet on page 130).

Another very interesting genus in family Sabellidae is *Bispira*. The generic name refers to the bispirality of the two halves of the crown in the type species, but this is not a reliable generic character, since several species have crown forming the usual two semi-circlesbranchial crown. The main branches normally carry paired compound eyes along their length (PERKINS & KNIGHT-JONES, 1991; KNIGHT-JONES & PERKINS, 1998).

The best known *Bispira* species within the aquarium hobby is *B. brunnea* from the Caribbean Sea. Like many other species of this genus, it has a significant capacity for asexual reproduction and so it forms dense colonies. It is only sporadically available in the aquarium trade, and according to our experience, it is not easy to keep. Moreover, we have also observed that brittle stars will readily attack the delicate colonies, pulling the worms out from under rocks, and eating them (see fact sheet on page 132).

Bispira tricyclia is an example of one of the few larger species in this genus, which has one half of the crown forming a single spiral and overlaying the other which is semicircular. It occurs in the central Indo-Pacific and is frequently available in the aquarium trade (see fact sheet on page 134).

Sometimes a small sabellid appears in a coral reef aquarium, where it then undergoes a virtual population explosion, establishing dense colonies of many individuals. The tube is thin and nearly transparent. The species involved is *Bispira viola.* Originally, *B. viola* was described from the Mediterranean Sea near Croatia, but it is also reported from other locations in the Mediterranean Sea (GRUBE, 1863; KNIGHT-JONES & ERGEN, 1991). GIBB (1971) described *Sabella melanostigma* from the Solomon Islands, but that is a misidentification (KNIGHT-JONES & PERKINS, 1998). His specimens are identical with the worms from our

This structure at the base of the tentacular crown and the paired ventral collar lobes just below the basis of the tentacular crown are typical for the larger *Sabellastarte* species.

tank and with those from the Mediterranean Sea and share the same morphology, but there are some differences in size (see fact sheet on page 135).

The best-known species from genus *Notaulax* is no doubt *N. occidentalis* with its yellow and black branchial crown. This sabellid occurs in the Caribbean Sea, near Florida and the Bahama Islands. We found some specimens near Puerto Rico in an area with algae and live rocks, but with only sparse coral growth. This corresponds to the details provided by HUMANN (1994), that *N. occidentalis* occurs most commonly in such habitats. It was very difficult to observe the specimens closely, since they were very shy. The tubes were buried deep within live rocks, which is not unexpected as *Notaulax* spp. usually take advantages of crevices and is capable of boring deep into rocks. We are not aware that *N. occidentalis* has ever been kept in an aquarium. With its beautifully coloured branchial crown this tube worm could be very attractive in a coral reef aquarium. Not quite as colourful is *N. nudicollis*, which lives in the same geographical region and occurs in the same habitat.

Notaulax species are also widely distributed in the Indo-Pacific. Small specimens can often be found on live rocks as well as living in association with corals. An example of this is given in fact sheet on page 136, involving a *Notaulax* sp. "KA5-POL-03", which may be undescribed, (KNIGHT-JONES, pers. comm.). PERKINS (1984) revised the genus *Hypsicomus*. With the exception of *H. stichophthalmus*, he places all other species into genus *Notaulax*.

Among the most attractive sabellids is *Anamobaea orstedii* from the Caribbean Sea, including Florida. The crowns, are 4 to 5 cm in diameter, display shades of lilac, red, orange, brown and white, the two halves forming a characteristic divided oval shape. In Puerto Rico we found this worm frequently in the same habitats as

Sabellastarte magnifica in a shallow reef in Puerto Rico. According to KNIGHT-JONES (pers. comm.) this name should be used for all *Sabellastarte* specimens from the Caribbean, pending a revision of this genus.

In this *Bispira* species (possibly *Bispira guinensis*) the pair-like arrangement of compound eyes is very well visible on the main branches.

Photo: Scott W. Michael

Sabellastarte spectabilis
Indo-Pacific Tube Worm (often misnamed as *S. indica* or *S. sanctijosephi*)

Distribution: Widely distributed throughout much of tropical Indo-Pacific.

Size and appearance: Tubes up to 20 cm long or even more, but normally shorter in aquaria with a diameter of 1 to 2 cm. Tentacular crown 5 to 10 cm in diameter. Lives in crevices amongst stones and corals.

Reproduction: Asexual reproduction possible under aquarium conditions, and has been observed. No information available about sexual reproduction in captivity.

Food: Collects plankton and other organic material with its tentacular crown.

Description: Colours of the tentacular crowns vary from one specimen to the next, and thus can not be considered a species characteristic. Large paired ventral collar lobes clearly seen above the tube rim. Posterior end of body is pointed. The tube is made of mud particles, and is normally not covered by coral fragments or sand grains.

Aquarium requirements: If sufficient food is being provided, the Indo-Pacific Tube Worm can be quite hardy and durable. If there is a lack of adequate food, the worm will quickly die. The tube should be placed in drilled holes among corals. After a while the tube will grow on to the substrate.

GA: +; **SE:** +/-; **CO:** +

Photos on the left:
Top: Fully expanded aquarium specimen of *Sabellastarte spectabilis*.
Centre: Close-up view of the ventral collar lobes and base of each of the sides of the tentacular crown.
Bottom: Worm released from its tube.

Photo on the right:
Upper row: *Sabellastarte spectabilis* amongst corals at Bunaken, Indonesia. Photos: R. Hansen
Centre left: Specimen at an Indonesia reef.
Photo: Scott W. Michael
Centre right: Specimen at Heron Island, Great Barrier Reef.
Photo: L. Newman and A. Flowers
Bottom row: Two different colour varieties in an aquarium.

Bispira brunnea

Distribution: Widely distributed throughout Caribbean, including Bahama Islands.

Size and appearance: Because of asexual reproduction lives in populations made up of several specimens, groups can measure 20 to 30 cm in diameter. Individual specimens only a few centimetres tall.

Reproduction: Asexual reproduction possible under aquarium conditions. The densely crowded groups of this worm found in its natural habitat are the result of asexual reproduction (AUGENER, 1927). No information available about sexual reproduction.

Food: Collects plankton and other organic particles, using the branchial crown.

Description: Tubes are parchment-like. Tentacular crowns circular-shaped and with variable colours. According to HUMANN (1993) the colours can be uniform within in certain geographical regions. Normally, the colouration in the vicinity of the mouth is more intense and becomes paler towards the outside.

Aquarium requirements: Occasionally imported, but must be categorized as difficult to keep. Requires an abundant food supply. The specimens within a group are only loosely attached to the substrate and can become detached during transport. We have observed that brittle stars tend to prey on *Bispira brunnea*, pulling the tubes under rocks where the worms are eaten. Ideally, this delicate tube worm should be kept in a special aquarium, together with other harmless, sessile invertebrates.

GA: +/-; **SE:** -; **CO:** +/-

Photos:
Bispira brunnea in typical colonies made up of several individuals at Puerto Rico.

Bispira guinensis

Distribution: Atlantic, Indo-Pacific; from West Africa to Indonesia.

Size and appearance: Body without crown 25-30 mm long and 4 mm wide. The crown about 12 mm long. The tube is usually between 5 and 10 cm long.

Reproduction: Nothing is known on the reproduction of this species in aquaria.

Feeding: Filter feeder.

Description: Bispira guinensis is one of the species in the genus with a bispiral crown. It differs from the other bispiral species in having ❶ the first ventral shield with an indistinct or trimarginate anterior margin and ❷ no flanges on the radioles. The crown curves inward at ventral margins to form 1-2 whorls. The radioles (about 50) have bands of light brown and dark brown, and many have paired red or pinkish red composite eyes. The body has up to 80 segments of which up to 15 are found on the thorax (based on KNIGHT-JONES & PERKINS, 1998).

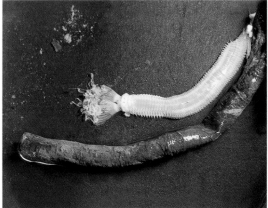

Aquarium Requirements: Occasionally seen in the trade. We have found this species to be very durable in the reef aquarium and have successfully kept a group of about ten individuals in our test aquarium. Here the animals dug themselves into the bottom layer consisting of medium sized coral gravel with the upper part of the tube projecting above the bottom. Like for all of the bigger sabellid tube worms a regular feeding with suspended food is necessary.

GA: + ; **SE:** +/-; **CO:** +

Photos:

Top: A beautiful group of Bispira guinensis on the bottom of our experimental aquarium.

Centre: Bispira guinensis removed from its tube.

Bottom: Close up of Bispira guinensis out of its tube.

Bispira tricyclia

Distribution: Occurring widely in the Indo-Pacific; very common in Indonesia and Papua-New Guinea and Taiwan; no further details available.

Size and appearance: Our aquarium specimen was 8.5 cm long, including branchial crown, and the tube was 16 cm long with a diameter of 8 mm.

Reproduction: No information available about captive breeding.

Food: Captures plankton and other organic particles with the branchial crown.

Description: First described by SCHMARDA (1861) from Sri Lanka. Was considered to be a synonym of *Sabella spallanzanii* for a long period of time. This is one of the two *Bispira* species which do not have a bispiral arranged crown. Branchial crown red with whitish tips or yellow, red paired compound eyes. Body whitish with red or pinkish patches and spots. Tube soft and normally without large attached fragments.

Aquarium requirements: With an adequate food supply, *Bispira tricyclia* can be quite durable, but will soon die without sufficient food. Best maintained in tanks with a soft bottom substrate. Continuous water current required.

GA: +; **SE:** +/-; **CO:** +

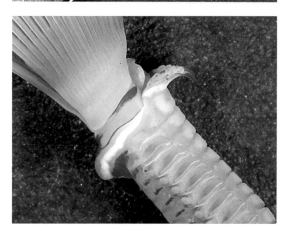

Photos:
Top: Typical appearance of *Bispira tricyclia* in an aquarium.
Centre: Worm removed from its tube.
Bottom: Close-up view of anterior body section and base of branchial crown. The pink spots and the yellow bristles of the body can clearly be seen here.

Bispira viola

Distribution: Originally described from Croatia, but has also been found in Italy and Turkey. GIBBS (1971) described specimens from the Solomon Islands, which he identified incorrectly as *Sabella melanostigma*. Until further taxonomic work has been on the original (type) specimens, it is presumed that this tube worm occurs in both temperate and tropical seas.

Size and appearance: Tubes up to 2 cm long and slightly curved. Worm approximately 0.5 mm in diameter, with a branchial crown 9 mm high and 4 mm in diameter. KNIGHT-JONES et al. (1991) report having seen specimens of twice that size. Forms dense populations.

Reproduction: Asexual reproduction by means of budding. No information available on captive sexual reproduction.

Food: Collects plankton and other organic particles with its branchial crown.

Description: First described by GRUBE (1863) as *Sabella viola*. Among the *Bispira* species, *B. viola* has an unusually long first segment, very low collar edges and large ventral sacs below the base of the branchial crown (KNIGHT-JONES et al., 1991 and pers. comm.). The main branches have violet compound eyes arranged in pairs. Colouration of branchial crown normally pale grey-blueish.

Aquarium requirements: Normally introduced in to an aquarium via live rocks. Sometimes thrives extraordinarily well and forms dense populations. Appears to do better in tanks with a somewhat higher organic load, sites with partially reduced light levels and reduced current flow. Fundamentally, a durable aquarium animal. It must be noted here that butterfly fishes, especially *Chelmon rostratus* like to feed on these delicate worms, and can decimate an entire population within a short period of time.

GA: +; **SE:** +/–; **CO:** +/–

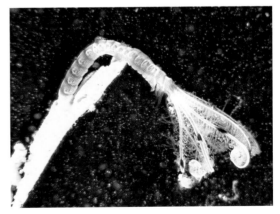

Photos:
Top: Aquarium population of *Bispira viola*. Photo: T. Luther
Bottom: Worm partially removed from its tube

Notaulax sp. "KA5-POL-03"

Distribution: Widely distributed in coral habitats through-out Indo-Pacific.

Size: Maximum diameter of branchial crown is 1 to 2 cm.

Reproduction: Presumably asexually, but no information available about captive breeding.

Food: Captures plankton with branchial crown

Description: Species of Notaulax have the main branches forming two semi-circles from each long base of the branchial crown. These are joined by a membrane up to one-third of their entire lengths usually with single lenticular ocelli either scattered along the outside or as in Notaulax sp. "KA5-POL-03" arranged in elongate groups – carried on main branches. Collar bristles arranged dorsally, in two oblique rows, on each side. There are at least three Notaulax sp., in the Indo-Pacific.

Aquarium requirements: Often introduced into aquaria inside coral or attached to live rocks; however, it is mostly overlooked. A robust tube worm, which can live for several years in an aquarium.

GA: +; **SE:** +; **CO:** +

Photos:

Left: Aquarium specimen of Notaulax sp. "KA5-POL-03".
Below: 1: A mainly ventral view of a worm released from its tube (branchial crown has become detached); a – details of a main branch showing a group of ocelli; b – region of the membrane; c – flange along edge of base of crown base; d – collar; 2: dorsal view of anterior thorax (arrow points an obliquely row of collar bristles).

Drawing: P. Knight-Jones

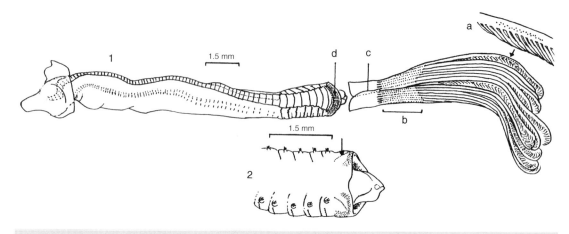

Megalomma vesiculosum lanigera

Distribution: Mediterranean Sea, south and west Africa and probably widely distributed in the Indo-Pacific.

Size and appearance: Our aquarium specimen had a length of 10 cm, including branchial crown, and lived in a 19 cm long and 0.8 cm diameter tube. The tubes are normally covered with sand grains and shell fragments, partially embedded in the surface.

Reproduction: No information available about reproduction under aquarium conditions.

Food: Collects plankton and other organic particles with its branchial crown.

Description: In *Megalomma vesiculosum lanigera* – as in all *Megalomma* species – the two most dorsally located main branches are stiffer and standing more upright, so that they protrude beyond the rest of the branchial crown. Moreover, the involution of the two halves of the dorsal crown tends to place these two branches in the centre so that they are easy to distinguish (see page 139), especially as each possesses a large compound eye. The remaining main branches of the branchial crown are not as stiff, (slightly bent towards the outside) with smaller subdistalt compound eyes. However, the two stiff dorsal branches are often bitten off by predators. *M. vesiculosum lanigera* is distinguished from *M. v. vesiculosum* by longer dorsal lips (KNIGHT-JONES, 1997; DAY, 1967) and higher dorsal collar margins. The genus *Megalomma* contains many species with variable numbers of tentacular eyes, some with eyes only along the dorsal-most pair.

Aquarium requirements: Often available in the aquarium trade. Rather robust tube worm. Best kept in quiet aquarium with deep sandy bottom. Requires an adequate water current, which transports food to the worm.

GA: +; **SE:** +/-; **CO:** +

Photos:
Top: Branchial crown of an aquarium specimen.
Bottom: Worm without tube.

Branchiomma cf. *curtum*

Distribution: The genus is widespread in cold, temperate and tropical seas. Our material originates from a live rock imported from the Suez area in Egypt. The type material of *Branchiomma curtum* described by EHLERS (1901) as *Dasychone curta* were specimens from Juan Fernandez Islands, 650 km west of the Valparaiso Province, Chile. Also collected from New Zealand (EHLERS, 1907) and the Cape Verde Islands (KNIGHT-JONES, pers. comm.).

Size and appearance Body up to 30 mm long and 3 mm wide, the crown up to 7 mm long. We have observed the tubes to be about twice the body length in our aquarium population.

Reproduction: Little is known on the sexual reproduction of the species from the aquarium. The species does, however, reproduce asexually by scissiparity. An adult worm forms a clone by discarding its posterior part of the abdomen, found deep inside the tube. The parent worm regenerates a new posterior, whilst the clone shed piece gradually develops a thorax and branchial crown. In populations that settle on the windows of the aquarium, scissiparity can easily be observed and studied in detail. When we collected worms in their tubes from our aquarium, we had no problem finding several developmental stages. By this form of asexual formation, the species can rapidly build dense populations, and its ability to reproduce by scissiparity is the main reason why *Branchiomma* cf. *curtum* so quickly can colonise the reef aquarium. The young specimens eventually leave the parent tube and settle on a suitable substratum by the help of mucus.

Food: Filter feeder.

Description: The crown has up to 20 radioles to each side, each with about 12 pairs of stylodes. Paired eyes are found between all but the most distal pairs of stylodes. The specimens in our material have a green body colour, while the crown appears brown and white or yellowish brown and white. EHLERS (1901) and AUGENER (1922) noted crown bands of brown violet, and KNIGHT-JONES (in prep.) notes that the body has dark, fairly dense irregular spots. The number of abdominal segments is variable. The thorax is short and usually consists of only 4 or 5 segments. There are also reports that the species can leave its tube and swim by wriggling the body.

Aquarium Requirements: This species can spread like crazy due to frequent asexual reproduction (scissiparity) and can colonise large areas of the substratum. We found it thrive best in shaded or medium illuminated areas. In our aquarium it settled on live rocks, on the glasses and among algae. Must be regarded as very easy to keep, and we never fed the population separately.

GA: + ; **SE:** +/-; **CO:** +

Photos:
Top: Three stages in the life cycle of the worm. In the middle an adult specimen, to the left a clone which has not yet formed thorax and crown and to the right a juvenile with thorax, head and a partly developed crown.
Bottom: Population of *Branchiomma* cf. *curtum* on the side window in our experimental aquarium. Do note that some tubes contain detached clones.

Notaulax occidentalis. It occurred in small groups, but also solitary in very shallow water, often together with lush algal growth. The tubes were buried deeply within the substrate. This tube worm was observed to be rather shy and would immediate retract when disturbed. It feeds on plankton and organic material, which is captured using the branchial crown.

The genus *Megalomma* is characterised by the fact that the two most-dorsally located main branches of the branchial crown are stiffer and stand more erect, so that they protrude beyond the rest of the crown. Moreover, the involution of the two halves of the branchial crown on the dorsal side allows the two dorsal branches to be positioned in the centre where they are easy to recognise, especially since each of them carries a large compound eye spot. The remaining branches of the crown are not as stiff and are slightly bent outward at the top, often with smaller compound eyes near eyespots their tips. Several species are commonly available in the aquarium trade; the most frequent one is *Megalomma vesiculosum lanigera*, with eyes on most radiol branches.

The genus *Megalomma* is characterised by the fact that two main branches are stiffer and more upright than the remaining radioles. They therefore protrude beyond the tentacular crown.

Family Serpulidae

Calcareous tube worms of the family Serpulidae are very popular in the marine aquarium hobby. There is hardly any coral reef tank that does not contain small white calcareous tubes with red or nearly transparent branchial crowns. Many species are regularly imported together with live rocks; a few are also available separately in the aquarium trade.

The family Serpulidae is quite large and in part known only insufficiently. FAUCHALD (1977) lists 54 genera for this family and 16 genera for family Spirorbidae. Nowadays, most taxonomists consider the family Spirorbidae merely as a subfamily. Accor-

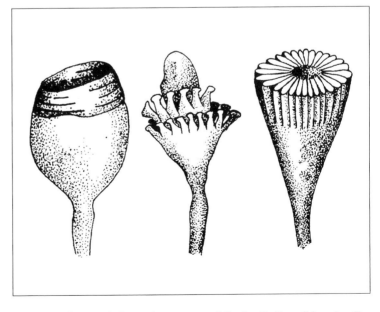

Examples of opercula for various genera of the family Serpulidae: A – *Vermiliopsis*; B – *Hydroides*; C – *Serpula*. Drawing after VINE (1986)

Spirobranchus corniculatus typically associated with *Porites* sp. in the Coral Sea.

dingly, it needs to be listed among the subfamilies of Serpulidae, as Spirorbinae, together with Serpulinae and Filograninae. Roughly estimated there is about 65 genera and 500 species in the family Serpulidae (TEN HOVE, pers. comm.)

Calcareous tube worms are richly represented in fossil finds, since their calcareous tubes maintain well as fossils. They have existed now for more than 100 million years. They were so numerous in ancient seas that they occasionally formed reef structures. Nevertheless, there is considerable uncertainty about their evolutionary relationships (TEN HOVE & VAN DEN HURK, 1993).

According to the shape of the calcareous tube, the serpulids can be divided roughly into two groups. In one group, the calcareous tubes are straight or twisted irregularly, while the tubes are spirally-shaped in the other group. In both groups the tubes can be sculptured with rings and grooves, or they can be round or

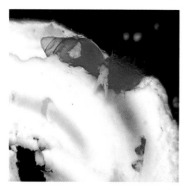

This photograph shows how the shape of the operculum in *Vermiliopsis* species. The operculum closes off the tube entrance, when the worm has withdrawn inside (magnification 20x).

Serpula sp. "KA5-POL-04" with a bell-shaped operculum, which is typical for this genus.   Photo: F. Verbiest

angular. The tube is usually attached to a substrate, which can be rocks, corals, clam shells or artificial material such as bridge pylons or anchor chains. In some species, such as the well-known *Spirobranchus* species it can also be deeply embedded into a coral. The calcareous tubes are built by the worm by removing calcium ions and carbonate ions from the water, and then mixing these with organic compounds given off by two glands located behind the mouth opening. During subsequent growth a new piece of tube is being added as a ring, placed at the end of the old tube.

Calcareous tube worms are generally small and usually occupy only the anterior part of their tube. If the worms are frightened, they retract lightning-fast into the interior of their tube. Serpulids capture food particles, by filtering them from water flowing over the branchial crown. The branchial crown is divided into two halves, which turn towards each other. These halves can be shaped as a bowl or as a spiral.

The most important characteristic for identifying many species is the shape of the operculum. The operculum is a modified radiole (one of the branches in the branchial crown) forming a protective plug or lid effectively locking the entrance of the tube once the worm has withdrawn

Hydroides sp.

Drawing after BARNES (1980)

into it. The structure is of evolutionary importance since not all serpulids possess an operculum. It is always absent in the family Sabellidae. Most evolutionary biologist consider the presence of an operculum as an advanced stage of development and the serpulids as further evolved than sabellids lacking an operculum. The perculum develops only after the larvae has completed its metamorphosis. For some weeks the radiole, which eventually develops into the operculum, remains a normal so that the serpulids look like a sabellid during the early life. Cal-

careous worms which do not develop an operculum at all (e. g. *Protula* spp. and *Microprotula* spp) belong to the more primitive species in the family Serpulidae (TEN HOVE, 1988). Generally speaking, species identification of calcareous tube worms is rather difficult.

The longevity of calcareous tube worms vary from a few months among the smaller worms of the subfamily Spirorbinae up to 4 to 8 years among the larger species, such as *Ficopomatus enigmaticus*, which lives in temperate or subtropical seas, or even 10 to 40 years in the *Spirobranchus giganteus*-complex (NISHI & NISHIHIRA, 1996).

Subfamily Serpulinae

The genus *Serpula* is one of the most common genera of small calcareous tube worms of the subfamily Serpulinae. The operculum is bell-shaped, hollow in the centre and has a corrugated edge. The branchial crown is generally coloured intensely red. Currently there is considerable confusion in respect to the various species. This applies particularly to the most frequently mentioned species *Serpula vermicularis*, which probably needs to be divided into several distinct species. There is some hope that there will be clarity soon, since

Spirobranchus tetraceros at the Seychelles.

Photo: W. Kolvoort

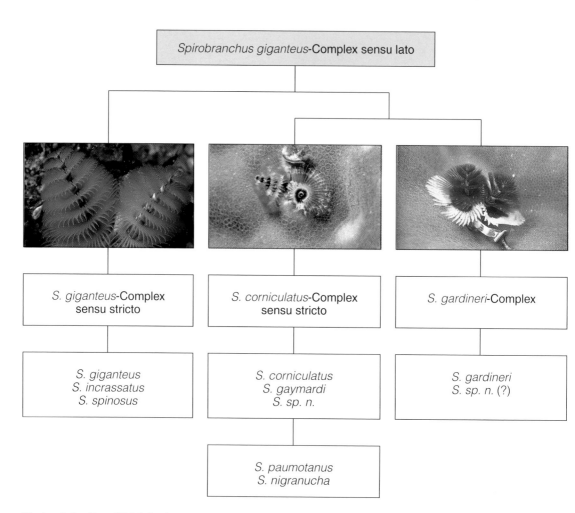

```
                    ┌──────────────────────────────────────────┐
                    │  Spirobranchus giganteus-Complex sensu lato │
                    └──────────────────────────────────────────┘
```

S. giganteus-Complex sensu stricto	S. corniculatus-Complex sensu stricto	S. gardineri-Complex
S. giganteus S. incrassatus S. spinosus	S. corniculatus S. gaymardi S. sp. n.	S. gardineri S. sp. n. (?)

S. paumotanus S. nigranucha

Photos: Left - Scott W. Michael; Centre - W. Kolvoort; Right - J. Randall

this genus is currently being revised by Dr. T. G. Pillai, Natural History Museum, London. Therefore, it does not make any sense to discuss this genus further at this time.

Hydroides species have the most artistically developed operculum. Once the larvae has settled on the bottom, the young worms commence their life without operculum. A few weeks later a primary operculum developes, which is rather similar to that found in *Serpula* species. After another six weeks the operculum, with two superimposed funnels, typical for this genus, is formed; the primary operculum with a club-shaped pseudo operculum.

There are many *Hydroides* species in the Indo-Pacific. *H. minax* is widely distributed in the western Indo-Pacific. It is one of the animal species which - following the completion of the Suez Canal - migrated to the Eastern Mediterranean Sea, where it now also occurs abundant. The calcareous tube of *H. minax* is chalky white, with a round cross-section. This species often lives in association with cnidarians, especially with the fire coral (genus *Millepora*) or stony corals from the genus *Porites*.

Hydroides albiceps occurs in shallow waters, and has an operculum with a vesicular, dorsal spine. According to TEN HOVE (1994) there are also deeper water forms, living at depths of 30-40 m, with a differently shaped operculum. These will probably turn out to be separate species.

The Caribbean Sea is the home of the sponge tube worm, *Hydroides spongicola*, which lives in symbiosis with the "don't touch me" sponge, *Neofibularia nolitangere*. It is relevant at this point to elaborate on the species name of both invertebrates: spongia, lat. = sponge and incola, lat. = inhabitant, occupant, as well as nolitangere, lat. = do not touch me. *Hydroides spongicola* may have a double, funnel-shaped operculum on a long stem. The juvenile worms settle on the sponges and are successively overgrown by the sponge resulting in their calcareous tubes becoming totally buried inside the sponge.

There are often small, white post horn-like worms on imported live rocks or at the base of corals. These belong to the genus *Vermiliopsis*, of which the species taxonomy still is unclear. Moreover, it is hard to distinguish from the genus *Serpula*. TEN HOVE (1994) described it as being extremely difficult to gain an overview of the *Vermiliopsis infundibulum/glandigera*-complex (see fact sheet on page 145).

The calcareous tubes worms best-known in the aquarium hobby are beyond doubt the *Spirobranchus* species. In the aquarium literature these worms are invariably included in the species *Spirobranchus giganteus*, but this is not correct. Today we know that a number of species are involved, distributed over several species complexes. However, much work remains yet to be done, in order to resolve the details about these complexes.

Spirobranchus species live in association with stony corals. The errant larvae settle on a stony coral, often on *Porites* colonies, but they are known to live associated with as much as 15 to 20 genera of stony corals. The larvae settle where there are weakened or dead polyps. There the young tube worms start building their tubes. The coral grows around the tube, so that soon it is totally enclosed by coral tissue and only the branchial crown remains visible. The crowns are very colourful, with shades from white and pink via blue, yellow and red and even up to jet black. There are also branchial crowns with variable colour shades. Populations, where all tentacles crowns are of the same colour, are rare indeed. Normally a population, which can include several hundred specimens in one and the same stony coral colony, consists of specimens with differently coloured branchial crowns. This is indeed a spectacular sight, which undoubtly motivates us as aquarists to realise such a population in a coral reef aquarium.

The species delineation in genus *Spirobranchus* is somewhat complicated. Fundamentally, we can distinguish two principal types: *S. giganteus* sensu lato (sensu lato = in the widest sense) and *S. tetraceros* sensu lato. In *S. giganteus* sensu lato the branchial crowns are composed of radioles arranged in two distinct spirals, while those in *S. tetraceros* sensu lato are arranged in a circle. Moreover, in *S. tetraceros* sensu lato the antler-like outgrowths of the operculum are more widely separate than is the case in *S. giganteus* sensu lato, where they more or less originate from a common base. Both taxa contain several species and species complexes.

Spirobranchus tetraceros sensu lato has not yet been investigated in respect to the individual species involved. This worm is not as closely associated with stony corals, and it often occurs in turbid water, while *S. giganteus* sensu lato is tied to reef areas with crystal clear, nutrient-poor water.

The *Spirobranchus giganteus*-complex sensu lato encompasses at least three species complexes with at least nine different species (probably more), and it encloses all circum-tropical species of the genus (TEN HOVE, pers. comm.). Originally, *S. giganeteus* was described from the Central American region. Nowadays, and at least three species can be distinguished in this area: *S. giganteus* in the Caribbean Sea, *S. incrassatus* near Panama and in the Gulf of California, and *S. spinosus* in the subtropical waters of California. These three species belong to the *S. giganteus*-complex sensu stricto (sensu stricto = in the strict sense). The species in this complex seem to have a more

A small group of *Filogranella* sp. at a depth of 10 m at Bunaken, Indonesia

upright branchial crown than the Indo-Pacific species.

Spirobranchus-species from the Indian Ocean are included in the *S. corniculatus*-complex sensu stricto or in the *S. gardineri*-complex. In order to be able to distinguish the individual species from each other, the shape of the operculum of several specimens from a population needs to be studied closely. In some cases even the colour of the calcareous tube and the shape of the branchial crown can provide some indications; however, details about the two complexes have not yet been fully resolved. The taxonomists involved in this work have, however, succeeded in coming with the scheme on page 142.

The *Spirobranchus corniculatus*-complex sensu stricto incompasses at least three species: *S. corniculatus*, *S. gaymardi* as well as a species of which the

A small, so far unknown species of genus *Protula* ("KA5-POL-05").

Photos: F. Verbiest

Salmacina sp. at Heron Island, Great Barrier Reef.
Photo: L. Newman and A. Flowers

scientific name has not yet been approved. It most probably should be named *Spirobranchus cruciger* (TEN HOVE, pers. comm.). These three species have low, more or less branched, antler-like outgrowths, on an oval opercular plate. A fourth species, *S. paumotanus*, lives on litoral reefs and in the inter-tidal zone. The fifth species, *S. nigranucha* lacks an operculum. This species lives on coral reefs, where it is found deeply between the branches of *Acropora* species.

In the *Spirobranchus gardineri*-complex the species have a circular opercular plate, which displays antler-like outgrowths on a long common stem. This species complex contains at least two species, of which one has yet to be described.

The scheme developed on page 142 provides an overview over *Spirobranchus giganteus* sensu lato. It was established on the basis of currently available data and through personal information provided by TEN HOVE, but do also see FIEGE & TEN HOVE (1999).

Except for *Spirobranchus*-species, *Floriprotis sabiuraensis* is the only other species from the Indo-Pacific, known to be a symbiont of corals. This species was described by UCHIDA (1978) from Japan. It often lives in association with brain corals of the family Faviidae,

and according to BAILEY-BROCK (1985) especially with *Goniastrea pectinata, Favia speciosa* and *Favites abdita*. Yet, we have also found this calcareous tube worm in other imported brain corals, and we have also observed the species ourselves on many reef locations, among others in Fiji where it was abundant on some shallow reefs. Its calcareous tube is also embedded deeply in the coral, so that only the golden-yellow to yellowish-white branchial crown is visible. Further details are listed in fact sheet on page 148.

Apart from *Spirobranchus giganteus* only *Pseudovermilia madracicola* lives in symbiosis with stony corals in the Carribean Sea, and as indicated in the species name, it associates with *Madracis* colonies. It is rather small, normally only about 8 mm long, rarely up to 12 mm. The width of the thorax region is about 0.4 to 0.5 mm, and the diameter of the thin-walled tube is about 0.7 mm. The body is orange coloured, with an orange-red collar at the thorax. The operculum is pear-shaped, slightly flattened at its white tip, otherwise it is transparent. The transparent branchial crown features shades of orange-brown or white.

The genus *Filogranella* (currently being revised by Dr. H. A. ten Hove, Inst. for Taxonomic Zoology, University of Amsterdam) includes some of the most suitable calcareous tube worms for marine aquaria. They live in dense colonies, which makes them very attractive in an aquarium setting. Reproduction by means of asexual division is rapid, so that colonies tend to spread quickly.

The characteristic feature of genus *Filogranella* has always been the absence of an operculum; however, recent studies have shown that within the population of a particular locality there can be specimens with a distinct operculum present, as well as specimens with a pseudo-operculum only, a small almost invisible button which may grow into a full-sized operculum eventually (TEN HOVE, pers. comm.).

Filogranella sp. "KA5-POL-07" (see fact sheet on page 150) occurs in the Caribbean Sea, Gulf of Mexico, near Florida and northward along to coast to Georgia, USA.

F. elatensis is occasionally available in the aquarium trade (see fact sheet on page 149). It has been recorded from America to Australia, however, according to TEN HOVE the material requires a revision, in order to resolve whether this is really one and the same species or whether there are several species involved.

Subfamily Filograninae

This subfamily includes some of the most attractive and popular calcareous tube worms, most notably the *Protula*- and *Salmacina* species. The latter are often referred to as *Filograna* species, but the taxonomy of genus *Filograna* is rather uncertain and still far away from being resolved (TEN HOVE, pers. comm.). The generic name *Filograna* should only be used for species from the Mediterranean Sea and the Atlantic, which have an operculum. In the tropical species (referred to as *Filograna*) the operculum is absent. Therefore, they must be placed in the genus *Salmacina*, characterised by the absence of an operculum. The colonies, with their filigrane appearance, consist of many specimens. VINE (1986) lists *Salmacina* (as *Filograna implexa*) for the Red Sea, where it occurs in shallow water, together with sponges, tunicates and other invertebrates.

Most calcareous tube worms are rather small. Only *Protula bispiralis* (often erroneously referred to as *P. magnifica*) is larger and also regularly available in the aquarium trade (see fact sheet on page 152). While *P. bispiralis* has a tube with a diameter of 2 to 3 cm and a branchial crown with three to eight spirals of radioles, there are (according to TEN HOVE, 1994) also *Protula* species with tubes which are only a few millimetres in diameter. The branchial crowns in these small species are arranged

Vermiliopsis infundibulum/glandigera-complex

Distribution: Widely distributed circum sub-tropically and circum-tropically. No further details available.

Size and appearance: Usually colied (rarely spirally coiled) calcareous tubes with funnel-shaped outer cross ribs. Sizes variable. The tubes of our aquarium population are 0.5 to 3 cm long.

Reproduction: Sexual reproduction can quickly establish a large population in an aquarium.

Food: Collects plankton and other organic particles with its branchial crown.

Description: The species within this complex are very difficult to identify. Our aquarium population probably consists of *Vermiliopsis pygidalis* (TEN HOVE, pers. comm.). The *Vermiliopsis* species have a pear-shaped operculum. Branchial crown red, body reddish to orange-coloured.

Aquarium requirements: Present in most coral reef aquaria which are decorated with live rocks. Populations expand quickly in areas where there is reduced illumination, including the filter chamber. Harmless and very durable.

GA: +; **SE:** +/-; **CO:** +

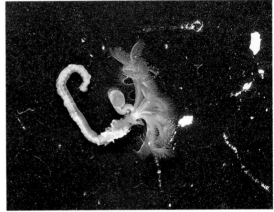

Photos:
Top: Typical appearance of an aquarium specimen.
Centre: Worm removed from its tube.
Bottom: Close-up view of operculum (50x magnification).

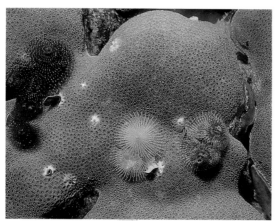

Spirobranchus giganteus-complex sensu lato
Christmas Tree Worms

Distribution: *Spirobranchus giganteus*-complex sensu stricto in Central America, *S. corniculatus*- and *S. gardineri*-complex widely distributed in the Indo-Pacific.

Size and appearance: Adult worms up to 8 cm long. Only the branchial crown protrudes from the coral. In the *S. giganteus*-complex sensu stricto the branchial crowns are slightly taller than in the other two species complexes.

Reproduction: Sexual reproduction via a larval stage. The larvae settle on locally damaged coral colonies, usually on *Porites* sp., their developing tubes then become embedded in the regenerating coral tissue.

Food: Suspension feeder, which removes small food particles from the surrounding water. A current is created by the cilia on the radioles. Appears to be adapted to nutrient-poor water (STRATHMANN et al., 1984).

Description: Normally associates with stony corals. Branchial crowns very colourful and within a population sometimes uniformly coloured. The individual species are distinguished on the basis of the operculum shape (see page 139). Formerly, all species of the various complexes were listed under *S. giganteus* (see page 143).

Aquarium requirements: Small *Porites* colonies with species of *S. corniculatus* are common available in the aquarium trade. The coral colonies accommodating worms can easily be adapted to aquarium conditions. During the purchase it is important to make sure that the coral colony is not dead, because this will also lead to the demise of calcareous tube worms. Other than that, these worm do well in a coral reef aquarium.

GA: +; SE: +/-; CO: +

Photos on the left:
Top: Adult worms in a large *Porites* colony at the Maldives.
Centre: *S. gardneri*.   Photo: W. Kolvoort
Bottom: *S. corniculatus* removed from its tube.

Photos on the right:
Upper row: *S. giganteus* at Puerto Rico (left) and at the US Virgin Islands   Photo to the right: Scott W. Michael
Centre row: *S. corniculatus*.   Photos: Scott W. Michael
Bottom row: *S. corniculatus* at Flinders Reef, Coral Sea (left) and *S. gardineri* in deep water at the Maldives.

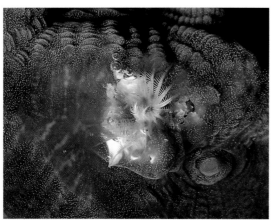

Floriprotis sabiuraensis

Distribution: Widely distributed in the Indo-Pacific; according to IMAJIMA & TEN HOVE (1984) including Japan, northern Queensland, Ponape, Truk and Belau; BAILEY-BROCK (1985) reports an occurrence at the Fiji Islands and we have found this worm in Fiji our selves also; apparently also in Indonesia (TEN HOVE, pers. comm.), the origin of our imported aquarium specimen.

Size and appearance: Lives associated with stony corals, mostly brain corals of family Faviidae. The worm as such is 20 mm long and about 1.5 to 2 mm thick. The round tube measures 2.0 to 2.5 mm in diameter (UCHIDA, 1978). The worm will die within a short period of time once the coral dies.

Reproduction: There is still uncertainty about the reproduction in the natural habitat of this species, however, since embryos have never been found inside the tube, there appears to be sexual reproduction through spawning in open water (UCHIDA, 1978). No records of breeding under aquarium conditions.

Food: Collects plankton and other organic material with its branchial crown.

Desription: Operculum absent. Collar well-developed with three lobes. Thorax with seven segments. Two types of collar chaetae: ❶ blade-shaped, ❷ cylindrical shaft with a short blade. The type of blade-chaetae is not found in another genus of this family, although it has some resemblance with that in the genus *Serpula*. Body light red, thorax orange, branchial crown whitish to yellowish with patches of red. Main radioles very long with slender tips, the dorsal ones are shorter than the ventral ones and not connected by a basal membrane.

Aquarium requirements: Normally only the branchial crown emerging from a brain coral is visible. Can live in an aquarium for a long period of time. Basically, easy to keep, however, symbiotic in the coral host and can not survive without it.

GA: +; SE: +; CO: +

Photos:
Top: Aquarium specimen in a brain coral.
Centre: Worm removed from its tube.
Bottom: Close-up view of collar.

Filogranella elatensis

Distribution: Originally described from the Red Sea. Reported from various localities in the Indo-Pacific region.

Size and appearance: Forms dense clusters of calcareous tubes. Worm about 7 mm long and 0.7 mm thick, branchial crown about 4 mm long.

Reproduction: Form dense aggregations possibly due to asexual reproduction or mass-settlements of larvae on intra-specific tubes. No signs of budding found, although this seems to be possible. No records of any sexual reproduction under aquarium condition.

Food: Collects plankton and other organic particles with the branchial crown.

Description: Described by Ben-Eliahu & Dafni (1979) from Eilat, Israel. The tubes are round with five longitudinal keels and faint growth rings. Colouration of tentacles variable, often red. Operculum or pseudo-operculum absent in the original colony from Eilat, but an operculum can be present in specimens in a populations from a specific locality.

Aquarium requirements: Occasionally available in the aquarium trade, unfortunately, however, this species is rather delicate and difficult to keep (Wilkens, pers. comm.). Must not be kept together with butterfly fishes, especially not with *Chelmon rostratus*. It is advisable to keep this worm in a separate aquarium.

GA: -; SE: -; CO: +

Photos:
Top: Large aquarium population.
Bottom: Close-up view of collar and the branchial crown.
Photo: F. Verbiest

Filogranella sp. "KA5-POL-07"

Distribution: Widely distributed and quite common throughout the Caribbean, including Florida, the Bahama Islands, in the Gulf of Mexico, the Antilles and possibly also at the Cape Verde Islands.

Size and appearance: Forms dense clusters of calcareous tubes. Worm about 10 mm long, branchial crown 3 mm. Tube diameter about 1mm and up to 6 cm long.

Reproduction: Dense aggregations possibly due to asexual reproduction or the release of fully grown, settling ready larvae. Julian Sprung (pers. comm.) has observed reproduction, probably asexuel, in an aquarium.

Food: Collects plankton and other organic material with its branchial crown.

Description: Each aggregation contains specimens with and without an operculum. If an operculum is present, it has a chitinous end plate, in contrast to the mostly conical operculum of the *Vermiliopsis* species (see fact sheet on page 145).

Aquarium requirements: Durable, but not frequently imported. Should be kept in an aquarium without fish, especially butterfly fish, which feed on these worms. A separate tank is most suitable, for observing the biology of this worm, especially any asexual reproductive activities.

GA: +; **SE:** +/-; **CO:** +

Photo:
Large aquarium population in a tank owned by J. Sprung, Miami.

Microprotula cf. *ovicellata*

Distribution: Tropical seas, Indo-Pacific; no details are known. As far as we know and according to UCHIDA (1978), the genus has not yet been observed in the nature, but is known from aquaria only. The specimens photographed here grew attached to rocks in a German aquarium shop ("marin" Meerwasser Aquaristik, Siegburg, Germany).

Size: UCHIDA (1978) describes *Microprotula ovicellata* having a tube diameter of 0.3 mm. Our material had a tube diameter of 0.45-0.55 mm. In the aquarium the fragile, calcareous tube grew to a length of about 5 cm. The crown has four pairs of branchial radioles, each 1.4-1.8 mm long. The lateral pinnules are about 0.15 mm in length.

Reproduction: Modified from UCHIDA (1978) who describes the reproductive behaviour from the only described species *M. ovicellata*: "The breeding season is spring (March to May). Before the spawning the worm makes a breeding chamber on the calcareous tube (the ovicell). The chamber is a swelling near the end of the tube in which the tube continues. *M. ovicellata* seems to be hermaphrodite as all individuals build ovicells. The life span may be one year, guessing from the absence of adults in summer and autumn. An adult may spawn 2 to 3 times in its life, because tubes with two or three ovicells are found at the end of the breeding season. The worm spawns the eggs just before finishing the building of the upper narrow projection of the ovicell. It winds its collar to the upper margin of the ovicell while the embryos develop inside the ovicell and hatch here. After the spawning is completed and the larvae have left the ovicell, the worm continues to grow the tube above the margin of the ovicell." It should be noted that ovicells were not observed on our material. However, we collected the material in the aquarium shop in December, which is out of the naturel breeding season.

Food: Filter feeder.

Description: The calcareous tubes are thin, white opaque, with round face in cross section where it is free, semicircular when attached. The tubes are most fragile. The tubes are coiled on the substratum, but the distall part grows vertically or horizontally from the substratum. An operculum is absent. The tiny crown consists of 4 (sometimes 5?) pairs of radioles. The radioles are colourless with a paired row of 4-5 bright red eye-spots. There is no interradiolar membrane present. The presence of all kinds of setae links the genus *Microprotula* to the *Protula*-group. There are two kinds of collar setae; simple blades and capillary. Thorax possesses three kinds of setae; simple blades, capillary and sickle-shaped. The thoracic uncini of the "*Protula*-type" with many rows of teeth and long peg also possessing rows of teeth. The abdominal setae are all sickle-shaped, usually called "apomatus-setae" The collar of our

material is trilobed, while that of *M.* cf. *ovicellata* described by UCHIDA (1978) is 4-lobed. Description based on UCHIDA (1978) and TEN HOVE (pers. comm).

Aquarium requirements: This is a most interesting species for the tiny reef aquarium. One of the reasons that this worm has not yet been observed in the nature might in fact be just the delicate and fragile tubes. Predation and wave action might prevent the worm from developing long tubes and the species can therefore be overlooked in habitats normally visited by humans? When we collected the material in the German aquarium shop, we could hardly touch the tubes without breaking them. There should be a big potential for studying the reproductive behaviour of this species in the reef aquarium. Should be given a small and peaceful aquarium where it can develop dense populations. *Microprotula* cf. *ovicellata* also represents an excellent example of how the modern reef aquarium can be a tool for biological studies.

GA: + ; **SE:** +/-; **CO:** +

Photo:
Group of worms with their typical, fragile calcareous tubes on a live rock in an aquarium of "marin" Meerwasser Aquaristik, Siegburg, Germany.

Protula bispiralis
Magnificent Calcareous Tube Worm

Distribution: Widely distributed in western Indo-Pacific. Originally described from the Indian Ocean.

Size and appearance: Lives in calcareous tubes with a diameter of 2 cm and a length of up to 30 cm. The calcareous tubes are usually coiled, however, with the opening pointing upward.

Reproduction: No records of breeding under aquarium conditions.

Food: Collects plankton and other organic particles using the branchial crown.

Description: Commonly (however, erroneously) referred to as *Protula magnifica*. The branchial radioles are arranged in two spirals, each with three to eight revolutions. Colour uniformly white or a mixture of white and red. Operculum absent. Under aquarium conditions the branchial crown is cast off after a certain period of time, and a new one develops. This is about the largest calcareous tube worm in family Serpulidae, and so it can hardly be mistaken for any other species.

Aquarium requirements: Usually categorised as too difficult to keep, but in our experience this is due to an insufficient food supply. If there is not enough food, *P. bispiralis* will not do well and usually dies after a while. Therefore, this species should be kept in a tank with a slightly elevated organic load and a moderate current. Frequently available in the aquarium trade.

GA: +/-; **SE:** +/-; **CO:** +

Photos on the left:
Top: Most common colour of branchial crown.

Photo: Scott W. Michael

Centre: Close-up view of base of branchial crown and upper edge of the calcareous tube.
Bottom: A new branchial crown is being developed.

Photos on the right:
Top row: Juvenile (left) and typical colouration of branchial crown (right) of *Protula bispiralis*. Photos: Scott W. Michael
Centre: White aquarium specimen.
Bottom row: White specimen at Seychelles.

Photos: W. Kolvoort

in a semi-circular or incomplete spiral pattern. In these species there are two types of tubes: a smooth one and one that is unevenly structured. According to TEN HOVE (1994), this indicates, that there may be at least two different species, which have been described under several names: *Protula palliata, P. procera, P. arafurensis* and *P. tubularia*. However, none of these species descriptions is complete enough to decide which name(s) should be used, so that here too a revision is urgently required. Until that has happened, we will list the small species always as *Protula* sp.

We have recently come across a colony of the fragile and most interesting *Microprotula* sp. in an aquarium shop in Siegburg in Germany. This worm seems only to be known from aquaria, and as far as we have been able to find out, the worm has never been seen in the wild. This is not only most interesting from a biological point of view, but also fully demonstrates how important the reef aquarium can be for detecting and observing reef animals (see fact sheet on page 151 for further details on *Microprotula*).

Subfamily Spirorbinae

The calcareous tube worms in this subfamily are generally referred to as post horn worms, most of the species are very small. The tubes are spiral-shaped and rather reminiscent of the a post bugle. On several occasions we

Protula sp. "KA5-POL-06" from the Caribbean.   Photo: Scott W. Michael

Post horn worms: left – *Neodexospira* sp. (photo: G. Rouse); right – *Pileolaria* sp. (photo: R. Brons).

have been able to observe developing populations of these worms, as shown in Volume 1 on page 171. It was probably the northern post horn worm, *Spirorbis borealis*, which we have inadvertently introduced with natural seawater (always used by us). Along the Norwegian coastline this worm sometimes occurs in vast numbers in the intertidal zone among algae and kelp. An example of a tropical post horn worm is *Neodexiospira* sp.

Phylum Echiurida – Sausages Worms

The sausages worms in phylum Echiurida are particularly fascinating animals, and are quite suitable for a coral reef aquarium. In our opinion, there is every possibility to keep them alive in the modern coral reef aquarium for a long time. Unfortunately though, they are rarely ever available in the aquarium trade.

Echiurids live in tubes, which are buried in sand, under rocks or anchored in crevices among coral rocks. In total there is about 130 known species which are all marine or live in brackish water. Many species occur at great depths, but there are also some which live in shallow water.

Echiurids do not have segments; they are sausage-shaped and closely related to annelid worms. The body is soft and there is little protection. At the anterior end of the body there is a proboscis, which can be considered as an extension of the head since it also contains the brain. It is probably homologous with the prostomium of the annelids. The edgess are rolled ventrally so that the underside forms a gutter. The proboscis can not be fully retracted, but instead it can be extended out along the bottom for several metres. In the *Bonellia* species an 8 cm long specimen can extend its proboscis for 2 m (BARNES, 1980). The proboscis gives off a mucus, to which food particles – usually detritus – adhere. The tip of the proboscis is often flattened, but it can also be divided into two halves in some species. At the base of the proboscis we find the mouth opening.

The taxonomy within genus *Bonellia* is unclear. Generally, *Bonellia viridis* has been considered a cosmopolitan species, but probably several species are involved, and a revision of the group is badly needed. For the time being it is best to refer to the respective species as *Bonellia* sp. only.

Bonellia species have a wide distribution; from cold seas to tropical seas and from shallow inshore water down to great depths. The echiurids display an extreme sexual dimorphism and their reproductive biology is especially fascinating. Females grow to a

When diving a coral reef one occasionally comes across a T-shaped, several meter-long proboscis searching the bottom for food. This is the visible part of an echiurid worm. The trunk is well hidden in a crevice among the coral boulders.

length of up to 8 cm with the typical shape of sausage worm. On the other hand, males are very small, reaching only a length of 1 to 3 mm, and live inside the uterus or body cavity of the female. The males are further more structurally modified in many ways. They do not have a proboscis, a circulatory system and only a reduced digestive tract. Their entire body surface is covered with cilia. Whether a larva develops into a male or a female is a function of larval contact with an adult female. Any larva that comes in contact with a female or enters her body cavity is induced by a female hormone and develops into a dwarf male. The first contact is made with the female's proboscis. After a few days on the proboscis, the juvenile presumptive male passes into the female's esophagus and eventually into the uterus where it becomes sexually mature in one to two weeks. The uterus of a single female will normally house some 20 males. Larvae that do not come in contact with a female, develope into females, and more than a year is needed to reach sexual maturity (BARNES, 1980).

MATHER & BENNET (1993) list two

echiurids for the Great Barrier Reef. *Pseudobonellia biuterina* is coloured dark green. The posterior body is 5 to 20 mm long. Like *Bonellia* species, these echiurids also exhibit sexual dimorphism, and females also accommodate the males in their body cavity. The second species is *Anelassorhyn-*

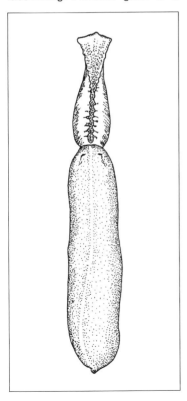

Echiurus sp.
Drawing after BARNES (1980)

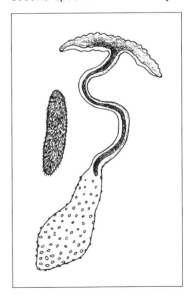

Dimorphism in genus *Bonellia*: left male; right female.
Drawing after BARNES (1980)

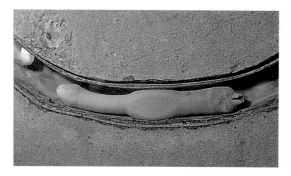

The innkeeper's worm, *Urechis caupo*, lives in a U-shaped tube (seen here at the Monterey Bay Aquarium, Monterey, California). Other organisms also tend to live in the same tube, which is the reason for the colloquial name.

This echiurid, *Listriobolus bulbocaudatus*, seen here at Stradbroke Island, Great Barrier Reef, has extended its trunk from the tube in search of food.

Photo: L. Newman and A. Flower

chus porcellus. It has a sack-like or elliptical posterior body, an undivided, 30 to 50 mm long proboscis, and lives in sand or under rocks. We did also ourselves observe hundreds of similar looking sausages worms living buried in a muddy beach in Fiji. When the tide was low and the beach dried out, their transparent proboscises could be seen searching the surface for food.

Urechis caupo is distributed along the coast of California. It builds U-shaped tubes in sand- or mud bottom. It is fascinating to see how this worm has adapted to a life "locked up" in its tubes. At the Monterey Bay Aquarium in Monterey, California, a PVC pipe has been cut open along its entire length, filled with sand and then

attached to the front glass of an aquarium. This way these worms were put on display for aquarium visitors. The tube normally also contains several commensals, such as gobies, two species of shrimp, a clam, among others. Therefore, *Urechis caupo* has been given the highly appropriate common name "The Innkeeper's Worm".

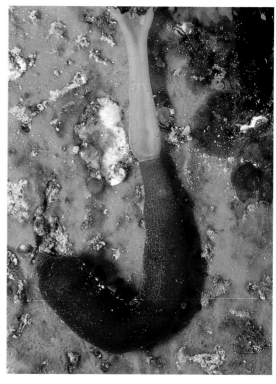

Bonellia sp. (left) and *Anelassorhynchus porcellus* (right) at Madang, Papua-New Guinea.

Photos: L. Newman and A. Flowers

Peanut-worms of phylum Sipunculida are exclusively marine. According to BARNES (1980) the phylum contains about 300 species. The body is divided into two sections: a relatively small, narrowed anterior section called the introvert, and a large posterior trunk. Although the introvert can be retracted into the anterior end of the trunk, it is not a proboscis, but represents the head and the anterior part of the body. Located in the anterior body is the mouth, which is often surrounded by tentacles covered with cilia. The tentacles are hollow but not connected to the coelom which extends the length of the body. Instead the tentacles are connected to each other by a system of canals with one or two blind tubular sacs that run parallel to the esophagus. These sacs are contractile and receive fluid from, or supply fluid to, the tentacles when they are contracted or expanded, (BARNES, 1980). The majority of peanut worms feeds on detritus or algae. The food is collected by the tentacles. Peanut-worms are eaten by fish and some snails, especially the predatory snails of genus *Mitra*.

Peanut worms are often brought into an aquarium together with live rocks (see Vol. 1, page 183). They occupy holes in the rocks and in coral skeleton and are actually the most numerous organisms in coral boulders, and important decomposers of the reefs. Settlement densities of 700 specimens per square metre have been reported from Hawaii (BARNES, 1980). Many peanut-worms are capable of boring into porous rock, but how they do that is still not totally resolved yet. Probably it involves chemical as well as physical means. In an aquarium it can happen that suddenly there are long, nearly transparent worms emerging from a live rock. We have seen this happen repeatedly in our experimental aquarium. The decoration consisted of live rocks, which had already been in the tank for ten years.

Peanut-worms are able to bury into the bottom substrate, as seen here at Eilat, Israel.   Photo: R. Brons

During the night, when we illuminated the decoration with a torch, we could observe numerous sipunculids stretching out of their burrows in live rocks. We have illustrated this with a photo in volume 1, page 183. The genus *Phascolosoma* also belongs to the boring peanut-worms. These species have along their ventral body surface distinctly pigmented papilla and longitudinal muscles. The posterior body can reach a length of up to 35 mm.

Other boring peanut worms are *Cloesiphon aspergillus, Lithacrosiphon cristatus* and *Themistes* sp. *Cloesiphon aspergillus* is known from the Great Barrier Reef. The posterior body, from which the anterior body emerges, is covered by pineapple-like shells. *Lithacrosiphon cristatus*, which also occurs on the Great Barrier Reef, has a white, conical cap over the anterior section of the posterior body. The anterior body does not emerge from anterior end of the posterior body, but instead from the abdominal part (MATHER & BENNET, 1993). *Themistes* sp. has a distinct tentacle crown with four to six bushy branches at the tips. *Sipunculus* sp. and *Siphonosoma* sp. are also reported from the Great Barrier Reef. They are stout, cylindrical and up zo 160 mm long. These species make unlined, and non-permanent burrows in sand. The genus *Phascolion* normally occupies emty shells of molluscs.

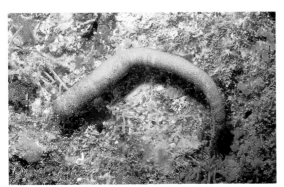

Two unknown peanut-worms at Madang, Papua-New Guinea.   Photos: L. Newman and A. Flowers

Beard worms are among the most extraordinary animals known. The first incomplete specimen was found in Indonesia about 1900, but this animal group was not described until 1963 when a complete specimen could be collected. Today about 100 species are known. The most famous collection of a beard worm was beyond doubt that of *Riftia pachyptila*. This beard worm lives in warm, sulphur-rich water in the proximity of submarine volcanoes at a depth of 2500 m near the Galàpagos Islands and elsewhere In the Pacific. Some researchers are of the opinion, that the species should be placed within its own phylum.

Riftia pachyptila lives symbiotically with chemo-trophic bacteria, which are able to oxidise sulfide. It has a specific haemoglobin, which can bind oxygen as well as the toxic hydrogen sulfide. The collection of *R. pachyptila* near the submarine volcanoes of the

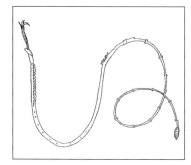

Beard worm.
Drawing after BARNES (1980)

Galàpagos Islands was the first, which showed that an ecosystem can exist solely from chemically derived energy, and in total independence of solar energy. No wonders that it created a worldwide sensation when it was discovered!

Beard worms have derived their scientific phylum name from the beard-like tentacle crowns at their anterior end (pogon, gr. =

beard and phoros, gr. = carrier). Most species are deep-sea forms, which occur below depths of 100 m. This is probably one of the principal causes why it took so long for these worms to be discovered. Beard worms are long and thin, whereby the ratio of length to width can be 500 : 1.

The majority of beard worms live in secreted, stiff chitinous tubes, which are fixed upright from the substratum. The animals often occur in dense aggregations with more than 200 individuals per square metres. *Scleronium brattstromi* has been found in decaying organic material, such as card board, wood or leather, e. g. along the coast of Norway.

The phylogenetic relationships of beard worms are not clear. The fact, that they possess a true abdominal cavity and also display a certain segmentation of the posterior body, seems to suggest that their closest relatives are the segmented worms (Annelida).

Phylum Chaetognatha – Arrow Worms

With very few exceptions, arrow worms of phylum Chaetognatha are planktonic. They are small, unattractive and early transparent organisms. Arrow worms are predatory and feed primarily on

planktonic crustaceans, as well as on fish larvae. At the very tip of the torpedo-shaped body is the head, which is equipped with many bent hooks. Planktonic food is captured with these hooks and

then manipulated into the mouth. Although arrow worms have a pair of simple, light-sensitive eyes located on their head, they can not perceive a pictorial image. Along the side the body there are

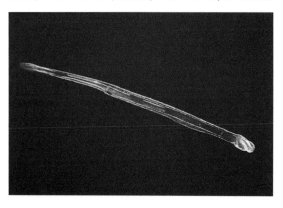

Arrow worms, shaped like arrows (left), are perfectly adapted for a planktonic life. They are equipped with powerful jaws (right), which are ideally suited for capturing plankton, their main food. **Photos: R. Brons**

two pairs of fins, which facilitate swimming, and tactile bristle which perceive movement and position in the water.

Although many attempts have been made to determine the evolutionary relationship of arrow worms to other animal groups, definitive answers are still outstanding. From an aquarist's point of view arrow worms are of significance only as food-organisms.

Phylum Hemichordata – Acorn Worms

Hemichordates are relatives of vertebrate animals (hemi, gr. = semi and chordata, gr.-lat.= cartilaginous axial rod as precursor of the vertebral column in the acrania, vertebrates, amphioxus and tunicates), but different only in that they do not have a notochord. Hemichordates also show many similarities to spiny-skinned animals. These are reasons why they are so interesting to biologists. In total there are 90 known species in the two classes Enteropneusta and Pterobranchia.

Acorn worms of class **Enteropneusta** are buried in sand or under rocks in shallow water. We found the group ourselves at Rarotonga, in the Cook Islands, where it was numerous buried in the sand in the near-shore coral beach. Many species, such as *Phycodera flava* or *Saccoglossa* spp. build U-shaped tubes in which they live. The only thing visible of acorn worms are large spiral-shaped waste piles above one of the opening to the tube, as well as one or more in-current openings in the sand somewhat away from the waste pile. If the waste piles were not so conspicuous if would be difficult to find acorn worms. Although most of them are rather large, some, like the Brazilian species *Balanoglossus gigas*, being up to 1.5 m long construction up to 3 m long burrows.

The cylindrical body is clearly divided into three sections. At the anterior end is conical proboscis, which in its shape is reminiscent of an acorn in its shell. This is followed by a collar and then by a long trunk. Behind the collar the trunk bears a longitudinal row of gill pores at each side of the mid-dorsal ridge. More laterally the anterior half of the body contains the sex organs. Occasionally there are also two large body lo-

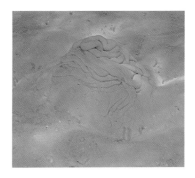

Only the large, spiral-shaped waste heaps (here photographed close to a coral beach in the Maldives) tell us that an acorn worm lives buried in the sand below.

bes, which enclose and protect the sex organs.

Acorn worms feed on organic material, which they filter from bottom material channelled through their digestive tract. Some species obtain their food by suspension feeding. Detritus and plankton that come in contact with the surface of the proboscis are trapped in mucus and transported posteriorly by

strong ciliary currents. This method of feeding is found among non-burrowing as well as burrowing species. Some of the burrowing soecies project their proboscis out of their burrow and move it about on the surface, not unlike what we see in some sausage worms. This is rather reminiscent of the feeding method of some annelid worms (see page 112).

There is little resemblance between winged gill worms of class Pterobranchia and acorn worms, and so the former are generally considered to be more primitive than the latter. They live in populations which can be made up of many individuals and where each animal lives inside a tube. On the back of the collar there are usually many tentacles, which are presumably used for catching food.

The majority of species in class **Pterobranchis** lives in deep water. *Rhabdopleura* sp. Is an example of a species, which lives in shallow water. It occurs in the Bahamas, among other places. Gill clefts are totally absent in this species.

Phycodera flava at Lizard Island, Great Barrier Reef.

Photo: L. Newman and A. Flowers

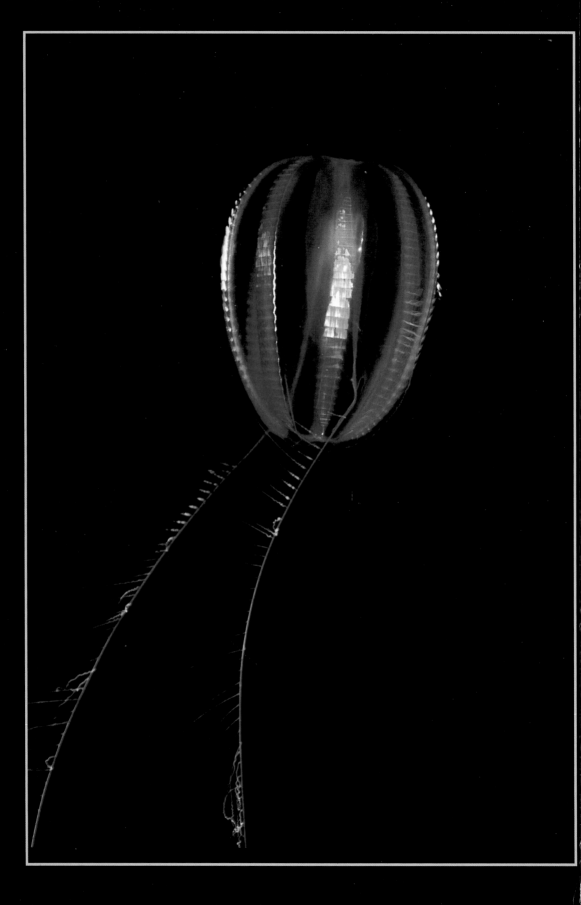

Chapter 5:

Comb Jellies, Entoprocts, Horseshoe Worms, Moss Animals, Lamp Shells, Water Bears, Sea Spiders, and Horseshoe Crabs

In this chapter seven animal phyla will be discussed, which are not directly related to each other (see List of Phyla discussed on page 162). Many of these organisms, such as the entoprocts (phylum Entoprocta) or the water bears (phylum Tardigrada), are strange creatures with a peculiar mode of life and an appearance which seems hardly real.

The three phyla Phoronida (horseshoe worms), Bryozoa (moss animals) and Brachipoda (lamp shells) are being treated as a joint phyla group referred to as the "Lophophorates", since they all possess a special feeding organ: the lophophore. The lophophore is a circular or horseshoe-shaped fold in the body wall, which encircles the mouth and bears many ciliated tentacles. The tentacles are hollow out-growths from the body wall. Each tentacle contains an extension of the coelom body cavity.

In addition to this joint characteristic, nearly all species in the three phyla are sessile organisms. They have a reduced head and live inside a protective shell, excreted by the organisms themselves. Furthermore, they posses a U-shaped intestine. All these characteristics point towards a

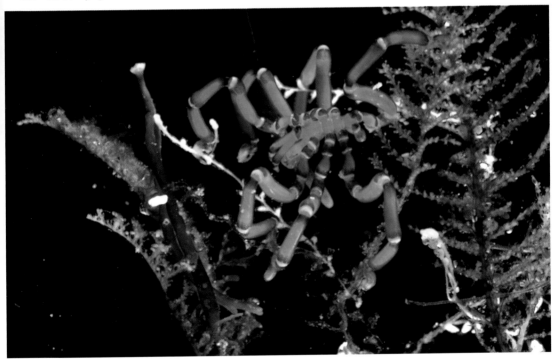

In this chapter we present many extraordinary organisms. Some of these are present and clearly visible in many coral reef aquaria, a few are very hard to find and others can not be kept at all in such aquaria. The sea gooseberry, *Pleurobranchia pileus* (photo on the left, by R. Brons) belongs to the latter group, although it is a cosmopolitan species and occurs seasonally in vast numbers in some regions. The small sea spider of genus *Pseudopallene* (photo above, by C. Bryce) lives among algae and hydroids. Occasionally, sea spiders appear in a coral reef aquarium.

All species in phyla Phoronida, Bryozoa and Brachiopoda possess lophophores, used for capturing food. The photo shows three lophophores of the moss animal *Electra pilosa*. Photo: R. Brons

convergent evolution. In other words, identical structures have developed independently in different unrelated groups as a result of their adaptations to common ecological conditions.

In term of the evolutionary aspects involved, the larval stage is the most interesting. At that stage the lophophorates display obvious similarities with sea urchins (phylum Echinodermata) as well as with acorn worms and related forms (phylum Hemichordata).

Both sea urchins and acorn worms represent the deuterostomal line of development (see chapter 1), while the lophophorates are nowadays included in the protostomal phyla. However, there is still some uncertainty about the phylogenetic position and development of this group (EMIG, 1977; NIELSEN, 1977). As in so many other phyla, increasing knowledge of their phylogeny is likely to alter the systematics in times to come.

Evolution has continuously created fantastic organisms and our approach to this phenomenon, as used in this chapter, is always with this point of view in mind. Even if many of these organisms are small and difficult to find and observe in the aquarium, they are, nevertheless, often there. Once again, this is a reminder that a coral reef aquarium can be much more than a mere display of just corals.

The Heritage of Prehistoric Times

Life on earth is incredibly rich and diversified. Over the last three centuries taxonomists have described about 1.5 million animal species, but this is only a fraction of animal species in existence. It is assumed, that there are at least 5 million – may be even 50 million animal species – on earth. More than 95 % of these are invertebrates, i. e. animals without a backbone. This enormous number is the result of evolution in species, which reproduced and survived; in other words, the survival of those specimens which succeeded in passing on their genetic material to the next generation. From a biological and evolutionary point of view, that is exactly what we mean by "survival".

From the very first algae and bacteria, which developed more than 3.8 billion years up to this very day, evolution has formed the most extraordinary creatures. Some of these are so well adapted to life, that they have survived the competition with other species since time immemorial, while other, less well-adapted species became extinct fairly quickly. Evolution is not a process that has been completed, but instead it is an ongoing process and as such unstoppable. Even our own species, *Homo sapiens,* is a product of evolution. Although the theory of evolution has its (mostly religious) opponents, and even if there is no consensus on how evolution occurs, there are no le-

gitimate scientists who doubt that a biological evolution is taking place. No other theory can explain the species diversity of organisms on earth. For further information about evolution, the reader's attention is drawn to DARWIN (1859, 1968, 1979, 1980), DAWKINS (1981), GOLDSMITH (1996), GOULD (1980, 1991, 1993), GORE (1993), JOHANSON & EDEY (1981), VERON (1995) as well as WALKER & SHIPMAN (1996) - just to list a few of the very many books and articles published on this topic.

While working on this series of books, we continuously encountered unusual organisms, such as the Gall Crab, *Hapalocarcinus marsupialis* (page 345), or the Inn-Keeper's Worm, *Urechis caupo*

Following the appearance of blue-green Cyanobacteria 2 billion years ago, it took about 1.4 billion years until the first invertebrates appeared on the stage of life. This was during the Pre-Cambrian Period, about 570 million years ago. At that time the climate was cold and vast areas of the earth were covered by ice. For a long time nothing was known about the fauna of that period. Then, an Australian geologist, R. C. Sprigg, discovered remarkable fossils in an area near Ediacara Hills in South Australia (photo on the right). Until that time the only fossil invertebrates had been those with shells or other hard body armor. The fossil fauna of Ediacara Hills contained the first soft-bodied invertebrates. They were clearly older than those fossils known to that date. Initially, it was assumed that the fauna of Edia-

cara Hills contained the ancestors of present-day animal phyla and classes, such as sea pens, sea jellies, bristle worms and "joint-footed" animals (Arthropoda). However, alt-

hough several Pre-Cambrium fossil sites have been discovered since Ediacara Hills, the conclusion has not yet been drawn and the discussion continues.

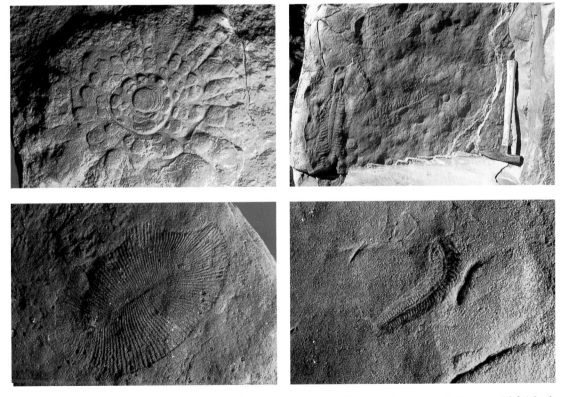

Centre row: *Mawsonites spriggi* (left) appears to have been a sea jelly-like organisms. *Charniodiscus* sp. (right) is similar to a sea pen. Bottom row: *Dickinsonia* sp. (left) and *Spriggina floundersi* (right) look similar to bristle worms.

When Charles Doolittle Walcott, Secretary of the Smithsonian Institute, at the time the most qualified authority on the Cambrian fauna, discovered in August 1909 – quite by accident – the fossil site in Burgess-Shale, he did not know what extraordinary discovery he had made. Burgess-Shales is a mountain chain in the Canadian Rocky Mountains, with an elevation of up to 2300 m. The Burgess-Shales locality is now a National Park, which is administered and supervised by the Yoho Burgess-Shale Foundation. In 1981 the UNESCO declared this area a world heritage site.

One of the reasons why the fossils of Burgess-Shale are so remarkable is that the majority of them have been well preserved. The animals of the Burgess-Shales lived during the Cambrian Period (about 515 million years ago) in the sea, along a steeply sloping cliff. Within a few minutes, hundreds of thousand animals had become buried 160 m deep by a submarine landslide (BRIGGS et al., 1994). The result was that many animals have been found with their internal organs still intact. 15-20 of the

Scientific field work under the direction of Dr. Collins, Royal Ontario Museum. It is grueling work to uncover the fossils. Photo: R. Robertson

species found at Burgess-Shale cannot be assigned to any of the recent, living phyla. One could get the impression that nature was experimenting with solutions for survival (see GOULD, 1991).

Each year various scientific institutions participate in excavations at

Burgess-Shale, so that our knowledge about the marine animals of the Cambrian Period constantly increases. Some of the animals are of very peculiar shape and they resemble some of the invertebrates discussed in this chapter - this may be unbelievable, but it is true!

Left: *Marrella* sp. (photo: Royal Ontario Museum) is the most common animal species in Burgess Shale. More than 15.000 specimens have so far been found. The maximum length of *Marrella* sp. was only about 2 cm, and it had a strange head shield with two pairs of long, curved spines and two pairs of antenna. Nowadays, *Marrella* sp., is categorized as an arthropod (phylum Arthropoda). It may have been an ancestral form for either of the large groups of marine arthropods: crustaceans, chelicerates or trilobites (see Chapter 6). Right: Another strange sea creature of the Cambrian Period was *Opabinia* sp. (photo: Dr. D. Bruton, Museum of Paleontology, Oslo). It had five eyes in the front of its head and a long, flexible proboscis, which terminated in a series of grasping spines. It was a highly unusual creature with a body structure, which was not successful enough to assure its survival. *Opabinia* is an example of one of the fossil species that cannot be assigned to any of the recent, living phyla.

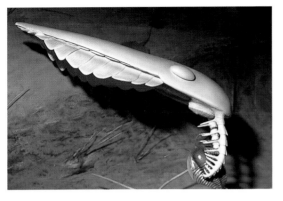

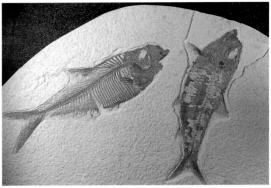

Left: Most life forms existed only during a certain period of the earth age. One example of this is the highly unusual sea predator, *Anomalocaris canadensis*, which lived during the Cambrian Period and like *Opabinia*, cannot be assigned to any of the now living phyla. It was reconstructed in painstaking work from fossils found in the Burgess-Shale; shown here is a model at the Museum of Paleontology in Oslo, Norway, holding a trilobite in its pincer. With a special, circular mouth below the head, it was able to crack the hard shells of trilobites. Incidentally, a single imprint of its mouth had originally been thought to have been a sea jelly-like organism (BRIGGS, 1979). Right: Vertebrates are often found in excellent condition as fossils, and so provide us with information about past life forms. Here we see two fish specimens from the Eocene Period (about 40 million years ago; 475 million year later than the fauna of the Burgess-Shale): *Diplomystus dentatus* (left) and *Knightia* sp. (right). These fossils came from the Green River Formation, Wyoming, USA.

(page 156). Organisms can posses bizarre and unusual characteristics that make them look strange or appear nearly unreal. Sometimes they live in extreme habitats where it seems virtually impossible for life to survive, or they exhibit a most peculiar behavior that, although it may look ridiculous to humans, is important for the survival of the species. During the more than 4.5 billion years of geological history of earth many extraordinary organisms have lived and again vanished. It is interesting, to compare extinct live forms with organisms alive today. Through the effort of placing recent species into an evolutionary perspective, we learn more about the process of evolution. We must keep in mind that our normal perception of time, which is often limited to a human's age, appears minuscule and so it is essentially useless within the time frame of evolution.

In order to study long-extinct animals, one need to examine fossils, that is, imprints of these animals left behind in rocks. Traces of prehistoric organisms left in rocks have provided science with invaluable information about how the current life on earth has

evolved. They are important pieces in the jigsaw puzzle of the history of earth. Fossils appear in a vast number of locations. In some places they are extremely numerous, like the fossil sea urchins that can be found almost everywhere along the Danish coasts. In other sites, like at Riversleigh in Lakefield National Park, Australia,

scientists have stumbled upon delicate and rare fossils that tell us how this present dry landscape in the outback Australia once was a diverse and damping rainforest (ARCHER et al., 1991).

The oldest, known fossils of bacteria and blue-green algae, found in the oldest rocks on earth, came from Isua and the Sirius

From an evolutionary point of the view, the oldest organisms currently still in existence include those blue-green Cyanobacteria that are known as stromatolites. Nowadays they are only found in a few locations with extremely high salinities, such as Shark Bay (seen here) in Western Australia.

Photo: L. Newman and A. Flowers

Pass in Greenland. In Pre-Cambrium age sites like Ediacara Hills in South Australia and Sonora in Mexico, fossils of the first multicelled animals, some of which are cnidarian-like, have been found and studied closely during the last years (MCMENAMINE, 1998). To see a rock that contains traces and imprints of life forms more than 600 million years old is truly exciting. While it was long thought that Pre-Cambrium sites like Ediacara were very rare, more and more fossils from this prehistoric age are found, among others in Canada, China, England, Newfoundland, Northern Norway, southwestern United States and northern Mexico and in several locations in Russia. Localities containing Pre-cambrium fossils are often referred to as "Vendian localities", see for instance SEILACHER (1992).

In Burgess-Shale, near the town of Field in Canada, a complete fauna has been found dating all the way back to the Cambrian Period (550 million years ago), which gave us an insight and invaluable information about the evolution of our current invertebrate fauna. The fauna of the Burgess-Shale contains a number of organisms, which must indeed be considered as "unusual". Yet, evolution and fossils are not the principal theme of this book, nevertheless, it appears useful to us to wander back – in our thoughts – a few hundred million years ago, and so to gain an insight into a prehistoric world. With this, the organisms discussed in this chapter will appear in another, more revealing perspective. For that reason, these localities and some of the extraordinary creatures from times long ago are presented on pages (163 and 164). Those readers, who would like to get more involved in this topic, are advised to commence with the following literature: BRIGGS et al. (1994), CASTER (1994), CLOUD & GLASSNER (1982), FENTON & FENTON (1989), FRICKHINGER (1991), FORTEY (1991), and GORE (1993).

Phylum Ctenophora – Comb Jellies

At first sight comb jellies look very similar to regular sea jellies ("jelly fish"). Although they are closely related to the phylum Cnidaria, they have their own phylum Ctenophora. Comb jellies and regular sea jellies, sea anemones, coral and related forms were formerly designated as Coelenterata. However, nowadays, comb jellies are considered to be phylogenetically a side branch of the cnidarians (corals, sea anemones, and related forms). There have been two fossil discoveries from the Devonian Period (STANLEY & STÜRMER, 1983 and 1989) and one record from the Precambrian Period.

General biology

Comb jellies are of a gelatinous structure. Most species are planktonic and exclusively marine. The popular name "comb jellies" refers to the eight rows of cilia combs, each consisting of up to 100,000 cilia grown together. The cilia contract in rhythmic movements. They stabilize the position of the comb jelly and are involved in propelling the animal in water. The wave-like movements of the cilia combs are being controlled by impulses from a sensory organ (apical organ), which actually serves as a balancing organ. It contains sensory epithelium with rows of extended cilia, which are supporting a small calcareous body - a statolith. The statolith exerts uneven pressure on the sensory epithelium, depending upon the respective position of the comb jelly in the water. The animal then controls it upright position with the aid of impulses, which the sensory hairs transmit to the cilia combs. Yet, the movements of the cilia are not

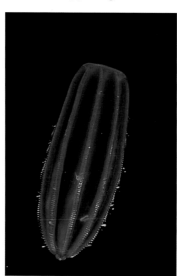

Left: Typical comb jelly of genus *Beroe* (photo: R. Brons). Right: *Kimberella quadrata*, a comb jelly fossil from Ediacara Hills, South Australia (photo: N. Pledge, South Australian Museum, Adelaide).

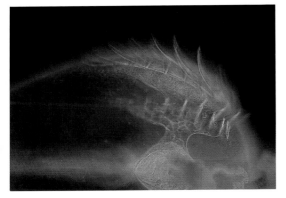
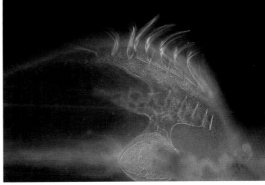

Movement of cilia combs in the sea gooseberry, *Pleurobranchia* sp.   Photos: R. Brons

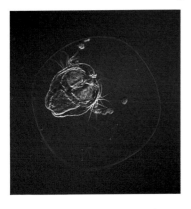
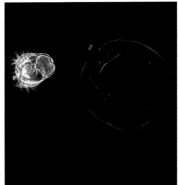

Hatching of a young sea gooseberry: Oocyte with fully grown larva (left), larva newly hatched from oocyte (centre), and 2 mm long juvenile (right).   Photos: R. Brons

particularly powerful, so that comb jellies are very much affected by currents. Therefore, they are considered primarily as planktonic organisms. While true sea jellies move mainly by means of rhythmic body movements, comb jellies move with the aid of cilia.

Moreover, comb jellies are known for their capability to give off biologically created light, called bioluminescence. This production of light takes place in meridional canals, extended in a longitudinal direction, located directly inside the cilia combs. Therefore, from the outside it looks like the cilia combs are emitting the colours of a rainbow.

Yet, the type of locomotion as well as the light being produced are not the only significant differences that set comb jellies apart from cnidarian animals. Many of the latter (classes Hydrozoa to Scyphozoa, see Volume 2, chapters 4 and 5) have two generations: the free-living, sexual medusa stage and the (in principle) sessile, asexual polyp stage. Comb jellies have only a free-swimming stage. Furthermore, cnidarian animals are also characterized by the fact that they have stinging cells (nematocysts)

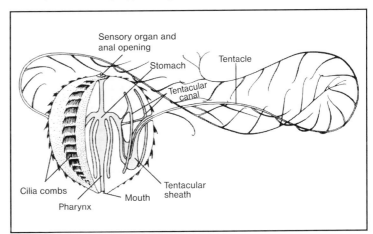

Schematic structure of comb jellies (Ctenophora).
          Drawing after SEMB-JOHANSSON (1988)

in their tissue (see Volume 2, pages 18-20). These are absent in comb jellies, except in the species *Euchlora rubra*. Instead, comb jellies have lasso cells (adhesive cells), also referred to as colloblasts found on the comb-jellies tentacles. These are specialised cells, serving as capture organs, in essence making comb jellies predators capturing other zooplankton. Many species have two very long tentacles, which contain numerous colloblasts, making them highly effective for prey capture. Other species collect plankton directly with their mouth. In terms of tissue structure, comb jellies are, however, very similar to cnidarians. They have – just like cnidarian animals – two cell layers (ectoderm and endoderm), separated by a non-cellular layer, the mesogloea.

All comb jellies are hermaphrodites, releasing their sex cells directly into the surrounding water, where fertilization takes place. In a few species the fertilization is internal. The zygotes develop into a cydippid larva, named after the comb jelly order Cydippida, where the adults have considerable resemblance to their larvae.

Systematics

Comb jellies are cosmopolitan with a world-wide distribution.

They are grouped in five orders with about 100 species (for a systematic overview see above).

Order Cydippida

The members of this order have ovoid bodies and branched tentacles that are retractable into pouches. The best-known comb jelly is probably *Pleurobranchia pileus*, which is also known colloquially as the "sea gooseberry". As suggested by the popular name, the sea gooseberry has a roundish, berry-like shape. It occurs in tropical seas as well as in the Atlantic Ocean. During the summer months it is also found along our North Atlantic coastlines, sometimes in very large numbers. The body has comb rows of equal length, extending from the aboral pole almost to the mouth. The spherical body can reach a diameter of up to 4 cm, and it is equipped with two pouches, into which the tentacles can be retracted. The tentacles, which can be up to 50 cm long, have filaments on one side and are used for capturing zooplankton as well as acting as a drift net. The lasso cells, present in large numbers, make this sort of prey capture highly effective.

Order Lobata

The animals in this order are of a more elongated shape and they are laterally flattened. These spe-

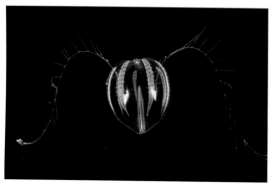

Left: The two body pouches are clearly visible in this *Pleurobranchia pileus* specimen. Right: Comb jellies sometimes occur in vast numbers, such as these *Pleurobranchia pileus* washed up on a beach in the Red Sea.　　Photos: R. Brons

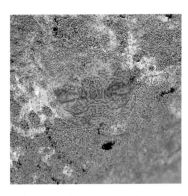
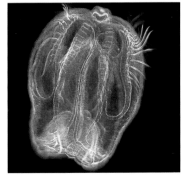

Left: *Ctenoplana* sp. at Madang, Papua-New Guinea. (photo: L. Newman and A. Flowers). Middle: 2 mm long juvenile *Beroe cucumis*. Right: Fully grown *Beroe cucumis* which has just swallowed a comb jelly of the genus *Pleurobranchia*.

Photos: R. Brons

cies have only very short tentacles and there are no pouches. The body possesses two large, oral lobes on each side of the mouth and four ciliated processes projecting above the mouth, serving as capture organs. *Mnemiopsis* is a genus with relative small species, which can – just like sea gooseberries – occur seasonally in vast numbers. In the *Mnemiopsis* species the body projections have four short and four long comb rows (SEMB-JOHANSSON, 1988).

Order Cestida

The comb jellies in this order have a body that is expended laterally into a ribbon-like form and so resemble elongated, gelatin-like bands, which are referred to as "Venus' Girdle". Their main tentacles are very much reduced, but numerous short tentacles occur along the entire lower edge of the body. These comb jellies move with gliding and sinusoidal movements of the entire body, which looks rather elegant. Locomotion is facilitated by a muscle layer within the mesogloea. The genera *Cestum* and *Velamen* are distributed in subtropical and tropical seas.

Order Platyctena

This order contains the most unusual comb jellies, but they include species that can be of interest to marine aquarists. Instead of a life as a planktonic organism in open water, these comb jellies are adapted for creeping. The animals crawl along the bottom or at the surface, or live on other invertebrates. Comb rows are reduced or totally absent in adult specimens and the cilia-covered ventral surface is part of the stomach cavity.

Species of genera *Coeloplana* and *Tjalfiella* live on the bottom. They are dorso-ventrally compressed, crawling organisms. In fact, *Tjalfiella* species can be considered as nearly sessile forms (SEMB-JOHANSSON, 1988). Comb jellies of genus *Gastrodes* are mostly specialised and live as pa-

rasites on salps. The genus *Lyrocteis* contains *L. imperatoris*, which varies in colour from light red, lilac to yellow, can reach a maximum size of 26 cm. It lives at a depth of about 75 m and presumably feeds on soft corals.

Genus *Ctenoplana* contains several species. Some can sporadically and inadvertently be introduced into coral reef aquaria together with other invertebrates, but so far we have not yet seen this. *C. astericola* lives on the sea star *Echinaster luzonicus* and occurs in the Central Indo-Pacific (GOSLINER et al., 1996). *C. gonoctena* has been seen on soft corals, for instance on *Cladiella*

Ctenoplana astericola lives on sea stars, especially on *Echinaster luzonicus*, photographed at Madang, Papua-New Guinea.

Photo: L. Newman and A. Flowers

species and others. On the other hand, *C. meteoris* lives freely on soft bottom substrates (GOSLINER et al., 1996). Both species are widely distributed in the Indo-Pacific. In Papua-New Guinea very colourful, as yet undescribed *Ctenoplana* species has occasionally been seen living on a sea cucumbers. No doubt, there are still many unknown and yet-to-be de-

scribed species in this genus; species, which are being overlooked while they are camouflaged on some host animal, or which are being mistaken for other organisms, such as flat worms.

Order Beroida

Tentacles are absent in comb jellies of this order. Food is captured

directly by the mouth. The best known species is *Beroe gracilis*, which occurs in the North Sea and Atlantic Ocean. It feeds exclusively on sea gooseberries (see photo on page 169), which can easily be manipulated because a large part of the body is made up by a stomach system and only to a lesser degree by mesogloea.

Phylum Entoprocta – Entoprocts

Entoprocts are relatively small (less than 1 mm), sessile filter-feeding animals, many of which are colonial or associated with other invertebrates. Occasionally, they can also appear in a coral reef aquarium (see Volume 1, page 190).

General biology

The simplest entoprocts are non-colonial and are attached to a substrate by means of a stalk. They often occur gregarious and in association with other animals, however, without inflicting any damage on the host organism. Some species can be found on bristle- and peanut worms, others are attached to the exhalent opening of sponges, and yet others are growing on shelled mollusks. Some are even species-specific in respect to their host. Much research has been done to determine the reasons for this peculiar behavior of entoprocts. Presumably, this way the entoprocts avoid mutual competition with each other, and at the same time they have an assured food source, as well as being afforded better protection against predators, than living alone.

The name Entoprocta refers to the location of the anal opening within the tentacle crown, in contrast to the Ectoprocta (see page 174), where the anal opening is

Two entoprocts of the genus *Berentsia* (magnification 130x).
Photo: R. Brons

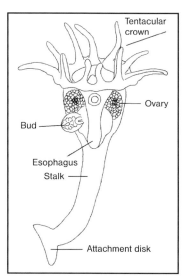

Schematic structure of Entoprocta.
Drawing after BARNES (1980).

located outside the tentacle crown (entos, Greek = inside, within; ectos, Greek = outside, and proctos, Greek = buttox, anus). Formerly, the Entoprocta and Ectoprocta were kept together in the "Polyzoa"; however, there is now a consensus that these organisms represent separate phyla.

Entoprocts have a simple body structure. Each zooid consists of a cup-or goblet-like body (= calyx), which is positioned on top of a long stalk. Both of these are made up of soft, pliable tissue. At its tip, the cup or calyx is constricted and forms a margin with about 40 hollow tentacles. The tentacles are flexible and can be

expanded for feeding or folded down to lie inside the tentacular membrane which joins their bases. In the center of the calyx within the tentacle crown there is the mouth and the anal opening. The latter is connected to a U-shaped intestine or digestive tract. In colonial forms the individuals (zooids) are connected to each other by a stolon which grows from its apices, branching and budding off successive zooids.

Entoprocts have a "false body cavity" (pseudocoelom), which is filled with gelatinous mesenchymatous tissue, surrounding the internal organs. The reproductive organs are located near the digestive tract and terminate in a brood chamber in the upper part of the chalice. A circulatory system and a respiratory system are absent. Gas exchange takes place by means of diffusion, directly through the cell walls. Entoprocts are filter feeders, straining organic particles or microorganisms from water currents passing by.

Many entoprocts reproduce asexually through budding from stalk, calyx or stolon depending upon the respective genus. Similarly, the type of growth of the colony is also dependent upon the genus. Some species are hermaphrodites, while others have separate sexes. Fertilization probably takes place within the calyx, and the larvae develop inside a brood chamber, before they hatch and enter open water.

Systematics

Systematically the entoprocts are divided into four families: Pedicellinidae, Urtanellidae (in freshwater only), Loxosomatidae and Barentsiidae (HAYWARD & RYLAND, 1996). The families are distinguished on the basis of the shape of zooids and the growth form of the colony.

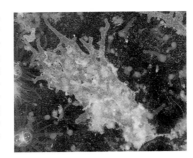
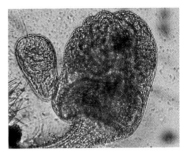

Left: This, only 24 mm² large, glass sheet from the sump of our experimental aquarium, with a steady flow of water, shows various organisms, which have settled on the glass within a period of four months. Among sponges, hydroids and young *Aiptasia* (glass roses), one can recognize about 30 club-shaped entoprocts, probably of genus *Loxosoma* (magnification 8x). Right: Many solitary entoprocts reproduce through budding. Here we see a new zooid being formed from the calyx of a *Loxosoma* species (?). The large, slightly brownish region inside the entoproct is the stomach. The digestive tract is U-shaped and terminate at the anus (the brownish dot), which is located close to the mouth inside the tentacle crown (magnification 260x).

Left: *Loxosoma* (?) sp. with expanded tentacles, which are hollow and covered on the outside with many small cilia. Right: Two entoprocts with their tentacle crowns closed. The juvenile, formed by budding and still attached to the adult, will soon leave the parent animal and attach itself to the substratum (both photos magnification 52x).

Family Pedicellinidae

There are no free-living species in this family, all members live in colonies. The individuals rise from a creeping and branching stolon. The stalks are without joints, flexible and entirely muscular. The calyx is off-set from the stalk by a distinct constriction and can be totally cut off, when the environmental conditions become too unsatisfactory or the calyx has been damaged. The stalk can, however, regenerate a new calyx, so that the zooids can have cups of different developmental stages. The zooids are usually less than 2 mm high. *Pedicellina* is a common genus.

Family Loxosomatidae

Species of family Loxosomatidae are among the most common entoprocts. They are solitary and usually found commensal with other organisms. In aquaria members of the family can be found free-living, however. The zooids are normally less than 0.5 mm high and have longitudinal mussels that are continuos throughout both stalk and calyx. The stalk always grows fluently into the calyx, which can not be cut off. Daughter zooids are budded off from the calyx. The two most common genera are *Loxosoma* and *Loxosomella*. In *Loxosoma* the stalk terminates in an attachment disk that makes the adult animals capable of moving from place to place. Buds lack foot glands. In *Loxosomella* the zooids are cemented to the substratum or to the host and are not capable of movement. A foot gland is present in buds, but disappears in the adult (HAYWARD & RYLAND, 1995).

Family Barentsiidae

Here the zooids are colonial, arising from a creeping or erect, branching stolon. The stolons are septate, of alternating zooid-bearing and barren segments. The stalks are divided into alternating rigid sections (internodes) and flexible muscular joints (nodes). The genus *Barentsia* is dominating (see HAYWARD & RYLAND, 1996).

Entoprocts in the coral reef aquarium

Entoprocts are not easy to observe in a coral reef aquarium, however, they are most certainly present in many tanks. It requires a (hand-held) magnifying glass to locate them on rocks and other solid objects. A rather efficient method for tracking settling organisms in the aquarium is to use small glass sheets (e. g. micros-

copy glass slides) and mount these in the sump or in a shady location of the aquarium itself, so that the glass is exposed to a steady flow of water. After a few weeks one will observe that the glass becomes covered with tiny organisms like sponges, hydrozoans, small anemones and very often entoprocts. We have found entoprocts, probably of the genus *Loxosoma*, to be very common settlers in the reef aquarium (NILSEN, 1999). The photos on page 171 show entoprocts collected from the authors' aquarium by the use of this method.

To the right: Entoprocts settle sometimes on other invertebrates. Here *Loxosomella* sp. on a see-quirt at Heron Island, Great Barrier Reef.
Photo: L. Newman and A. Flowers

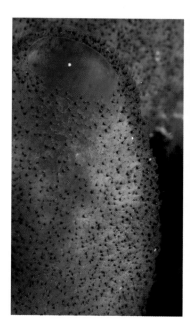

Phylum Phoronida – Horseshoe Worms

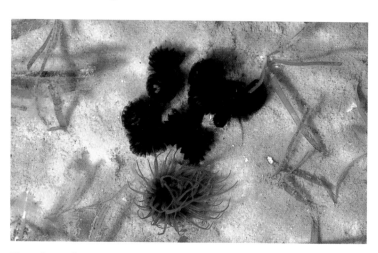

These horseshoe worms, *Phoronis australis*, live in association with a tube anemones of genus *Cerianthus* at Stradbroke Island, Great Barrier Reef.
Photo: L. Newman and A. Flowers

Phoronids resemble moss animals (phylum Bryozoa, see page 174), however, in comparison to the latter, phoronids represent only a rather small group of animals. The phylum contains no more than about 20 known species in two genera. All known species are marine and sessile, and most of them occur in subtro-

pical and tropical seas. A few species of the genus *Phoronis* are known from the North-East Atlantic where they can appear in great abundance in some habitats (HAYWARD et al., 1996). Phoronid larvae are known from Nordic coasts, but the adult animal has traditionally not been observed along the Norwegian coast. We

have, however photographed horseshoe worms ourselves during dives in about 10 meters depth off the coast of southern Norway, an observation that confirms its presence in cold water habitats. It is likely, that the low number of known species from cold waters is due to a lack of field research. Consequently, it stands to reason, that "new" phoronids will be discovered in the future.

General biology

Horseshoe worms live in a chitinous tube, excreted by the animals themselves, as sessile organisms attached to a solid substrate. Usually they bury themselves in mud bottom or bore into the shells or tubes of other organisms (they are particular common in tube anemones of genus *Cerianthus*, see page 197). Through their boring activity horseshoe worms play a major ecological role by breaking down large shell debris and opening limestone surface to other borers.

Horseshoe worms have elongated bodies with a posterior bulge, which serves as an anchor, maintaining the animal in its tube or burrow. The mouth is overhung by a short lip (epistome), and surrounded by the lophophore. They are small organisms, normally substantially smaller than 20 mm.

One of the largest and most frequently encountered species is *Phoronis australis* which has been found associated with several tube anemone species. *P. australis* penetrates the tissue of the tube anemone, but is does not harm its host in any way. This species occurs in subtropical and tropical seas. What a fantastic aquarium it would be to keep tube anemones with their tubes occupied by many horseshoe worms!

Phoronids have an elongated head and a lophophore, which carries a well-developed, horseshoe-shaped tentacle crown located at the upper end of the animal. Phoronids belong to the coelomate phyla, which have a true body cavity. The tentacle crowns have rows of tentacles arranged in a crescent pattern, inside each other. Located among them is the mouth opening. In some species the tentacle crown shows a spirally wound arrangement.

Phoronids are filter feeders. The cilia create a downward water current directed to a groove between the two lophophoral ridges. The current follows the groove inward on each side towards the mouth opening. The food is pulled into the mouth with a mucus net secreted by the worm. The mouth leads to a pharynx, which passes the food further down to the stomach located at the lowest end of the organism. From there a U-shaped intestine leads to the rectum and on to the anal opening, located below the lophophore at the anterior of the body coelom.

The body wall has an outer epithelial layer, which covers a thin circular muscle layer. The circular muscle can contract, cau-

Phoronis hippocrepia. The popular name of phylum Phoronida refers to the horseshoe-shaped tentacle crown. We have observed similar looking colonies along the coast of southern Norway. Photo: Prof. Dr. P. Wirtz

sing the body to become long and thin. Within the circular muscles are strong longitudinal muscles, which can contract the body, and so facilitate the withdrawal of the worm back into its tube. The muscles are controlled by a simple nervous system, located in the tentacle crown. Phoronids have a distinct circulatory system with red-coloured, haemoglobin-containing blood.

Most phoronids are hermaphrodites. They produce eggs and sperm cells within the fluid of the body cavity, which are then given off into the surrounding water, together with the excretory products. Fertilization takes place in open water and the fertilized eggs are either planktonic or brooded in the concavity formed by the two arms of the lophophore. The elongated ciliated larvae (actinotroch) undergo, like in the related phyla Bryozoa (page 174) and Brachiopoda (page 181), a development stage during which the body is divided into three segments and each segment retains

An unidentified moss animal species ("KA6-BRY-01"), with a growth form reminiscent of a hydroid colony, at One Tree Island, Great Barrier Reef.
Photo: L. Newman and A. Flowers

a small contribution from the body cavity. The most anterior segment will be reduced and disappears almost totally. The center segment retains the coelom and forms the tentacle crown around the lophophore. The posterior segment of the larva becomes the principal part of the animal's body and produces the body cavity. Organisms, which display this sort of development, are referred to as being "oligomerous", that is, they possess only a few segments. This distinguishes them from animals with many segments like the segmented worms and crustaceans. At least one species of horseshoe worms, *Phoronis ovalis* is known to reproduce asexually by budding and can in this way colonize large areas.

Phylum Bryozoa – Moss Animals

The phylum Bryozoa, sometimes also referred to as phylum Ectoprocta, has the largest number of species of the three lophophorate phyla. Moss animals are rather frequently occurring organisms and they live – without exception – in colonies only. The colonies take on variable shapes, a factor used to distinguish individual genera. The vast majority of the about 4000 known species live in the sea. Although this group has the largest species diversity within the lophophorates and is in general an important group of invertebrates, the phylum has been poorly studied and many species remain to be described.

About 50 species of class Phylactolaemata live in freshwater (see systematic overview on page 176).

General biology

Moss animals are most numerous in shallow water, however, individual colonies can occur as deep as 8200 m (BARNES, 1980). The colonies are sessile and grow on algae and kelp or directly on the substratum. Encrusting colonies, growing on the large leafy brown algae of the genus *Laminaria*, are very frequent in North Atlantic coastal waters.

A colony is being formed when a larvae settles on a suitable site. The larvae develop into an adult specimen, which then divides and so starts up a new colony. Since a growing colony is the product of asexual reproduction, all specimens within that colony are genetically identical.

The small individuals of a colony live within a protective chamber (zoecium), which is secreted from the epidermis by the organism itself. The chamber is often square and box-like, but it can also have an oval or cylindrical shape. In class Gymnolaemata, the protective chamber consists of an organic material (essentially proteins, chitinous or other organic compounds) covered by a layer of calcium carbonate. For this reason, many moss animal colonies appear rigid and substantially stiffened, which in some instances can be reminiscent of coral. The protective chamber possesses an opening for the protrusion of the lophophore, and

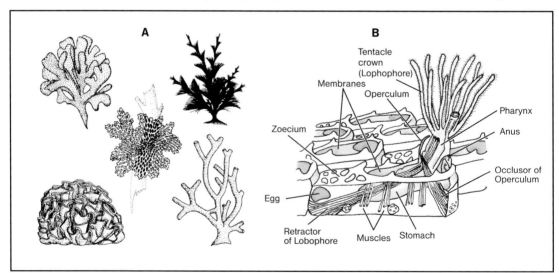

A: Various Bryozoa colony formations. Drawing after SEMB-JOHANSSON (1988). B: Schematic structure of a moss animal. Drawing after BARNES (1980).

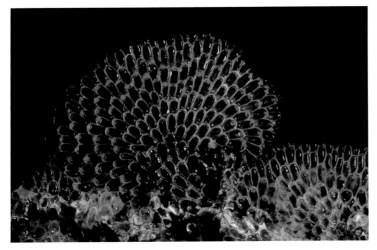

Two different colony formations of moss animals: Branched colony of *Bicellariella* sp. (right) and the crust-like (encrusting) shape of *Conopeum* sp. (left). Photos: R. Brons

the opening is equipped with a lid (operculum). The shape of this tiny lid is highly variable within this group; a characteristic that is associated with differential phylogenetic adaptations and it represents an important taxonomic criterion.

The mouth is located in the center of the tentacle crown of the lophophore. It leads into a simple pharynx, stomach and intestine. The anal opening is outside the tentacle crown. This particular character has led to the alternate phylum name "Ectoprocta" ("outside-anus" in contrast to the Entoprocta, see page 170).

The diet of moss animals is rather variable. The tiny organisms usually less than 0.5 mm in length utilize organic particles of different sizes, often depending upon the size of the lophophore. Digestion occurs within as well as outside of the cells. Waste material is passed on to the rectum and excreted through the anal opening. The gas exchange takes place by diffusion across the body surface. The main system for spreading metabolic products across the colony is the funiculus, a band of mesoblastic tissue extending from the stomach to the body wall.

Most moss animals are hermaphrodites. Eggs and sperm always develop independently and migrate into the body cavity upon

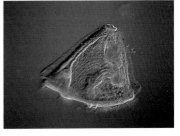

Moss animal larva, referred to as Cyphonates larva.
Photo: L. Newman and A. Flowers.

maturation. Some species (*Electra* spp. and *Membranipora* spp.) expel their sex products into the surrounding water, where fertilization takes place. However, the

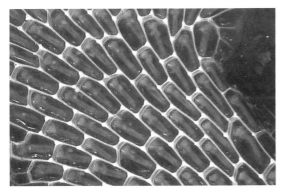

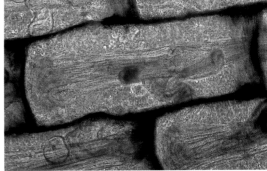

Structural details of moss animal colonies can be recognized under a microscope. The photo on the left (magnification 80x) shows that the animals live in box-like zoecia; the photo on the right (magnification 200x) shows a single specimens inside its zoecium.

The photo on the left reveals that the zoecium of this *Electra* species possesses a protective spine. On the right we can see how the lophophore is extended out from the zooecium (magnification 70x).   Photos: R. Brons

vast majority of moss animals practice brood care, most often outside, but occasionally also inside the body cavity. Normally there are few, but large eggs, which are expelled through special pores in the body wall. In terms of shape, the developing larvae are rather variable, however, all have certain mutual traits such as a ring of cilia which are used for locomotion (BARNES,

1980). Larvae from moss animal with brood care do not feed, and their larval stage is short. The larvae of species that do not brood, have a digestive tract and are actively feeding. Their larval stage can last for several months.

The longevity of moss animal colonies is rather variable, and some live only for a year. This applies especially to those species that normally grow on algae; ho-

wever, others can live longer. The lophophore and digestive tract of individual specimens tend to degenerate already after a few weeks, but are then regenerated.

Systematics

For a comprehensive review of tropical moss animals we recommend the publication by MATHER & BENNET (1993), with its clearly arranged overview of the most common genera and species of the Indo-Pacific. The discussion below is confined to the most fre-

---

**Systematic overview of the phylum Bryozoa
with the most important tropical genera
(after MATHER & BENNETT, 1993)**

Phylum Bryozoa
    Class Phylactolaernata
    Class Stenoiaemata
        Order Cyclostomata
            Mesonea, Cristia, Lichnopora, Nevianopora
    Class Gymnoiaemata
        Order Ctenostomata
            Nolella
        Order Celiostomata
            Suborder Anasca
                *Bugula, Scrupocellaria, Thalamoporella,
Retiflustra, Caberea, Nellia, Poricellaria,
Steginoporella*
            Suborder Cribrimorpha
            Suborder Ascophora
                *Euthyrisella, Margaretta,
Tetraplaria, Tremogasterina, Celleporaria,
Hippopodina, Clayptotheca, Stylopoma,
Cigcisuia, Pleurocodonellina, Parasmittina,
Sinupetralielja, Schedocleidochasma,
Rhynchozoon, Reteporelja, Reteporellina,
Iodictyum, Sertella, Triphyllozoon,
Schizoretepora, Hippellzoon*

Mesonea radians at Heron Island, Great Barrier Reef.
Photo: L. Newman and A. Flowers

Retiflustra cornea is one of the most peculiar moss animals. It lives on a muddy bottom close to shore. Small "feet" project the colony off the substrate.   Photos: P. Colin, Coral Reef Research Foundation

quent genera (see systematic overview, page 176).

Order Cyclostomata

The colonies in this order grow erect and branched, with or without joints, or forming discoid, hemispherical or irregular incrustations. The body walls of the individuals are strongly calcified and are orifice terminal and circular. Stippled, swollen regions of the colony are indicative of the development of brood chambers (gonozooids).

In genus *Cristia* the colonies are small and upright. They form tufts of branching, jointed stems. *C. elongate* is the most common species, where the colonies reach a maximum height of up to 15 cm. *Mesonea radicans* has bifurcate stems spreading to a saucer shape with a maximum dia-

meter of 25 mm. In cross-section the branches are triangular. *Nevianopora* species have thin, irregular branches and form colonies of at least 45 mm in cross-section. *N. pulcherimma* is a common species. *Lichnopora* species are small, encrusting, and domed, often with an elongated outline. Their size is typically less than 10 mm. Representatives of this genus can be numerous, but they are often found in cryptic, inaccessible habitats, such as in narrow crevices or in caves, and among coral boulders.

Order Celiostomata

The colonies of order Celiostomata may be encrusting or growing erect, and frequently jointed. The membrane in which the operculum is set, comprises a part of the frontal surface and

may be underlain by a concave calcareous shield or overarched by ribs (MATHER & BENNETT, 1993). The opening as such is often surrounded by thin spines. The two suborders Anasca and Ascophora are distinguishable from each other by the structure of the frontal membrane.

Species of **suborder Anasca** have a partially or totally transparent frontal membrane, so that the internal organs become visible. The rather unusual *Retiflustra cornea* thrives on a muddy bottom, usually in shore of the actual reef, that is, in areas from where live rocks are frequently collected for the aquarium trade. Therefore, there is a chance for this species to be introduced into aquaria. The colonies are dish-shaped and are supported above the bottom by many "legs". The bottle-green *Bugula dentata* forms bushy colo-

Left: *Cigcisula (?)* sp. at One Tree Island, Great Barrier Reef. Right: *Cigcisula* sp. at Heron Island, Great Barrier Reef.
Photos: L. Newman and A. Flowers

Left: *Bugula dentata* at One Tree Island, Great Barrier Reef. Right: Unknown moss animal species ("KA6-BRY-2") in the Truk Lagoon, Micronesia.

Photos: L. Newman and A. Flowers

nies, which reach a maximum height of 6 cm. These colonies display bifurcate branching, coming off a more or less distinct axis. In genus *Scrupocellaria* the colonies are clearly branched. Instead of thick, bush-like structures they are spread out over a substrate, where they are often attached by means of "hair roots". *S. maderensis*, *S. diadema* and *S. spatula* are the most frequent species of the Indo-Pacific.

Species of **suborder Ascophora** have a stronger and often calcified frontal membrane, than the Anasca. MATHER & BENNETT (1993) separate the genera on the basis of their colony- and branch shapes. *Euthyrisella clathrata* has flat, flexible bifurcate branches with a chitinous (horn-like) struc-

ture. The branches have a diameter of 3 to 6 mm; they are rounded off at their tips and are positioned parallel to each other. At their bases (point of attachment to the substrate) they are narrowed. They are coloured brick red or pink lilac. The zooids are located only along one side of the branches. Normally the colonies are 10 cm high, but they can reach a maximum height of up to 19 cm. *E. clathrata* is only known to occur along the coast of Queensland.

Low-growing, stiffened branches occur in *Cigcisula* species, where the flat and rigid branches form a three-dimensionally colony shape. The zooids are located on both sides of the branches, in strongly calcified small box-shaped chambers. There are at

least two species in the Indo-Pacific: *C. occlusa* and *C. cautium*. The genera *Margaretta* and *Tetraplaria* have species with cylindrical and jointed branches.

Among the most frequently encountered moss animals on a coral reef are the so-called "lacecorals", which resemble small corals- or hydroid colonies, and which are sometimes mistaken for them. In these moss animals the colonies grow fenestrate; they branch repeatedly and regularly, and anastomose forming a web of branches and windows. Most of the lace corals from coral reefs belong to family Phidolophoridae, and are common animals on coral reefs. They form cup-like, saucer-like or scrolled colonies. The zooids are located only along one side of the branches. They are usually pointed towards the inside of the colony. At the base of the colony there are special reinforcing individuals (kenozooids). The kenozooids do not take in food, and all external structures are absent. Their main task is to strengthen the colony. The genera are distinguished primarily by the structure of the brood chamber and the structures of the opening to the "box".

Reteporella and *Reteporellina* species have both a typical fan shape. In *Reteporellina* species the branches are more brittle and delicate than in *Reteporella* species. Without a precise examination of the position of the zooids and of the structural details of the

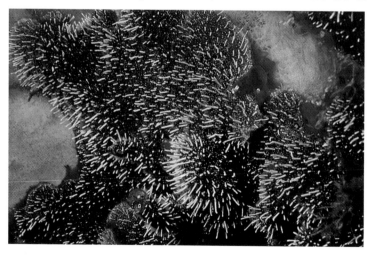

Celleporaria sibogae.   Photo: P. Colin, Coral Reef Research Foundation

colony, the species are very difficult to identify. *Iodictyum* species have a particular crimson-red or lilac colour, as well as a dense dish-like fan shape. They are among the most easily recognizable moss animals on a coral reef. According to GOSLINER et al. (1996), the distribution of genus *Iodictyum* is concentrated in western parts of the Pacific Ocean. On the basis of colony colouration, the same authors distinguish three species: *I. axillare*, *I. buchneri* and *I. sanguineum*.

The species of genus *Triphyllozoon* resemble *Iodictyum* species. Without detailed examinations of the macro structures of respective colonies, the 15 species are indistinguishable from each other. Some species are typically found in deeper areas of a reef.

The number of moss animal species growing encrusting is nearly innumerous; however, the majority of them has so far only been insufficiently investigated. One of the most frequently encountered genera is *Celleporaria*, where the colonies grow in many layers, often with intensive colours, a reason why they are rather conspicuous. *Stylopoma* is yet another genus, which often produces massive or nodular layered colonies, with strongly calcified feeding zooids.

Moss Animals in the coral reef aquarium

There are a number of genera and species of moss animals which can conceivably be introduced into a coral reef aquarium, together with live rocks or – inadvertently as "stowaway passengers" – attached to corals, mollusks or other invertebrates. Unfortunately as a group, the bryozoans have so far not been sufficiently researched yet. Moreover, species and

Moss animals, principally those of family Philolophoridae, which are reminiscent in their growth forms of small coral- or hydroid colonies, are often referred to as "Lace Corals".

Reteporella is a genus of moss animals commonly found on coral reefs. Individual species can only be identified on the basis of structural details of their zooecia.
Photos: L. Newman and A. Flowers

Left: *Iodictyum* species are usually coloured red and build fan-shaped colonies, which are rather stiff and firm. They typically live in caves or crevices. Right: *Triphyllozoon* (?) sp. at One Tree Island, Great Barrier Reef.
Photos: L. Newman and A. Flowers

Encrusting moss animal colonies
Photos top and centre left: L. Newman and A. Flowers; photos centre right and bottom: P. Colin

"KA6-BRY-03" at Lizard Island, GBR.

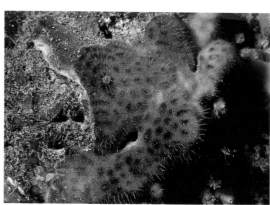

Steginoporella cf. *magnilabris* at One Tree Island, GBR.

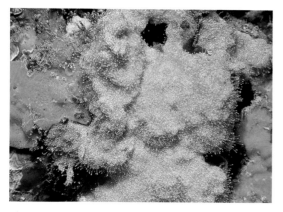

"KA6-BRY-04" in the Wistari Reef, GBR.

"KA6-BRY-05" at the Fiji Islands.

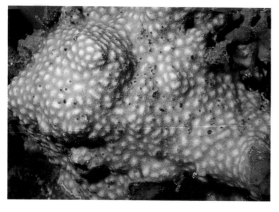

"KA6-BRY-06" at the Fiji Islands.

"KA6-BRY-07" at Zanzibar.

genus characters are generally so complicated that it is difficult – if not impossible – to identify the species and genera involved. Only time will show us whether we will be successful in keeping moss animal in aquaria. This animal group probably represent the most difficult of aquarium animals, most certainly when we are talking about a nutrient-deficient coral reef aquarium. Chances of their survival may be better in an aquarium where the animals are being given a more generous diet. Indeed, in an aquarium filtered over biological filtration only, or a biological filter in combination with a careful skimming, the nutrient content will rise and one might have better luck with moss animals in such a tank than in a traditional reef aquarium.

Moss animals may be introduced into a coral reef aquarium attached to live rocks, corals or various shelled mollusks.

Phylum Brachiopoda – Lamp Shells

No animal group deserves the name "living fossils" more than the lamp shells of phylum Brachiopoda. Lamp shells were very numerous from the onset of the Cambrian Period (almost 600 million years ago) and reached their peak of abundance and distribution during the middle of the Palaeozoic Period about 225 million years ago. More than 30,000 fossil species of brachiopods are known. In some fossil localities brachiopods are very numerous. The recent species of lamp shells occur in all seas. Some species have retained their ancient structural characteristics, and so they are indeed "living fossils". However, as an animal group the brachiopods are nowadays undergoing a regressive development. Currently we know barely 300 living species.

General biology

Most lamp shells live in shallow water, where the vast majority is attached to rocks or other solid substrates. A few species will bury in muddy bottoms. Among these are *Lingula* species, which

Sometimes tiny lamp shells can occur in large numbers; left *Pjandina flatica* and right *Megathiris* sp.

Photos: Prof. Dr. P. Wirtz

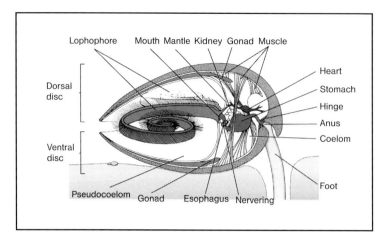

Lophophore Mouth Mantle Kidney Gonad Muscle

Dorsal
disc

Ventral
disc

Heart
Stomach
Hinge
Anus
Coelom

Foot

Pseudocoelom Gonad Esophagus Nervering

Schematic structure of a lamp shell.   **Drawing after** SEMB-JOHANSSON **(1988)**

Above: Unidentified lamp shell from Micronesia.
Photo: P. Colin, Coral Reef Research Foundation

are probably the best-known of all lamp shells. They live in mud bottoms of subtropical and tropical seas. Overall, the distribution of lamp shells is only sparse in tropical seas, and they are more numerous in most colder seas.

At first sight lamp shells are reminiscent of mollusks as they have a bivalved shell. In fact, until the middle of last Century they were classified as such. The shells of the brachiopods are however orientated dorsal and ventral rather than the lateral shell-orientation found among the mollusks. The dorsal valve is usually smaller than the ventral, which is usually attached to the substratum. Like in the mollusks, the shell of the brachiopods protects the organisms against predators and heavy wave action. In most species the valves are convex shaped. In burying forms, like *Lingula* spp, the valves can be dorso-ventrally compressed. The shells can be equipped with teeth and spines. Colouration varies from orange and red to yellow and gray.

The body is surrounded by a mantle, which is located between the two valves. The shell contains the lophophore, which projects anteriorly as two arms, or brachia, from which the name "brachiopod" is derived. The lophophore effectively collect food particles suspended in the water. Most lamp shell species have separate sexes. Except for a few brooding species the gametes are shed into the water where the fertilization occurs at the time of spawning.

To the left: *Lingula reevi*, is a lamp shell, which has remained virtually unchanged since lamp shells dominated the oceans 225 million years ago. The animals bury in small holes in mud or sand bottom. When disturbed they can quickly retract in to their holes, and then only small slots remain visible on the substrate surface.
Photo from the Philippines:
P. Colin, Coral Reef Research
Foundation

Although some lamp shell species do occur in coral reef aquaria, this is generally a rare phenomenon, and indeed they are of little interest to the marine aquarium hobby. We are not aware of any information available about the suitability of lamp shells as aquarium animals. In order to survive in an aquarium, these organisms will no doubt require substantial amounts of supplementary feeding of very fine particulate food, which they remove by filtering the water.

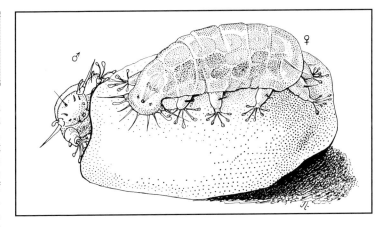

Water Bears which live among sand grains on beaches have developed telescopic legs with six toes each, and where the claws have been modified into suction discs. The drawing depicts *Batillipes noerrevangi*.

Drawing after Kristensen (1989)

Phylum Tardigrada – Water Bears

Water bears are strange creatures. They resemble microscopically small teddy bears! There are about 600 described species, which are all tiny and measure no more than 0.05 to 1.25 mm in length, which places them amongst the smallest multi-cellular organisms known. Moreover, it is assumed that the described species of water bears make up only a small fraction of the species expected to exist (KRISTENSEN, 1989). Many species are tied to a damp environment, most live in mosses found among vegetation on damp forest floors. There are also a number of species in freshwater sediments and in the marine environment, as for instance in coral sand. Some species are also found in extreme environments such as in very dry habitats among lichens in the Namibian Desert. Tardigrads can be rather colourful, possessing colours from yellow and red to olive green, however, because of their tiny size they are, of course, not particularly conspicuous.

Water bears are distributed worldwide and live at great ocea-nic depth, as well as in the highest mountain regions. KRISTENSEN (1989) reports in detail how numerous these organisms can be at certain localities. On the inland ice of Greenland small "micro aquaria" are formed, when some of the ice melts in the summer sun. Dust accumulates in such puddles, and KRISTENSEN found 285 water bears per gram of dust in such dust accumulations. If one takes into consideration that 80 % of Greenland is covered in ice, water bears must be the most common animals of Greenland. As if this was not already impressive enough, in Turkey 20.000 specimens were found in a gram of moss!

The phylogenetic relationships of the Tardigrada are disputed, since the day the German priest GOEZE in 1773 described for the first time the organism as a "small water bear". The Dane MÜLLER was the first in 1785, who placed bear animals into a zoological system. Today there are two groups of opinions. Europe's taxonomic specialist believe the Tardigrada to be related to the arthropods.

However, America's evolutionary taxonomists believe water bears to be closely related to rotifers

Water bears, like *Echiniscoides sigismundi* look like miniature teddy bears. No doubt, they are among the most extraordinary animals known to man, and their natural history is extremely interesting.

Scanning electron microscope photo:
R. M. Kristensen

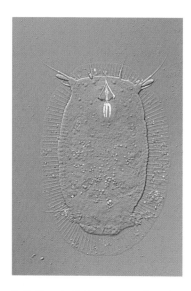 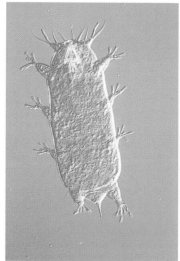 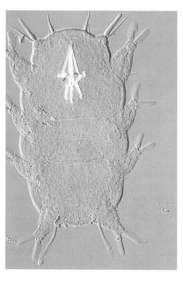

Left: Female *Raiarctus aureolatus* (magnification 800x). Centre: *Batillipes tubernatis* (magnification 400x). Right: Larvae of *Orzeliscus* sp. (magnification 800x).

Photos: R. M. Kristensen

and nematods (KRISTENSEN, 1989). Prof. R. M. Kristensen, Zoological Museum, Copenhagen has done much research on marine water bears. He is of the opinion that these have evolved during the early Cambrian Period (570 million years ago) in the marine environment, and had already separated from the ancestral arthropods at that time. One 535 million years old fossil form, found in Middle Cambrium lime stone layers of Siberia, looks very similar to marine tardigrads of today. Anyway, today the tardigrads are considered to be an independent phylum with 15 families in three orders.

General biology

The anatomy of the Tardigrada is rather complicated. Most species have four pairs of short legs without true segments, while the body carries distinct signs of segmentation. The external skin is covered by a layer of cuticle with chitin, which is regularly replaced throughout the life of the organism. The longevity lasts from three to thirty months. The exter-

nal cuticle can develop segment plates or be distinctly segmented. Freshwater tardigrads move slowly, supported against the substrate by 2 to 4 small claws at the end of each leg. Many marine species, which live between sand grains on a beach, have developed telescopic legs with six digits on each leg, whereby the claws have been modified into suction discs. An example of this is *Batillipes noerrevangi* which also occurs in Nordic oceanic waters.

Most water bears live on plant juice which they suck up. This is done by means of a sharp, pointed maxillary tube, which is pierced through the cell walls of algae and terrestrial plants. Few species are predators, which hunt for rotifers, nematods or other water bears. Moreover, there are three known marine species, which occurs as parasites on sea cucumbers, barnacles and bryozoans respectively (KRISTENSEN, 1989).

Tardigrada are so small, that respiration can take place via diffusion across the body cell walls. Respiratory organs, a heart and blood vessel system are absent; however, a large brain is present, as is a well-developed nerve cord, which extends along the ventral side of the animal.

Most Tardigrada have separate

sexes. Normally there are far more females than males, in fact, in some species males have not yet been found. Parthenogenesis has been observed in females of some species, whereby new individuals are developed without any fertilization having taken place. Usually Tardigrada reproduce by copulation and internal fertilization. Especially in marine species, the male can be seen courting the female prior to the actual mating, by touching the female with its long tactile bristles. Some females can store sperm cells in special pouches and then lay one to thirty eggs at once. In others, egg deposition takes place inside an old skin layer, which is cast off during the replacement ("moult"). In such case the male releases the sperm into the skin sack. The eggs have often a thick and attractive shell, which is rather resistant and can survive an extended period of unfavorable environmental conditions. On the other hand, the egg shell can also be thin, leading to an early hatching. The newly hatched larvae are identical to the adult, but may have fewer claws and digits, which then develop during subsequent growth, but there is no increase in the number of cells. Instead, each cells increases only

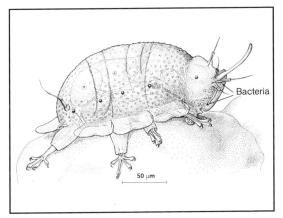

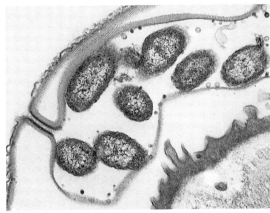

Left: *Wingstrandarctus corallinus* (drawing after Kristensen, 1984) and other water bears have pouches around the head and mouth, used to accommodate symbiotic bacteria. The bacteria supply nutrients to their host. Right: Cross-section of a pouch containing seven bacteria (SEM photo, magnification appr. 13.000x: R. M. Kristensen).

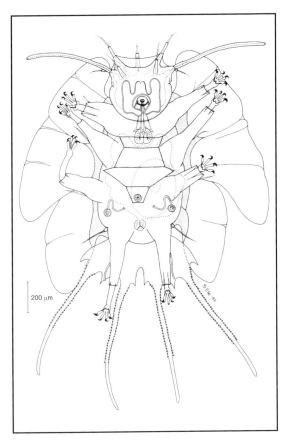

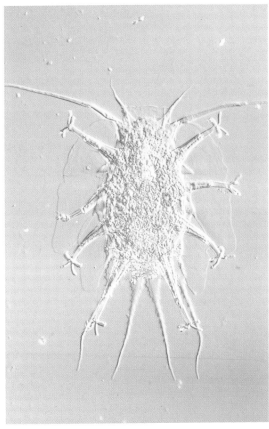

Female water bear found among coral sand at New Caledonia, scientifically described in 1965 as *Florarctus heimi*. Several years later it was discovered that the male is only about one-third the size of a female and looks totally different. Consequently, it is not surprising to learn that it was described as a new species, *F. cervinus*. Professor Kristensen found thousands of *F. heimi* in coral sand at Heron Island, Great Barrier Reef. He was able to observe that during copulation *F. cervinus* acted as the male, which confirmed that *F. cervinus* is actually the male of *F. heimi*. The drawing (S. Elle) and the photo (R. M. Kristensen) show females of *F. heimi*.

its volume; this is an extraordinary phenomenon, which may be related to the microscopically small size of the animals (SEMB-JOHANSSON, 1983).

One other peculiarity of terrestrial and tidal tardigrads is their extraordinary resistance against deteriorating environmental conditions. When these become extremely unfavorable, water bears can survive better than any other animal. The Italian SPALLANZANI stunned the scientific community when, in 1776, he insisted that he could totally desiccate water bears in a soil sample, and bring them back to life when he added some water to the sample. In his time, such claims were deemed unbelievable. However, today we know that SPALLANZANI was right. Tardigrada can go into a state of dormancy, (called "latent life" or cryptobiosis), which can last for years. This way, they can – for instance – survive periods of extreme drought. It is being reported that such dormancy under conditions of normal air- and room temperature can last for seven years, and in a deep-frozen condition even considerably longer. Dry tardigrads have been brought to the boiling point and cooled down to -227 °C in liquid Helium, they have been exposed to radioactive radiation, placed in a vacuum, and kept in dry ethanol or ether, and they still have survived (KRISTENSEN, 1989). Under extreme environmental conditions, water bears must somehow be able to put their metabolism on hold. Such period of dormancy is particularly typical for freshwater and terrestrial species, while most marine species can not tolerate any desiccation. One exception is *Echiniscoides sigismundi*, a species common in inter-tidal waters; it is considered to be one of the most resistant animals in nature. Other Tardigrada have developed different methods to survive extreme environmental conditions, such as *Halobiotus crispae*, which changes its appearance depending upon the season - a phenomenon generally referred to as cyclomorpho-

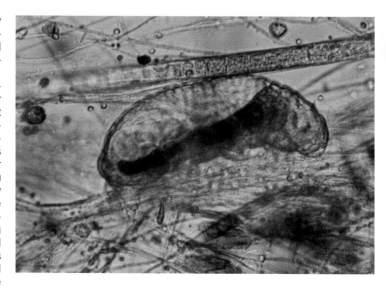

In our small experimental aquarium (NILSEN, 1999 and in press) we for the very first time in a coral reef aquarium discovered a population of water bears. Some of the animals were sampled and shipped to Professor R. M. Kristensen in Copenhagen for identification. The species is a new species of the genus *Archechniscus*.

sis and also found e.g. among Rotifers.

Systematics

The order Mesotardigrada contains a single species, which has only been found once in a warm sulfur spring in Japan (KRISTENSEN, 1989). The order Eutardigrada contains many species, which live in soil, on mosses or in freshwater, while the species of order Heterotardigrada are principally terrestrial and marine, however, there are only a few known freshwater forms. Coral sand contains numerous species from the order Heterotardigrada, and *Wingstrandarctus corallinus* is common in this type of habitat. This species has three "head sacs" located around the nervous system of the head. These structures also occur in other species, especially in genus *Florarctus*, where several species live frequently in coral sand. These head sacs contain symbiotic bacteria, cultured by the organisms themselves. For this, the head sacs contain a system of pores, which are usually close off by a mucus layer. This prevents substances getting out of the sacs. The bacteria produce small molecules, such as glucose and amino acids, which are passed on through these pores to the host. Most likely, then the bacteria provide food for their host in the form of assimilation products. Tardigrada can distort the shape of these sacs and so dispose of bacteria, as a form of regulating their numbers. Similar symbiotic relationships with bacteria are known from other animal groups, especially those that live under conditions of marginal food availability. Symbiotic relationships are known from deep sea bacteria which live in association with host animals without a digestive system; these include the giant pognophore *Riftia* sp., which lives symbiotically with sulfur-oxidizing bacteria. Tardigrada with symbiotic bacteria are found in algae-free coral sand, an environment with only a sparse food supply. It is therefore conceivable, that under these conditions the bacteria provide a crucial food supplement; not, because they are feeding on them, but because the bacteria actually provide food for their host (KRISTENSEN, 1984). KRISTENSEN & HIGGINS (1989) describe marine Tardigrada from south-eastern America. KRISTENSEN & STERRER (1986) report on the Tardigrada of Bermuda. Water bears are rather common in coral sand. In fact, 4 l of sand may reveal 10 to 15 different species.

Water Bears in a coral reef aquarium

Tardigrada can also be found among crushed coral and in the sand of a coral reef aquarium. In fact, one species was first scientifically described from an aquarium population, but many species could be present. Probably the only difficulty is finding them in an aquarium.

During 1997 and 1998 we operated a small experimental aquarium with the purpose of observing some of the chemical and biological changing taking place (NILSEN, 1999 and in press). The aquarium developed an interesting growth of algae and micro- and macro-organisms. When we used a microscope and searched samples of algae, we discovered a population of water bears. This was the very first time we observed this group of animals in a reef aquarium and it was most fascinating to observe the tiny animals crawling among the algae, clinging to the algae threads with their tiny claws. We sampled some of the animals and shipped them to Professor R. M. Kristensen in Copenhagen who could state that our population consisted of a new species of the genus *Archechniscus* (see photo on page 186 and drawing on page 197).

To our knowledge this is the very first time water bears have been observed in a home reef aquarium. The animals were most frequently sampled among diatoms and other algae growing on the windows of the aquarium, but could also be found among algae growing from the live rocks. When sampling on the bottom of the aquarium among gravle, the water bears were almost completely lacking. These observations definitely show how well suited a marine aquarium can be for studying the tiny marine life. To investigate the water bear fauna in an aquarium, one needs to wash bottom (substrate) samples through a 63 μm plankton net, and then check the filtered solution under a microscope. Similar samples can also be made of algal accumulation; however, actively searching for Tardigrada in an aquarium is a task best left to advanced and specially interested aquarists.

Phylum Arthropoda – "Joint-footed" Animals

The "joint-footed" animals represent the largest phylum in the Animal Kingdom. It contains more than 1 million known species, and there are at least just as many still undiscovered species. The majority of animals in this phylum belong into the class Insecta (insects), which makes up about 85 % of all known arthropod species. The systematic overview provided on page 188 shows the categories of arthropods up to class level. For aquarium purposes we are interested only in three groups of arthropods: two of these, the sea spiders of class Pycnogonida and the horseshoe crabs (horseshoe crabs) of class Merostoma, will be discussed in this chapter. The group of arthropods of greatest interest to aquarists, the crab- and shrimp-like animals of subphylum Crustacea, will be discussed in detail in chapter 6.

Arthropods are found in virtually any habitat. They are represented in large numbers in the sea, in freshwater as well as on land. The most important reason for the enormous success of this group is probably the skin skeleton, the cuticle, which affords very effective protection to the animals. At the same time, the cuticle necessitates a size limit for the terrestrial forms. Difficulties in oxygen supply via the cuticle-lined air ducts (tracheae) limits the size of insects to maximally about 20 cm - fortunately! Some of the aquatic forms reach significantly larger sizes, and there are some very few "giants" among the arthropods, e. g. the American Lobster and the Asian King Crab. The latter may actually reach a good 5 m between its legs!

"Joint-footed" animals developed probably about 500 to 600 million years ago during the Cambrian Period. They arose from segmented worm-like ancestors, which were reminiscent of today's bristle worms. Segmented worms (Annelida) and arthropods have many traits in common. Apart from the fact that both have segmented bodies, there are large similarities in the nervous system. There was (and still is) uncertainty whether the Arthropoda constitute a monophyletic or a polyphyletic assemblage, that is, whether the group arose from a common ancestor through a single line of development or via several (independent) lines of development. Some researchers believe that there have been three principal lines separately leading to Crustacea, Chelicerata and Uniramia respectively. In that case, the three groups must be considered as independent developmental series. Variable shape and position of the jaws and walking legs are (among other details) the basis for the polyphyletic theory. However, arthropods have many external and internal similarities in their structure, e. g. the compound eyes, the musculature, the genital organs, the sperm cells and the circulatory system. Mutual characteristics are far more common than those that differ. This is essentially the basis for the prevailing modern opinion, that the Arthropoda are a mono-phyletic group. The three groups: Crustacea, Chelicerata and Uniramia are normally given the status of subphyla, as shown below, although even this is already being debated.

Subphylum Chelicerata – Spiders

Pseudopallene cf. *dubia* at Southern Australia.   Photo: K. Kates

---

Systematic overview of "Joint-footed" Animals down to class level

Phylum Arthropoda - "Joint-footed" Animals
    Subphylum Uniramia
        Superclass Myriapoda
            Class Diplopoda
            Class Chilopoda
            Class Symphyla
            Class Plauropoda
        Superclass Hexapoda
            Class Insecta – Insects
            Class Protura
            Class Diplura
            Class Collembola
    Subphylum Chelicerata
        Class Arachnida – Spiders
        Class Pycnogonida – Sea Spiders*
        Class Merostomata – Horseshoe Crabs*
        Class Trilobita – Trilobites †
    Subphylum Crustacea – Crustaceans **

              *   dealt with in this chapter
              ** dealt with in chapter 6
              †   extinct

Spiders are often associated with horror movies, damp jungles and night mares – but certainly never with a coral reef. The fact, however, remains that there are also something like "spiders" under the sea, not only on coral reefs but also in the oceans worldwide. The name of this subphylum refers to the first pair of walking legs (chelicerae, sing. chelicera), which has become modified for food intake. These are outgrowth typical for spiders. The second pairs of walking legs has been modified into the so-called "pedipalps", which have different functions in the various classes of spiders. Sometimes, as for instance in the dreaded scorpions, the pedipalps can take on the shape of powerful pincers. We also encounter these characters again in the marine forms of the Chelicerata.

Sea spiders of class Pycnogonida are among the most beautiful and extraordinary creatures of the sea. Their systematic position is uncertain. They have probably become separated from the main line of arthropod development rather early during the evolutionary process. Although they are (externally) similar to actual spiders, they are only distantly related to them. Among the Chelicerata we also find the horseshoe crabs of class Merostomata. These are a relict group, having been rather numerous on earth about 300 to 400 million years ago, and they have retained their ancient structural features. Apart from these animals, there is also marine mites from order Acari in class Arachnida.

Class Pycnogonidae – Sea Spiders

There are about 1,200 species of sea spiders, which are exclusively marine. To call sea spiders "beautiful" animals may be a somewhat courageous statement! They are probably more unusual and fascinating. One of the largest known species was collected in the Antarctic at a depth of 7000 m. Once anyone has seen such a large sea spider (genus *Colossendeis*) with a span of 70 cm between the walking legs, will probably always remember sea spiders. However, most species are rather small, often less than 1 cm. Apart from their diminutive size they also possess good camouflage markings and colours, and so they are easily overlooked. On the other hand, some species living on coral reefs are very colourful and quite attractive. At least one species with bright colours has been shown to possess defensive alkaloids, and its bright colours are warning colours that signal: "Don't eat me, I am poisonous!" Unfortunately,

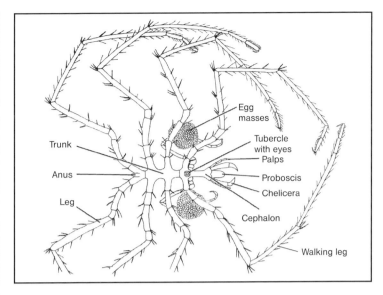

Schematic structure of sea spiders.   Drawing after Barnes (1980)

many sea spiders are predators. Sea spiders found on coral reefs are often parasites, feeding on the tissue of their host. They are commonly found on cnidarian animals such as corals and hydroids, but they can also live on other invertebrates (e. g. sponges). A few sea spiders are herbivores, and it is conceivable that they could be kept in a coral reef aquarium. In the sea, small sea spiders are common in the intertidal zone

They occur from the polar oceans to tropical seas, but they are rarely ever seen, primarily because of their excellent camouflage. From the 1200 known species about 350 occur in the Indo-Pacific (GOSLINER et al., 1996).

General biology

Sea spiders have a series of unique structural characters, which places them no doubt among the most extraordinary creatures in the sea. They have a short straight body, which is divided into segments, whereby parts of the body are substantially reduced. At the anterior end there is the head (cephalon) equipped with a proboscis with a mouth opening at the tip. This is used by the sea spiders to effectively suck tissue from the host or from any prey, e. g. from live coral polyps in a colony. At the top of the cephalon there is a tubercle which carries two pairs of eyes, one directed forward and the other pair directed towards the back of the animal. These may be useful features for being constantly on the look out in all directions for enemies, although nobody have ever tested the vision of sea spiders. Behind the head there are at least three thoracic segments and far

Nymphon sp. with egg masses attached to ovigerous legs.   Photo: E. Svensen

Left: *Parapallene obtusirostris* (photo: M Cufer). Right: *Propallene* sp. (photo: C. Bryce).

back a small posterior body segment, conventionally called the abdomen. Located on the head is, a pair of pincers or claws (chelicerae), a pair of antennae (palps) and a pair of modified legs (pregenital) which serves to carry the eggs ("ovigerous" legs). This may be found in males as well as in females. In the latter, however, they are often reduced in size, since males carry the eggs. In many species (e. g. families Nymphonidae and Colossendeidae) the ovigera function as cleaning devices. Their terminal four articles

roll around the legs and by the special spines on the concave face of the curvature they may rub off any detritus or small larva trying to settle on the leg surface. Moreover, there are four pairs of walking legs, which in sea spiders are often much longer than the body they support. The walking legs have always at least nine segments, with the last one being the terminal claw, which has (usually paired) auxiliary claws at its base. Sea spiders can move only slowly, often rather "clumsily". They are dependent

upon the claws at the end of their legs in order to get an adequate hold, and so remain securely attached to the host on which they live. Some of the large species have such long legs, that they can practically be used for swimming.

Sea spider have an open circulatory system, whereby the blood circulates freely within the body. This is accomplished with the aid of a heart and a blood vessel along the back of the animal, whereby the blood is being transported forward to an effluent opening immediately behind the eye tubercles on the back of the head segment. Many small pores which are regularly distributed over the entire body surface take care of the gas exchange as well as of excretion products. The small body can not hold all internal organs, so that parts of the very long intestine or the sex organs are located inside the walking legs.

Sea spiders have separate sexes. The female lays eggs via genital pores located on one or more of the walking legs. Mating and spawning in the wild has been observed in a few species. In some species the male hangs up-side-down on the ventral side of the female and fertilizes the eggs as soon as they are laid and then gathers them up with the legs attached to the pre-genital segment. In the common *Pycnogonum litorale* (see photo on page 193) the male mounts up-side-up on top of the female! The

Systematic overview of the class Pycnogonida

Class Pycnogonida
    Family Ammotheidae
        Achelia, Cilunculus, Nymphopsis, Ammothella
        Ascorhynchus
    Family Nymphonidae
        Nymphon, Nymphopsis
    Family Callipallenidae
        Callipallene, Parapallene, Propallene,
        Pseudopallene, Stylopallene
    Family Phoxichilididae
        Phoxichilidium, Anoplodactylus
    Family Endeidae
        Endeis
    Family Colossendeidae
        Colossendeis
    Family Pycnogonidae
        Pycnogonum

male excretes mucus from glands located dorsally on all of the eight femora, in order to hold the egg mass securely in place. Up to 1000 eggs can be held together and carried around in a single egg cluster. Within a particular season, males of tropical species can fertilize eggs several times and carry around several clusters of eggs. Atlantic and Mediterranean species just have two generations a year, while in Polar Regions the development of new generations may take many years. A planktonic larval stage is absent in sea spiders, which may be the reason why there are so many endemic species.

Systematics

On page 190 there is a systematic overview of class Pycnogonida. It is impossible within the limited space available, to discuss individual species of the various genera.

- Family Nymphonidae

The species within this family are all very similar. Usually they have a longish body and a rather wide and short proboscis. Either sex possesses the full complement of accessory - that are cheliphores, palps and ovigera - as well as at least four pairs of walking legs. Several swimming species have been observed. It appears that the species in the family are among the most active sea spiders. The genera are *Nymphon*, *Boreonymphon*, *Pentanymphon*, *Sexanymphon* and *Heternymphon*.

- Family Ammotheidae

The species in this family display age dimorphism in their structure. In comparison to juvenile specimens, adults have fewer digits on their palps, and there is a marked tendency for the body segments to fuse in members of this family. The proboscis is movable and curved. *Achelia* and *Nymphopsis* are common genera in this family. *Achelia* is rather numerous in shallow water.

A *Cilunculus-* or *Nymphopsis* species of family Ammotheidae seen here on an Indonesian coral reef.

Anoplodactylus evansi at Albany, Western Australia.   Photo: C. Bryce

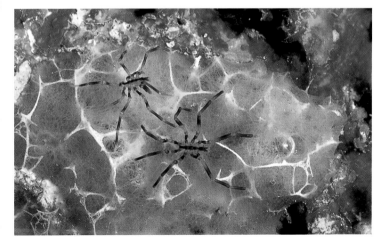

Two males of an *Anoplodactylus* species at Madang, Papua-New Guinea.
Photo: L. Newman and A. Flowers

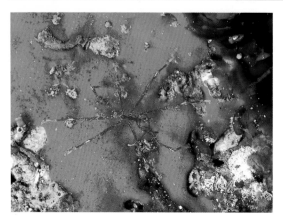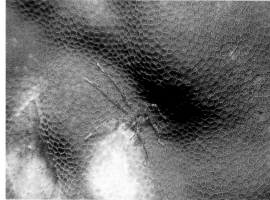

Left: Possibly a female *Endeis* species at Madang, Papua-New Guinea (photo: L. Newman and A. Flowers). Right: *Endeis* species at the Fiji Islands (photo: J. Cairns-Michael).

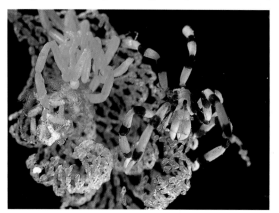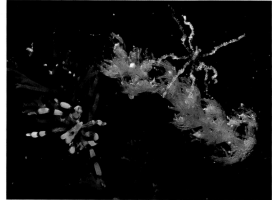

The left photo shows a *Pseudopallene* species (orange) and an adult *Stylopallene* species (with dark-coloured rings on appendages). This species has currently been shown to be chemically protected by alkaloids derived from its normal food, which is moss animals from the genus *Amathia* (Prof. F. KRAPP, pers. comm.). Right: Probably the same *Stylopallene* species, as well as an *Anoplodactylus* species.   Photos: C. Bryce

Left: Juvenile stage of *Pseudopallene* or *Stylopallene* (photo: K. Kates). Right: *Pseudopallene ambigua* (photo: M. Cufer).

- Family Phoxichilidiidae

In this family some of the species have a long proboscis and large "ovigerous" legs. The palps on the head are absent or reduced to mere stumps. *Anoplodactylus evansi* is a magnificently coloured species. Its base colour is made up of shades of orange. The legs are solid blue and narrow, yellow bands along the segments.

- Family Endeidae

All species in this family have an elegant, longish body and long, slender walking legs, which have a curved tarsus (penultimate segment of the legs) and strong claws on the prodopus (outermost segment of the legs). The body is equipped with many spines, which are larger in males than in females, and these are arranged in a species-specific pattern. Moreover, they have small tubercles, which are depressed at their ends. According to KING (1974) the function of these tubercles has not yet been determined. Small pores equipped with sensory hairs are located among the tubercles. In adult males the ovigerous legs are particular, while these are absent or just starting to grow in juveniles. The palps are absent in adults, while these are present in juveniles; again, this is a form of age dimorphism. The sole genus is *Endeis*.

- Family Callipallenidae

The family Callipallenidae is rather diverse in tropical seas, especially throughout the Indo-Australian Archipelago. In contrast to several other groups, both males and females have "egg-carriers". According to KING (1974) it is impossible to identify individuals down to species level, from immature European specimens. *Callipallene* is among the common genera in this family.

- Family Colossendeidae

The largest species in this family normally live in the deep sea, but in Polar Regions they can be found in rather shallow water. The family is characterized by the fact, that all species have a very slender body, a long proboscis and long pedipalps. The species also have extra pairs of walking legs (5 or 6 pairs in contrast to the normal 4 pairs) and have large chelipores shaped like ice tongs. while chelicerae are absent. The best known species is *Colossendeis colossea*, which is distributed in the Arctic Ocean and in parts of the Atlantic. According to GEORGE & GEORGE (1979) the extended legs of this species can measure up to 50 cm.

- Family Pycnogonidae

In the Pycnogonidae the body is short and stout, and the legs are only slightly longer than the body. Claws are absent from the tips of the walking legs in some species. *Pycnogonum littorale* is a common species along European shores, but the genus is also known to have several tropical species.

Pygnogonium litorale
Photo: E. Svensen

Class Merostomata – Horseshoe Crabs

Horseshoe crabs are a strange group of animals, and it is hard to imagine that they are suitable for aquarium keeping. Yet, they are periodically available in the aquarium trade. At first sight, these animals are reminiscent of crabs, but they are not at all closely related to them. In fact, they are placed together with the long-extinct sea scorpion in the order Xiphosura. These two animal groups once lived side-by-side with the famous Trilobites (also rather closely related to them), during a time period, which commenced about 500 million years ago. The fearsome-looking sea scorpions, which reached a size of up to 3 m, became extinct 300 million years ago, while the Trilobites disappeared about 230 million years ago. However, horseshoe crabs continued to live to this day, even though only in small numbers compared to their earlier abundance. Consequently, these animals are among the oldest living creatures on earth. As far as we know, their recent mode of life is the same as it was hundreds of million years ago, and their appearance has also remained remarkably unchanged.

A closer view reveals, that horseshoe crabs had a worldwide distribution 60 to 180 million years ago. There are many fossil sites of these animals, such as in Solnhofen, Germany (MIKKELSEN, 1982; WALKER & WARD, 1993). Today there are only four known species in three genera. Their distribution is restricted to eastern North America, the Caribbean and southern Asia, from India to Japan.

General biology

Horseshoe crabs have a protective dorsal shield or carapace, which forms a horseshoe-like shield over the anterior body and the anterior part of the hind (posterior) body. If one lifts up an horseshoe crab to look at its ventral side, the outline of the shield looks like the shape of a horseshoe, which has given rise to the popular name. The shield makes excellent protection against enemies. Horseshoe crabs themselves are by far not as dangerous as their appearance may suggest and under predator attack they have

Horseshoe Crabs, *Limulus polyphemus* at Florida.   Photo: M. Awai

mellae, very much like the leaves in a book. Therefore, they are also referred to as book gills, structures which are a unique adaptation in horseshoe crabs (SEMB-JO-HANSSON, 1988). When a horseshoe crab moves, water is being pushed through the book gills, which are heavily vascularised. A simple heart pumps blood through the body.

The Danish researcher Tom MIKKELSEN refers to horseshoe crabs in a jocular fashion as "invertebrate aristocrats". This is not only in reference to the long and impressive pedigree of these animals, but because the most interesting phenomenon is that their blood is actually coloured blue! The blue colour is due to copper-containing protein, called haemocyanine, which – just as the red, iron-containing haemoglobin in most other animals – is responsible for oxygen transport. In contrast to haemoglobin, which is carried in red blood cells, haemocyanine is never bound to cells. Instead, haemocyanine is present in giant molecules, which drift freely in the blood of horseshoe crabs. Incidentally, their blood is also used in the production of modern test procedures used to detect endotoxins from gram-negative bacterial infections in humans. For instance, it has proven to be highly effective in the early diagnosis of blood poisoning caused by gram-negative bacteria, urinary tract infec-

few options but to rely on the shield and crawl away into security. Like crustaceans, horseshoe crabs also have a fixed exoskeleton that has to be moulted in order for the animal to grow. To do this, the old shell splits around the front edge and the horseshoe crab crawls out. At first the new shell is very soft, but it soon hardens, and the animal is about one quarter larger than it was before the moult.

Outside of each of the two dorsal lateral ridges is a large oval, protruding compound eye, and to each side of the median ridge is one of two small median eyes. In addition, the horseshoe crabs are equipped with five light-sensitive organs, located underneath the shield.

A sword- or arrow-like tail protrudes from below the posterior part of the shield. The tail is about half as long as the total length of the animal. It is rigid, pointed and hollow. Depending upon the species, the upper side of the tail can either be smooth or saw-like serrated.

On the ventral surface of a horseshoe crab, well protected below the shield, are the chelicerae (just as in spiders, the first pair of legs has been modified into pincers or claws) and five pairs of walking legs. The legs of the posterior part of the body is substantially reduced. The first pair covers the remaining five pairs, which carry leafy gills. Each pair of gills, joined at their midline, is equipped with 150 leaf-like gill la-

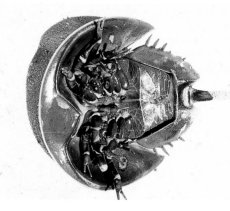

Horseshoe crab males (left) have extended chelicerae (pincers) and they are smaller than females (right), where the chelicerae are not extended.
Photo: J. Yaiullo

When mating, the male very firmly grasps the posterior part of the female's body. The female deposits the eggs in a sand pit, where the male subsequently fertilizes them.
Photo: J. Yaiullo

tions and meningitis. For further information about these test procedures and the respective research activities, the reader's attention is drawn to MIKKELSEN (1982). Additionally, horseshoe crabs have been used in eye research for more than 50 years. Their large eyes and large optic nerves make them easy to study, and scientist have learned a great deal even on how human eyes function from research done on horseshoe crab eyes.

Horseshoe crabs live on soft substrate bottoms and bury through the upper most layer of sediments. The shape of the shield is ideally adapted to such mode of life. Horseshoe crabs move forward by the aid of the five pairs of walking legs. Should an animal unfortunately land on its back, the tail is an important lever for returning to the correct position. Horseshoe crabs are primarily scavengers and feed mainly on dead clams, mussels and worms. Food material is picked up by the chelate appendages, and passed on to the serrated basis of the legs (gnathobases), where it is macerated. Thereafter it is moved anteriorly to the mouth. The powerful sixth pair of legs can effectively crush clams and mussels.

Horseshoe crabs breed during certain times of the year, when the adults gather together – sometimes in very large numbers – in the intertidal zone. Males grasp

the posterior body of females and hold on so tightly that it is nearly impossible to separate the animals, until the eggs are laid. Such persistent behavior is probably the reason why the Thai name for horseshoe crabs is "Maeng da", which actually means "pimp" (DAVIDSON, 1977).

The eggs are deposited in a pit about 15 cm deep, dug into the sand by the female. This is followed by fertilization of the eggs by the male. In *L. polyphemus* each clutch can contain up to 900 eggs, while those of the Asiatic species are smaller, usually only about 200 to 300 eggs. Each pair deposits eggs in many pits. Overall, a female of *L. polyphemus* can lay 100 clutches (90 000 eggs!) in one breeding season. The 1 cm long larvae will hatch in two to three weeks, and the young animals will reach sexual maturity in three years. The larvae of horseshoe crabs have particularly many similarities to trilobites, and for that reason they are also called "trilobite larvae".

It must also be noted, that the eggs of horseshoe crabs are considered to be delicacies in many parts of south-east Asia. For that purpose, the eggs are normally removed from the body cavity of collected females. But in some areas, such as in Vietnam, the eggs are also dug up from spawning pits. The typical preparation involves frying the eggs, sometimes also with some of the blue

blood mixed in. In Thailand and Vietnam the meat and gills of horseshoe crabs are also being used, for instance, as ingredients in soups and salads, together with pineapple, mango, grapefruit and/or cucumbers (DADVIDSON, 1976). Interesting enough, there are also published studies indicating that horseshoe crabs can be fatally toxic, at least during certain times of the year.

- Genus *Limulus*

The genus *Limulus* is monotypic with *Limulus polyphemus* as the only species. The Atlantic horseshoe crab lives on the bottom along the east coast of North America, from Nova Scotia in the north, southward to the Florida Keys. It is also found sporadically along the coastline of the Gulf of Mexico down to the Yucatan Peninsula. Probably *L. polyphemus* also occurs at Jamaica. MIKKELSEN (1982) claims to have proof, that this species has also crossed the Atlantic, and occurs off Senegal (Africa).

Atlantic horseshoe crabs have always been in abundance along the east coast of North America. The North American Indians were also familiar with them. The pointed tail was used, for instance, as a spear head. The dorsal shield served as food bowl and drink container and the flesh was eaten. The European settlers also became fascinated by horseshoe

Juvenile *Limulus polyphemus*, about 8 cm long, in an aquarium at Kölle Zoo, Stuttgart, Germany.

crabs. Reports about live animals, as well as their utilization by the Indians emerged during the 16th Century, following the discovery of Virginia by Sir Walter Raleigh.

Since horseshoe crabs were numerous along the beaches, settlers also started to use them soon. The helpless animals were gathered in large numbers to be used as fertilizer for the fields and as food for pigs and chickens. In the year 1856 more than 1.2 million horseshoe crabs were collected in Delaware Bay along a few kilometers length of beaches. The peak of horseshoe crab collecting occurred in 1930 with the slaughter of not less than 5 million animals along the American east coast (MIKKELSEN, 1982).

A fully grown female of *Limulus polyphemus* (in all horseshoe crab species the female grows substantially larger than the male) can reach a size of up to 90 cm and reach a weight of 4 kg. At such a size, the respective specimen must be rather old, may be up to 30 years.

- Genus *Tachypleus*

The genus *Tachypleus* occur in Asia. *T. gigas* can already be encountered in India (Bay of Ben-

gal). Its distribution extends eastward via Thailand, Indonesia up to the Philippines. Probably this species also occurs in the Torres Straits, between New Guinea and Australia. *T. tridentatus* is reported to occur in Vietnam, China, Taiwan, the Philippines and southern Japan.

Although the scientific name means exactly the opposite, *Tachypleus gigas* is practically the smaller of the two species. The maximum length is reported to be 50 cm, whereby the shield makes up about 30 cm. The largest females of *T. tridentatus* reach a total length of 75 cm.

- Genus *Carcinoscorpius*

Carcinoscorpius rotundicauda is the sole species in this genus. It occurs together with *Tachypleus gigas* along the east coast of India. It is also suspected to be on both sides of the Malayan Peninsula. This species has also been found in the Philippines, Borneo and the Sunda Islands. The shield diameter can be up to 25 cm. This species is clearly distinguishable from the other horseshoe crabs by the oval outer profile (cross-section) of the tail, which in the other three genera is always tri-

angular. *C. rotundicauda* often lives in the brackish water of river estuaries, e. g. Ganges Delta at Calcutta and Bangladesh, while the other three horseshoe crab species are purely marine species.

Aquarium care

Horseshoe crabs, especially *Limulus polyphemus* are relatively often available in the aquarium trade. However, these animals must be provided with a dedicated (separate) tank featuring a large open sandy bottom area! The recommended temperature for *L. polyphemus* is between 14 and 24 ° Celsius and for the Asian species between 20 and 26 ° Celsius.

They should be offered mussel- and shrimp meat as food. Since it can be sometimes difficult to persuade horseshoe crabs to feed, it may be advisable to lift the animals out of the water and actually place the food between the pincers (chelicerae). Horseshoe crabs are relatively insensitive to drying out and can actually feed in this position. There is evidence of horseshoe crabs living for as much as 10 to 15 years in aquaria.

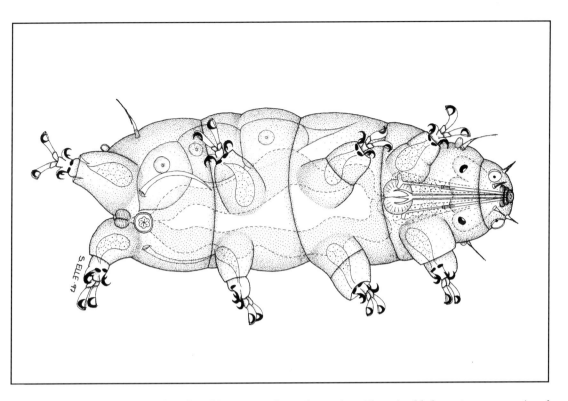

A detailed drawing of the water bear found in our experimental aquarium. The animal belongs to a new species of *Archechnischus*.   Drawing: S. Elle

Phoronids often live in association with Cerianthid anemones like here at 40 metres depth at the Commonwealth of Dominica.   Photo: L. Newman and A. Flowers

Chapter 6:

Crustaceans

The diversity of crustacean animals (phylum Arthropoda; subphylum Crustacea) is enormous (for a systematic review see page 201). There are at least 32,000 known species, and some scientists assume that there may be as many as 39,000 species. Crustaceans have invaded practically any moist habitat on earth, be it terrestrial, freshwater or marine. In other words, in contrast to the other arthropod subphyla, crustaceans are predominantly aquatic. The majority are marine forms, and representatives are found all over the world, from shallow inshore waters and inter-tidal regions down to oceanic depths of more than 9,000 metres. At the other end of the spectrum, there are a few species that spend most of their lives actually out of water.

Crustaceans play a significant

Crustaceans play a significant role on coral reefs – visually as well as ecologically. There are minuscule planktonic species, carried over the reef by currents, as well as large, conspicuous lobsters, prawns and crabs (order Decapoda), with spectacular colours aquarists dream about.
Top: Mysiids, ostracods and copepods are amply represented in this plankton sample taken at Heron Reef, Great Barrier Reef.   Photo: L. Newman and A. Flowers
Left: Hermit crabs (shown here is *Phimochirus operculatus*) are herbivorous and make excellent algae grazers in the aquarium.

Habitats: The banded cleaner shrimp, *Stenopus hispidus*, lives hidden in crevices and caves, as seen here at Bunaken, Indonesia (left; photo: R. Hansen), while the soldier crab, *Mictyris* sp., wanders across land at low tide, in search of food, as seen here at Bintan, Indonesia (right; photo: C. Bryce).

role in the coral reef environment, ecologically as well as visually. In fact, they are one of the truly dominant animal groups living on reefs. The large, generally well known and highly conspicuous species, such as crabs, shrimps, crayfish and lobsters occur on coral reefs in virtually countless numbers. Yet, even more numerous are the tiny macro- and microscopic species, such as copepods, ostracods, amphipods-mussel shrimps, etc., which are often overlooked or ignored by divers and aquarists alike. Because of the very small size and cryptic life of most of them, both their numbers and their influence on coral reef ecology tends to be largely underestimated.

Coral reefs provide a huge number of suitable habitats for crustacean animals. Myriads of these small organisms live in crevices, cracks and holes among and on corals and other invertebrate animals, as well as in coral rubble and in sand. Small cladocerans, ostracods, copepods, mysiids and the larvae of the larger crustaceans make up a significant component in the planktonic fauna in water on and around coral reefs. Beyond that, the interstitial fauna (for a detailed explanation of this term see pages 96-97) is also rich in crustaceans. A particularly large number of crustaceans living in the coral reef environment have established symbiotic relationships with other reef organisms, be it as parasites or as commensals. For instance, the close and intimate coexistence of many sea anemones and certain shrimps, between corals and some crabs or shrimps, as well as between copepods and fishes, is for many species obligatory.

Because of these numerous interrelationships of life on coral reefs, crustaceans, of course, also play an inevitable role in the coral reef aquarium. Therefore, it is imperative for aquarists to have a certain understanding and working knowledge of crustaceans. In this chapter we will discuss in detail all the major groups of crustaceans that are important for aquaria, in some way or another. Admittedly, some crustacean groups that are omitted, could certainly also be of casual interest to the dedicated marine aquarist. However, because of the inherent space limitations in a book like this, we could only select those species – available from within the vast army of crustace-

 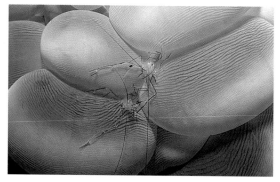

Co-existence: Pistol shrimps often live in association with gobies, such as this *Alpheus* sp. seen here together with *Cryptocentrus cinctus*, in an aquarium (left). The shrimp *Vir philippinensis* lives in pairs on a bubble coral (right; photo: J. Cairns-Michael).

Body shapes: The broken back shrimp, *Thor amboinensis* (left; photo: Scott W. Michael) looks like a typical shrimp or prawn, while the decorator crab, *Camposcia* sp. (right: photo: M. Cufer) at first sight bears little resemblance to a crustacean animal.

ans – which are likely to be acquired, kept and observed by the average aquarist.

In respect to size, shape, colour and mode of life, crustaceans are incredibly diverse. Their size range extends from the tiniest of parasites or planktonic organisms, to proverbial giants walking the ocean floors. For instance, whereas the Japanese Giant Spider Crab, *Macrocheira kaempferi* can reach a leg span of more than 5 m, there are many other crustaceans which do not even reach .25 mm as adult.

Systematics

Only a few groups of crustaceans have so far been scientifically investigated in detail. Most are known only insufficiently. Consequently, the systematics of crustaceans, compared to other groups of marine invertebrates, can only presented in a less than satisfactory fashion. Moreover, any systematic overview is being complicated further in that the enormous diversity of organisms requires a more comprehensive hierarchy of taxa for their classification, than is needed for other animal groups. Therefore, the systematic overviews provided to the right must all be considered

Systematic overview of the subphylum Crustacea

Based on BARNES (1980);
BRUSCA & BRUSCA (1990);
GEORGE & GEORGE (1979); GONZALEZ (1995); INGLE (1997) und
JONES & MORGAN (1994)

Class Remipedia *
Class Cephalocarida *
Class Branchiopoda
Class Maxillopoda – Jaw-footed Crustaceans
    Subclass Ostracoda - Mussel - or Seed Shrimps
    Subclass Mystacocarida *
    Subclass Copepoda - Oar-footed Crustaceans
Class Branchiura
Class Cirripedia - Barnacles
Class Malacostraca – Soft shelled Crustaceans
    Subclass Phyllocarida *
    Subclass Eumalacostraca
      Superorder Hoplocarida
        Order Stomatopoda - Mantis Shrimps
      Superorder Syncarida *
      Superorder Eucarida
        Order Euphausiacea *
        Order Amphionidacea *
        Order Decapoda - Ten-footed Crustaceans
        Order Peracarida
          Suborder Isopoda - Sea Lice, Pill Bugs
          Suborder Mictacea *
          Suborder Tanaidacea
          Suborder Amphipoda - Beach Fleas, Whale Lice
                         Skeleton Shrimps
          Suborder Mysidacea - Mysiids
          Suborder Lophogastrida *
          Suborder Cumacea *
          Suborder Spelaeogriphacea *
          Suborder Thermosbaenacea *

The Taxa marked with an asterisks (*) are not dealt with in this book.

Co-existence: Coral crabs have become specialized for a life on stony corals, such as this *Trapezia* sp. on a bush coral in an aquarium (left). Sea urchins also serve as hosts, in this case for *Zebrida adamsii* (right; photo: J. Cairns-Michael).

as substantially simplified presentations.

There is some debate in the scientific community as to whether Crustacea should be given the rank of phylum or merely be considered as a subphylum of Arthropoda. We have adopted the more conservative view, that the crustaceans represent a subphylum, and in doing so we have ignored the work by MANTON (1977). This is, however, triggered more by the need to take a specific position on this issue, rather than by any strong conviction. An abridged presentation of the phylum Arthropoda and some marine forms related to the Crustacea is given in Chapter 5, pp. 187.

For a long period of time it had been customary to divide crustaceans into two major groups, the classes Entomostraca and Mala-

costraca. The entomostracans included the majority of smaller species, like brine shrimp, water fleas, copepods and barnacles, whereas the malacostracans covered the larger, more familiar crustaceans, such as crabs, shrimps and lobsters. However, modern phylogenetic researchers have determined that the class Entomostraca is an artificial, polyphyletic assemblage, while Malacostraca is considered monophyletic and is thus to be maintained (MOORE, 1969; BRUSCA & BRUSCA, 1990). Those groups formerly combined in class Entomostraca, are nowadays placed in a variable number of separate classes. Our systematic overview, which is based on several sources (shown here on the 201), contains, in addition to Malacostraca, six further classes.

Co-existence: Copepods attached to the head of a hammer head shark.
Photo: Scott W. Michael

General biology

External body structure

All crustaceans are characterized by a rigid, calcium-carbonate based external skeleton (**exoskeleton**), formed over a multilayered epidermis (cuticle). The outermost layer (epicuticle) is thin and comparatively flexible, since only a small amount of calcium compounds is embedded in it. Furthermore, it does not contain any chitin ($C_{15}H_{26}O_{10}N_2$), which is usually the strengthening factor of the exoskeleton in most arthropods. The layer below (endocuticle) is composed of chitin, with the upper 2/3 heavily impregnated with calcium compounds, rendering maximum hardness and strength to the skeletal structure. The surface of this layer also contains the pigments, which provide the vast diversity of fascinating colours and patterns in crustaceans. The internal surface of the exoskeleton is covered by numerous projections, which provide a complicated framework for the attachment of muscles and internal organs. At the same time, they also lend additional rigidity to the body armour.

Furthermore, crustaceans are also characterized by a segmented body structure, although individual segments may be covered up by an external shell. Basically, the crustacean body is divided into two main (structural) sections:

• The **cephalothorax** (= 'head and chest' section) is the anterior and main part of the body, and towards its posterior region it is often partially covered by a carapace, while
• the **abdomen** (= 'belly', also called **pleon**) represents the posterior part of the body.

Beyond that, jointed body appendages that are connected to internal muscles, are also a typical feature. These appendages have variable functions in different groups of crustaceans, for instances, for locomotion, as sensors, for respiration and for food intake. Originally, the appendages were rather numerous and fundamentally identical in shape and function. In the course of their evolutionary development the crustaceans, just like other arthropods, have displayed a tendency towards appendage reduction, and so to transfer specific functions to particular appendages. In most groups of recent crustaceans the most conspicuous appendages are:

– **walking legs (pereiopods)**

This crab of family Xanthidae (seen here at the Maldive Islands) displays its large pincers (chelae) in a threatening posture.

– **swimming legs** or **swimmerets (pleopods)**
– two pairs of **antennae**
– **pincers (chelipeds** or **chelae)**

Furthermore, there are specialized appendages for transferring sperm, for brooding eggs and for food intake.

The ancestors of modern crustaceans were probably small, benthic swimming animals, a mode of life still found to this day in some groups. Propulsion while swimming is created by oar-like or propeller-like beating of various appendages. These appendages are normally covered with fringe-like bristles (setae), in order to increase the surface area for better propulsion. Yet, most current crustaceans move by walking. Although the swimming capability has been maintained (in most cases, at least), the appendages used for walking and digging have become larger, stronger and more robust.

The **head section (cephalon)** in all crustaceans is more or less uniformly constructed. Apart from eyes it also has five pairs of ap-

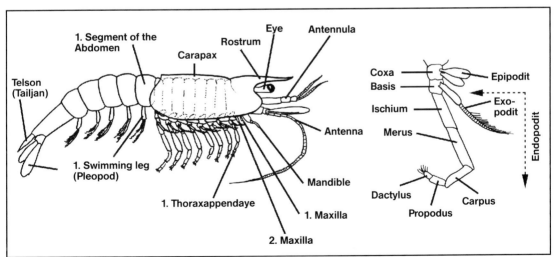

Schematic representation of a Crustacean from class Malacostraca: Side view (left) and structure of a thorax appendage (right). After BARNES (1980)

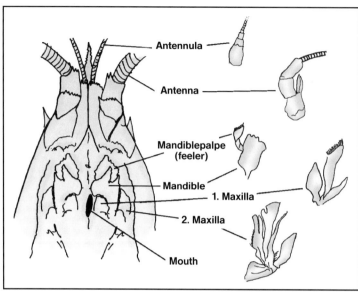

Schematic structure of head (ventral view) with its appendages.

pendages (see drawing page 203). The most anterior ones of these are two pairs of antennae, of which the first pair is called **antennules** (= small antennas) and the second pair is referred to as **antennae** (= antennas). The presence of two pairs of antennae is an identifying characteristic for crustaceans, distinguishing them from other arthropods. Frequently the antennas bear filamentous flagella, which are used for "tasting" the water.

The following three pairs of head appendages make up the chewing apparatus: a pair of **mandibles** (first pair of mouth appendages) and two pairs of **maxillae** (pairs of mouth appendages used as lower jaw). These mouth appendages are movable and function as grinding and chewing implements. The mouth has sturdy, immovable structures, referred to as **labrum** and **labium**. Behind these there are still three pairs of appendages, the **maxillipeds**, which facilitate holding and macerating food.

Walking legs (pereiopods) are appended to the **thorax** (or **pereion**, = chest), and are – as indicated by the name – used for walking and for defence. The first pair of chelae **(chelipeds)** are used for defence, for courtship and sometimes also for holding food. The following two pairs possess smaller chelae and are used for transporting food to the mouth parts, and for cleaning the body and its appendages. Below the abdomen are the **pleopods** (swimmerets or swimmer legs). The posterior end of the abdomen is formed by a tail that consists of the **uropods** (= tail feet) and a **telson** (tail fan). The telson is not actually a body appendage, since it is formed already during the early embryonic stage, prior to the development of body segmentation.

In most crustaceans one will find **gills (branchiae)** associated with the appendages. There are, however, some crustaceans where gas exchange is facilitated directly across the body surface. The gills of crustaceans vary considerably in shape and arrangement, however, the water current necessary for respiration is nearly always created by beating movements of some body appendages. Gas transport occurs either directly within the circulatory system (see page 209) in dissolved, or indirectly in pigment- (e.g. such as in haemoglobin or in hemocyanin) bound, form of oxygen.

In most of the more familiar crustaceans the head-chest section is covered by a **dorsal shield (carapace)** (see drawing on page 203). The lateral edges of this carapace are normally extended downward, often all the way to the ventral side. In ostracods the carapace even encloses the entire body, similar to the shell of a clam. Frequently, the carapace continues forward into a more or

Important sensory organs in crustaceans are located on the head, specifically the antenna serving as tactile organs and the compound eyes (as seen here in the dancing shrimp, *Rhynchocinetes durbanensis*).   Photo: T. Luther

Definitions of descriptive terms used in the anatomy of crustaceans

Abdomen
Segmented, posterior part of the body, between thorax and telson; with or without appended legs; sometimes also referred to as **pleon**.

Antennae, (singular: antenna)
Two pairs of tactile organs ("feelers"), protruding anteriorly from the head, between the eyes. Those of the first pair consist of a single branch (= uniramous), each possibly with two or three flagella. The feelers of the second pair have two branches (= biramous), where one branch is similar to a uniramous feeler, while the second branch is flattened and scale-like. The term "antennae" is actually only applicable to the second pair of tactile feelers, while the first pair should be referred to as **antennulae** (singular: antennula).

Caecum (plural: caeca)
Blind gut; terminal ending of an evagination of a tubular organ, e.g. appendix.

Carapace
Dorsal shield, the exoskeleton that covers the upper (dorsal) and lateral (ventro-lateral) part of the cephalothorax.

Cephalon
Head section, with antennules, antennae, eyes, mandibles and maxillae.

Cephalothorax
Head and "chest" section; cephalon and thorax fused into a single structural unit. Enclosed by the carapace above and along the sides (laterally), and by the sternum along the abdomen (ventrally).

Chela
Pincer with one movable finger (dactylus, also known as dactylopodite) and one fixed finger (propodus; also known as propodite). The dactylus is the fifth segment and the propodus the sixth segment of a pincer (chela; plural: chelae).

Chelipeds
Legs modified with pincers; one or more pairs of legs attached to the thorax in decapod crustaceans of order Decapoda. A cheliped has a chela (pincer) at its tip.

Endopodite
Inner branch of a biramous body attachment and also the main branch of an appendage, arising from its basis.

Epipodite
Branch-like outgrowth, originating from the basal region of a body appendage.

Exopodite
Outer branch of a biramous body appendage and also side branch of an appendage, arising from its basis.

Haemocyanine
Copper-containing respiratory pigment in the blood of crustacean animals of class Malacostraca.

Haemoglobin
Oxygen-carrying protein in the red blood cells of vertebrate animals, also present in the plasma of some crustaceans.

Labium
Paired, plate-like (laminar) part of the mouth, immediately behind the mandibles.

Continued on page 206

Continuation from page 205: Definitions of descriptive terms used in the anatomy of crustaceans

Labrum
Unpaired outgrowth directly in front of the mouth opening, which more or less cover it.

Mandible
Appendages of the fourth segment of the cephalon; forms a pair of jaws (first pair of mouth segments).

Maxillae
Paired appendages of fifth and sixth segment of cephalon. Both pairs of maxillae are part of the mouth apparatus (singular: maxilla).

Oesophagus
Anterior part of the food pathway between pharynx or mouth opening and stomach. Also spelled Esophagus.

Ommatidium
Single eye; cylindrical or prismoid component of a compound eye, which is covered by a transparent cornea.

Pereiopods
Walking legs; paired appendages of thorax, used for locomotion, food intake and defense.

Pleopods
Swimmerets or swimming legs; paired appendages of abdominal segments.

Rostrum
Extension of forehead; beak-like (anterior) projection from carapace.

Sternum
Thoracic shield; covers the ventral area of the cephalo-thorax.

Telson
Tail fan; attached posteriorly at the sixth (last) abdominal segment (but it is not a body segment).

Thorax
"Chest" section; central body area of crustacean animals.

---

less pointed projection, which is referred to as the **rostrum**. This structure can be extraordinarily well developed in some crustaceans.

Moulting

Crustaceans exhibit more or less continuous growth throughout their entire life, so that the exoskeleton eventually becomes too tight and too small. It must then be discarded and renewed. This process is known as "moulting". Prior to moulting the calcium compounds of the old exoskeleton are partially reabsorbed, while the new skeleton is already starting to develop underneath the old one. Once the old exoskeleton has been cast off by means of more or less elaborate contortions, the new one, which remains soft and pliable for a certain period of time, becomes visible. The cast-off exoskeleton is referred to as exuvia. Once the crustacean animals has liberated itself form its "prison", it can expand the new exoskeleton, before it starts to harden. At that stage crustaceans are virtually unprotected against predators, and so until the new exoskeleton has hardened they tend to seek out cover in crevices, cracks or other hiding places.

Moulting appears to be a traumatic event for crustaceans, so that the normal behaviour of the animals is suspended for a period of time prior to, during and after the moult. Often moulting takes place at night, when the risk of being discovered by predators is lowest. Just prior to the moult, water is being absorbed, so that the body swells up. A small crack appears in the membrane between cephalothorax and abdomen, through which the entire animal including its appendages and eyes carefully withdraws. The time required for the new exoskeleton to harden is very variable. In large decapod crustaceans (lobsters, crabs) this typically takes one to three days; however, in some species it can take a few weeks (INGLE, 1997). Only after the new exoskeleton has totally hardened, will the animal resume its normal behaviour.

Moulting is necessary for crustacean animals when the external skeleton has become too small. Like an acrobat, the animal has to twist through a tiny crack between thorax and abdomen, such as this candy-striped cleaner shrimp, *Lysmata californica* is seen doing here.   Photos: Scott W. Michael

Many hermit crabs, like this *Calcinus laevimanus*, are herbivorous and as such they are very useful in an aquarium as algae grazers.

The porcelain crab, *Petrolisthes maculatus*, is a suspension feeder and collects plankton, by waving its thoracic appendages – equipped with brushes – through the water.

Mantis shrimps, like this *Odontodactylus scyllarus*, are carnivorous and aggressive predators, even in an aquarium. Photo: Scott W. Michael

Feeding

The spectrum of food requirements and food preferences among the crustaceans is wide. There are carnivores (meat eaters), herbivores (plant eaters) and filter feeders (feeding on suspended particles and organisms). Many are also more or less omnivores, feeding (non-preferentially) on animal- and plant material. Typically, certain appendages of the cephalothorax are adapted for capturing prey or picking up food. The maxillae and mandibles are being used for holding, macerating and passing the food to the mouth. In practically every order there are also suspension feeders, which filter their food (plankton or detritus) out from the surrounding water. These species use "setae", which are elaborate bristle like structures (see the drawing on page 209), instead of simple cilia, as is common in other filter feeding organisms. This type of feeding can easily be observed in an aquarium, in anemone crabs of genus Petrolisthes, or better yet in barnacles (class Cirripedia). Fine-bristled setae on certain body appendages function as a filtering screen and retain edible particles. The required water current is created either by whipping motions of the filtration appendages as such, or by appendages specifically modified for that purpose. The particles retained in these filter setae are then raked out by comb-like or broom-like setae, to be passed on to the mouth by yet other appendages or sometimes via a ventral feeding groove.

The mouth is in a ventral position, at the anterior part of the crustacean animal, and the digestive tract is nearly always straight. The foregut is developed as a tubular esophagus or as a refined gastric mill (triturating stomach). The midgut varies in size, however, nearly always one or several pairs of caeca are present. One pair of caeca is normally modified into large digestive glands, producing digestive juices. These are made-up of ducts and blind,

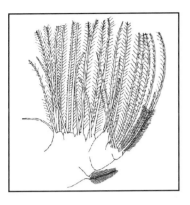

Filter brush of copepods (*Calanus* sp.). Drawing after BARNES (1980)

secretions-producing tubules. The absorption of nutrients takes places across the midgut walls, as well as inside the tubules of the digestive gland. The hindgut, which serves as viscera, forms the terminal section of the digestive tract.

Circulatory- and nervous systems

The circulatory system is developed rather variably in crustaceans. In some of the smaller and more primitive forms it is confined to a tiny, unbranched artery, while in the more advanced forms it may consist of a network of heavily branched arteries, which lead into various parts of the body. Most groups of crustaceans also have some type of heart. This can vary in shape from a long, simple tube to a spherical vesicle. The blood contains amoebocytes, which facilitate phagocytosis as well as supporting blood clotting in case of injuries.

The nervous system consists of a double chain of ganglia. A ganglion is an accumulation of nerve cell (neuron) bodies (web-like aggregations of nerve fibre endings and nerve cells). Primitively, ganglia were present in each body segment, however, in due course development became concentrated on a few large ganglia. This tendency towards concentration and fusion of ganglia is common in all Arthropoda.

Sensory organs

The sensory organs in crustaceans are:

– the eyes,
– the statocysts (balancing organs)
– proprioceptors (elements for the transfer of perceptions from within the own body)
– tactile receptors (nerve fibre endings or specialized cells conveying touch perceptions or sense of touch)
– chemoreceptors (sensory cells or sensory organs for the perception of chemical stimuli)

There are two types of eyes: **median eyes** and **compound eyes**. The median eye is a characteristic of nauplii larvae (see page 210). In adult crustaceans it has either regressed or it can still be present. Most likely, this very simple eye, consisting of only three or four small ocelli (eye spots), functions to determine the direction of incoming light, and so to facilitate the orientation towards top and bottom within the environment.

The compound eyes, present in most adult crustaceans as a pair, represent a much more advanced development than median eyes. Normally, one compound eye is located on each side of the head. This physical separation of the eyes permits stereoscopic and wide-angle vision, whereby each eye covers a large angle (in some species in excess of 180 degrees). The term "compound eye" (also known as a facet eye) has been derived from its structure. It consists of many long, cylindrical individual eyes (ommatidia), and when viewed from above, its surface looks like as if it is composed of many facets (small angular surfaces). Each ommatidium is covered on its outside end by a translucent cornea which functions as a lens. The number of ommatidia various considerably. In the more primitive crustaceans a compound eye may consist of 20 to 30 ommatidia, while in the advanced forms there can be several thousand ommatidia.

The image of the environment, composed by a compound eye, can be compared roughly to the image produced on a TV screen, where the picture is made up of several dots of light. The compound eye image is composed of a mosaic of smaller elements, which are assembled into a total picture. When compared to the image created by the highly deve-

Crustaceans like this ghost shrimp, *Stenopus pyrsonotus* (aquarium photo) are well equipped with sensory organs.

The stalked compound eyes of mantis shrimp are the most advanced eyes found in any crustaceans. They play an important role in prey capture. These eyes are not only used for detecting moving objects, but also to determine the correct distance to the prey and the most opportune moment for actually seizing the prey.

Photo: Scott W. Michael

loped mammalian eye, the compound image is very crude and of a rather low resolution. However, resolution improves with an increasing number of ommatidia. Consequently, some of the decapod crustaceans (shrimp, lobsters, crabs) have a rather good visual acuity. There are also indications that some of them have at least marginal colour vision (BARNES, 1980).

Reproduction

Most crustaceans have separate sexes, but hermaphrodism does occur in some groups. Some species are protandrous hermaphrodites, whereby, in the early part of their lives they function as males, and later on change in to fertile females. This type of hermaphrodism has been particularly well documented in certain shrimp species. In some cleaner shrimps like *Lysmata amboinensis* and *L. grabhami* (Decapoda: Hippolytidae), there are even simultaneous protandrous hermaphrodites, i.e. initially they functionally as males, and then later simultaneously as males and females (WIRTZ, 1996).

But this type of hermaphrodism is not common among crustaceans, and has not yet been reported from other decapod crustaceans.

The gonads are usually pairs of elongated organs, located dorsally in the thoracic section, or in the abdomen or in both. Egg- and sperm ducts are typically simple tubes, arranged in pairs with an opening to the outside either at the base of one of the pairs of appendages or at the underside of one of the abdominal plates (sternites). This varies considerably from one group of crustaceans to the next.

As a rule, fertilization takes place through copulation. In most species, the male posses specifically adapted appendages with which it can grasp and hold a female. Reproduction is closely associated with moulting. The female of many species are receptive to mating only when the

Juvenile harlequin shrimp, *Hymenocera picta*, bred at the Waikiki Aquarium (Honolulu, Hawaii), which has settled on a sea star.

Photo: A. Nelson, Waikiki Aquarium

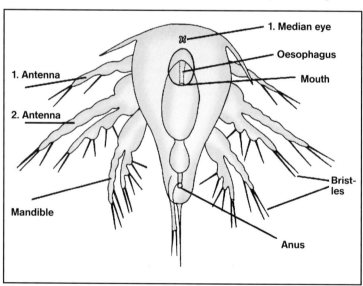

Nauplius larva of a barnacle (*Balanus* sp., class Cirripedia).

Drawing after FREEMAN & BRACEGIRDLE (1971)

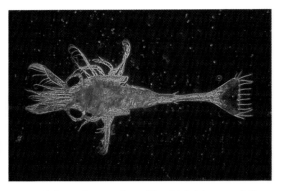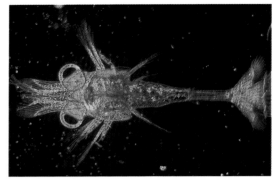

Young (left) and somewhat older (right) larvae of the rock pool shrimp *Palaemon elegans*. During the larval stage, there are significant changes in the shape of the larvae, following each moult. Photos: H. Schöne

exoskeleton is soft. Often females produce aromatic substances (pheromones) in conjunction with their moulting process, which are attractive to males. The males of some species carry a female around with them for some time prior to it moulting, to make sure that she is available for breeding at the right time (INGLE, 1997).

Most crustaceans are brooders, but incubation periods for the eggs can vary substantially between individual species. The eggs may be attached to particular appendages, accommodated in a brood chamber or stored in a sac, formed at the time the eggs are discharged. But there are also some species which simply disperse their eggs into the open water.

In the primitive crustaceans, a free-swimming planktonic larva, referred to as a **nauplius**, always hatches from the egg. The nauplius larvae are characteristic for many marine species, as well as for some freshwater forms. Among the more advanced crustaceans, such as those in order Decapoda, the eggs give rise to advanced larvae, which have already several body segments as well as body appendages. In cases like that, there will still be a nauplius stage within the egg.

A nauplius larva has three pairs of appendages: a single-branch (uniramous) first pair of antennas, a two-branched (biramous) second pair of antennas, and two-branched (biramous) mandibles. At that stage, the mandibles have not yet attained the hardness required in most crustaceans for chewing. Normally, the nauplius has a simple eye, located on top of the head (median position), often referred to as the "nauplius eye", or as median eye.

Through successive moults, new segments are added, sequentially proceeding from the anterior part towards the tail.

Each segment receives a pair of two-branched appendages. The first appendages to appear, successive to the three pairs already mentioned (antennas and mandibles; see above), are the first maxillae, followed by the second maxillae. The subsequent development of larval stages depends on the group of crustaceans involved. In higher developed forms of class Malacostraca, one speaks of a **zoea** larva, once the first eight pairs of body appendages are no longer enclosed by the carapace. In barnacles (class Cirripedia), the second larval stage is referred to as a **cypris** larva, and in the oar-footed crustaceans of subclass Copepoda it is a **copepodid** larva.

For further information about the biology of Crustacea the reader is advised to see BARNES (1980), BRUSCA & BRUSCA (1990), MANTON (1977) and McLAUGHLIN (1980).

Class Branchiopoda -
Fairy Shrimps, Shield Shrimps, Water Fleas

The members of class Branchiopoda are small and their occurrence is almost entirely restricted to freshwater and inland salt lakes. There are only a few marine water fleas (order Cladocera), including some which make up part of coral reef plankton, but they are extremely difficult to find and by no means evident to the casual observer. Actually, the branchiopods are really only of academic interest to coral reef aquarists; however, since they play a significant role as food organisms in all areas of aquarium- and aquaculture husbandry they are briefly discussed here within that context. Without doubt, brine shrimp of genus *Artemia* (order Anostraca, fairy shrimps) are among the most important food organisms for marine (and freshwater) aquarists.

Brine shrimps (*Artemia*) live in saline water bodies, including lakes, ponds, and rain pools, and are adapted to extremely highly salinities, for instance, as those prevailing in the Great Salt Lake (Utah, USA) and Lake Mono (California, USA). In both of these "salt lakes" *Artemia* species are the only macro-invertebrates present. All fairy shrimps are characterized by an elongated cephalo-

Adult male (left) and adult female (right) of brine shrimp (genus *Artemia*). In males the antennae are developed into exceptionally large claspers, with ...

... which it clasps the female during copulation.

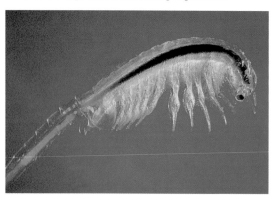
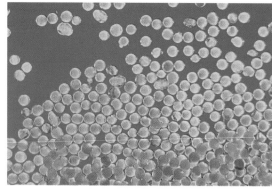

Lateral view of female (left) revealing the brood sacs on the posterior abdomen, where nauplii hatch from eggs (at water densities of up to 1.129 g/cm^3). From a density of 1.130 g/cm^3 on up, brine shrimp produces only encysted eggs. Empty (hatched) *Artemia* egg shells can pose a problem in the aquarium. For some time now the aquarium trade has been supplying chemically "shelled" eggs (as shown right). **Six photos: H. Linke**

Lake Mono, one of the salt lakes in the United States, where Artemia are being collected and processed for the aquarium trade. Photo: H. J. Mayland

thorax, consisting of 20 or more segments. The anterior 11 to 19 segments carry appendages. Since a carapace is absent (as indicated by the name of the order Anostraca *an*, Greek = without, and *ostrakon*, Greek = shell), all segments are clearly visible.

Artemia swim up-side-down; i.e. on their "back". The antennules are small and resemble those of insects. In mature males the second antennae are modified as graspers with which they cling to the female and hold her during copulation. In females the antennae are not modified. Following the second pair of maxillae the appendages are leaf-like and

used for swimming as well as for filtering food particles (microplankton) from the water.

Artemia are perfectly adapted to a life in temporary water bodies. Their eggs are enclosed by a shell made of scleroproteins, which makes them resistant against desiccation. Following rain fall, the nauplii hatch from the eggs in a very short period of time. They develop and grow quickly, so that a population tends to exhibit explosive growth. This is also a reason why *Artemia* have conquered the aquarium hobby and aquaculture worldwide.

The eggs are easy to transport, to store and to hatch. These fac-

tors assure a stable supply of live food, either as brine shrimp nauplii or as adults. *Artemia* are excellent food for a marine aquarium, since they can survive in seawater for a long time. WOLFRUM (1996) reports on long-term culturing of *Artemia*.

The order Cladocera also contains a number of interesting feeder animals, such as various water fleas of genera *Daphnia* and *Moina*. These are also important food organisms for the aquarium hobby; however, these are pure freshwater organisms that do not survive for long in a marine aquarium.

Class Maxillopoda - Jaw-footed Crustaceans

Systematically, the *jaw-footed* crustaceans represent are somewhat complicated group, since there is considerable disagreement within the ranks of taxonomists about the higher taxa and their respective hierarchal position. Those three subclasses (Ostracoda, Mystacocarida, and Copepoda) selected by us for

discussion, are in part given separate class status by some systematists. On the other hand, one may also encounter the view that the class Maxillopoda is much more extensive, and actually include Branchiura and Cirripedia as mere subclasses. We, however, have decided to treat the latter as separate, indepen-

dent classes. Overall, it is therefore difficult to provide an exact delineation of class Maxillopoda; however, the two subclasses Ostracoda (mussel- or seed shrimps) and the Copepoda (oarfooted crustaceans) are clearly definable, and so these are discussed below.

Subclass Ostracoda - Mussel- or Seed Shrimps

For the casual observer the mussel shrimps of subclass Ostracoda look indeed like small clams or mussels. The body is totally enclosed by a bivalve (two-shelled) carapace. Each shell half (valve) is round or elliptical, and impregnated with calcium carbonate deposits in the outer wall. Along the dorsal side there is a distinct hinge line, formed by a non-calcified strip of cuticle. Furthermore, the shell halves can be opened and closed by a cluster of transverse adductor muscle fibres (closing muscle). These muscle fibres are attached near the center of each valve. In some species the shell halves are also locked together by hinge teeth. Altogether, this construction is almost identical with that found in class Bivalvia (phylum Mollusca).

Mussel shrimps have a worldwide distribution. They live in freshwater as well as in the sea and practically in all climatic zones. More than 2,000 species have so far been described. The classification of individual species is usually based upon characteristics of the carapace valves, as for instance their shape, colouration and texture. In spite of their cryptic mode of life and small size, mussel shrimps are very common and have been so for millions of years. Fossil records date back about 500 million years. Oil bearing strata often contain an abundance of ostracod fossils, and therefore they are often considered as indicator organisms in the search for new oil fields.

Today's mussel shrimps are tiny organisms, with a normal size range of about 0.3 mm to 5 mm. Only a few reach larger sizes, such as the pelagic (living in open water) deep sea species *Gigantocypris mulleri*, with a maximum size of up to 2.5 cm. Colouration of the Ostracoda is highly variable. More often than not these organisms are pale and translucent, but any shade of grey, brown, green, red and yellow may be found.

Since body and legs are enclosed in a bivalve carapace, propulsion can be facilitated only by the sole, long appendages, which protrude to the outside: the antennae. The antennae (sometimes also the antennules) have been modified into implements for swimming, crawling or digging. In free-swimming ostracods both pairs of antennae are covered with long setae, in burrowing species the antennules are blunt and covered by short spines.

It is fascinating that mussel shrimps were the first crustacean animals, from which bioluminescence were described. "Bioluminescence" means, that an animal is capable of producing light by biological means. *Gigantocypris mulleri*, already mentioned above, is among those mussel shrimps which have been reported to produce bioluminescence (MARSHALL, 1979). In addition, there are three or four other marine genera, from which bioluminescence is also known. A cloud of bluish light is created from a secretion produced by a gland located in the labrum. When this secretion is ejected into the water, there is an instantaneous development of light flashes, which shine for one or two seconds. The exact significance of this light is uncertain, but it is assumed it may serve to confuse or frighten off predators.

For sexual reproduction, copulation does normally take place, during which the female is clasped by the male's antennae or first pair of legs. Many species can be seen swarming in huge numbers during this reproductive ritual. Parthenogenesis also occurs, however, principally in freshwater ostracods, whereby the eggs develop successfully without having been fertilized by a male - a process also known to us from water fleas. Normally the eggs are released into the open water, or at the bottom substrate

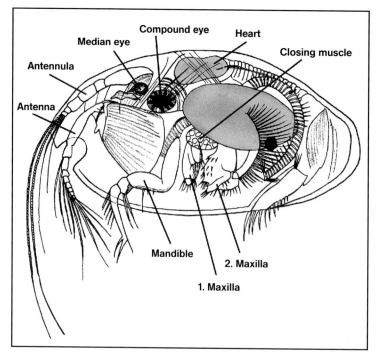

General body structure of a mussel shrimp (Ostracoda).

Drawing after BARNES (1980)

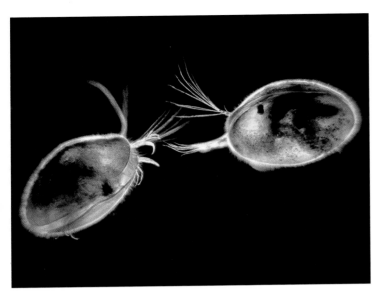

Mussel shrimps.　　　　　　　　　　　Photo: R. Brons

* benthic species of genera *Cyclolebris*, *Cylindrolebris*, *Cypridina*, *Cypridinotes*, *Euphilomedes*, *Philomedes*, *Rutiderma*, and *Synasterope*.

Aquarists will hardly ever see ostracods in their tanks without specifically searching for them. But there is a good chance to find some by using either powerful binoculars or a microscope and looking through strained detritus or a carefully scraped off algae sample. It is highly unlikely that mussel shrimps are totally absent from any healthy coral reef aquarium, since they will nearly always be introduced into an aquarium attached to live rocks, corals or algae. Many species thrive under aquarium conditions and readily reproduce over several generations. There is virtually no reason to assume that ostracods will ever become a nuisance in an aquarium. In fact, quite to the contrary; many mussel shrimps play a positive role within the community of waste-reducing organisms. Yet, one can never totally exclude the possibility that there may be some ostracod species, which can harm those animals we wish to keep in our coral reef aquarium. We have, however, never encountered any reports indicating so.

or attached to vegetation or algae. A few species are egg brooders. The specialised nauplii emerging from the eggs have already a bivalve carapace, just like adult mussel shrimps.

In a coral reef environment ostracods are predominantly benthic (living on the bottom), but there are also a few planktonic species. In addition, there are also species that live as commensal organisms on echinoderms (spiny-skinned animals, phylum Echinodermata). The benthic forms swim only occasionally, or dart over or dig through the detritus layer on the bottom. Most mussel shrimps on a coral reef are suspension feeders or detritus feeders. From a few species it is known that they are carnivorous (feed on meat), some are scavengers and others live as predators. A number of species are also known to be herbivorous (plant eaters).

Mussel shrimp which inhabit coral reefs include the following:

* planktonic species of genera *Asterope*, *Cypridina*, *Euconchoe-*

Subclass Copepoda - Oar-footed Crustaceans

With more than 9,000 known species and certainly thousands more yet to be described, subclass Copepoda is a very important taxon in the class Crustacea. Not only in terms of species numbers but also in their overall abundance, copepods are among the most significant animals on earth. Although there are many freshwater species and even a few which live in mosses or even soil water films, the vast majority of copepods are marine. Copepods are best known as planktonic grazers of diatoms and other phytoplankton, but there are also many benthic species, which use their head- and jaw appendages to scrape food off rocks. Others are even predators and very many live as parasites. The most advanced copepod parasites are barely recognizable as crustacean animals, and only their characteristic larvae reveal the systematic relationship.

Since diatoms and dinoflagellates are among the leading primary producers in the sea and as such represent a biomass which is just about the same as that of

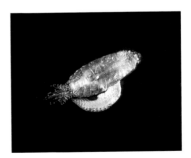

A copepod of the order Calanoida carrying a parasitic isopod of the suborder Isopoda.
Photo: L. Newman and A. Flowers

Many copepods live as parasites or commensals on other animals, such as those here on the head of a moray.

Photo: K. Kates

all terrestrial plants, the copepods are equally abundant. In fact, copepods make up the principal component of zooplankton at all oceanic depths. In a study from around Bermuda, DEEVY & BROOKS (1977) found that the relative proportion of copepods in the total zooplankton catch ranged from 73.5 % at the surface, to 91 % at depths of 1,500 m to 2,000 m. Marine copepods exist in such enormous numbers, that they are the principal connecting link between phytoplankton and the higher trophic levels in the food chain. Moreover, they provide most of the food for many adult fishes as well as for newly hatched juveniles, and for many invertebrates. Therefore, it is of paramount importance for aquarists to be informed about copepods and be able to identify them as such, when confronted by them.

The majority of copepods are rather small in size. The total length of free-living forms ranges from 0.3 to 17 mm. Parasitic species are generally larger. A species of the genus *Penella*, (a so-

called "anchor worm" that live as a parasite on fishes and whales) can reach an astonishing length of 32 cm! Copepods are highly diverse in body shapes, even when ignoring the extreme parasitic forms. Typically their head is fused with the first, and sometimes also the second, (of the altogether six) thoracic segment. The abdomen consists of five segments, all without appendages. The five pairs of biramous pereiopods of the thorax function as swimming legs (swimmerets). The anal segment carries two tail branches (caudal rami), which can be spectacularly developed in some species. Compound eyes are absent in subclass Copepoda. Most free-living species have a single dorsal median eye, while eyes are totally absent in parasitic species.

When free-living copepods move about in water, they row with their swimming legs in an alternate rhythm, the obvious reason for the scientific name "Copepoda" (*kope* or *kopos*, Greek = the beating and *pous*, genetive *podos*, Greek = foot), and the popu-

lar name as "oar-footed" crustaceans. The main propulsion organs are, however, the two branches of the antennae, which can also execute rowing or paddling movements. The long antennules can be used for rapid escape movements; when startled they pull the antennules violently backward, so that the copepod virtually is flung about in a totally random fashion. This somehow resembles a form of leaping about, a curious "popping" motion that is easily observable in copepod cultures. Yet, the main function of the antennules is to exert parachute-like braking action and so to prevent the organism from sinking. In addition, they also serves as supporting sensory organs when searching for food.

Bottom dwelling copepods crawl over the substrate or dig into it, or they live interstitially among sand grains. The thoracic appendages are used for crawling, sometimes supported by wriggling movements of the body.

The suspension feeders among copepods filter their food

from the surrounding water with the aid of long, fine bristles on their maxillipeds or – if the phytoplanktonic cells are large enough – grasp them one by one. It is assumed that dinoflagellates make up most of the food used by filter-feeding copepods, but also included in their diet are radiolarians, ciliates, foraminiferans, diatoms and various flagellates, as well as bacteria. Some species are heavily dependent upon detritus and other dead organic matter as food sources. Carnivorous species often feed on mussel shrimps (Ostracoda), arrow worms (Chaetognatha), euphausiids, amphipods, as well as on larvae of decapod crustaceans and fishes. Beyond that, there are also omnivorous copepods, which utilise more or less the entire food spectrum mentioned above (HARDING, 1974).

Copepods have separate sexes. There are either one or two ovaries present, while free-living species normally have only one testicle. Copepods are one of very few groups of Entomostraca, which produce spermatophores (sperm packages enclosed in a capsule); which – on the other hand – is common among the "ten-footed" crustaceans (lobsters, prawns, etc.) of order Decapoda. During copulation, the male embraces the female with its antennules, and inserts a spermatophore into her gonopore, with the aid of one of his thoracic appendages. The spermatophore is adhered to the receptacle by means of a special adhesive cement.

Copepod females can carry their eggs for a long period of time, before they are fertilized and deposited. Most species are egg brooder, whereby the extruded eggs are stored in one or two **ovisacs**, brood sacs that are produced during the egg laying process by an oviduct secretion. The ovisacs remain attached to the female's genital segment until the larvae start to emerge from the eggs. Each egg sac can store from a few to as many as 100 eggs. There are also some copepods that release their eggs into

Copepod of the order Calanoida.   Photo: R. Brons

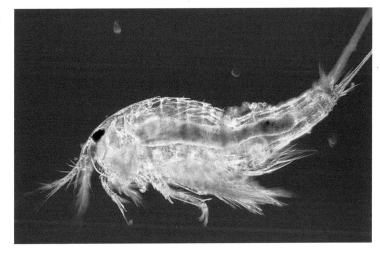

Copepod of the order Harpacticoida.   Photo: R. Brons

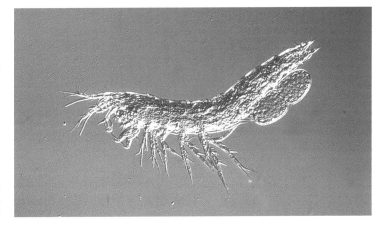

Female copepod of genus *Cylindropsyllus*, (order Harpacticoida) carrying eggs (280 X magnification).   Photo: R. M. Kristensen

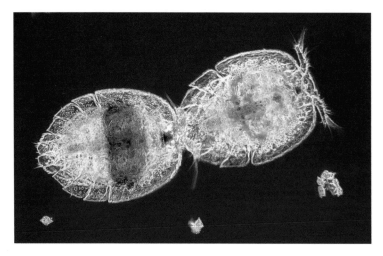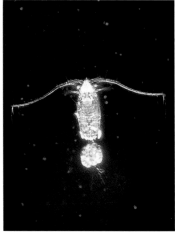

Left: *Porcellidium* sp. (order Harpacticoida) just prior to copulation; male on the left (photo: R. Brons). Right: Female copepod of the order Calanoida with eggs (photo: L. Newman and A. Flowers).

open water immediately after they have been fertilized. Yet again others produce thick-shelled dormant eggs, which can survive unfavourable environmental conditions, and only develop after more favourable conditions have been re-established.

Each egg gives rise to a nauplius larva, which undergoes a series of moults to become a copepodid (post-larva; juvenile copepod). The copepodid, in turn moults ten more times, before it will have grown into a mature copepod. In most cases, the development of the nauplius and copepodid progresses rather rapidly, so that a female can give rise to several generations within a single reproductive season.

The size of newly hatched nauplii is normally between 20 and 40 µm. They are an important food source for the larvae of larger invertebrates and fishes. In aquaculture and in the aquarium hobby, the nauplii of copepods are also an excellent starter food for newly hatched fish larvae and for many invertebrates. Species of order Harpacticoida are the most frequently cultured copepods. These organisms can be raised on a diet of yeast, ground rice bran, phytoplankton and other, foods also used for culturing rotifers and brine shrimps. LAMM (1988) and DÜRBAUM (1997)

provide directions for the culture of copepods on a small scale. However, for sustained culturing success it is advisable to consult relevant scientific literature pertaining to commercial aquaculture, such as HOFF & SNELL (1989) and LAVENS & SORGELOOS (1986).

Taxonomic work on copepods requires sensitiveness and skill. Most species can only be identified on the basis of dissections of the antennules, antennae, mandibles, maxillae, maxillipeds and other appendages. When one considers the minute size of most species, it becomes obvious why we had difficulties in identifying the species discussed here down to species level.

Currently, the subclass Copepoda contains ten orders with a total of about 180 families (BRUSCA & BRUSCA, 1990). Within a coral reef environment, the most common planktonic copepods belong into the orders Calanoida and Cyclopoida, and the most frequently encountered benthic species are those of order Harpacticoida (but there are also a few benthic forms in order Cyclopoida). The principal anatomical features of these three orders, can be summarized as follows (also see the drawings on page 219):

Order Calanoida

These are principally free-living planktonic species. The antennules, consisting of 16 to 26 segments, are long, at least half as long as the body, but often even longer than the body. The antennae are biramous. The fused cephalothorax is oval, and off set from the abdomen by a conspicuous constriction. In most species, the females carry fertilized eggs in a single ovosac, but some also release fertilized eggs directly in to open water.

Order Cyclopoida

Most are free-living planktonic and (some) benthic species, however, this order also includes a several parasitic species. The antennules are normally shorter than the length of the cephalothorax, and are made up of 10 to 16 segments. The antennae are uniramous. These copepods have a pear-shape body with a distinct constriction between the fourth and fifth postcephalic segments. The females carry fertilized eggs in two ovosacs.

Order Harpacticoida

Most of the species in this order are benthic forms, and several of them live interstitially; a few species are parasitic and some are planktonic. The antennules are very short, consisting of five to nine segments. The antennae are biramous. The abdomen is nearly as wide as the thorax. Often the body is worm-shaped, such as in *Cylindropsyllus* spp, but it can also be roundish, such as in *Porcellidium* spp. Although there is an anatomical articulation located between the fourth and fifth post-cephalic segments, there is rarely any perceptible external constriction. The females carry normally only a single ovosac.

Beyond that, a coral reef also accommodates commensal and parasitic copepods, which largely belong into the other seven orders (in addition to those already mentioned). Sponges, corals, echinoderms and fishes are usually the hosts for these copepods.

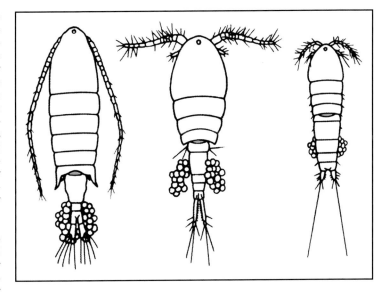

Basic body structure of copepods of the three most important orders: Calanoida (left), Cyclopoida (centre), and Harpacticoida (right).

Drawings after Jones & Morgan (1994)

There will always be copepods present in a modern coral reef aquarium, especially benthic and interstitial forms. These are usually introduced with live rocks, and do especially thrive in cracks and holes of the rocks as well as among filamentous algae. If we shine a flashlight at night into the aquarium, directing the beam into caves and crevices, we will soon discover swarms of small copepods darting about. Taking a look at samples of filamentous algae under a microscope, we will also usually find evidence of the presence of large numbers of copepods in the aquarium. These copepods contribute significantly to the well-being of many other aquarium inhabitants. One classic example of this are the mandarin fishes of genus *Synchiropus*, which would hardly survive in a tank without these microscopic crustaceans. In a well-conditioned coral reef aquarium, with a balanced number of small predators feeding on these organisms, there may often be growing populations of copepods and other microorganisms, to such an extent that there is sufficient food for most of these aquarium inhabitants. Moreover, copepods in an aquarium also play a significant role in the stability of such a small ecosystem, since they contribute greatly to the decomposition of food remnants and detritus. Admittedly, harmful and parasitic species can also get into an aquarium, but they are most certainly less common than the beneficial copepods.

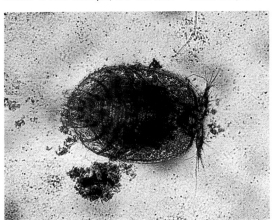
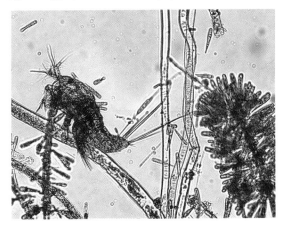

Various copepods of the order Harpacticoida occur frequently in coral reef aquaria: (left) a young copepod (possibly a *Porcellidium* species) and (right) an adult copepod among green filamentous algae.

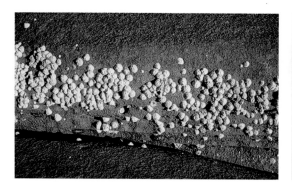

Barnacles of genus *Balanus* (left) and goose barnacles of genus *Lepas* (right).   Photos: L. Newman and A. Flowers

Class Cirripedia – Barnacles

The barnacles should be well known to all who have ever visited the seashore. In fact, they are quite common also along our northern Atlantic and Pacific shores. The most familiar barnacles live permanently attached to rocky substrate in the intertidal zone, where they form dense settlements recognizable as a white interface line. But not all barnacles look or live like that. In fact, the class Cirripedia contains a fascinating array of diverse life forms.

Barnacles make up the only sessile-living group of organisms within the Crustacea, except for parasitic-living forms of some other classes. Since they look vastly different from what is commonly perceived to be a crustacean animal, the layman may find it difficult to accept that barnacles are indeed members of the Crustacea. In the most common groups of barnacles the actual animal is somewhat reminiscent of a shrimp turned upside down, completely enclosed by interlocking shellplates. Only a small opening at the apex is left for the animal to extend its legs through. The legs are covered with feathery setae, used for catching microorganisms from the surrounding water. There are, however, also some members of the Cirripedia which look totally different. Parasitic species exhibiting a more or less extreme mode of

life, and species boring into calcareous rocks, coral skeletons or mollusc shells, do not produce their own enclosure. Some of the barnacles that extrude their own shell cover, attach themselves to the substrate via a long flexible stalk, which often lacks calcareous plates itself. This group is commonly known as goose barnacles. There are various explanations for the origin of this name. One is that people during the Middle Ages, that these (barnacles) would hatch into ducks, specifically into the Eider duck. Another explanation (FRIESE, pers. comm.) has it, that naturalists during the Middle Ages had seen branches and tree logs washed ashore to which these (stalked) barnacles had attached themselves. They assumed that they were actually fruits of these trees, and they believed that the appendage of the barnacle, often hanging out of the shell, were the tail feathers of a small bird. This then gave rise to the myth that a seabird (the Barnacle Goose) originated in the fruit of a tree that grew along the coast. From there on stalked barnacles were known as goose (or goose neck) barnacles.

The relationship of Cirripedia to Crustacea in general, is not obvious in any of the groups of barnacles. Even biologists did not consider these animals to be cru-

staceans, until 1829, when it was discovered that they actually went through a nauplius larval stage. Before that, barnacles had been classified as soft bodied animals (phylum Mollusca).

Barnacles are exclusively marine. There are more than 1,000 species, which occur in highly variable habitats. Many species are parasites or live as commensals on other animals. The class Cirripedia has four orders, of which the order Thoracica is (numerically) the largest and for aquarists and divers it is probably also the most interesting. Consequently, we will take a somewhat closer look at these animals in the course of this discussion.

Some very odd parasites are found in the orders Ascothoracica and Rhizocephala. The former contains about 45 to 50 small species, which are parasitic on echinoderms and black corals of order Anthipatharia (see Volume 2, pages 98-100). *Syngoga* spp., which are ectoparasitic on feather stars (crinoids), have still retained some anatomical characteristics of crustaceans. On the other hand, *Laura* spp., which live attached to black corals, are extraordinarily degenerated and consists of little more than a bivalved carapace, which is embedded in the host polyp. Species of family Dendrogastridae, which live inside the bodies of sea stars and sea urchins, have a very small body surrounded by a large, branched ovary. These parasites essentially bathe in the body fluid of their host, where they are completely entrapped. Only the eggs have the opportunity to escape through a small hole drilled by the adult through the body wall of the echinoderm host (ZANN, 1980).

"Root-footed" barnacles of order Rhizocephala live as parasites on decapod crustaceans and on tunicates. They bathe with their root-like body in the body fluid of their host. Only little more than their reproductive organs are visible from the outside. Best known from among the nearly 250 species of "root-footed" barnacles are probably the *Sacculina* spp., which live attached to the abdomen of crabs (order Brachyura). The visible body part, which consists principally of the reproductive organs, looks somewhat like a lump of sponge, which is covered by a pale brownish-yellow skin. These parasites are found under the abdominal "flap" of crabs, attached in a position where the eggs of the host would normally be found. The remainder of the parasitic barnacle consists merely of internal rooted threads, which have approximately the same function as the hyphae (filamentous, cellular segmented base structures) of fungi. Nutrients are removed from host tissue by the threaded roots. Similar root-footed barnacles of genus *Peltogaster* attack hermit crabs and those of genus *Thompsonia* infest shrimps and crabs.

The order Acrothoracica contains about 50 very small species, which bore into calcareous substrates, such as rocks or the shells of other animals. They are rarely more than a few millimetres in size, often only 0.5 mm. In terms of body shape they are rather similar to acorn barnacles, but they have a soft carapace and a reduced number or total absence of calcareous plates. Their bore hole sites are visible from the outside as narrow slots.

Order Thoracica Acorn-, Rock- and Goose (Neck) Barnacles

The order Thoracica is the only one of particular interest to aquarists. It is structured into three suborder, and with 700 species in 17 families it is the largest order within the class Cirripedia. The rock and acorn barnacles of suborders Verrucomorpha and Balanomorpha are fundamentally sessile, while the goose (neck) barnacles of suborder Lepadomorpha are stalked (pedunculate). But a few parasitic forms have also developed within this order, however, only three of the free-living groups will be discussed below.

Goose barnacles

The majority of stalked goose barnacles attach themselves to floating objects or to other animals, such as to ships and driftwood or sea turtles and whales. Thus, they change their position regularly, but not because of their own volition, but instead due to ambient currents or because of a whim of their host. Commonly, they can be seen in colonies attached to objects washed up on a beach. This mode of life is typical for species of genera *Lepas* and *Conchoderma*, although there are some stationary species, which are attached to sessile animal hosts or on to rocks. *Ibla* spp. adhere to the underside of corals or coral rock, while *Pollicipes* spp. are attached to rocks in the intertidal area, very much like acorn barnacles. *Scalpellum* species live among colonies of hydroids and bryozoans.

The long stalk of goose barnacles sticks with one end to the substrate, while the other end carries the major part of the body, which is enclosed within calcareous plates. The body capsule (capitulum) accommodates all parts of the animal, except for the pre-oral (in front of the mouth) end, which has been modified into the stalk.

Acorn- and rock barnacles

It is assumed, that the rock- and acorn barnacles have evolved from stalked ancestors, where the stalk has gradually disappeared. The large adhesive surface and the low, strong and round shell is a substantial adaptation for a life on rocks and stones pounded by waves and swept by current in the intertidal zone. Although there are some deep water species, the occurrence of most barnacles is restricted to the intertidal zone and to the area immediately below. Furthermore, each species is specifically adapted to a very particular zone. Intertidal barnacles commonly occur in extraordinarily dense aggregations. Densities of 40,000 to 50,000 individuals per square metre are not uncommon.

Some barnacles are adapted to a sessile life on other surfaces, such as on large crustaceans, sea turtles or whales, to gorgonians, stony corals and to other cnidarian animals. Although also barnacles that live on stony corals secrete their own calcareous shell, they will eventually be covered by the coral's skeleton as well.

Most barnacles are suspension feeders. In order to gather food, they extend their cirri-covered feet (specialized for that purpose) through the opening of the shellplate cover. In fact, the scientific name of this class (Cirripedia) refers to the peculiarity of these feet: *cirrus*, Latin = creeping/climbing hair curl and *pes*, genitive *pedis*, Latin = foot. When extended, the cirri on each side of the foot form a separate side of a basket-like structure. In most species, the capture of food particles occurs in periodic, rhythmic beating. Both sides of the cirri fan towards each other and downwards, thus gathering food particles from the water. Food

Goose barnacles, *Lepas anserifera*, attached to a cuttle fish "bone" (*Sepia* sp.), washed ashore at Alexandra Bay, Great Barrier Reef.
Photo: L. Newman and A. Flowers

Barnacles of the genus *Balanus*.
Photo: L. Newman and A. Flowers

ted in the proximity of the cirri.

In certain other species, such as those of genus *Ibla* and a few of genus *Balanus*, there are also miniature males, which attach themselves to a female or hermaphroditic individual. Frequently the morphology of such dwarf males has been modified through loss or degeneration of various body structures.

The eggs of common barnacles and goose barnacles are incubated in an ovosac (brood sac) within the mantle cavity. Following the incubation period, which may last anywhere from a few weeks to six months, the hatchlings are released at an early nauplius stage. A single mature individual can produce several thousand larvae in one brood. Larval development proceeds through six nauplius stages and ends as a non-feeding cypris larva. This is the time for settling down. The cypris larva searches for a suitable substrate and attaches itself by means of special adhesive glands, located on the antennules. Prior to their attachment, barnacle larvae have to test the environmental properties of the site such as composition of substrate, water quality,

Barnacle (*Balanus* sp.) removed from its shell: the tendril-like cirri along the feet and the long penis (the longish, horizontal organ in the centre of the picture) are now clearly visible.

particles suspended in the water are trapped by the setae and the first one to three pairs of cirri are used to scrape these particles off and transfer them to the mouth. The food gathered is of variable nature. In some species, small crustaceans, such as copepods and amphipods make up the main component, while for other Cirripedia species micro- and phytoplankton are more important.

Barnacles and goose barnacles are the largest group of crustaceans, which are basically hermaphrodites. Although each individual is male as well as female simultaneously, cross fertilisation is the rule. All individuals have an extremely long and well-developed penis, which is easily used for copulating with other individuals in close proximity. Individuals functioning actively as males can recognize those functioning as females. Several males may inseminate an active female. For copulation the penis is protruded from the body and inserted into the mantle cavity of an active female. The sperm mass is deposi-

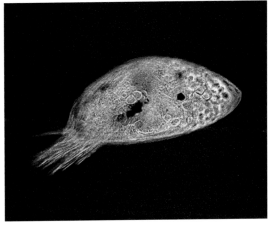

Barnacle larvae of genus *Balanus*: left: nauplius larvae and (right) a cypris larva.

Photos: R. Brons

wave action and currents. Once a larvae has become established, it is tied down for life to this particular spot on the substrate. There is no chance of a second attempt.

It has been found, that a protein in the exoskeleton of older, attached individuals has an attracting effect on larvae about to settle. This enhances the opportunity for a larva to find a suitable site. Once attachment has been successfully completed, metamorphosis occurs, during which the larva is being transformed into a miniature version of the adult organism. In the event it is not eaten, it should be able to survive for two to six years.

Common barnacles and goose barnacles are fairly abundant on coral reefs. The Great Barrier Reef has 23 genera with a total of about 43 species (MATHER & BENNETT, 1993). Barnacles, as animals of the intertidal zone, live on rocks and coral boulders along the reef flat and on beach rocks. The most common genera are *Balanus* of family Balanidae and *Tetraclita* of family Tetraclitidae, but there are still other genera in a coral reef environment. Family Pyrgomatidae contains species, which live more or less embedded in stony corals. Goose barnacle, of which there are several cosmopolitan, drifting species, are often found washed up on beaches after storms. *Lepas anatifera* and *L. anserifera* are the two species,

which are most often encountered.

Normally, aquarists will never see barnacles in their aquarium. But it does happen that they get into an aquarium as "stowaways" on live rocks or corals. It is not unusual to discover pyrgomatids in an aquarium attached to stony

corals such as *Euphyllia* spp. Under normal conditions they should be able to survive if plankton or plankton substitute is available as food. So far there are, however, only very few publications on aquarium observations of barnacles, and our own experiences are also rather limited.

Barnacle of the family Pyrgomatidae in a hammer (or anchor-) coral, *Euphyllia ancora*.

Photo: L. Newman and A. Flowers

In crustaceans of the class Malacostraca the female genital pores are located on the sixth thoracic segment or its appendages (left); however, those of the male are at the eighth (right) segment, as shown here on the Australian freshwater crayfish, *Cherax destructor*.
Photo: U. Werner

Class Malacostraca – Soft-shelled Crustaceans

The class Malacostraca (*malakos*, Greek = soft, and *ostrakon*, Greek = shell) embraces nearly three-quarters of all known crustacean species. That makes it an extremely diversified class, which contains a large number of fascinating species. It includes crabs, shrimps, prawns, crayfish and lobsters – better known from dinner menus than from aquaria – as well as some lesser known crustaceans.

In our discussion below we are going to concentrate on three orders: Stomapoda, Decapoda and Peracarida.

The body of malacostracans is typically composed of 14 segments and the telson. The first eight segments make up the thorax and the remaining six the abdomen. Corresponding to the fundamental body plan of crustaceans (see the drawing on page 203), all segments are equipped with appendages. A pair of compound eyes, usually biramous antennules, and antennae with a large scale-like flattened exopodite are the visible sensory organs of the head. The female sexual openings (gonopores) are located on the sixth thoracic segment or its appendages, whereas those of the male are on the eighth thoracic segment or its appendages.

Order Stomapoda – Mantis Shrimps

Mantis shrimps of the order Stomatopoda, which represent the only order in superorder Hoplocarida, are extremely successful predators, feeding principally on fishes, molluscs and other crustaceans. The fact, that mantis shrimps are placed in their own order, separate from all other crustaceans of class Malacostraca, clearly indicates that also in an evolutionary sense they represent something special; and indeed so they are.

The external appearance of mantis shrimps is vaguely reminiscent of shrimps or prawns. The body is dorso-ventrally compres-sed (flattened from top to bottom), and is often armed with ridges and spines. The carapace is short and covers only the head and part of the thorax. Yet, one feature is very particular: the first five pairs of pereiopods are all equipped with pincers; moreover, the second pair is extremely large and well modified for lightning-fast prey capture (raptorial feeding). The inside edge of the movable pincer digit is armed with long spines or with a cutting edge like a sharp knife, which curves back on itself into a deep groove. Because of such weaponry, mantis shrimps are capable of captu-ring prey in a manner similar to that used by the preying mantis, a well-known insect species, which has given these crustaceans there common name.

There are basically two structural versions of the second pair of legs, separating mantis shrimps into two groups: **smashers** and **spearers**. Among the "smashers", which predominate in superfamily Gonodactyloidea, the appendages are club-like, suitable for crushing animals with strong shells, such as crabs, clams and gastropods. "Spearers", on the other hand, which are characteristic for all other superfamilies, have the forelimbs equipped with numerous spines, suitable for capturing mainly soft-bodied prey, such as fishes and shrimps. Smasher mantis shrimps tend to hide preferably in crevices and cracks in hard substrate, such as coral or rock. The effectiveness of their heavily calcified weapons is so high, that they often attack and conquer well-armoured crustaceans, which are larger than they themselves. They smash claws, legs and carapace of their prey, before dragging the carcass into their hiding place to devour it there. Smaller seized prey, such as molluscs, is often taken directly to the hide-out, and there to be smashed against the wall, before breaking it open. For some of the larger smasher mantis shrimps it has been estimated that the impact of a blow equals that of a bullet from a 22-caliber gun - comparable to a compressed air jack hammer! No wonder that there are reports about mantis shrimps having smashed thick aquarium windows (JUAN, 1998).

Spearers are basically larger than smashers; however, they are less aggressive. These mantis shrimps tend to hide in burrows excavated by themselves in soft substrate, such as in sand or mud. The rapid projection of the capture legs can reach a speed of a magnitude of 10 m per second (!), and is accompanied by an incredible accuracy of aim, so that even fish swimming past at considerable speed can still be seized and killed (JUAN, 1998).

Traditionally, the more than 400 known species of mantis shrimps have been sorted into only four families: Squillidae, Lysiosquillidae, Gonodactylidae and Bathysquillidae. We have decided to follow the new classification proposed by MANNING (1995), which is supported by AHYONG (1997). According to this latest classification there are about 109 genera in 20 families, within five or six superfamilies (see the systematic review on page 226).

The maximum size of mantis shrimps is very variable; it can

On this *Gonodactylus* species it can be seen that the carapace in mantis shrimps covers only the head and a minor part of the thorax. This is a characteristic feature, which distinguishes mantis shrimps from decapod (order Decapoda) crustaceans. Photo: C. Bryce

range from less than 2 cm, as in *Nannosquilla* spp., up to 40 cm in the largest *Lysiosquilla* species. But the majority of species are between 4 and 10 cm long. Mantis shrimps occur in variable habitats, yet most live in crevices and cracks of rocks, or in burrows, excavated by themselves or by other animals in soft substrate. These burrows are often used as hideouts, where they lay in waiting for suitable prey to pass by.

Excellent visual acuity is mandatory for a successful hunt. Consequently, mantis shrimp have distinctly well-developed compound eyes, which permit three-dimensional and probably

even colour vision. It has been proven, that the eyes of mantis shrimps contain at least ten spectral classes of photo receptors (JUAN, 1998), while humans, on the other hand, have only three!

Apart from sea lice and related forms of suborder Isopoda, mantis shrimps are the only crustaceans in class Malacostraca, which have abdominal gills. Gas- and nutrient transport is facilitated by a rather advanced circulatory system with a tubular heart, which extends nearly throughout the entire thorax and abdomen. Hemocyanin is present in the blood and provides the oxygen transport.

This *Odontodactylus* sp., seen here just leaving its hiding place in a crevice, is a "smasher". Photo: Scott W. Michael

This *Lysiosquilla* species (seen here in Indonesia) is partially buried in sand waiting for prey. It is a "spearer". Photo: Scott W. Michael

The eggs give rise to zoea larvae, which have already large, conspicuous compound eyes and well-developed capture appendages.

The majority of species are tropical, however, there are also a few in subtropical and temperate seas. For instance, the genus *Squilla* is represented in the Mediterranean Sea by *S. mantis*, and in the Mediterranean Sea and the Atlantic Ocean northward to the British Channel by *A. desmaresti*, while the similar *S. empusa* is found along the North-American Atlantic coastline.

Mantis shrimps occur frequently as by-catch in shrimp- and prawn trawls. Fisherman have great respect for these powerful crustaceans, since they can inflict severe wounds to fingers and other unprotected parts of the body. All three above-mentioned species taste delicious! Especially in Italy there is a long-standing tradition to serve "Cannocchia". They can be eaten steamed, fried or grilled or as "Brodetto di Cannocchie" (= mantis shrimp soup) (DAVIDSON, 1981).

In most species, the females carry the eggs around with them as a agglutinated mass, held together by an adhesive secretion from specialised glands. The egg mass is held by the smaller chelate, anterior thoracic appendages, and it is continuously turned and cleaned. This assures that each of the several thousand eggs in the bundle is afforded identical development conditions. There are, however, also species, where the females hide inside their burrow, holding the egg mass on top of their carapace.

Similarly in Asia, mantis shrimp are also highly prized as food (DAVIDSON, 1977). *Squilla raphidea* is preferentially eaten in Japan, where it is known as "Sako". *Harpiosquilla harpax* and *Oratosquilla nepa* are frequently offered in the fish markets of Thailand and many other south-east Asian countries. In Thailand they are called "Kang takaten", in Malaysia "Kamun", in the Phillipines "Tatampal" and in Hong Kong "Taan ha".

From our perspective as aquarists, it is most interesting that mantis shrimps often are brilliantly coloured. Coral reef species of genera *Lysiosquilla*, *Gonodactylus* (see factsheet on page 227) and *Odontodactylus* (see factsheet on page 228) are of particular interest to the aquarium hobby. *Lysiosquilla* spp. are typical spearers, while the species of *Gonodactylus*- and *Odontodactylus* are smashers. Yet, all species are capable of capturing fish and killing them. Many species of these three genera are very beau-

Systematic overview simplified of the order Stomatopoda

Based on AHYONG (1997) and MANNING (1995)

Superfamily Lysiosquilloidea
Family Nannosquillidae
Nannosquilla
Family Lysiosquillidae
Lysiosquilla, Lysiosquillina
Three more families

Superfamily Erythrosquilloidea
One family

Superfamily Gonodactyloidea
Family Gonodactylidae
Gonodactylus, Neogonodactylus
Family Odontodactylidae
Odontodactylus
Six more families

Superfamily Bathysquilloidea
Two families

Superfamily Squilloidea
Family Harpiosquillidae
Harpiosquilla
Family Squillidae
Oratosquilla, Squilla

Gonodactylus spp.
Mantis shrimps

Distribution: Circumtropical.

Size: Most species reach a length of up to 5 cm, but some grow to more than 10 cm.

Reproduction: Details unknown. In aquaria females have often been observed carrying eggs, however, larvae have never been raised.

Food: Carnivorous; very aggressive predators. Generally of the "smasher" type (see description on page 224). In captivity, mantis shrimps prefer live food, but they will readily adapt to substitute food. CAUTION: If a mantis shrimp is to be hand-fed, it is imperative to use long forceps.

Description: Mantis shrimps live on coral reefs, where they hide in cracks and crevices of coral rocks or underneath cliffs. The body is elongated and flattened. The first five pairs of thoracic appendages have been modified into dangerous, strong "weapons". The abdominal appendages are typical swimmerets (pleopods). These animals display strong inter- as well as intra-specific aggression. The genus contains a large number of species. VINE (1986) lists 10 species from the Red Sea alone.

Aquarium requirements: *Gonodactylus* spp. are commonly introduced into an aquarium together with corals and live rocks. In many instances they are not discovered until after the rocks are placed in the tank. Some of the smaller species are not overly aggressive, but they too tend to attack free-living invertebrates, especially shrimps as well as small fishes. The best way to remove a mantis shrimp from an aquarium is simply to take out the rock it is hiding in. In general, *Gonodactylus* spp. are very hardy and interesting animals for a special aquarium.

GA: +; SE: +; CO: -

Photos:
Three *Gonodactylus* species from Heron Island, Great Barrier Reef: male *G. chiragra* (top), female *G. mutatus* (centre), and male *G. platysoma* (bottom).
Photos: L. Newman & A. Flowers

Odontodactylus scyllarus
Harlequin Mantis Shrimp

Distribution: Occurs widely throughout the Indo-Pacific.

Size: One of the larger mantis shrimps, may attain a length of up to 15 cm.

Reproduction: Details unknown. In aquaria, females have often been observed carrying eggs, however, young have never been raised.

Food: Carnivorous; a very aggressive predator of the "smasher" type (see description on page 224). Also in captivity, this mantis shrimp prefers live food when available, but it will readily adapt to substitute food. CAUTION: If a mantis shrimp is to be hand-fed, it is imperative to use long forceps.

Description: Occurs down to a depth of at least 40 m, where it lives in burrows dug in sand or coral rubble. These burrows are U-shaped, and for a 10 cm long specimen they can be about 1 m long and 40 cm deep. They are lined with small coral and shell fragments, as well as with pebbles. The various materials used are meticulously fitted together, to form a rather sturdy structure. Locations with a moderate current are preferred. The animals will leave their burrows repeatedly during day and night in search of food or for a partner. Consequently, they are often seen wandering from coral to coral (JUAN, 1998). The body is elongated and flattened. The first five pairs of thoracic appendages have been modified into dangerous "weapons", equipped with sharp, pointed spines. The abdominal appendages are typical swimmerets (pleopods). The eyes are spherical, and divided by two parallel lines through their centre. The males of this species are the most colourful of all mantis shrimps, with a shiny green body, blue head, and reddish orange thoracic appendages and antennas. Females are normally brownish or olive-coloured.

Aquarium requirement: Has been imported in small numbers for a long time. It is fundamentally a hardy species, but it is not suited for a community tank. It should preferably be kept in a separate, specially set-up aquarium, but it can also be maintained in the company of large fishes (CAUTION: Small and medium-size fishes are invariably welcome prey). Strong intra-specific aggression, and therefore this species is best kept in solitary specimens.

GA: +; SE: +; CO: -

Photos:
Odontodactylus scyllarus at Sulawesi (top and centre; photos: Scott. W. Michael), and at Madang, Papua-New Guinea (bottom; photo: L. Newman and A. Flowers).

tifully coloured: with prevailing shades of green, blue and red, often mottled or with intense contrasting patterns. Very attractive species occur in the Indo-Pacific, and Eastern Pacific, as well as in the Caribbean, where they should be easy to find. In the aquarium trade, however, mantis shrimps are generally cursed as "castouts". So it is indeed a lucky opportunity if one is offered a mantis shrimp for sale. Here one must hasten to add, that mantis shrimps are NOT a good choice for the average coral reef aquarium, although as aquarium specimens they adapt readily and they are hardy and tend to live for a long time.

Under aquarium conditions, mantis shrimp are nearly always very aggressive and predatory, as they are in the wild. Therefore, they should always be kept in a separate tank, and there only as single individuals, since intraspecific aggression is the rule for mantis shrimps. It may work out in combination with selected corals and other less "edible" invertebrates, but all potential prey, such as other crustaceans, molluscs and fishes, should be avoided. It is very important that the animal is provided with appropriate hiding places, which – depending upon the species – could be either a deep sand layer to dig in, or some form of artificial burrow or cave.

Although mantis shrimp are predators and hunters, in an aquarium they will adapt rather readily to feed on dead organisms or substitutes like pieces of fish-, shrimp-, squid- and clam meat. Here we must hasten to add the CAUTION, that any hand feeding of mantis shrimp must be done with long forceps; otherwise, the aquarist may be in for a very painful encounter when the mantis pounces on its food. When all prerequisites for keeping these animals are met, mantis shrimps can be most interesting, and very much worthwhile for taking a closer look at in an aquarium.

Apart from the rare opportunity of being able to buy a mantis shrimp in an aquarium shop,

Mantis shrimp of the genus *Squilla*, seen here at Cockburn Sound, Western Australia.   Photo: C. Bryce

there is yet another, less voluntary way of acquiring these animals. It does happen, that specimens are introduced into an aquarium (where it may be less than desired) as a "stowaway" in live rocks. If it is a small individual and belongs to a species that does not get too large, there may be not necessarily a problem. Unfortunately though, mantis shrimps create anxieties for the aquarist concerned, because they may

well prey on small aquarium inhabitants and severely damage larger ones.

Often it takes some clicking sounds from a tank to alert the aquarist that there may be a mantis shrimp in his tank. These sounds can indeed come from a mantis shrimp pounding on the carapace of some crustacean or on a the shell of a clam. But more likely these are "gun shots" from pistol shrimps of family Alphei-

Lysiosquilla sp., buried in sand (Indonesia). It too is a "spearer".
                                      Photo: Scott W. Michael

dae. These shrimp are generally no problem at all and indeed they are welcome guests in most aquaria (see pp. 236). Therefore, an "invader" should never be indiscriminately killed before one knows exactly what kind of animal it is!

Positive identification of a mantis shrimp requires sight contact, or a continuous decimation of the fish and invertebrate population in the tank. Once the trouble maker has been discovered and a decision has been made to get rid of it, one needs to proceed as follows: determine its hiding place (ideally in a rock), because mantis shrimp tend to utilize the same place most of the time. If this is a rock, it is cautiously removed and transferred to another aquarium. Another possibility is to immerse the rock in soda water, which will

cause the mantis shrimp to leave its hiding place (JUAN, 1998). Afterwards the rock must be returned to the aquarium as quickly as possible so that all the other life forms on the rock are not destroyed. To save the mantis shrimp, this must of course also be transfered to sea water right away. Another alternative is to use a trap, which is available from an aquarium- or fishing tackle shop (= bait traps). Make sure that the construction material of such a trap is not affected by seawater. JUAN (1998) recommends a "suction method" to remove an undesirable mantis shrimp from an aquarium. The suction hose of a strong cannsiter filter is secured tightly over the hole where the animal hides, and left running over night. When the shrimp emerges from its hideout, it will be

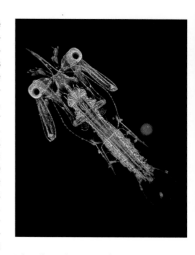

First larval stage of *Odontodactylus scyllarus*.   Photo: R. Brons

"sucked up" into the filter cannister, from where it can be safely removed the next morning.

Order Decapoda – Ten-footed Crustaceans

The members of order Decapoda are indeed the best-known crustaceans, not only to divers and aquarists but virtually to everybody. In fact, with at least 8,500 described species, it is also an extremely comprehensive group of crustaceans. Among them are crabs, shrimps, hermit crabs, crayfish and lobsters, as well as many inconspicuous species. This group includes some highly colourful species, which are easily spotted in their surroundings, but also many more cryptically coloured, and in their habitat well camouflaged, species.

The order Decapoda is a very variable group, but its members occur mainly in the sea. Only relatively few live in freshwater and even less on land. Decapod crustaceans have invaded nearly all substrate areas in the ocean, from the shore (or even above the shore) down to great depths. Compared to other crustacean groups, the decapods have, however, only relatively few deep sea species (MARSHALL, 1979). Many decapod species are permanently planktonic, and prac-

tically all species undergo some planktonic larval phase. Decapod crustaceans inhabit all tropical seas and they are particularly abundant on coral reefs.

Worldwide numerous decapod crustaceans are important for commercial fisheries for human consumption, see for instance HOLTHUIS (1980 and 1991). In Norway alone, more than 50,000 to 60,000 tonnes of the deep sea shrimp, *Pandalus borealis* are caught annually. Additionally, many species are important aquaculture organisms.

Systematics

Traditionally, decapod crustaceans have been divided into two groups: **Natantia** ("swimmers") and **Reptantia** ("crawlers"). The Natantia used to include shrimps, while the Reptantia covered lobsters, crabs, crayfish etc. Modern phylogenetic research does, however, imply that this was a highly

artificial constellation without foundation in the evolutionary history. Moreover, this also applies to the reproductive physiology, which is among those traits that in general tend to change very slowly through evolution. Consequently, modes of reproduction are considered good characters for interpreting the phylogeny of animals. Besides, fundamental morphological features of these animals suggest, that dividing decapod crustaceans into two other groups, that is, into the suborders **Dendrobranchiata** and **Pleocyemata** is more logical.

The species of suborder Dendrobranchiata are shrimp-like, and characteristically laterally flattened and equipped with multi-branched gills (*dendros*, Greek = branch, and *branchia*, Latin = gill). They release their eggs into open water, and the first larval stage is a nauplius. In the Pleocyemata, which embraces the majority of crustaceans, including most shrimps, the gills are not branched, but plate- or thread-like. Moreover, they are egg brooders (*pleon*, Greek = po-

Decapod crustaceans (Order Decapoda) include most of the crustaceans popular in the aquarium hobby, such as this dancing shrimp, *Rhynchocinetes durbanensis* (left; photo: G. Spies), and the banded cleaner shrimp, *Stenopus hispidus* (right; photo: Dr. D. Brockmann).

lys, Greek = many and *kyema, genetive kyematos* = fruit in maternal body, embryos), and the first larval stage is a protozoea or a zoea.

Although there is an on-going discussion about the higher level taxonomy of decapods, we have decided to follow the general scheme proposed by BOWMAN & ABELE (1982), and use the taxa Dendrobranchiata and Pleocyemata, rather than Natantia and Reptantia. Furthermore, in respect to the systematics involved we have also assessed several other sources and, to some extent, interpreted according to personal opinions. The systematic overview (see page 232) conveyed here contains only the taxa down to superfamily or section level, respectively. In the separate section on the respective infraorders there will then be a classification down to genus level.

General biology

Typical for all ten-footed crustaceans of order Decapoda, is that the first three pairs of thoracic appendages have been modified into maxillipeds ("jaw feet"). Thus, five pairs are left for use as wal-

king legs, that is a total of ten walking legs (*deka*, Greek = ten and *pous*, genitive *podos*, Greek = foot, leg). The first (sometimes also the second and third) pair of walking legs is normally (but not always) equipped with **chelae** (pincers), which serve as defensive weapons and/or as tools for handling prey. Head and thorax are fused dorsally into the headchest section (cephalothorax), and covered by a carapace, which extends down the sides and so cover the gills. Usually there are several rows of gills, so that a large respiratory surface is formed. The total number of gills varies from only 3 up to 24 on each side of the body.

In some groups, such as shrimps and lobsters, the abdomen is well developed and carries appendages in the form of swimming legs (swimmerets), plus a tail fan, consisting of the telson and the uropods. In others, such as crabs, the abdomen is strongly reduced and frequently hardly visible.

The blood of decapod crustaceans contains hemocyanin, which is responsible for the principal share of oxygen transport. The hemocyanin is dissolved in the blood plasma and not embedded in blood cells. The heart is a coffin-like vesicle, located in the thorax. Five arteries emerge from

the front of the heart and a median abdominal artery from the back. A sternal artery emerges from the ventral side of the heart or from the base of the abdominal artery. All arteries are heavily branched and supply various organs and body structures.

Except for the members of a few highly specialized groups, all decapod crustaceans possess ingeniously developed compound eyes. The eye-stalk consists of two or three segments, which are sometimes elongated to such an extent, that very conspicuous "pop eyes" are formed. In any case, the eyes are always much more movable than in most other crustaceans. From that, one concludes, that eye sight is a very important sense for decapods. Moreover, the antennae, as sensors for environmental information - especially for those of a chemical nature -, are significant.

At the base of the antennules, most decapod crustaceans have a pair of statocysts (balancing organs). The statocysts are always open towards the outside, and inside they accommodate the statoliths, which provide information about the direction of gravity, when they come into contact with the various regions of the statocyst walls. Frequently, the statoliths have been formed from fine sand particles that have entered from the outside and become glued together by special secretions given off by the walls of the statocyst. The most advanced statocysts, as those found in true crabs of infraorder Brachyura, provide information not only about gravity, but also about the position of the animal relative to its movements.

The dietary requirements and the food gathering habits of decapod crustaceans cover a wide spectrum. Most species feed – in some form or other – as scavengers of dead plant- and animal matter, including detritus, but there are also predatory and filter-feeding species. Many of the scavengers can become more or less predatory if given the opportunity. Moreover, predators may also utilise carrion if necessary. Predatory species feed on larger invertebrates, such as molluscs, bristle worms, echinoderms, as well as on other crustaceans and on many planktonic organisms. Strictly, or predominantly, herbivorous species are also found in many groups of decapods.

Most decapod crustaceans have separate sexes, and well-defined sexual dimorphism is conspicuous in many species. This is particular obvious, in species like fiddler crabs (*Uca*), where one pincer of the male is extraordinarily enlarged. A similar sexual dimorphism occurs in the well-known marbled shrimps of genus *Saron* and the dancing shrimps of genus *Rhynchocinetes*. In all of these, males have much longer and more powerful pincers, than females. Sometimes the colouration between the sexes is also different enough, so that males and females can be clearly distinguished. On the other hand, there are also those species where sexual dimorphisms is less distinct or absent altogether.

WIRTZ (1996) demonstrated, that the white-banded cleaner shrimps *Lysmata amboinensis* and *L. grabhami* are simultaneous protandrous hermaphrodites (male first, and then male and female at the same time). It is

---

Systematic overview of the order Decapoda

Based on BARNES (1980), GEORGE & GEORGE (1979), GONZALEZ (1995), INGLE (1997), JONES & MORGAN (1994) **as well as some personal communications**

Suborder Dendrobranchiata
  Infraorder Penaeidea

Suborder Pleocyemata
  Infraorder Caridea – among others symbiosis-, dancing-, marble- and harlequin shrimps
  Infraorder Stenopodidea – Scissor shrimps
  Infraorder Astacidea – Cray fish and Lobsters
    Superfamily Astacoidea – Cray fish
    Superfamily Parastacoidea – Cray fish
    Superfamily Nephropoidea – Lobsters
  Infraorder Thalassinidea – Ghost shrimps and Lobsters
    Superfamily Thalassinoidea – Ghost shrimps
  Infraorder Palinura – Spiny Lobsters and Slipper Lobsters
    Superfamily Palinuroidea – Spiny Lobsters and Slipper Lobsters
  Infraorder Anomura – Hermit crabs, porcelain crabs, mole crabs
    Superfamily Paguroidea – Hermit crabs
    Superfamily Galatheoidea – Porcelain crabs
    Superfamily Hippoidea – Mole crabs
  Infraorder Brachyura – True crabs
    Section Dromiacea
    Section Oxystomata
    Section Cancridea
    Section Oxyrhyncha – Decorator- and spide crabs
    Section Brachygnatha – Among others Swimmer-, black-finger-, coral-, hairy-, shore- and gall crabs

---

known from many other species, especially shrimps, that they change sex - from male to female - in the course of their life.

Generally, the testicles and ovaries are elongated, paired organs, which are located dorsally in the thorax, and in some instances extending well into the abdomen. Normally, the terminal ends of the sperm ducts of males are muscular to facilitate ejaculation. Their openings are on the eighth thoracic segment or its appendages, that is, the fifth pair of walking legs, the female's oviducts open on the sixth thoracic segment or its appendages, that is, the third pair of walking legs (see illustrations on page 224). In males, the first two pairs of swimming legs are usually somewhat modified to support sperm transfer. Sometimes they have been

restructured into a type of penis, as in some hermit crabs, or into a pair of penises, as in crabs. The sperms (spermatozoa) of decapods are of a stellar shape and without tails. Often spermatozoa are transferred to the female in the form of a sperm package (spermatophore), which is attached to the ventral side of the first abdominal segment inside a sperm receptacle. The spermatophore can contain significantly more spermatozoa than required for a single batch of eggs, so that subsequent clutches can be fertilized without prior copulation.

As is typical for crustaceans, copulation takes place immediately after moulting. Yet, sexually mature males are ready to copulate at any time, while it is necessary for females to have undergone a moult just prior to mating.

Visual acuity appears to be very important in decapod crustaceans. They have well-developed compound eyes, located on long stalks in some groups, where they become conspicuous stalked eyes, as seen here in the red hermit crab, *Dardanus megistos.*, in the Maldives. Photo: P. Lange

Later on, she no longer reacts to the courtship behaviour of a male. As soon as moulting has been completed, or even when it is still going on, the male approaches the female. In many decapods, copulation is preceded by courtship activities, which take on various forms of nudging, tapping, stroking and caressing.

To copulate, the male mounts the female. In shrimps the pair is typically oriented at right angles, with the genital openings opposing each other. In crabs the female is usually below the male, often in reverse positions, so that the genital openings are facing each other. In some crayfish the male turns the female on her back and takes up a head-to-head position.

In most species, the females will deposit their eggs shortly after copulation, however, in those with a sperm receptacle, the spermatozoa may be stored for subsequent spawning at the correct time. In crabs it has been shown that true internal fertilization takes place, whereas in most other decapods the eggs are probably fertilized at the moment when they are laid. With the ex-

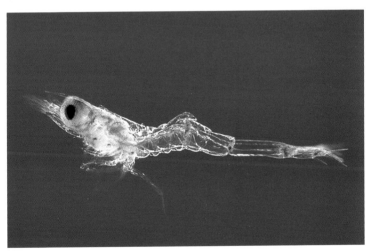

This zoea larva of *Rhynchocinetes durbanensis* bears hardly any resemblance to an adult dancing shrimp. Photo: R. Brons

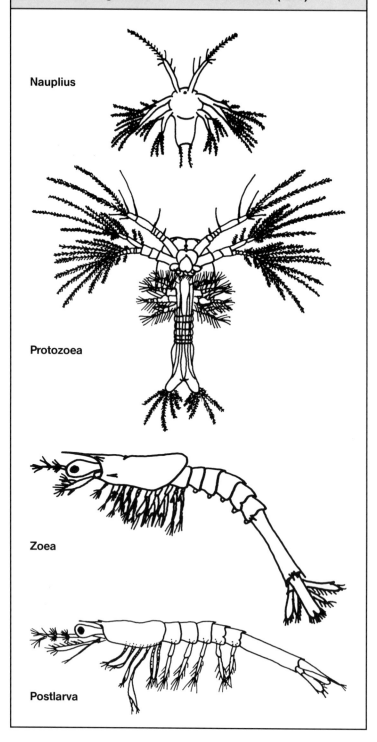

Larval stages in decapods (order decapoda)

Drawings based on DOBKIN in ANDERSON (1973)

Nauplius

Protozoea

Zoea

Postlarva

ception of king- and tiger prawns, belonging to the infraorder Penaeidae of suborder Dendrobranchiata, which release their eggs directly into open water, all other decapods are egg brooders, where the females hold their eggs against the abdomen with their swimmerets. The individual eggs cells stick to each other by means of an adhesive substance that associates with the egg membranes. The eggs remain at the abdomen until they hatch, but the incubation period is highly variable within the order; not only from species to species but also from one population to another. The time span involved ranges from one week to one month; in most reef-dwelling decapods it is between 10 and 20 days. In the pelagic spawning tiger- and king prawns the eggs develop much faster, normally within 12 to 24 hours.

In most marine decapod crustaceans, the newly hatched larvae immediately take up a planktonic life. During this planktonic phase, which passes through various larval stages, the morphological characteristics change quite considerably (see the drawings to the left). The table (on page 233) depicts the larval stages of some typical groups of crustaceans.

Decapod crustaceans in the coral reef aquarium

Generally speaking, decapod crustaceans make excellent aquarium inhabitants, in terms of their hardiness and their attractive colouration, as well as their intriguing behaviour patterns. Beyond that, some can be a valuable addition, because of their ecological role. Most certainly this includes cleaner shrimps, which clean the parasites off fishes, as well as the algae-grazing hermit crabs, just to mention a few. Over the following pages we will discuss a selection of 34 families that – in our opinion – are of particular interest to aquarists and divers. However, this does not mean that there are not other families of decapods inhabiting coral reefs, but it is simply our very own, personal selection from the vast multitude of crustacean animals in the order Decapoda.

Typical larval stages of decapods
Based on BARNES (1980)

Groups	Larval stages
Suborder Dendrobranchiata Infraorder Penaeidea	Naplius → Protozoea → Zoea → Postlarva
Suborder Pleocyemata Infraorder Caridea Infraorder Stenopodidea Infraorder Astacidea Infraorder Palinura Infraorder Anomura Infraorder Brachyura	 Protozoea → Zoea → Postlarva Protozoea → Zoea → Postlarva Zoea → Postlarva Zoea → Postlarva Zoea → Postlarva Zoea → Postlarva

Suborder Dendrobranchiata

Shrimps and prawns of this suborder are the most primitive decapods, with distinctly primitive, evolutionary characteristics, such as branched gills, releasing the eggs into open water and starting the larval phase as a nauplius. They are excellent swimmers with very well-developed, large, fringed swimming legs. In addition, they can propel themselves backwards at great speed through rapid flexions of the abdomen with the attached tail fan. The first three pairs of pereiopods are more or less of equal length and are equipped with tong-like pincers. Many species lead a pelagic life, some at great depths down to at least 5,000 m (MARSHALL, 1979),

however, there are also species which live as benthic organisms in shallow water.

Infraorder Penaeidea

The infraorder Penaeidea is made up of five families (see systematic overview on page 236), but here we will only discuss briefly the tiger- and king prawns of family Penaeidae.

Family Penaeidae

Tiger- and king prawns are neither conspicuous on the coral reefs nor are they of any great significance to the marine aquarium hobby. On the other hand, they are very important for the commercial fisheries as well as for aquaculture, because world-wide they are generally highly prized culinary food items. Some species reach remarkable sizes of 20 to 30 cm, and weights of 100 g to 200 g are not uncommon.

Most species are nocturnal feeders on algae, detritus and other organic material, including a wide range of small invertebrates and fish larvae. During the day, they tend to hide, often buried in sand or mud. Darkness appears to be the deciding factor for their activities, so that divers

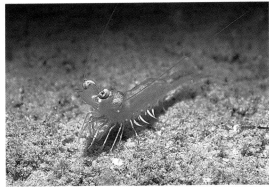

King- and tiger prawns (family Penaeidae) are fundamentally nocturnal. *Penaeus* sp., is seen here burying itself (Indonesia) left; photo: Scott W. Michael. *Penaeus* cf. *indicus*, also in Indonesia, is a typical representative of this family (right; photo: C. Bryce).

usually encounters them during night dives only.

King- and tiger prawns have only very few representatives as regular inhabitants on coral reefs. In the Indo-Pacific region we find e.g. *Penaeus longistylus, P. indicus, Metapenaeopsis* spp. and *Heteropaeneus longimanus*, while *Penaeus aztecus* and *P. duorarum* are common species in the Caribbean. It appears unlikely, that these species have ever been imported for the aquarium trade; we are certainly unaware of any reports to that effect, since most are rather plainly coloured and usually lead a cryptic existence. Yet, a few *Metapenaeopsis* spp. are spectacularly mottled in red and white. There are no known details about their aquarium requirements, but we assume that the benthic species, at least, should be cared for just like other shrimps.

Systematic overview of the infraorder Penaeidea

Family Solenoceridae *
  Haliporoides, Hymenopenaeus

Family Aristeidae *
  Aristaeomorpha, Bentheogennema, Benthesicymus, Gennadas, Plesiopenaeus

Family Penaeidae
  Funchalia, Metapenaeus, Metapenaeopsis, Parapenaeus, Penaeopsis, Penaeus

Family Sergestidae *
  Petalidium, Sergestes, Sergia

Family Luciferidae *
  Lucifer

The families marked with an asterisks (*) are not dealt with in this book.

Suborder Pleocyemata

This suborder contains the more highly developed decapod crustaceans. They are all egg brooders where the eggs give rise to protozoea- or zoea larvae. Moreover, this suborder contains most of those crustaceans that are of interest to the aquarium hobby, such as shrimp, crayfish, crabs and lobsters.

Infraorder Caridea

This is the largest group of shrimps and it contains nearly all the species which are important to the aquarium hobby. Basically, these crustaceans have a more or less cylindrical cephalothorax. The first two pairs of walking legs are equipped with pincers, and here is either the first or the second pair distinctly more powerful and/or larger than the other, especially in sexually mature males. The gills consists of a central stem with plate-like branches. In all species, the female carries the eggs attached to her abdominal appendages, until they hatch as protozoea larvae.

There are several hundred known species, which are incorporated in at least 22 families (see the systematic overview on page 237). We will discuss only six families, but these contain very many species that are highly suitable for a coral reef aquarium. For those reader who wish to acquire further information, the best guide through this infraorder is the publication by HOLTHUIS (1993).

Family Alpheidae

This family contains the symbiosis- or pistol shrimps, which are of particular interest to aquarists, biologist and divers alike. The reason for this is the extraordinary habits of many of the species, which live in symbiosis with various gobies, principally of the genera *Amblyeleotris* and *Cryptocentrus*, in burrows dug into the sandy substrate. This commensal association between shrimp and goby is one of the most often cited examples of symbiosis in the animal kingdom.

It is often stated that the eye sight of the alpheid shrimp is rather poor, or even that they actually are blind. BRUCE (pers. comm., 1999) has, however, never located any positive evidence of this being the case. In fact, it is possible that it actually is nothing but an often repeated myth, with no foundation in reality. In some species, there may be an anatomical reason for weakened eyesight, as the anterior margin of the carapace extends over the eyes. The ecological reason for this could lie in the fact that the eyes need to be protected while the shrimp is digging into the substrate. Yet, the cornea appears well developed and the carapace extension is probably thin enough for the shrimp to see through it. The notion that the shrimp is practically blind and totally dependent on the goby, for instance, to provide a warning against intruders or possible predators, is therefore probably not correct. Although the pistol shrimps that lives together with gobies are the best-known representatives of the family, there are also several species with other modes of life. Most notable are species which live symbiotically with sponges, corals (specifically with stony corals of genera *Seriatopora*, *Stylophora* and *Pocillopora*), as well as with various other invertebrates. The shrimps that associate with sponges appear to be particularly numerous. In one study, 16,000 individuals of *Alpheus* spp. were recorded in a single sponge colony (ZANN, 1980).

The popular name "pistol shrimp" (and also "snapping shrimp") refers to the ability of some of the better known species, to produce distinctly audible clicking sounds with a significantly enlarged pincer (for details see fact sheet on page pp. 240). However, most alpheids do in fact not produce any sounds.

The family Alpheidae is made up of 11 genera, of which genus *Alpheus* and *Synalpheus* are by far the ones most commonly encountered. The two genera can be distinguished from each other by the shape of the front edge of the carapace and by the shape of the movable pincer digit (dactylus) on the third walking legs. In *Alpheus* species the anterior edge of the carapace is rounded underneath the antennas, while in *Synalpheus* it is angular. In *Alpheus* species, the dactylus on the third walking leg comes to a single point, however, in *Synalpheus* species there are two or three points (JONES & MORGAN, 1994). Other genera often represented on coral reefs include *Alpheopsis*, *Amphibetaeus*, *Athanopsis*, *Automate*, *Betaeopsis*, *Racilius* and *Salmoneus*. The colouration is highly variable in all genera, and ranges from a dull overall grey or greenish to extremely colourful, spectacular species. The aquarium trade offers *Alpheus* spp. far more commonly than other genera, in imports from the Indo-Pacific region as well as

from the Caribbean. Many of these shrimps are virtual jewels for a coral reef aquarium, with incredible colours - often in red and white. Moreover, it is not uncommon to find *Alpheus*- or *Synalpheus* species getting inadvertently into an aquarium as "stowaways", with live rocks or colonies of corals. Generally, all alpheids are carnivorous (meat-eating) and feed principally on small invertebrates, but they will readily accept substitute foods in

an aquarium; sometimes algae are also eaten.

There is no reason to be mistrusting towards pistol shrimps in coral reef aquaria. In particular the gobiid associated species are extremely interesting aquarium animals. In addition, their digging activities is decidedly advantageous for the aquarium ecology; it loosens up the bottom substrate and cleans it at the same time. A few shrimp together are easily able to work through the sub-

Systematic overview of the infraorder Caridea

Familie Alpheidae – Symbiosis- and pistol shrimps
  Alpheopsis, Alpheus, Amphibetaeus, Aretopsis, Athanas, Athanopsis, Automate, Beataeopsis, Racilius, Salmoneus, Synalpheus
Family Pasiphaeidae *
  Eupasiphae, Pasiphae
Family Oplophoridae *
  Acanthephyra, Ephyrina, Hymenodora, Meningodora, Notostomus, Oplophorus, Systellaspis
Family Nematocarcinidae *
  Nematocarcinus
Family Hippolytidae – Cleaner- and marble shrimps
  Hippolyte, Latreutes, Ligur, Lysmata, Parhippolyte, Saron, Thor, Tozeuma, Trachycaris
Family Rhynchocinetidae – Dancing shrimps
  Cinetorhynchus, Rhynchocinetes
Family Stylodactylidae *
  Stylodactylus
Family Bathypalaemonellidae *
  Bathypalaemonella
Family Gnathophyllidae – Harlequin shrimps
  Gnathophyllum, Hymenocera
Family Palaemonidae – Rockpool shrimps
  Subfamily Palaemoninae – Rockpool shrimps
    Leandrites, Macrobrachium, Palaemon, Palaemonetes, Urocaridella
  Subfamily Pontoniinae – Commensal pontoniin shrimps
    Allopontonia, Anapontonia, Anchistioides, Anchistus, Apopontonia, Cavicheles, Conchodytes, Coralliocaris, Dasella, Dasycaris, Fennera, Hamodactylus, Hamopontonia, Harpiliopsis, Harpilius, Ischnopontonia, Jocaste, Metapontonia, Onycocaris, Palaemonella, Paranchistus, Parapontonia, Paratypton, Periclimenaeus, Periclimenes, Philarius, Platycaris, Pliopontonia, Pontonia, Pontonides, Pontoniopsis, Propontonia, Stegopontonia, Thaumastocaris, Typton, Vir, Zenopontonia
Family Processidae *
  Processa
Family Pandalidae
  Bitias, Heterocarpus, Plesionika, Pandalus, Stylopandalus
Family Crangonidae *
  Philocheras, Pontocaris, Sabinea
Family Glyphocrangonidae *
  Glyphocrangon
Family Atyidae - Freshwater shrimps *
  Atya, Caridina

The families marked with an asterisks (*) are not dealt with in this book.

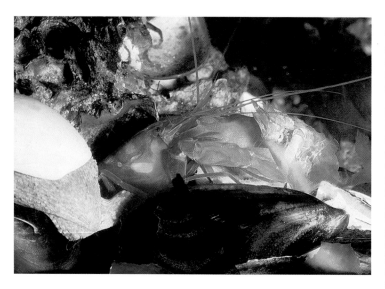

In order to protect itself against predators during and after the critical moulting phase, this pistol shrimp of the genus *Alpheus* has gone into hiding.

Photo: C. Bryce

strate of even relatively large tanks within the time span of a few weeks. Alpheids are usually hardy and can live for years in an aquarium.

Family Hippolytidae

This is another family made up of many shrimp species that are of particular interest and display value for coral reef aquaria. Without doubt, the best-known species is the Pacific white-banded cleaner shrimp *Lysmata amboinensis*, which has been a favourite among marine aquarists for many years. In fact, together with banded cleaner shrimp *Stenopus hispidus* (family Stenopodidae, infraorder Stenopodidea; see page 271), this was the first shrimp we had opportunity to keep in our aquaria. Of course, there are many more species of interest to the marine aquarium hobby, from different genera in this family. Individual species play ecologically different roles and they vary considerably in their appearance.

Most shrimps of family Hippolytidae commonly occur under coral ledges, in caves and in protected crevices. There are also species, which live in association with anemones or sponges. Cleaner shrimps, which remove and feed on parasites from the skin of fishes, are well known. Apparently these shrimps also clean up injured tissue and so prevent infections. This symbiotic relationship is so perfect, that cleaner shrimp are often virtually invited to clean even the inside of the mouth and gills of fishes which are potential predators; and under normal circumstances with immunity from being eaten. This type of cleaning behaviour contributes no doubt to the well-being and health of the fish populations of coral reefs. It may even be justified to consider cleaner shrimps, together with cleaner fishes (e.g. cleaner wrasses, *Labroides* spp.), as so-called key organisms in the ecosystem of coral reefs, similar to herbivores and detritus feeders. In experiments where all cleaning organisms were removed from particular reef areas, declining numbers of fish were noted a few weeks later, together with an increased number of fish with frayed fins and ulcerated sores (et LIMBAUGH al., 1961).

This type of cleaning behaviour has also been observed under aquarium conditions, in such species as *Lysmata amboinensis* and its Caribbean sibling species *L. grabhami* as well as in the cardinal shrimp *L. debelius*, the candy-striped cleaner shrimp *L. californica* and the peppermint or veined cleaner shrimp *L. wurdemani*. Fishes as well as the hand of an attending aquarist are eagerly "cleaned". With the exception of *L. californica*, all the abovementioned species are presented in detail in separate fact sheets on pages 244 to 248. If one were to select a cleaner shrimp on the

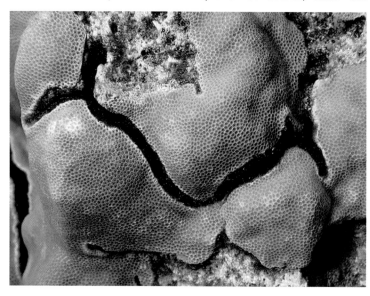

Channels dug into a coral by pistol shrimps.

Pistol shrimp *Alpheus* sp. "KA6-CRU-01" in an aquarium. Photo: R. Balven

basis of its "cleaning effectiveness" alone, the choice would clearly have to be *L. amboinensis*, at least under aquarium conditions. However, none of the above-mentioned species are actually obligate "full-time" cleaners. In fact, all of them utilise other food sources too, such as microscopic invertebrates. In an aquarium they will accept most substitute food, and often they are quite satisfied by snatching particles of whatever food that is offered to the other aquarium inhabitants.

Many aquarists have reported that the presence of cleaner shrimps has a positive effect on the well-being and health of their fishes; this is particularly the case for more sensitive and delicate fish species. All cleaning *Lysmata* spp. have highly conspicuous colouration, which makes it easy for those fishes wishing to be "cleaned", to recognise the clea- ner shrimps as such. Additionally, cleaner shrimp also display particular ways of movement ("dance"), which appear to neutralize the innate instinct in fish to eat the shrimps.

Apart from the listed – very colourful – cleaner shrimp, a few other *Lysmata* spp. are periodically imported for the aquarium trade. These species are usually pale-pink with patterns of darker red stripes, as is very common

Alpheopsis yaldwyni is one of the rarely encountered species of family Alpheidae. It lives among coral rubble and it occurs from Australia to Japan. Photo: L. Newman and A. Flowers

Alpheus spp. and *Synalpheus* spp.
Pistol shrimps, symbiosis shrimps, snapping shrimps

Distribution: Widely distributed in all tropical seas. A few species also occur in subtropical and temperate seas, and two *Alpheus* species are found in cold, northern European seas.

Size: From less than 1 cm in those species that are commonly found on live rocks, to slightly more than 5 cm in species which live in association with gobies.

Reproduction: Details unknown.

Food: Carnivores; these shrimps feed on very small invertebrates. Easy to feed in an aquarium.

Description: Some species live in symbiosis with sponges, corals and other invertebrates, while many others live associated with gobies. These shrimps occur mainly on the sandy bottom of lagoons and close to beaches. *Alpheus*- and *Synalpheus* species are distinguished from each other by 1) the shape of the front edge of the carapace and 2) by the shape of the dactyl of the third leg. In *Alpheus* the front edge of the carapace below the antennae is rounded while it is angular in *Synalpheus*. The dactyl of the third leg has usually only one digit in *Alpheus* while there are two or three digits in *Synalpheus*, (JONES & MORGAN, 1994). In both

Photos:

Top: *Alpheus armatus* from the Caribbean, in an aquarium.
Photo: T. Luther

Centre: *Alpheus* cf. *bellulus* with a goby partner from the Indo-Pacific, in an aquarium.

Bottom: *Alpheus bisincisu* (left) and *A. lottini* (right; photo: Scott W. Michael) from the Indo-Pacific, in an aquarium.

genera the first pair of legs is generally built differently than the other pairs. It is has always one claws, which is heavier and larger, than those in the other pairs. Normally there is a peg on the dactylus of the large claw, which fits tightly into a socket on the fixed finger (pollex). When the peg snaps very quickly back into the socket on the fixed digit, a loud snapping- or pistol-shot-like - sound is generated. This "shot" plays a role when attacking prey (stunning effect) and in the defence against predators (which are driven off), as well as in intra-specific communication ("I am here") within a population (JONES & MORGAN, 1994). The colour varies from a drab grey and greenish to very colourful, depending on the species.

Aquarium requirements: Pistol shrimps are well suited for a community tank as well as for a special aquarium. They are often introduced as stowaways on live rocks. These shrimps must be carefully acclimatised. Although they are frequently not seen, their "pistol shots" are often heard in the evening and at night. We prefer to keep snapping shrimps in a sandy area aquarium (see Volume 1, pages 138-144), together with their symbiotic goby partner.

GA: +; **SE:** +; **CO:** +

Photos

Top: *Alpheus ochrostriatus* with goby, at the Solomon Islands.   Photo: M. Awaii
Centre: *Alpheus* sp. "KA6-CRU-01" from the Indo-Pacific, in an aquarium.   Photo: Scott W. Michael
Bottom: *Alpheus* sp. "KA6-CRU-02" from the Indo-Pacific (left), and *Synalpheus* sp. "KA6-CRU-03" at Rottnest Island, Western Australia (right; photo: C. Bryce).

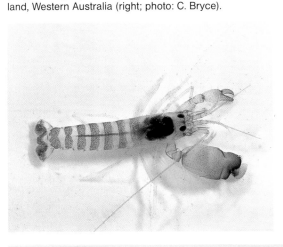

Many species of the family Hippolytidae are cleaner shrimp, which can also be very effective in the removal of parasites from aquarium fish, such as this *Lysmata amboinensis* seen here cleaning the butterfly fish *Chaetodon aya* (left). These crustaceans can become so conditioned, that they will even attempt to clean the hand of the aquarist (right: *Lysmata debelius*).
Photos: Scott W. Michael

within the genus. To identify them to species is often very difficult. In general, all *Lysmata* spp. make excellent aquarium inhabitants, which are rather easy to care for. They are, however, slightly sensitive to rapid changes in water quality. It is therefore important that these crustaceans are very gradually and cautiously acclimatised.

If the tank is large enough, several specimens can be accommodated, possibly with the exception of *Lysmata debelius*, which tend to be slightly more aggressive than the other species. Yet, also this species tend to do better when kept in pairs, than alone. In any case, there must be several hiding places (or suffi-

cient sight barriers), so that separate territories can be established. Fully grown specimens rarely ever reach a size of more than 6 cm. As far as we know, there are no reports of damage to corals or other large invertebrates by cleaner shrimp in an aquarium. Therefore, we can unequivocally recommend cleaner shrimp for a coral reef aquarium, although their crawling activities may irritate delicate corals if they are walked over too often by the shrimps.

All *Lysmata* spp. are frequently observed carrying eggs, however, successfully raising the larvae requires much work and dedication. One principal problem is probably inappropriate feeding. In order

to succeed it requires readily available food sources, such as plankton, which is sufficiently balanced to meet all nutritional demands of the larvae. Copepod naupliii (see pp. 215 and the literature references listed) are one particularly interesting alternative. Unfortunately, for obvious commercial reasons, successful breeders of *Lysmata* spp. rarely ever publish their methods.

Apart from genus *Lysmata* there are still other genera in family Hippolytidae of interest for coral reef aquaria. These are primarily the genera *Saron* and *Thor*, of which *Thor* is without doubt the more valuable for our purposes. The circum-tropically distributed, broken-back shrimp, *Thor amboinensis* is one of our favourites among shrimps (for further details see the relevant fact sheet on page 253). If an opportunity affords itself, one should not hesitate to purchased this shrimp (see NILSEN, 1988).

The Indo-Pacific marbled shrimps of genus *Saron* are often available from aquarium shops. These are virtually all spectacular shrimps, which make very interesting aquarium inhabitants. However, in many cases it has turned out that they are omnivorous food opportunists, which can not always be trusted for keeping together with corals and other sessile invertebrates. In a specifically set up tank, where the other inhabitants have been carefully cho-

The candy-striped cleaner shrimp, *Lysmata californica*, is found in the Eastern Pacific.
Photo: Scott W. Michael

sen to be able to cope with this, *Saron* spp. make incredibly interesting aquarium animals, though. Although *Saron marmoratus* is the most often imported species, other species like *S. inermis* and *S. rectirostris* and other, still undescribed species can also often appear in the aquarium trade (see fact sheets on pages 250-252).

Occasionally, we also encounter species from other genera within family Hippolytidae in the aquarium trade, such as genera *Hippolyte, Latreutes* and *Parhippolyte* (see fact sheet on page 249).

Family Rhynchocinetidae

This family contains the so-called dancing shrimps, which have derived their common name from their graceful movements, reminiscent of ballet dancing. This family is made up of only two genera, *Rhynchocinetes* and *Cinetorhynchus*.

Only one dancing shrimp, *Rhynchocinetes durbanensis*, is commonly available from aquarium shops. For a long period of time it was traded as *R. uritai*, however, OKUNO & TAKEDA (1992) proved that these are two different species (see fact sheet on page 255). Beyond that, we can expect occasionally to find *R. rigens*, which occurs in the tropical Atlantic and the Caribbean, as well as some Indo-Pacific *Cinetorhynchus* species. Occasional imports may occur of many species.

In the natural habitat of dancing shrimps it is not uncommon to find aggregations of many hundred individuals in caves and under ledges. During the day, they remain virtually motionless, however, with the onset of dusk they become increasingly active. Their natural habitat can easily be reconstructed in an aquarium, so that they can display their normal behaviour. It may be a uniquely different idea to display 30 to 40 dancing shrimps in a specifically set up tank, together with some peaceful fishes. On the other hand, these shrimps also do quite well in smaller numbers, for in-

The stellar marble shrimp, *Saron* sp. "KA6-CRU-04" (here a female at Suva Suva, Fiji Islands), is very attractively coloured. It has been found on many occasions at various localities from the Indo-Australian Archipelago eastward to the Fiji Islands, but it has still not been scientifically described yet.

Photo: Scott W. Michael

stance one male and three or four females in a community tank. However, single specimens alone do not seem to do well. Dancing shrimps are generally extremely shy and will run into hiding upon the slightest disturbance. In an aquarium it can take a long time before they have adjusted to their new environment and lose their inhibition.

Sexually mature males are easy to distinguish from females by their larger pincers, which serve mainly to impress other males. They are no threat to other animals of equal size or larger ones. Once peculiarity in dancing shrimp is the hinge on the long rostrum (head projection). This hinge permits an up and down movement of the rostrum relative to the carapace (= "hinge-beak shrimp" is another popular name for these shrimps).

Family Gnathophyllidae

By far the most widely known species of family Gnathophyllidae is the spectacularly coloured harlequin shrimp, *Hymenocera picta*. It is particularly well known among aquarist because of its food selection. As a food specialists it feeds on sea stars, especi-

ally on *Nardoa*- and *Linckia* species, but also on other species, including the infamous crown-of-thorns sea star, *Acanthaster planci*. Although this shrimp hardly grows larger than 5 cm, it readily attacks even very large sea stars. It is well known in aquarist circles, that it will also feed on other echinoderms if sea stars are not available, preferably on sea urchins. Consequently, *H. picta* is clearly no choice for combination with echinoderms, however in order to keep it alive in an aquarium, it must be given sea stars as food. Fortunately, it does well on many sea star species, such as *Asterias rubens*, which is common in the Northeastern Atlantic. It stands to reason that it will also feed on other temperate or cold water sea star species, and its food requirement is not very large (see fact sheet on pages 258-259).

Provided the correct type of food is available, harlequin shrimps do very well in an aquarium; in fact, it has already been successfully bred in captivity. Ideally, it should be kept in pairs, preferably in a small coral reef aquarium, where food and feeding can be closely controlled and monitored. Understandably, it

Lysmata amboinensis
Indo-Pacific white-banded cleaner shrimp

Distribution: Indo-Pacific, including Red Sea.
Size: Maximal length about 5 cm.
Reproduction: This is a protandrous, simultaneous herm-aphrodite, i.e. it is first a male and then (simultaneously) male and female (WIRTZ, 1996), which lives as a "pair". The greenish eggs are carried on the abdomen, and upon hatching the larvae are released into the open water. There

Photos:
Lysmata amboinensis in an aquarium (top), as a cleaner on *Pseudanthias* sp., (centre and bottom row; photos: Scott W. Michael)

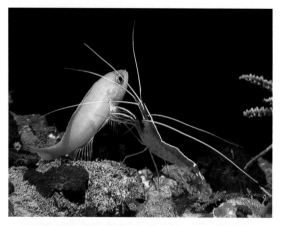

have been repeated reports of successful breeding in a coral reef aquarium, for instance by WOLFRUM (1993).

Food: In its natural habitat this shrimp feeds by removing parasites off fishes. This behaviour is maintained under aquarium conditions. In addition, it will also accept substitute food, such as flake food, or live and frozen plankton.

Description: The rostrum is long and straight, with five or six spines along the upper edge. The abdominal region and sides of the body are orange-coloured, the back is red, separated by a white longitudinal band, which terminates just in front of the tail fan. The tail fan has some white markings, and the antennas and the first pair of walking legs are also white. This species was formerly called "*Hippolysmata grabhami*"; however this is either a junior synonym (*grabhami* was described in 1935, whereas *amboinensis* was described in 1888) or it refers to another species. The name *L. grabhami* is now commonly used for what may be a separate Caribbean species, which is practically identical to *L. amboinensis*, except for small differences in the colouration of the telson (a white border line around the telson in *L. grabhami*, vs. white dots in *L. amboinensis*). It is, however, uncertain wether or not *L. grabhami* constitutes a valid species, or if it may be a geographical colour variety only.

Aquarium requirements: This species has been commonly available in the aquarium trade since the early days of the marine aquarium hobby. Easy to keep, but requires careful acclimatisation. It is advisable to keep it in small groups, with the numbers depending on the size of the tank.

GA: +; SE: +; CO: +

Photos:

Top: *Lysmata amboinensis* with eggs attached to the abdomen. Photo: T. Luther

Bottom row: Zoea larvae of *Lysmata amboinensis*: first stage (left) and second stage (centre), as well as a one month old larvae (right). Photos: R. Brons

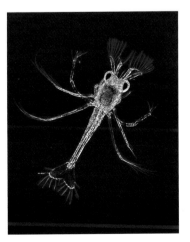
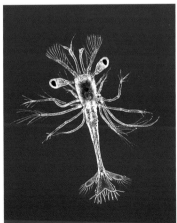

Lysmata debelius
Cardinal cleaner shrimp

Photos:
Lysmata debelius in aquaria (photo below: Scott W. Michael).

Distribution: Indo-Pacific; from the Maldives to Japan and the Society Islands.

Size: Maximal length about 4 cm.

Reproduction: This species was captive-bred and successfully reared for the very first time in the hatchery of Tropical Marine Centre (England) in 1998. Currently, this company is engaged in improving its techniques for rearing the species on an economically viable, commercial basis.

Food: In its natural habitat, this shrimp feeds on ectoparasites removed from fishes. This type of behaviour is maintained under aquarium conditions. In addition, it also accepts substitute food, such as flake food, or live and frozen plankton. It will also feed on minute animals, such as copepods and roundworms, found in all reef tanks and live Artemia is also an excellent food.

Description: A very beautiful cleaner shrimp, which has been known to the aquarium hobby for a long time, but it was not scientifically described until 1983, by BRUCE. The

antennas and legs are white. The cardinal red body is marked with a few distinct, white patches. This is probably an adaption to a life in deep water (from 20 m down) and in habitats where permanent twilight prevails. Lives together as a "pair" (separate sexes or protandrous, simultaneous hermaphrodites?), and strongly defends its territory.

Aquarium requirements: Very shy, but basically easy to keep. Should be given a tank conforming to the natural habitat of this species, and provided with dark caves and similar hiding places. Although this species lives naturally in pairs, we have kept a group together with a group of *Lysmata amboinensis* successfully for years, in a medium-size tank. It is possible that their natural behaviour had been suppressed by the prevailing aquarium conditions. Acclimatisation of *L. debelius* must be done carefully, and this species requires a long period of adjustment to its new habitat.

GA: +; **SE:** +; **CO:** +

Photos:
About 10 weeks old larvae of *Lysmata debelius* (top and centre), and juvenile shrimps after the last larval moult (bottom left and right).   Photos: Tropical Marine Centre

Lysmata wurdemanni
Peppermint or veined shrimp

Distribution: Caribbean; from New Jersey, Florida and the Bahamas, southward throughout the Caribbean Sea and on to Brazil.

Size: Maximal length about 5 cm.

Reproduction: Protandrous hermaphrodite, where the oldest male changes into a female, or possibly into a protandrous (simultaneous) hermaphrodite (as reported for *L. amboinensis*) (see fact sheet on page 244-245), usually living together as "pairs". This species has already been bred repeatedly under aquarium conditions (RILEY, 1994; GELLINGER-TUNZE, 1995; SCHÖNE, 1995). Breeding occurs continuously throughout the year. RILEY (1994) kept his brood stock at a water temperature of 20 to 30 °C and a salinity of 33 to 37 ‰, with an illumination period of 12 hours daily. The animals were fed regularly. Under these conditions eggs were produced every ten to twelve days, which developed for nine to eleven days while attached to the pleopods, below the abdomen. The number of eggs varied from 579 to 1707. GELLINGER-TUNZE (1995) reports, that the number of eggs depends upon the size of the female, and that the larvae are released at night, three weeks after fertilization and at a water temperature of 27 degrees Celsius. It is strongly recommended, to have the larvae hatch in a separate tank with the same water condition as in the main tank, and to remove the female immediately. Newly released larvae were about 2.2 mm long. The first moult occurred after two days, when stalked eyes and a red median line are present. The larvae moult at regular intervals,

usually every two to three days. From the 14th day onward a pair of long hind legs develops to twice the size of the body length. After ten to twelve weeks the juvenile shrimps had reached a size of about 10 mm. The survival rate of the larvae appears strongly dependent upon the type of food offered. In that respect, SCHÖNE (1995) comments that he was only able to rear juvenile shrimps, when the first food offered was a mixture of *Artemia* nauplii, two-day old *Artemia* raised on *Dunaliella* algae, and *Brachionus plicatilis*, which had been placed for at least three hours in a *Dunaliella* algae culture, prior to the feeding. RILEY (1994) lists a maximum survival rate of 22 %, when he offered as first food *Artemia* larvae, which were less than 6 hours old, to newly hatched *Lysmata* larvae. With increasing growth of the larvae, he fed larger *Artemia*, which in turn had been fed on the algae *Isochrysis galbana* and *Nannochloropsis oculata*, as well as on "Super Selco", a type of food developed by Aquarium Systems, Incorporated (Mentor, Ohio, USA) for feeding Artemia. Following metamorphosis into juvenile shrimps (40 to 45 days after release), he fed macerated fish and shrimp meat. Later on, the juvenile shrimps would take the same food as the adults.

Food: In its natural habitat, this species feeds on ectoparasites removed from fishes. This behaviour is maintained also under aquarium conditions. In addition, this shrimp will accept substitute food, such as flake food, or live and frozen plankton.

Description: Generally solitary or as a "pair", often associates with sponges of genus *Aplysina*. (RILEY, 1994). Pale pinkish white body colour; body and legs covered with thin bright-red or orange-red stripes.

Aquarium requirements: Easy to keep. Can be kept as a group in an aquarium.

GA: +; **SE:** +; **CO:** +

Photos:
Lysmata wurdemanni in an aquarium (left) and juvenile shrimp after two moults (top). Photos: H. Schöne

Parhippolyte uveae
Sugarcane shrimp

Distribution: Widely distributed throughout the entire Indo-Pacific region.
Size: Maximal body length 3 cm.
Reproduction: Details unknown.
Food: Habitat food and feeding behaviour unknown. Under aquarium conditions, this species will accept most substitute food.
Description: Primarily found in intertidal pools with variable salinities; where it lives solitary, in pairs or in small groups. According to GOSLINER et al. (1996), this species is closely related to *Koror misticius*, which lives primarily in submarine caves and has orange body stripes, while *Parhippolyte uveae* has red stripes. The resemblance between both species is quite considerable, so that they can be mistaken for each other. While *K. misticius* prefers shaded areas in an aquarium, *P. uveae* tends to stay in brightly illumina-

ted areas. *P. uveae* has a very short rostrum, which extends up to the eyes only. The legs and antennas are very long. The body is elongated and is encircled by five or six orange and white rings. The legs, antennas and abdominal appendages are red and white.
Aquarium requirements: A rather shy species. It is best kept in an intertidal aquarium, or alternately as a small group in a community tank, with ample hiding places.

GA: +; **SE:** +/-; **CO:** +/-

Photo:
Parhippolyte uveae in an aquarium.

Photo: Scott W. Michael

Saron inermis
Pinecone marble shrimp

Distribution: Indo-Pacific; Details are unknown.
Size: Maximum body length about 3 cm.
Reproduction: Details unknown.
Food: Carnivore, but details about food and feeding behaviour are unknown. We and other aquarists have observed this species feeding in an aquarium on corals with small polyps and on encrusting anemones.
Description: The female has a whitish body with numerous, more or less diffuse brown to brownish orange patches; the chelipeds are short. Abdomen of the male is covered with numerous brown to orange-brown spots, except the tail fan, which appears dark. Its chelipeds are longer than those of the female. In both sexes the chelipeds and pereiopods are white and purple banded. The ventral side of the carapace carries four sharp, pointed spines. The an-

tennas, the anterior part of the rostrum and the oral region are coloured purple to reddish-purple.
Aquarium requirements: It is advisable to keep this species in a small special aquarium with many hiding places. It is nocturnal, very shy and so in a community tank it will probably remain in hiding most of the time, rarely to be seen out in the open. Therefore, this species is more difficult to keep than the other *Saron* species, especially since it can also harm corals and other sessile invertebrates.

GA: +/-; **SE:** +/-; **CO:** +/-

Photo:
Saron inermis (male) in an aquarium.
Photo: Scott W. Michael

Saron marmoratus
Common marble shrimp

Distribution: Indo-Pacific, from the Red Sea and East Africa eastward to Hawaii.

Size: Body length about 4 cm, but the total length, including chelipeds, is considerably larger in mature males.

Reproduction: Details unknown.

Food: This species feeds in various ways. In its natural habitat we have observed it at night searching for food among algae and on sessile invertebrates. Aquarium observations have revealed that a wide range of substitute food are accepted, such as brine shrimp, plankton, flake food, frozen food, and larger pieces of "squashed" shrimp and fish meat. However, we have also seen this species feed on coral polyps and also damage other sessile invertebrates. This type of feeding behaviour is perhaps a consequence of nutritionally deficient substitute food or in fact, because of substitute food. It is recommended to feed this shrimp in the evening, after the main tank lighting has been turned off.

Description: Active during crepuscular and nocturnal conditions in protected habitats, where this shrimp tends to hide in crevices and cracks during the day. The colouration is mysterious and indistinct. With basic tones of brown or greenish-brown, the body also has a scattered pattern of numerous greenish patches, which in turn have a variable number of tiny brilliant white spots. The rostrum is long and spiny, covered by tufts of long cirri along its ventral side and on its base. The legs, chelipeds and antennas have bands shaded in brown and white. The chelipeds in adult males can be as long or longer than the body. In females they are shorter, but not less powerful.

Aquarium requirements: Frequently imported species, but in our experience the aquarium trade usually carries only females or sub-adult males, which have not yet developed the long chelipeds of adults. This is a very hardy and spectacular aquarium animal, which is best kept in a special aquarium, which does not need to be large, but it should contain a few caves and other suitable hiding places for a small group of these shrimps. If they are kept in a community tank, an aquarist may have to accept the fact that some corals and other sessile invertebrates could be damaged by this species.

GA: +/-; **SE:** +; **CO:** +/-

Photos:
Saron marmoratus in an aquarium: male (top; photo: Scott W. Michael) and female (centre and bottom).

Saron rectirostris
Violet-legged marble shrimp

Distribution: Indo-Pacific; details are unknown.
Size: Maximum body length about 4 cm.
Reproduction: Details unknown.
Food: Carnivorous, but details about food and feeding behaviour are unknown. In an aquarium, other aquarists and we have observed this species feeding on corals with small polyps and on encrusting anemones.
Description: The appearance of the body is reminiscent of a fragment of dead coral. The colour is white with pale brown patches of different sizes. The legs and the tail fan are violet. Males have longer chelipeds than females. The dorsal margin of the carapace has about six sharp, pointed spines, which are covered by small cirri.
Aquarium requirements: This species should be kept in a small, special aquarium with many hiding places. It is nocturnal, very shy and in a community tank it is likely to remain mostly in hiding, rarely to be seen out in the open. Therefore, it is more difficult to keep than the other *Saron* species, especially since it may harm corals and other sessile invertebrates.

GA: +/-; **SE:** +/-; **CO:** +/-

Photo:
Saron rectirostris (female) in an aquarium.

Thor amboinensis
Broken back shrimp, "sexy shrimp"

Photos:
Thor amboinensis in an aquarium (top) and at Sulawesi (bottom; photo: Scott W. Michael)

Distribution: Circumtropical.
Size: Maximum body length 2 cm.
Reproduction: Details unknown.
Food: Probably feeds on small organisms, but details unknown. In an aquarium most substitute food are accepted, including brine shrimp, frozen and freeze-dried plankton, as well as dry food.
Description: The base colour is brown; the thorax and the abdomen are covered by a few opalescent large saddle patches and dots, which are bordered by a thin, purple line. The chelipeds are small and barely developed. This species lives in association with anemones and corals, normally in pairs, but sometimes also in small groups.
Aquarium requirements: A very attractive shrimp, which – unfortunately – is rarely ever imported. Should be kept in a special aquarium, together with other animals that live symbiotically with anemones. We have kept this species successfully together with anemones of genus *Phymanthus*. Can also be easily kept together with small fishes and small shrimps of genus *Periclimenes*. Acclimatisation must be done very carefully.

GA: +; **SE:** +; **CO:** +

Cinetorhynchus concolor in Christmas Island.　　　Photo: C. Bryce

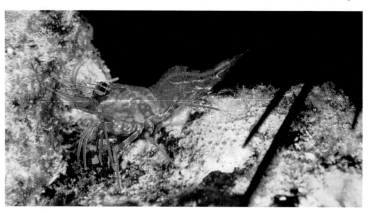

Cinetorhynchus hendersoni in the Maldives.

Cinetorhynchus hiatti in an aquarium.　　　Photo: Scott W. Michael

is important to remove all uneaten remnants of a sea star from the aquarium promptly, once the shrimps have stopped feeding on it.

There are different views on the systematics of harlequin shrimps, because some authors actually see two species: *Hymenocera picta* from the Pacific and *H. elegans* from the Indian Ocean. This separation, apparently first proposed by DEBELIUS (1983), is based only on colour differences. *H. picta* has red colour blotches, while *H. elegans* has brownish ones. We have difficulties finding scientific support for this assumption, nor other justification for regarding them as anything more than geographical variations of a single species. However, recent studies by Nancy KNOWLTON and colleagues on shrimp sibling species (BRUCE, pers. comm., 1999) has indicated that the number of shrimp species in general is underestimated by a factor of five. Thus, it may very well be that *H. picta* and *H. elegans* are distinct species. It would be a most interesting topic to study the possibilities of interbreeding in an aquarium!

The family Gnathophyllidae contains yet some other shrimps, but most of these do hardly ever appear in the aquarium trade. Only *Gnathophyllum* species are occasionally imported. They are rather small shrimps (maximum length 2 to 3 cm), and because of their characteristic colouration they are generally referred to as bumble bee shrimp. *G. americanum* is a particularly strikingly coloured species and, because of its circumtropical distribution, also the one, which is most likely to be imported. It too is a food specialist and feeds on the tube feet of sea stars, sea urchins and sea cucumbers.

Family Palaemonidae

This family incorporates some highly variable shrimps with a multitude of body shapes and sizes, and a wide range of habits. There are representatives in the

Rhynchocinetes durbanensis
Common dancing- or hinge-beak shrimp

Distribution: Indo-Pacific; from South Africa to Indonesia, Papua-New Guinea, the Phillippines and the Ryukyu Islands.
Size: Maximum body length 4 cm
Reproduction: Details unknown.
Food: Carnivore, which feeds mainly on tiny organisms. Under aquarium conditions, it will quickly accept most substitute food, including brine shrimp, frozen or freeze-dried plankton, as well as flake food.
Description: Occurs mainly in larger groups deep in caves, cracks and crevices. The male has much longer chelipeds than the female. For many years this species has been erroneously considered as *Rhynchocinetes uritai*, however, the real *R. uritai* is confined in its distribution to Japan and Korea (OKUNO & TAKEDA, 1992), and so there is little reason to assume that *R. uritai* will be imported for the aquarium trade. Colour patterns of the two species are very similar, with red lines on a translucent background, coupled with some white markings. However, in *R. durbanensis* the white markings are made of white ocelli and white lines in the interspaces between each red line, and a Y-shaped white mark on the dorsal surface of the carapace; whereas in *R. uritai* there are only small white ocelli scattered among the red lines. The red is somewhat brighter in *R. durbanensis* than in *R. uritai*.

There are also some morphological differences, but of these only the structure of the rostrum is clearly discernable on live animals in an aquarium. The rostrum of *R. durbanensis* has 9-10 teeth on the upper margin and 16-18 teeth on the lower margin, while the rostrum of *R. uritai* has 7-8 and 13-15 teeth respectively.
Aquarium requirements: *Rhynchocinetes durbanensis* has been established in the aquarium hobby already for a very long time. It is a hardy and highly suitable animal in particular for a cave aquarium, where it should be kept in a large group. This, however, involves a tedious feeding regimen. Keeping these shrimps together with large fish, e.g. *Calloplesiops altivelis* must be avoided, since the fish will gradually decimate the group of prawns.

GA: +; **SE:** +; **CO:** +

Photos:
Large group of *Rhynchocinetes durbanensis* at Sulawesi (top; photo: Scott W. Michael) and a male (centre) as well as a female (bottom; photo: Scott W. Michael) in an aquarium.

Two harlequin shrimps, *Hymenocera picta*, feeding in an aquarium on *Asterias rubens*, a sea star native to the Northern Atlantic.   Photo: W. A. Tomey

oceans as well as in freshwater habitats, and a very large number of species are found on coral reefs. The family is divided into two subfamilies: Palaemoninae and Pontoniinae. The species of these two groups have very different modes of life, and have thus different significance to a coral reef aquarium.

The subfamily Palaemoninae is known mainly for the large freshwater shrimps of genus *Macrobrachium*. These are extremely important aquaculture species throughout south-east Asia, and regarded as superior eating, especially in Thailand and Burma.

Beyond that, it is worthwhile to note the so-called rock pool shrimps of the genus *Palaemon*, which occur worldwide in the sea as well as in brackish water. With their greenish or brownish, transparent bodies, marked with patches or lines of different colours, they are fairly inconspicuous; however, a closer look often reveals considerable subdued beauty. This genus is very common all over the world, including in tropical habitats, but so far we have never encountered tropical spe-

cies in the trade. The aquarium hobby is acquainted with a few *Palaemon* species from the Mediterranean Sea and the Atlantic Ocean, which are easy to keep. It stands to reason, that the tropical *Palaemon* species are equally durable as aquarium inhabitants, and that they would be easy to keep, hardy and thriving on most kinds of substitute foods. Generally, *Palaemon* spp. do, however, not occur on properly developed coral reefs, but they are commonly found in adjacent rock pools.

Perhaps more interesting, subfamily Palaemoninae also includes the genus *Urocaridella* known to aquarists for *U. antonbruunii*. It is not a very conspicuous shrimp, but it is nevertheless attractively coloured. It lives as a cleaner of fishes (see fact sheet on page 261).

The majority of the reef-dwelling species of this family belongs to the subfamily Pontoniinae, which contains about 35 genera with at least 200 species inhabiting coral reefs. A few are free-living micro-predators, but the overwhelming majority are com-

mensals on various other invertebrates, such as sponges, anemones, hydroids, corals, molluscs, echinoderms and ascidians. Some few pontoniines also act as cleaners on fishes, but this kind of association does not occur widely in this group. It is probable that the shrimps are not totally dependent upon their cleaning activities for food, and capable of supplementing their diet by predation or scavenging. For fishes, however, this relationship can be of significance. The Appendix of this book (pages 424-429) gives an overview of the most important commensal species of the subfamily and their hosts, but it does not include the shrimp-fish relationships.

Although we, in accordance with other authors, choose to refer to these symbiotic relationships as commensalism, this is not necessarily 100 % correct. In most cases very little is known on the exact trophic relationship between host and shrimp. In probability a range of different relationships are involved here, which can conceivably extend through the entire spectrum from outright

Gnathophyllum americanum
Bumblebee Shrimp

Distribution: Circumtropical.

Size: Maximal length 2 to 3 cm.

Reproduction: Details unknown.

Food: Feeds principally on suction feet of spiny-skinned animals (Echinodermata), but according to BAENSCH & DEBELIUS (1992) this species will also accept substitute food.

Description: Generally solitary or in pairs, free-living or parasitising sea stars, sea urchins and sea cucumbers. The head-chest section is blunt and the rostrum is only short. The claws are of variable size, and the larger one is usually as long as the body. The body is white covered with many black-bronze-coloured bands. Tail fan and chelipeds are marked with yellow-orange patches.

Aquarium requirements: This species should be kept in a special aquarium, together with sea stars, sea urchins or sea cucumbers. Such a tank need not be larger than 50 litres.

GA: +; **SE:** +/-; **CO:** +/-

Photos:

Gnathophyllum americanum, at Muiron Island, Northwest Cape, Western Australia (top; photo: C. Bryce) and in Papua-New Guinea (bottom; photo: L. Newman and A. Flowers).

Hymenocera picta
Harlequin shrimp

Distribution: Indo-Pacific; occurs widely from the Red Sea and East Africa eastward via Indonesia, northern and north-eastern Australia to Hawaii.

Size: Maximal length about 5 cm.

Reproduction: Separate sexes. This species has been bred successfully at the Waikiki Aquarium (Honolulu, Hawaii). The following breeding details after KRAUL & NELSON (1986): The male fertilises the female immediately after moulting. One female can produce anywhere from 200 to 5,000 eggs per month, whereby the egg numbers are clearly dependent upon the food supply. The females attaches the red (0.8 x 0.6 mm) eggs to its pleopods. The larvae hatch a few days prior to the next moult of the female, and then go through a larval stage for five to seven weeks. Newly hatched larvae are about 1.4 mm long, 0.64 mm wide and 0.43 mm high. For the first few days they do not need any food; however, after the first moult, when the stalked eyes are developing, they require planktonic food, such as rotifers, *Artemia* nauplii and copepods. When live copepods are fed, the survival rates of the larvae increase substantially. After five to seven weeks the larvae are about 3 mm long and 2 mm wide. This is the final larval stage. The pleopods have become branched, and life commences as

Photos:
Hymenocera picta in an aquarium (top; photo: Scott W. Michael), in Papua-New Guinea (centre; photo: L. Newman and A. Flowers), and on a *Nardoa* sea star (bottom left; photo: P. Schupp), as well as feeding on a Crown-of-thorns sea star, *Acanthaster planci*, at Papua-New Guinea (bottom right; photo: L. Newman and A. Flowers)

a shrimp. Juvenile shrimps settle down on corals, sea stars or on other firm substrates, or sometimes swim rather elegantly through open water. The body is still almost transparent. During the following weeks pink, purple and cream-coloured pigments start to appear. During this stage, the young shrimps can survive for at least two weeks without food. Probably, they accept only *Linckia* sea stars during this stage. The juvenile are not particularly aggressive.

Food: A carnivorous shrimp, which feeds exclusively on sea stars, specifically on *Nardoa*- and *Linckia* species, but may also take Crown-of-thorns sea stars *Acanthaster planci*. It is assumed, that harlequin shrimps anaesthetize a sea star, then turn it over and attack its arms (COLIN & ARNESON, 1995), but only a small piece of the sea star is actually eaten. It is possible that in the natural habitat, a sea star can sewer the arm attacked by these shrimps, and then flee and regenerate that arm again. Under aquarium conditions, harlequin shrimps must be fed with sea stars. There are reports, that they will also accept sea star species native to the North Sea, such as the common *Asterias rubens* (BAENSCH & DEBELIUS, 1992). The feeding rate of harlequin shrimps is not particularly high. KRAUL & NELSON (1986) indicate, that only one feeding per month is required; however, the growth rate of these shrimps and egg development is clearly dependent upon the availability of food. These authors also report, that newly established juvenile harlequin shrimps accept only *Linckia* sea stars as food. The feeding rate was such that five juvenile shrimps consumed only a single *Linckia* specimen (7 to 8 cm large) in a three months period, which corresponds to a rate of less than 0.1 *Linckia* per juvenile shrimp per month. It has been proven that *Hymenocera picta* is an efficient predator on *Asterina* spp., the tiny microphagous sea stars that are so common in many reef aquaria, and that it may be used as a means to control the populations of these (PINTAK, 2000).

Description: The second pair of walking legs is enlarged and flattened. The mouth is strongly developed and very well equipped for feeding on sea stars. The body is white with red or brownish patches, with or without a blue margin, in a harlequin-like fashion. There is an on-going debate whether there is more than one species. The literature carries two scientific names, that is, *Hymenocera picta* and *H. elegans*. Yet, there are also reasons to believe, that the colour differences may be mere variations of *H. picta*, possibly as stable colour forms. Harlequin shrimps live always in pairs, and female secrete pheromones, which act as attractants for males.

Aquarium requirements: Hardy and docile aquarium inhabitants, which will readily accept small tanks. If the correct food is available, they are easy to keep, but they really must be kept as a pair in special aquarium. Well suited for captive breeding trials.

GA: +/-; **SE:** +/-; **CO:** +/-

Photos:

Left: newly settled (left) and a one-week old juvenile *Hymenocera picta* after settling down. (right).

Photo: A. Nelson, Waikiki Aquarium

Right: *Hymenocera picta* specimens bred at the Waikiki Aquarium.

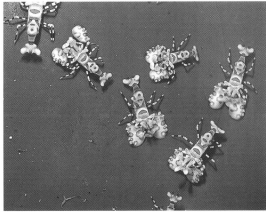

Left: Many rock pool shrimp are nearly transparent, like this unidentified specimen at Shark Bay, Western Australia (photo: C. Bryce). Right: This palaemonid shrimp *Leandrites cyrtorhynchus* is widely distributed throughout the Indo-Pacific. It has frequently been observed cleaning fish (photo: Scott W. Michael).

predation or parasitism to true commensalism. Nevertheless, we are reasonably comfortable with retaining the term "commensalism", especially since all aquarium observations on this have revealed a fundamentally commensal relationship. However, it is still conceivable that a commensal shrimp, living on a cnidarian animal, may take a bite from a tentacle or ingest mucus off the host, to such a degree that the host suffers. This is simply the way nature operates; it is not a dream world established for the benefit of man kind (nor for aquarists, for that matter).

There is considerable variation among the commensal shrimps in terms of the degree of host specificity. Some are specialised over their entire geographical distribution on a single, particular host, while others can live on many different hosts, even within a small area. Depending upon what host particular shrimps are associated with, the shrimp display different forms of adaptation in respect to morphological modification to their basic body structure. Free-living pontoniines, such as e.g. *Periclimenes tenuipes*, are basically slender, with a well-developed, strongly toothes rostrum and slender, elongated pereiopods (*tenuis*, Latin = thin, slender, delicate; and *pes*, Latin = foot). According to BRUCE (1976b), frequently occurring host specific

adaptions can be categorised in five main groups:

1. **Adaptation to small niches:** Many of the commensal pontoniines are very small, e.g. *Fennerea chacei*, which lives on stony corals of genus *Pocillopora*, reaches a maximum adult size of 6 mm.

2. **Adaptation to narrow spaces:** The body may be strongly dorso-ventrally flattened or sideways compressed, e.g. *Platycaris latirostris*, a dorso-ventrally flattened species, which lives inactively among corallites of *Galaxea fascicularis*, while *Ischnopontonia lophos*, a laterally compressed species, lives actively among the corallites of the same coral species.

3. **Adaptation to tubular spaces:** Particularly among shrimps living in the channels of sponges, such adaptations may be necessary. For instance, *Onycocaris amakusensis* and *Typton* spp. have vermiform bodies with elongated, nearly cylindrical abdomens and very small thoracic regions.

4. **Adaptation to confined spaces:** Shrimps that live enclosed in small confined rooms, for instance, inside bivalve molluscs or inside galls (formed by the shrimp itself) on stony corals,

may develop greatly swollen bodies. For instance, *Conchodytes* spp. inside clam shells and *Paratypton siebenrocki*, which creates galls on *Acropora* spp.

5. **Adaptation to exposed situations:** In order to avoid detection, commensal shrimps which live at exposed sites, may have modifications which assure camouflage. Since most pontoniin shrimps are rather cryptic in habits, such adaptations are not common; however, one example is the extremely slender, elongated body of *Stegopontonia commensalis*, which lives among the long spines of *Diadema* sea urchins.

Beyond that, colour adaptations are common. Many coral reef-dwelling shrimps have striking colour patterns, and often they are multicoloured. Yet in their natural habitat they remain quite inconspicuous. BRUCE (1976b) divides colour patterns into two main groups:

1 those that blend into the surroundings, and
2 colour patterns which are in contrast to the surroundings.

The first main group includes shrimp, which resemble their host in terms of colouration, such as species of genera *Stegopontonia*,

Urocaridella antonbruunii
Cleaning rock pool shrimp

Distribution: Widely distributed throughout the Indo-Pacific.

Size: Maximum body length about 3 cm.

Reproduction: Details unknown.

Food: Feeds on ectoparasites removed from fishes.

Description: Occurs in large groups, living in caves, where individual specimens mostly "float" in the open water area. In the Maldives we have observed this species removing parasites from large fishes, and so this is a genuine cleaner shrimp. The body is transparent, marked with white and red patches. The rostrum is long. The pereiopods and chelipeds are banded white and red. Often listed erroneously as *Leandrites cyrtorhynchus* in the literature.

Aquarium requirements: A rarely imported shrimp, which should be kept in a special aquarium. It is possible (and even likely) that this species will be eaten by large fish in an aquarium. Must generally be considered as difficult to keep in an aquarium; a shrimp which requires special care and attention.

GA: -; **SE:** +/-; **CO:** +/-

Photos:
Urocaridella antonbruunii in an aquarium (top; photo: Scott W. Michael) and at Sabolan Island, Indonesia (bottom; photo: C. Bryce)

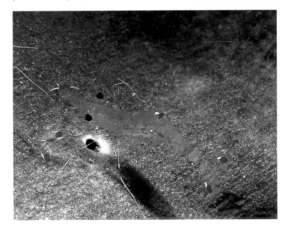

The commensal shrimp *Allopontonia iaini* can easily be mistaken for the porcelain shrimp *Allogalathea elegans*. While the porcelain shrimp associate with feather stars, the commensal shrimp lives on sea urchins (as here on *Asthenosoma varium*).   Photo: Scott W. Michael

Dasycaris and *Pontonides*. In others the colour pattern has been structured in such a way, that the outline of their body is being optically dissolved, as in species of genera *Harpiliopsis* and *Jocaste*. Yet others are more or less transparent, so that they appear almost glassy, for instance, like the rather transparent *Periclimenes diversipes, P. kempfi* and *P. inornatus*.

At first thought, it may appear somewhat incomprehensible, why there are species with a colour pattern, which is in strong contrast to their surroundings. There are, however, good reasons for this as well. Many shrimps can virtually afford to be colourful and multicolored, since such conspicuous colouration does not pose any danger in their well protected habitats of narrow cracks and crevices. *Coralliocaris superba* and *C. graminea* are good examples of this. They are shiny white and iridescent green, respectively, but they are well-protected among the branches of their host corals. In other cases, conspicuous colouration can have a signal effect, which assure these shrimps a certain advantage within their natural surroundings. This, for instance, is the case with the popular aquarium species *Periclimenes brevicarpalis*, which exhibits a striking colour pattern, in particular on its tail fan. The reason for such obvious coloura-

tion is hard to explain, however, it has been demonstrated that these shrimps are hardly ever molested by fishes, while other shrimps of the same size are readily eaten (BRUCE, 1976b). Moreover, under aquarium conditions it has been observed, that some fishes will actually entice *P. brevicarpalis* to "clean" them, in cases when legitimate cleaner species were not available. But this shrimp has never been observed cleaning fish. Could this be a case of mimicry?

Furthermore, at night some pontoniin shrimps can change their normal colours into more conspicuous colour patterns, than those displayed during the day.

Commensal pontoniines make very interesting inhabitants for a coral reef aquarium. It is particularly rewarding to keep them in small tanks, where the association with their host can be studied closely and in greater detail. It is very important to keep in mind, that they are rather delicate creatures, which require gentle handling while in transit, during acclimatization and in terms of aquarium care and maintenance. Most species must also be given a correct host, if they are expected to live a prolonged period of time. Some species will accept many different hosts (see the list in Appendix, on pages 424-429), so that it is not difficult to provide a suitable partner for them. The

easiest way, of course, is to purchase a host together with a commensal shrimp, at the same time. Most of our own experiences have been gained from species that live in association with sea anemones. The reason for that is simply that species which exhibit this sort of association are much more readily available in the aquarium trade than most others. Essentially these commensal shrimps will accept sand or rock anemones of the genus *Phymanthus* (see Volume 2, page 259) quite willingly. Also, these anemones have the advantage that they are less troublesome to keep than most of the larger sea anemones, which frequently are hosts of commensal shrimps in the sea.

Following below we present some interesting commensal shrimps on fact sheets, pages 266 to 270.

Family Pandalidae

Shrimps of the family Pandalidae occur only very rarely on coral reefs. From a European perspective though, they are, nevertheless, very important because they are eaten in huge quantities. The northern deep sea prawn, *Pandalus borealis*, which lives in the North Atlantic, is commercially fished in huge masses by trawl. Normally, the entire catch is cooked on board, right after capture, so that the average person rarely ever gets to see the live shrimp. This is a pity, since it is a very beautiful species with its faint, glassy-red colouration. It would indeed make an excellent inhabitant for a cold water marine aquarium.

In other parts of the world different species are important for human consumption, such as *Plesionika edwardsi* in the Mediterranean region, and *Pandalus danae* as well as *P. platyceros* along the eastern coastline of the United States and eastern Canada. At this very point it appears highly relevant to mention the fact, that we as aquarists remove only very few shrimp for their natural habitat, compared to

Periclimenes colemani in Indonesia.
Photo: Scott W. Michael

Perclimenes magnificus in Indonesia.
Photo: J. Cairns-Michael

Periclimenes ornatellus in the Maldives.
Photo: Scott W. Michael

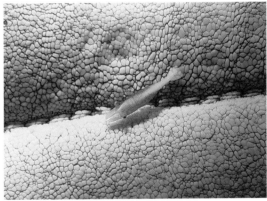

Periclimenes soror in Indonesia.
Photo: C. Bryce

Periclimenes cf. *tosaensis* in Papua-New Guinea.
Photo: L. Newman and A. Flowers

Periclimenes venustus in the Great Barrier Reef.
Photo: L. Newman and A. Flowers

Periclimenes cf. *commensalis.*
Photo: Scott W. Michael

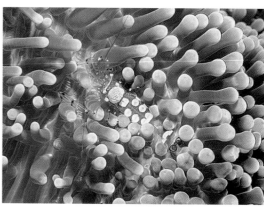

Periclimenes sp. "KA6-CRU-06".
Photo: J. Cairns-Michael

Periclimenes cf. *holthuisi* ("KA6-CRU-07").
Photo: J. Cairns-Michael

Periclimenes cf. *brevicarpalis* ("KA6-CRU-08").
Photo: J. Cairns-Michael

Periclimenes cf. *brevicarpalis,* ("KA6-CRU-09").
Photo: Scott W. Michael

Periclimenes cf. *brevicarpalis,* ("KA6-CRU-10").
Photo: J. Cairns-Michael

Left: Unidentified commensal shrimp, possibly a *Hamodactylus* sp., at Bintan Island, Indonesia (photo: C. Bryce). Right: *Stegopontonia commensalis* lives normally among the long spines of *Diadema* sea urchins (photo: Scott W. Michael).

Left: *Pontonides* cf. *unciger* (seen here at Bintan Island, Indonesia) has adapted its colours and shape to a life on black corals (photo: C. Bryce). Right: Pair of the free-living commensal shrimp *Periclimenes* cf. *tenuipes* in the Maldives (photo: Scott W. Michael).

the many thousands of tonnes which go towards human consumption. Commercial prawn trawling is also heavily criticized, rightfully or wrongly - depending on the local situation, for destroying marine habitats and adding to overfishing. In any event, such trawling is of course highly non-selective, resulting in large by-catches of no commercial value. We too enjoying eating prawns, but we find it unjustified, that the focus of environmentalists far too often is directed to the small scale catching with hand nets done for the aquarium trade. After all, one should never forget that being involved in the aquarium hobby opens the eyes of many to the magnificence of nature and so enhances environmental awareness! Please see also chapter 14 of this book series' Volume 1, pages 327-345, on "Marine Aquaristics and Nature Conservation".

The spot prawn, *Pandalus platyceros* (family Pandalidae), is common in temperate and tropical regions of the eastern Pacific Ocean.

Photo: Scott W. Michael

Periclimenes brevicarpalis
White-patched anemone shrimp

Distribution: Indo-Pacific; from the Red Sea and East Africa to the Line- and Marshall Islands.

Size: Maximum body length for males is 4 cm; females only to 2 to 3 cm.

Reproduction: Details unknown.

Food: Carnivorous, but details unknown. Under aquarium conditions most substitute food is eagerly taken, including brine shrimp, frozen or freeze-dried plankton, as well as flake food; will also feed on detritus.

Description: Lives in association with anemones, especially with the Pizza Anemone *Cryptodendrum adhaesivum* (see Volume 2, Page 263). The transparent body is covered with large white patches. Males have more patches than females, which are also smaller. The tail fan is white and reddish brown.

Aquarium requirements: The most frequently available anemone shrimp in the aquarium trade, but it is not a species that is hardy and easy to keep. It can really only be recommended to experienced aquarists, and does also require careful acclimatisation. It is imperative that a host anemone is available. Ideally, this shrimp species and its host anemone should be kept in small, peaceful aquarium. We have maintained this species successfully together with anemones of genus *Phymanthus*.

GA: +/-; **SE:** +/-; **CO:** +

Photos:

Top: Pair of *Periclimenes brevicarpalis* on a *Cryptodendrum adhaesivum* anemone, at Bunaken, Indonesia.

Photo: R. Hansen

Centre: *Periclimenes brevicarpalis* in an aquarium.

Bottom: *Periclimenes brevicarpalis* at the Great Barrier Reef.

Photo: M. Cufer

Periclimenes holthuisi
Holthuis' anemone shrimp

Distribution: Widely distributed throughout the Indo-Pacific, including the Red Sea.

Size: Maximum body length about 2 cm.

Reproduction: Details unknown.

Food: Carnivorous, but details unknown. Under aquarium conditions, this species feeds on detritus and uneaten food (BAENSCH & DEBELIUS, 1992). Also active as a cleaner shrimp on fishes.

Description: Lives in association with numerous cnidarian animals, such as sea anemones and stony corals of genera *Heliofungia, Plerogyra, Goniopora* and *Catalaphyllia,* as well as with Upside-down (or Mangrove-) sea jellies of genus *Cassiopea* (see Volume 2, page 92-93). The body is transparent, covered by purplish blue patches, with white, variably-sized dots in their centres. The pereiopods and pleopods are transparent, while the chelipeds are banded in purplish blue. The eyes are deep red.

Aquarium requirements: Occasionally available in the aquarium trade, but it is not a hardy and easy to keep shrimp. It requires careful acclimatisation, and can only be recommended to experienced aquarists.

GA: +/-; **SE:** +/-; **CO:** +

Photos:
Periclimenes cf. *holthuisi* at Bintan, Indonesia (top; photo: C. Bryce), and at Chuuk (bottom; photo: P. Schupp).

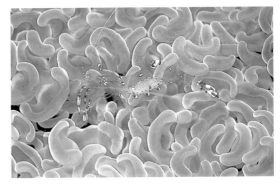

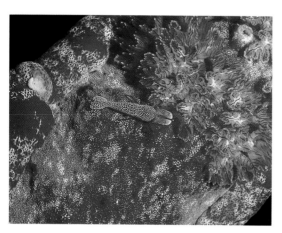

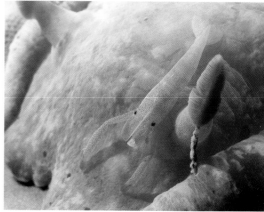

Periclimenes imperator
Emperor anemone shrimp

Distribution: Widely distributed throughout the Indo-Pacific, including the Red Sea.
Size: Maximum body length about 2 cm.
Reproduction: Details unknown.
Food: It is assumed, that this species feeds on mucus produced by its host. BAENSCH & DEBELIUS (1992) report, that in an aquarium small, substitute food is taken (e.g. finely ground flake food).
Description: Lives individually or in pairs, in association with numerous hosts, including the nudibranch Spanish dancer, *Hexabranchus sanguineus*, sea cucumbers of genera *Stichopus*, *Bohadschia* and *Synapta*, and together with various feather stars. The body colour is invariably adapted to that of the host. The head is flattened and the antenna dish is equipped with a large lobe, which lends a somewhat peculiar appearance overall to the head. The rostrum is equipped with 30 to 36 small spines.
Aquarium requirements: According to BAENSCH & DEBELIUS (1992), aquarium observations suggest, that there is a close relationship between this shrimp and the Spanish dancer, but that the relationship to echinoderms is of a somewhat looser nature. We have no personal experience, but we believe that this shrimp is rather difficult to keep. It is probably best to provide it with a small, special aquarium.

GA: +/-; **SE:** +/-; **CO:** +

Photos:
Periclimenes imperator on a Spanish dancer, *Hexabranchus sanguineus*, at Heron Island, Great Barrier Reef (top right; photo: L. Newman and A. Flowers), and at Aldabra Atoll (top left; photo P. Lange) and on the eyespot sea cucumber, *Bohadschia argus*, (bottom; photo: Scott W. Michael).

Periclimenes pedersoni
Pederson's commensal shrimp

Distribution: Tropical West Atlantic, including the Caribbean, but absent from Bermuda.

Size: Maximum body length about 2 cm.

Reproduction: Details unknown. According to COLIN (1978), females, carrying pink-coloured eggs, have been observed in the Virgin Islands, between February and August.

Food: Feeds on ectoparasites removed from fishes. Normally, this species does not require supplementary food in an aquarium.

Description: Lives as individuals or in pairs and occasionally in larger groups, associated with various anemone species, in particular with *Bartholomea* spp., *Lebrunia danae* and with *Condylactis gigantea*. When this species live together in a larger group, there is clearly a hierarchical social structure. The symbiosis with its host anemone does not guarantee total protection against predators. According to COLIN (1978), this shrimp will be eaten by large fish, if it moves too far away from its host anemone. The body and legs are transparent, covered with purple and lavender-coloured patches and dots. The hair-like antennas are long and white.

Aquarium requirements: This shrimp should be kept in a special aquarium, together with a sea anemone from the Caribbean region. A large group of *Periclimenes pedersoni*, together with two or three *Bartholomea annulata* or other sea anemones from the western Atlantic, possibly also with some small fish from the same area, would indeed make a fascinating and interesting observation and study object. We have noticed that this shrimp is somewhat difficult to keep in a community aquarium.

GA: +/-; **SE:** +/-; **CO:** +/-

Photos:
Periclimenes pedersoni in an aquarium at Hagenbecks Tierpark, Hamburg (top), at Bonaire (centre; photo: Scott W. Michael), and at the Cayman Islands (bottom; photo: Scott W. Michael).

Periclimenes yucatanicus
Yucatan commensal shrimp

Distribution: Tropical western Atlantic, including the Caribbean.

Size: Maximum body length about 2 cm.

Reproduction: Details unknown. According to COLIN (1978), females, carrying pink-coloured eggs, have been observed at the Virgin Island, between February and August.

Food: According to some authors, this shrimp removes parasites off fishes. LIMBAUGH et al. (1961) postulate, that the cleaning behaviour is merely a form of mimicry of cleaner shrimp, possibly as a protection against being eaten. In contrast to *Periclimenes pedersoni* (see fact sheet on page 269), this shrimp never leaves its host anemone, unless it is cleaning a fish (or pretending to do so).

Description: Generally solitary or in pairs and occasionally in larger groups, in association with various sea anemone species, in particular with *Bartholomea* spp., *Lebrunia danae* and with *Condylactis gigantea*. The body is transparent, covered with three or four bronze-coloured and white, saddle-shaped markings across the back of the abdomen; there are a few white patches along the sides of the body. Legs and tail fan with purple and white bands.

Aquarium requirements: This shrimp should be kept in special aquarium, together with a sea anemone from the Caribbean region. A large group of *Periclimenes yucatanicus*, together with two or three *Bartholomea annulata* or other anemones from the western Atlantic, possibly also with some small fish from the same area, would indeed make a fascinating, interesting observation and study object. We have noticed that this shrimp is somewhat difficult to keep in a community aquarium.

GA: +/-; **SE:** +/-; **CO:** +/-

Photo:
Periclimenes yucatanicus at Bonaire.

Photo: Scott W. Michael

Pair of banded cleaner shrimp, *Stenopus hispidus*, together with a honeycomb moray, *Gymnothorax favagineus*, in a cave in the Maldives.

Infraorder Stenopodidea – Scissor Shrimps

This infraorder contains two families: Stenopodidae and Spongicolidae, with four or five genera respectively. In scissor shrimps the first three pairs of walking legs are equipped with pincers, and the third pair is also much larger than the other two. The gills have a central stem, giving rise to unbranched filaments.

Family Stenopodidae

This family is of great importance to the marine aquarium hobby because of one single genus: *Stenopus*. *Stenopus* contains some species that are very common in the marine aquarium hobby. The banded coral- or cleaner shrimp, *Stenopus hispidus*, has been a "regular" in the aquarium trade for decades. In fact, it will have been most likely one of the very first invertebrates in the

marine aquarium of many early aquarists. *Stenopus* species are cleaners, similar to the *Lysmata* spp. discussed earlier. Yet, for unknown reasons, the cleaning activities of these shrimps tend to decline in an aquarium. On coral reefs, however, they set up regular cleaning stations, where fish aggregate and wait in line to be relieved of their parasites and have their wounds cleaned up.

Scissor shrimps tend to stay in caves or under ledges, nearly always in pairs. If one of the shrimps is ready to "clean" it waves its antennae back and forth, in order to attract the attention of potential clients. When a fish approaches, the shrimp first touches it with its antennae, so that it becomes passive. At that point the shrimp is allowed to search the surface of the fish, its mouth and gills for parasites and to

clean any wounds.

All *Stenopus* spp. have very large, conspicuous pincers, which are always pointed forward in a kind of defence- or attack position. When they "dance" along the substrate, they are full of beauty and grace. The pincers and antennae are then extended as far as possible, in order to appear as large and impressive as it can.

Stenopus hispidus is a circumtropical species, which is imported on a regular basis from the Caribbean as well as the Indo-Pacific. Although in the wild these shrimps are always seen in pairs, it is possible to keep them individually in an aquarium. If there are two it is important to make sure that they actually are a pair, because if they are the of the same sex they are totally incompatible in an aquarium, and it will lead to the demise of one or both speci-

Stenopus hispidus eating a bristle worm.

Photo: G. Spies

mens. Intraspecific aggression, as well as aggression towards similar species, is great. In fact, we have several times seen ourselves that even specimens of *Lysmata amboinensis* have been killed. All this depends very much on the size of the tank and the possibility for the shrimps to develop adequate territories. For

further details about *Stenopus hispidus* see the relevant fact sheet on page 274.

During the last few years more and more other *Stenopus* spp. have been imported. These are usually a bit more delicate than *S. hispidus*, but they are, nevertheless, interesting and highly suitable aquarium inhabitant (see fact

sheets on pages 273-277). In the moment other genera of the family have no position in the reef aquarium hobby.

Family Spongicolidae

The family Spongicolidae has mainly deep-sea members that live as commensals with sponges, however one *Microprosthema* species deserves to be mentioned here: the robust scissor shrimp, *M. validum*. This is a small shrimp, with a maximum length of only 2.5 cm. It occurs in the Indo-Pacific, where it lives among rocks and coral rubble down to depths of about 20 m. With its very long and flattened pincers, it is somewhat reminiscent of a small lobster. As far as we know, this species has so far never been imported, and so there is no information available about its aquarium requirements. We would expect though, that it would be fairly easy to keep in a coral reef aquarium.

There are also some shallow water members of the genus *Odontozona*, which occur in coral reef habitats.

Robust scissor shrimp, *Microprosthema validum*.

Stenopus cyanoscelis
Blue-legged cleaner shrimp

Distribution: Indo-Pacific

Size: Maximal length 3 cm.

Reproduction: The female carries blue-grees eggs attached ventrally on the abdomen. Likely to spawn regularly in a coral reef aquarium, similar to other species in this genus.

Food: Feeds on ectoparasites and dead tissue removed from fishes. This shrimp will accept most substitute food, such as flake food and live or frozen plankton. In addition, it also feeds on tiny organisms (e.g. copepods), which commonly occur in any coral reef aquarium.

Description: Normally lives in narrow crevices, caves or under overhanging ledges, where a pair or a group establishes a territory, which serves as a cleaning station for fishes. The body is yellow; the abdomen and chelipeds are covered by red and white bands; the antennas are white. This species looks similar to *Stenopus tenuirostris* (see fact sheet on page 277) and to *S. zanzibaricus*, however, the latter has a yellow cephalothorax, white legs and red antennas.

Aquarium requirement: Very shy in an aquarium, and should therefore be kept in a special aquarium, together with other small shrimps and small fishes. Under the correct conditions, this species is easy to keep.

GA: +; **SE:** +/-; **CO:** +/-

Photo:
Stenopus cyanoscelis in an aquarium.   Photo: T. Luther

Stenopus hispidus
White-banded cleaner- or coral shrimp

Distribution: Circumtropical and partially subtropical.

Size: Maximum body length of females 9 cm; males remain smaller and more slender.

Reproduction: Breeds regularly under aquarium condition. The fertilised eggs are clearly visible as a green, granular mass along the ventral side of the female. After 14 to 16 days, 3 mm long, free-swimming larvae are released. Unless they are immediately removed, they are quickly eaten by the other aquarium inhabitants. Rearing the larvae is difficult, but quite feasible with the proper food and careful attention. Normally, larvae are being released once a month, even when a male is not present, since sperm cells form earlier copulations are being stored by the female (see pp. 233). There are now some hatcheries which produce commercial quantities of this species.

Food: Feeds on ectoparasites removed from fishes. This shrimp will accept most substitute food, such as flake food and live or frozen plankton. In addition, it also feeds on tiny organisms (e.g. copepods), which commonly occur in any coral reef aquarium.

Description: Normally lives in narrow crevices, caves or under overhanging ledges, where a pair or a group establishes a territory, which serves as a cleaning station for fishes. The carapace, the abdomen and the third pair of pereiopods are equipped with spines. The anterior segment of the fourth and fifth pair of walking legs is numerously segmented (JONES & MORGAN, 1994). The body and the third pair of walking legs, which is extended and has chelae, are covered by a pattern of red and white bands. The antennas are long and white. This species moults often.

Aquarium requirements: Well established in the marine aquarium hobby since its early days. Very hardy and easy to keep, but only individually or as a pair. A subsequent introduction of a third specimen into a small or medium-size aquarium inevitably fails, because it is invariably killed within a few days, by the already established siblings. However, in a large tank (with appropriate sight barriers) it may be possible to keep several specimens together.

GA: +; SE: +; CO: +

Photos:

Stenopus hispidus in an aquarium (top), a pair (centre), and its egg-carrying female - on the left in the photograph - in an aquarium, and a zoea larva (bottom; photo: R. Brons)

Stenopus pyrsonotus
Ghost cleaner shrimp

Distribution: Indo-Pacific; few details are known. Fairly common around Hawaii, and according to BAENSCH & DEBELIUS (1992) also common at Mauritius, along the coast of East Africa and in Papua-New Guinea.

Size: With a maximal length of about 10 cm, this is one of the larger shrimps in this genus.

Reproduction: Around Hawaii, this species spawns in July. The female carries the blue-green egg mass along the ventral side of the abdomen (RUSSO, 1994).

Food: Feeds on ectoparasites removed from fishes. This shrimp will accept most substitute food, such as flake food and live or frozen plankton. In addition, it also feeds on tiny organisms (e.g. copepods), which commonly occur in any coral reef aquarium

Description: Normally lives in narrow crevices, caves or under overhanging ledges, where a pair or a group establishes a territory, which serves as a cleaning station for fishes. This species is reminiscent of *Stenopus hispidus* (see fact sheet on page 274), but its legs and the tail fan are white, while the abdomen is transparent whitish. A single red, longitudinal stripe extends along its dorsal region. The antennas are white and up to 20 cm long.

Aquarium requirements: Rarely available in the aquarium trade; only occasionally imported. It is a hardy and easy to keep shrimp, but only as individuals or as a pair. Strong intra-specific aggression.

GA: +; **SE:** +; **CO:** +

Photo:
Stenopus pyrsonotus in an aquarium.

Photo: Scott W. Michael

Stenopus scutellatus
Golden coral shrimp

Distribution: Caribbean.

Size: Maximal body length about 2 to 3 cm.

Reproduction: Spawns regularly in a coral reef aquarium. The female carries the blue-green egg masses attached to the ventral side of the abdomen.

Food: Feeds on ectoparasites and dead tissue removed from fishes. This shrimp will accept most substitute food, such as flake food and live or frozen plankton. In addition, it also feeds on tiny organisms (e.g. copepods), which commonly occur in a coral reef aquarium

Description: The body and legs are golden yellow; the chelae and the abdomen are covered by red-, sometimes also by white bands. The antennas are long and white. The third pair of pereiopods is enlarged and equipped with chelae.

Aquarium requirements: Only little is known about the aquarium care for this species, but it appears to be relatively easy to keep, but preferably only as a pair in a small, special aquarium.

GA: +; **SE:** +/-; **CO:** +/-

Photos:
Stenopus scutellatus in an aquarium. The photo below illustrates how well this shrimp is camouflaged in its natural habitat.

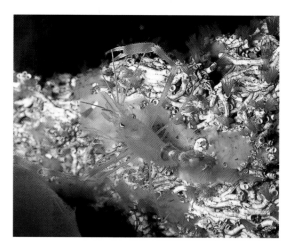

Stenopus tenuirostris
Blue-bodied cleaner shrimp

Size: Maximal body length about 2 to 3 cm.

Reproduction: Spawns regularly in a coral reef aquarium. The female carries the blue-green egg masses attached to the ventral side of the abdomen.

Food: Feeds on ectoparasites and dead tissue removed from fishes. This shrimp will accept most substitute food, such as flake food and live or frozen plankton. In addition, it also feeds on tiny organisms (e.g. copepods), which commonly occur in any coral reef aquarium.

Description: Normally lives in narrow crevices, caves or under overhanging ledges, where a pair or a group establishes a territory, which serves as a cleaning station for fishes. The body and legs are purple with blue insets; the chelae and the abdomen are covered with white, yellow and red bands; the antennas and the legs are transparent purple. This species looks similar to *Stenopus cyanoscelis* (see fact sheet on page 273) and *S. zanzibaricus*; however, the latter has a yellow cephalothorax, white legs and red antennas.

Aquarium requirements: This species is very shy in an aquarium. Therefore, it is best to accommodate it in a special aquarium, together with other small shrimps and small fishes. Under appropriate conditions, this species is easy to keep.

GA: +; **SE:** +/-; **CO:** +/-

Photo:
Stenopus tenuirostrus in an aquarium.

The best known representatives of this infraorder are the freshwater crayfish (including "yabbies", "crawdads", etc.), which are "regulars" on gourmet menus in many parts of the world. Yet, for marine aquarists, the reef lobsters of family Nephropidae are more interesting representatives of this group. In general, all crustaceans in infraorder Astacidea (see the systematic overview 278) are rather robust forms. Their carapace is cylindrical and not fused with the sternum in front of the mouth. The first three pairs of walking legs terminate in long pincers; however, the first pair is substantially larger and heavier than all the other ones. The gills are composed of unbranched filaments, and the long, straight and well-developed abdomen ends in a broad tail fan.

Family Nephropidae

Again we have to refer back to the world of gastronomy, where we find the best known members of this family. The European lobster, *Homarus gammarus* is indeed a culinary experience for the initiated gastronomic expert. Equally famous, but not quite as expensive is the "Norway lobster", *Nephrops norvegicus*, which is highly prized in the Italian kitchen under the name of "scampo" (plural: scampi).

In tropical seas, there are a number of genera represented, but only a single one stands out as important to the aquarium hobby; *Enoplometopus*, the reef lobsters. It must be noted here, that some authors include this genus in family Axiidae, but we have decided to remain conservative on this issue. *Enoplometopus* spp. are brightly coloured crustaceans, principally in red. They are distributed throughout all tropical seas, but only Indo-Pacific species are regularly imported. A selection of common reef lobsters are presented in fact sheets on pages 279-281.

All reef lobsters have large, strong pincers on the first pair of walking legs. The pincers are used for threats and in defence against opponents. Reef lobsters make excellent aquarium inhabitants, which rarely reach a length of more than 10 to 12 cm. They tend to hide during the day, but at dusk they crawl out in search of food (left over food particles, dead organisms and other organic material). In spite of their powerful pincers they are generally peaceful towards most other species. Yet, in respect to small fishes and other crustaceans, they are not entirely trustworthy. Therefore, care should be taken when selecting animals to be kept together with reef lobsters. Intra-specifically, however, reef lobsters are very aggressive, so that only a single specimen should ever be kept in an aquarium, unless it is a very large tank with suitable hiding places and adequate sight barriers.

All reef lobsters must be given protected hiding places, preferably in the form of dark caves directly on the bottom substrate, so that they can dig and rearrange their home themselves. Attempts should be made to structure such cave in a manner that offers views in to its interior, so that the reef lobster can be observed also during the day. Reef lobsters react very quickly to feeding. Once a specimen has settled into an aquarium, it will leave its hiding place whenever food of some sort is added to the tank. With the antennas moving back and forth, reef lobsters "taste" the water to detect the presence of food close by. In captivity, they are not particularly selective and will accept a wide variety of foods, however, there seem to be a distinct preference for raw clam and shrimp meat.

Systematic overview of the infraorder Astacidea

Superfamily Astacoidea – Fresh water cray fish*
    Family Astacidae *
    Family Cambaridae *
Superfamily Parastacoidea – Fresh water cray fish*
    Family Parastacidae *
      Astacopsis, Cherax, Euastacus
Überfamilie Nephropoidea
    Family Nephropidae – Reef lobsters
      Enoplometopus, Homarus, Metanephrops, Nephrops, Nephropsis

The families marked with an asterisks * are not dealt with in this book.

Enoplometopus daumi
Violet reef lobster

Distribution: Central Indo-Pacific, around Indonesia and the Philippines.
Size: Maximal length about 11 cm.
Reproduction: Separate sexes. Frequent aquarium observations have shown females carrying eggs, but young have never been raised.
Food: Feeds on food and small invertebrates. Under aquarium conditions, this species will readily accept most substitute food.
Description: Lives in caves and crevices along reef slopes. The colouration is reminiscent of *Enoplometopus debelius* (see fact sheet on page 280), however, the body is more yellowish, and the sides of the carapace have violet stripes. The chelae, which are very large and are used for defence, are covered by long, red cirri and white spines along the edges. The walking legs are yellow, and the antennas red to violet. Two rows of projecting spines are located on the dorsal side of the carapace.
Aquarium requirements: This species is occasionally imported for the aquarium trade. It is quite suited for a coral reef aquarium, however, only as a single specimen per tank, because of strong intra-specific (usually fatal) aggression towards sibling specimens. Ideally suited as a scavenger in a fish aquarium.

GA: +; SE: +; CO: +

Photos:
Enoplometopus daumi in an aquarium (top; photo: Scott W. Michael) and (bottom) in an aquarium owned by Kenneth Olsen, Oslo, Norway.

Enoplometopus debelius
Debelius' reef lobster

Distribution: Central and eastern Pacific, from Indonesia to Hawaii.

Size: Maximal length about 10 cm.

Reproduction: Separate sexes. Frequent aquarium observations have shown females carrying eggs, but young have so far never been raised.

Food: Feed on food and small invertebrates. Under aquarium conditions, species will readily accept most substitute food.

Description: Lives in caves and crevices along reef slopes. The base body colour is whitish and pale violet, with numerous red to violet spots. The chelae, which are very large, are used for defence. The digits of the chelae have red bands. The walking legs are bright orange. The body is covered by numerous cirri. Two rows of projecting spines are located on the dorsal side of the carapace.

Aquarium requirements: This species is frequently available in the aquarium trade, since it is popular with aquarists. It is very hardy and ideally suited for a coral reef aquarium. We had no problems keeping two specimens together in the same tank for several years. Aquarium specimens tend to hide during the day among the tank decoration, but they will become rather active when food (such as live brine shrimp) is offered.

GA: +; SE: +; CO: +

Photos:
Enoplometopus debelius in an aquarium shop tank.

Enoplometopus occidentalis
Hairy reef lobster

Distribution: Common throughout the Indo-Pacific, including the Red Sea.

Size: Maximal length about 12 cm.

Reproduction: Separate sexes. Frequent aquarium observations have shown females carrying eggs, but young have so far never been raised.

Food: Feeds on uneaten food and small invertebrates. Under aquarium conditions, this species will readily accept most substitute food.

Description: Lives in caves and crevices along reef slopes. VINE (1986) reports that this species occurs in the Red Sea at considerable depths. The basic body colour is pale- or light red, with white spots surrounded by a dark red margin. With long, white bristles on body and chelae. The latter are very large, with spines along the edges, and are used for defensive purposes. The walking legs and the digits of the chelae are poorly developed and carry light orange bands. Antennas same colour as the body. There are rows of projecting spines on the dorsal side of the carapace.

Aquarium requirements: Often available in the aquarium trade. This species is very hardy and ideally suited for a coral reef aquarium, but only as individual specimens. There is strong (usually fatal!) intra-specific aggression if more than one specimen is kept in the same tank. Very useful as a scavenger in a fish aquarium. It hides during the day, but it is not as timid as other reef lobsters.

GA: +; SE: +; CO: +

Photo:
Enoplometopus occidentalis in an aquarium.
Photo: Scott W. Michael

The members of this infraorder represent a peculiar group among decapod crustaceans. They lead an extremely cryptic life, normally inside cave systems in sand or mud substrate. Therefore, it is unlikely to come across them, unless in a specific search for them. Their normal geographical distribution covers temperate, subtropical and tropical seas, including coral reefs. Depending upon the viewpoints of different taxonomists, there are four to eight families in the infraorder. We

Systematic overview of the infraorder Thalassinidea

Superfamily Thalassinoidea – Ghost shrimps and Mud Lobsters
    Family Thalassinidae - Mud Lobsters *
      Thalassina
    Family Callianassidae – Ghost shrimps
      Callianassa, Callichirus, Corallianassa, Glypturus
    Family Upogebiidae – Ghost shrimps*
      Upogebia

The families marked with an asterisks * are not dealt with in this book.

Californian ghost shrimp, *Callianassa californiensis*, occurs in temperate and tropical waters of the Eastern Pacific. In this display tank at the Monterey Bay Aquarium, these specimens have accepted a man-made tunnel system.

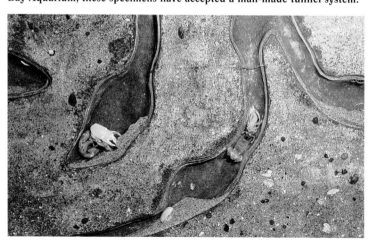

have decided to present this group on the basis of family Callianassidae, in superfamily Thalassinoidea (see the systematic overview), as an example.

Family Callianassidae

There are more than 160 species, classified in some 20 genera, within this family, which makes it the most species-diverse in the infraorder. The genera *Corallianassa*, *Callianassa* and *Callichirus* are known from coral reef habitats, where they live in sand or fine gravel along the reef flat. The most extreme burrows can extend down to as much as 2 m below substrate surface, within an elaborate tunnel system. The food consists mainly of organic particles in the substrate, which fall into the tunnel system. Ghost shrimps do well in an aquarium, but it is highly unlikely that they ever will become available through regular trade. Moreover, they should be given a specifically set up aquarium, otherwise there little point in keeping these unusual crustaceans. A combination with other burrow dwelling organisms like the inn keeper's worm, *Urechis caupo* (see page 156), is particularly interesting.

For those who would like to obtain further information about this infraorder, we recommend the publication by DWORSCHAK & HÖDL (1994), which also gives hints on collecting techniques.

Adult spiny lobster, *Panulirus penicillatus*, seen here in the Fiji Islands, is characterised by a series of conspicuous white, black-edged spots. This is the most common large spiny lobster in the Indo-Pacific region, which is also of considerable commercial fisheries importance.
Photo: M. Cufer

Infraorder Palinura – Spiny Lobsters and Slipper Lobsters

This infraorder contains crustaceans generally referred to as spiny lobsters or langusts, as well as slipper lobsters. They are principally lobster-like animals, which are distinguished from the North American (Maine)- and European lobster (*Homarus*), in that they have only small pincers on their pereiopods. The sides of the carapace are fused to the sternum in front of the mouth. The carapace as such is typically rather spiny, which has given rise to the popular name "spiny lobster". The gills are made up of unbranched filaments.

Three families (Synaxidae, Palinuridae and Scyllaridae) are of some interest to the aquarium hobby, although on a limited basis only (see the systematic overview). Most species of this infraorder are suitable for large specially set up tanks only, where

they can be hardy and durable inhabitants. They feed principally on dead organisms and other organic remains. Other invertebrates are hardly ever endangered by these animals, however, large specimens can become a problem when climbing about on aquarium decoration and on corals. All are dusk- and night active, and

require adequate hiding places during the day.

Families Synaxidae and Palinuridae

The species of these two families are rather similar. They all look very much like those spiny lobsters we know from restaurant

---

Systematic overview of the infraorder Palinura

Superfamily Palinuroidea
    Family Synaxidae - Spiny Lobsters
        Palinurellus
    Family Palinuridae - Spiny Lobsters
        Jasus, Justitia, Linuparus, Palinurus, Panulirus, Puerulus
    Family Scyllaridae - Slipper Lobsters
        Arctides, Evibacus, Ibacus, Parribacus, Scyllarides, Scyllarus, Thenus

The Spanish- or slipper lobster, *Scyllarides aequinoctialis*, lives on coral reef in the Caribbean, from the Bahamas and southern Florida southward to the West Indian islands.   Photo: Scott W. Michael

menus. The most frequently encountered spiny lobsters in the aquarium trade are those of genus *Panulirus*. It must be noted here, that there is also a genus *Palinurus*, which has given rise to the family name. The similarity between these two generic names is unfortunate, but we have to live with it.

Painted crayfish, *Panulirus versicolor,* are often available in the aquarium trade as juveniles, with a beautiful black, white an azure-blue colour pattern. They look indeed magnificent and so lead many aquarists into temptation to buy them. We have to point out though, that with a total length of 40 cm they get far too large for the average aquarium. Moreover, the colouration of adult specimens is no longer so attractive (see fact sheet on page 288). Most other spiny lobster species reach similar sizes, but *Palinurellus wieneckii* (family Synaxidae)

and *Justitia longimanus* (family Palinuridae) are exceptions. Their maximum sizes are only about 15 cm and 10 cm, respectively (for further details see fact sheets on pages 285-288).

Family Scyllaridae

The slipper lobsters of this family have many characteristics in common with spiny lobsters of families Synaxidae and Palinuridae. They are, however, clearly distinguishable by their much broader and dorso-ventrally flattened body shape. Moreover, they do not have the long antennae that are such visible features of spiny lobsters and many other crustaceans. Instead, the antennae have been modified into broad, shovel-like appendages, which are used for digging in sandy or muddy substrates.

Slipper lobsters draw attention primarily because of their pecu-

liar shape, but in terms of colouration they are not particularly conspicuous, with dominant shades of grey and brown in most species. Moreover, they are predominantly nocturnal as well as rather shy, and so they are not likely to be the first choice for most aquarists.

If they are kept in an aquarium, the tank needs to be set up specifically for them, in company with smaller and docile animals which are not likely to disturb the slipper lobsters. It is, however, important to keep in mind, that molluscs, worms and other small invertebrates are part of the natural diet of these crustaceans. Beyond that, feeding slipper lobsters in captivity is not particularly difficult. The aquarium trade offers mainly slipper lobsters belonging to the genera *Arctides, Parribacus* and *Scyllarides*. Slipper lobsters occur in all tropical and subtropical seas.

Palinurellus wieneckii
Australian miniature spiny lobster

Distribution: Central and eastern Pacific; from Indonesia to Hawaii.
Size: Maximal length about 15 cm.
Reproduction: Details unknown.
Food: Feeds mainly on uneaten food, but will readily accept most substitute food.
Description: This species lives on coral reefs in caves and crevices, or tends to bury in sand. It is coloured uniformly red or orange. Carapace and abdomen covered with small, closely spaced spines. Long spines (as those in other spiny lobsters) are not present. The first pair of walking legs is enlarged, but without chelae. The antennas are shorter than in other spiny lobster species, but in comparison to the body, they are large and distinctly pointed.
Aquarium requirements: Ideally suited for a coral reef aquarium. We have kept this small spiny lobster in a community tank successfully for years, without ever seeing other invertebrates damaged. This species is principally nocturnal, and so it is rarely seen during the day.

GA: +; **SE:** +; **CO:** +

Photos:
Palinurellus wieneckii in an aquarium.

Justitia longimanus
Long-handed spiny lobster

Distribution: Circumtropical.
Size Maximal body length of about 15 cm.
Reproduction: Details unknown.
Food: This species feeds on food remains and on smaller invertebrates. Under aquarium conditions it will accept most substitute food.
Description: During the day it hides in caves and crevices along the outer reef slope down to a depth of about 35 m; will emerge at night in search of food. The body is marked by a red pattern. The antennas, legs and chelae with orange to red and with white bands. The chelae are very long, with their tips curved inwards.
Aquarium requirements: Small specimens are occasio-

nally imported. Acclimatisation must be done carefully, and it is then ideally suited for a large coral reef aquarium. Several specimens can be kept together in very large tanks. Must be given ample hiding places.

GA: +; **SE:** +; **CO:** +/-

Photo:
Justitia longimanus in a display tank at the Waikiki Aquarium, Honolulu (Hawaii).

Panulirus argus
Caribbean spiny lobster

Distribution: Caribbean, including Florida and the Bahamas.

Size: Maximal length about 25 cm.

Reproduction: The spawning season of this lobster extends from March through June, and has its peak in April. The males attach their spermatophores to the legs of female. The eggs are not fertilized until they are fully developed, when the females attaches them to the ventral side of its abdomen, where they are distinctly visible as an orange or blackish, granular mass. At the latest after three weeks, Phyllosoma-larvae will hatch from these eggs. The larvae lead a planktonic life for about six months, when they undergo a metamorphosis and then settle to the bottom as juvenile spiny lobsters. It takes several years until they reach maturity.

Food: Feeds on dead organisms; scavenger. Will accept fish and mussel meat, dead shrimps and sometimes even dry food.

Description: Remains in hiding during the day, and emerges at night in search of food. The carapace with brown or bronze-coloured areas, covered by a few dark patches. The abdomen with brown, bronze-coloured bands, and has a mottled pattern of lighter spots. The carapace carries a number of strong, sharp thorns, as well as an extended rostrum. The antennas and the lower edges of the abdominal plates are also equipped with thorns.

Aquarium requirements: This species is occasionally imported for the aquarium trade, but it requires a large aquarium, where it can be kept together with large fishes and hardy invertebrates, such as sea anemones. It needs ample hiding places.

GA: +; **SE:** +; **CO:** +/-

Photo: *Panulirus argus* at Curacao.   Photo: Dr. I. Illich

Panulirus versicolor
Painted spiny lobster, Painted crayfish

Distribution: Widely distributed throughout the Indo-Pacific.

Size: Maximal body length about 40 cm (carapace length 15 cm).

Reproduction: Males attach their spermatophores to the legs of females. The eggs are not fertilized until they are fully developed, when the females attaches them to the ventral side of the abdomen.

Food: Feeds on dead organisms; scavenger. Will accept fish and mussel meat, dead shrimps and sometimes even dry food.

Description: Lives on coral reefs in shallow water down to a depth of about 16 m. Remains in hiding during the day, and emerges at night in search food. The abdominal segments are without a distinct partitioning groove. The pleopods of males are three-times longer than wide (JONES & MORGAN, 1994). The carapace is greenish-blue, but the dorsal side is deep dark blue with a white, reticulated pattern. The antennas are long, orange at their bases, and covered with black spines. The abdominal segments carry white cross bands with black margins. Legs with white stripes; chelae only moderately developed.

Aquarium requirements: Small specimens are frequently imported. Following a careful acclimatisation, these lobsters are very well suited for large coral reef tanks. Must be given ample hiding opportunities.

GA: +; **SE:** +; **CO:** +/-

Photos:
Panulirus versicolor: juvenile in an aquarium (top; photo: Scott W. Michael), sub-adult specimen in the Maldives (centre), and adult specimens in their natural habitat (bottom; photo: P. Schupp).

Parribacus antarcticus
Sculptured slipper lobster

Distribution: Circumtropical.
Size: Maximal length about 20 cm (carapace length only about 9.5 cm).
Reproduction: Females carry the red egg masses attached to modified pleopods under the abdomen.
Food: This lobster feeds primarily on molluscs and other small invertebrates, but will also take dead organisms and other organic uneaten food. Can be adapted to take substitute food, which may not be always be easy in a community tank since it is rather timid and invariably loses out when competing for food.
Description: A nocturnal species, which lives in shallow water down to a depth of about 20 m. Can usually be found on sandy areas between corals and rocks. The second pair of antennas have been developed into shovel-like structures, which gives the head a paddle-shaped appearance. Along the edges, the "shovel" is armoured with strong spines. Chelae are not present. The carapace is strongly flattened. The base colour is ochre or pale brown with a scattering of dark brown or grey-brown dots.
Aquarium requirements: This species is occasionally imported for the aquarium trade. It should be given a special aquarium with large sandy areas, where it can bury itself.

Very shy; clearly uncomfortable in the company of very active animals.

GA: +/-; **SE:** +/-; **CO:** -

Photos:
Adult (top) and sub-adult (bottom) specimen of *Parribacus antarcticus* in Indonesia.

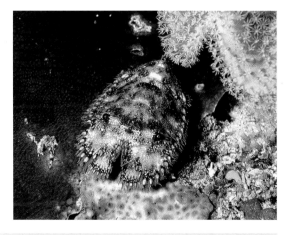

Left: Many small hermit crabs of the family Diogenidae, especially the genera *Calcinus* and *Clibanarius* (see fact sheets on pages 296 and 298) have become very popular in the marine aquarium hobby during the last decade or so. As very effective algae grazers they have become firmly established with coral reef aquarium hobbyists. Right: The red and white spotted *Dardanus gemmatus* is an extremely attractive hermit crab; however, like most *Dardanus* species it tends to get rather large and it is very aggressive. This specimen, seen here in Papua-New Guinea, carries a bright red sponge around on its mollusc shell (photo: L. Newman and A. Flowers).

Infraorder Anomura
Hermit Crabs, Porcelain Crabs and Mole Crabs

The infraorder Anomura contains many interesting reef-dwelling crustaceans, such as hermit crabs, porcelain crabs and mole crabs. Despite their common names, they are not true crabs, and can be distinguished from them, for instance, by the last pair of walking legs (the fifth pair), which is reduced and/or turned upwards. The shape of the abdomen varies within this infraorder. It is long and slender in some species, while it is small and tugged under the thorax in others, just as in the true crabs.

Below we will discuss in some detail six families, which belong into three different superfamilies (see systematic overview on page 291). These families are: Diogenidae, Paguridae and Coenobitidae from superfamily Paguroidea, and the families Galatheidae and Porcellanidae from superfamily Galatheoidea and the family Albuneidae from superfamily Hippoidea.

Paguristes purpureantennatus (here at Mullaloo Beach, Western Australia) is a predatory and rather large hermit crab.   Photo: C. Bryce

Hermit crabs of families Diogenidae, Paguridae and Coenobitidae

Hermit crabs have received their popular name from the fact, that their "house" consists of abandoned snail shells or sometimes they reside inside sponges or worm tubes, in a manner similar to the Greek philosopher and hermit Diogenes, who lived in a wine barrel. It is vitally necessary for hermit crabs, to hide their long, soft and coiled abdomen inside a strong shell; otherwise they would be without protection and exposed to predators. With increasing growth, this accommodation is periodically exchanged for a larger one. But there is one exception to this rule. The well-known terrestrial coconut hermit crab, *Birgus latro* (family Coenobitidae) does not require a snail shell, since its protect itself with its own thick armour.

Hermit crabs belong to the best-known invertebrates for the coral reef aquarium, and have been available in the aquarium trade since the infancy of the marine aquarium hobby. In the course of time, however, there has been a large change in the selection of species available. The first hermit crabs introduced to the aquarium hobby, were large predators, such as the *Dardanus* spp. Nowadays, there is a much larger interest among aquarists for the small, herbivorous species, which have proven to be excellent algae grazers. During the period of rather sterile aquariums, these hermit crabs did not do well, and were considered as being difficult to keep. On the other hand, the large predatory species hardly presented any problems when kept in aquariums with fish only, which is different than the modern marine community tanks with their large variety of invertebrates.

In addition to their attractive and entertaining character, hermit crabs play an important ecological role in a coral reef aquarium. Specifically, the family Diogenidae contains many species,

Systematic overview of the infraorder Anomura

Superfamily Paguroidea – Hermit Crabs
   Family Diogenidae - Hermit Crabs
      Aniculus, Calcinus, Cancellus, Clibanarius, Dardanus, Diogenes, Paguristes, Petrochirus, Trizopagurus, Troglopagurus
   Family Paguridae - Hermit Crabs
      Anapagurus, Catapaguroides, Catopagurus, Cestopagurus, Cestopagurus, Manucomplanus, Nematopagurus, Pylopaguropsis, Pagurus, Paguritta, Phimochirus, Spiropagurus
   Family Parapaguridae – Deep sea hermit crabs *
      Strobopagurus, Sympagurus, Parapagurus
   Family Coenobitidae – Land hermit crabs
      Birgus, Coenobita
   Family Lithodidae *
      Lithodes, Neolithodes, Paralithodes, Paralomis
   Family Lomidae *
      Lomis
Superfamily Galatheoidea – Porcelain crabs
   Family Chirostylidae *
      Chirostylus, Uroptychus
   Family Galatheidae
      Allogalathea, Cervimunida, Galathea, Lauriea, Munida, Munidopsis, Pleuroncodes
   Family Porcellanidae - Porcelain crabs
      Pachycheles, Petrolisthes, Pisidia, Polyonyx, Porcellana, Porcellanella
Superfamily Hippoidea - Mole crabs
   Family Hippidae – Mole crabs *
      Hippa
   Family Albuneidae - Mole crabs
      Albunea, Ptychodera

The families marked with an asterisks * are not dealt with in this book.

which feed on micro-algae, leftover food, dead organisms and detritus. Some sift through sand and mud or accumulated detritus in their search for food. In doing so, these species turn over the substrate, thereby "ventilating" it, which lessens the risk of anaerobic zones developing. Snails have traditionally been considered the best algae grazers, but many hermit crabs are not only more persevering but also more efficient in the fight against algae. In fact, some hermit crabs even feed on the red slime algae (a form of blue-green algae, Cyanophyta, see Volume 1, pp. 276), which are being avoided by most other algae feeders. A large number of hermit crabs are also rather effective for getting rid of dead fish and invertebrates, which are in-

accessible or unnoticed by the aquarist, before their decay becomes a pollution problem.

The most important genera, which include small species feeding on algae, detritus and dead organisms are *Calcinus* and *Clibanarius* (as well as a few *Paguristes* species) of family Diogenidae and *Phimochirus* of family Paguridae. Many of these are also very beautifully coloured, which makes their aquarium care that much more interesting. The staghorn hermit crab, *Manucomplanus varians*, is also a peaceful species, but it is among those which are hardly ever imported in large numbers.

Hermit crabs are really only effective in an aquarium in large numbers. One or two specimens have hardly any effect at all in a large tank; however, when one specimen for every 20, 10 or even 5 l water is kept in an aquarium, their impact is getting more noteworthy. None of the above-mentioned hermit crabs will get very large. Most reach a length of only 1.5 to 2 cm, with very few reaching 3 or even 4 cm.

Normally it is not necessary to feed the small hermit crabs specifically. In a healthy, well-conditioned coral reef aquarium there is always sufficient organic material present to cover their basic food requirements. If one is worried

Some predatory species of genus *Dardanus* (family Diogenidae) are still regularly available through the aquarium trade. The large *Dardanus megistos*, which – in extreme cases – can reach a total length of 30 cm, is easy to identify. With its hairy carapace and appendages, together with a deep red colouration covered by white spots, it is a uniquely beautiful species. Unfortunately, it is not suitable for the standard coral reef aquarium, because of its aggressive and predatory behaviour. Everything edible and wit-

therefore effectively unsuitable for the average coral reef aquarium.

There are yet some other interesting hermit crabs in family Diogenidae, which appear occasionally in the aquarium trade. This includes the extremely hairy *Aniculus* spp. (*A. aniculus* see fact sheet on page 295), the approximately 25 cm long *Petrochirus diogenes* (see fact sheet on page 305), and the red-orange-striped *Trizopagurus strigatus* (see fact sheet on page 306).

When keeping hermit crabs it is important to make sure that there

The staghorn hermit crab, *Manucomplanus varians*, from the eastern Pacific (here in an aquarium) leads a fascinating commensal life with the fire coral *Janaria mirabilis*. The fire coral encrusts and possibly also dissolves the mollusc shell inhabited by the hermit crab. The hermit crab, on the other hand, "tailors" the access hole so that it remains open as the coral grows.
Photo: Scott W. Michael

that there is not sufficient food available, in case there are extraordinarily many hermit crabs in a tank, possibly yet together with other animals with similar food requirements (e.g. snails and serpent stars), one can always offer some of the standard substitute foods. Fish- or shrimp meat are always excellent choices, as are many dry foods.

hin its reach, is likely to become its prey. Yet, in a specifically set up aquarium, in the company of large fish and robust invertebrates, it can be an attractive and interesting observation object. Many other *Dardanus* species (see fact sheets on pages 300-303) may well remain smaller, but with sizes of "only" 6 to 10 cm, they are still extremely predatory and

are sufficient numbers of empty snail shells in various sizes available for "changing house". Attempts should be made to find snail shells of similar shapes to those in use by the hermit crabs at the time of their purchase. Although, in their natural habitat, individual hermit crab species prefer specific species of snail shells, under aquarium conditi-

The genus *Paguritta* contains hermit crabs, which live inside empty tubes of calcareous tube worms in coral boulders. This forces them to lead a sessile life, feeding on plankton. So they rake plankton from the surrounding water with their long, feathered antenna. Above *Paguritta corallicola* at Heron Island and below *Paguritta* sp. "KA6-CRU-11" on Wistari Reef, Great Barrier Reef.   Photos: L. Newman and A. Flowers

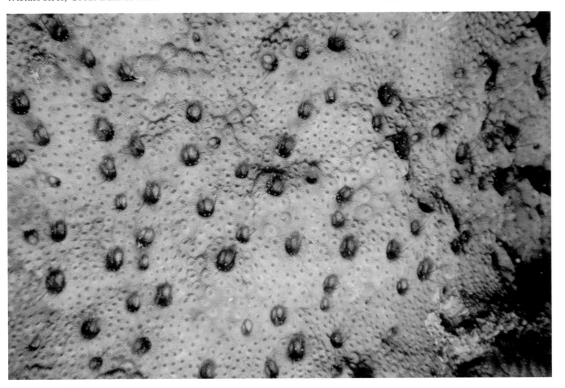

Land hermit crabs (here a group of *Coenobita perlata* at Flinders Cay in the Coral Sea) are not suitable for a traditional coral reef aquarium, but they are easy to keep in an aqua-terrarium.

ons many different kinds will also be accepted if the preferred species is unavailable.

Two particular groups of hermit crabs deserve to be mentioned, although they are hardly of much significance for the average aquarium. Firstly, there is genus *Paguritta* of family Pagurida. It is made up of very small species, which live in vacated serpulid worm tubes (*Spirobranchus giganteus*) (see page 142) in massive stony corals. They feed on plankton, which they strain out of the water, using their feathered antennae. When they withdraw into the tube, they use the large, left pincer to block off the entrance. *Paguritta* species are very cute crustaceans, often occurring in large populations on the same coral colony. Sometimes they are introduced into an aquarium, as inadvertent stowaways, attached to e.g. *Astreopora-, Montipora-, Cyphastrea-, Goniastrea-* or *Porites* stony corals. Regrettably, we have never seen them in aquaria ourselves. Because of their specific food requirements they may be difficult to keep; however, we believe, that it should be possible with a mixture of fresh and frozen plankton, as well as with plankton substitutes of high quality.

The other group of more peculiar hermit crabs is found in the genus *Coenobita* (family Coenobitidae). These are land hermit crabs, which spend their entire life outside water, once their larval stage has been completed. In order to do so, they have large gill chambers where they store moisture, so that the gill apparatus can function like a lung. Yet, they have not lost contact to the sea altogether. In addition to the need to replenish liquid in the gill chambers, the female has to return to the sea, in order to release her eggs. The larvae that emerges from the eggs go directly to a planktonic stage, just like in other hermit crab species. When the larvae settle, they have developed into small crabs, which find themselves tiny snail shells and move onto land. In spite of the fact, that land hermit crabs have direct contact to a coral reef, they are not suited for the traditional coral reef aquarium. On the other hand, they would certainly make interesting inhabitants for a reef-profile aquarium or an aquarium with a large sandy beach section, specifically set up for land hermit crabs.

These crabs are regularly imported for terrarium keeping, but it would certainly better to keep them in an true coral reef aqua-terrarium. Land hermit crabs can be fed adequately with most substitute foods, including dried foods. Some species will also readily take vegetable matter as well as fruit. For further information about the care of land hermit crabs in an aqua-terrarium, see HORSTMAN & VENZLAFF (1996).

Coconut hermit crab, *Birgus latro* (seen here in Indonesia), does not use a mollusc shell as a house, since it is already suitably armored. It reaches a maximum length of 35 cm and with its giant claws it looks indeed fearsome. In fact, its bite is quite powerful!

Aniculus aniculus
Scaly hermit crab

Distribution: Central Indo-Pacific.
Size: Carapace length about 10 cm.
Reproduction: Details unknown.
Food: Very aggressive predator, with a wide food spectrum, including molluscs, spiny-skinned animals (echinoderms) and worms. In an aquarium, this species will readily adapt to substitute food, such as raw clams and fresh fish.
Description: Occurs on the reef flat among rubble and rocks. It has sturdy, powerful chelipeds and large walking legs, which are – together with the sides of the carapace – covered with tubercles and brushes (setae). The carapace is olive green with red lines and dots. The eye stalks are olive green. Normally, this species lives in snail shells of genus *Turbo*. The genus *Aniculus* also contains other, similar looking, very hairy species, e.g. *A. maximus* from the Indo-Pacific, and *A. elegans* from the eastern Pacific; they are also rather large hermit crabs and equally predatory.

Aquarium requirements: This is a highly predatory hermit crab, which feeds on virtually anything of suitable size, including small fishes. It is basically unsuitable for coral reef aquarium; however, it would make a hardy and interesting inhabitant for a special aquarium or for a fish aquarium with large robust fishes. Rarely ever available in the aquarium trade.

GA: +/-; **SE:** +; **CO:** -

Photo:
Aniculus aniculus at One-Tree Island, Great Barrier Reef, Queensland, Australia.   Photo: L. Newman and A. Flowers

Calcinus spp.

Distribution: Widespread in the Indo-Pacific. At least one species also in the Caribbean, and some species in sub-tropical seas, such as the Mediterranean Sea and the eastern Atlantic.

Size: Most species are rather small, with carapace lengths of only 1 to 2 cm. Overall, the maximal body length of these hermit crab species ranges from about 3 to 6 cm.

Reproduction: Details unknown.

Food: In general, all species feed on algae and uneaten food.

Description of genus: These hermit crabs live in rocky areas the intertidal zone or just below it, or on coral reefs down to a depth of 40 m. The left chela is larger than the right one. The outer surface of the chelae is without spines and only slightly "hairy". There is a protruding nap on top of the carpus on the left chela. The right chela of the female is without spines. Colouration is highly variable, but these are all very attractive hermit crabs (JONES & MORGAN, 1994).

Description of species:

- *Calcinus californiensis* occurs from the central Gulf of California to Acapulco. Pereiopods deep orange or red; Chelae and eye stalks greenish-black with reddish margins; carapace length 12 to 19 mm. In the southern Gulf of California this species is often found in association with stony corals of genus *Pocillopora*. Can occur in large aggregations.

- *Calcinus elegans* found along the Australian coastline. With conspicuous deep blue and black bands; the tips of the chelae are white; the antennas are orange and eye stalks and eyes (cornea) are blue.

- *Calcinus gaimardii* (not illustrated) is distributed throughout the Indo-Pacific in two colour forms; one with dark brown chelae, orange walking legs, and bright orange antennas; the eye stalks and eyes are deep blue. The other colour form with a longitudinal brown stripe on the eye stalks, and with light- and dark blue cross bands directly under the eyes; the walking legs are rusty brown and orange with a narrow white cross band close to the darker chelae (MATHER & BENNETT, 1993). Both forms have a greenish white carapace, which is covered by shades of brown.

- *Calcinus latens* (not illustrated) is one of the most common hermit crabs on Australian reefs. Greenish-pink eye stalks, eyes black with white dots; the antennules are blue-white, antennas uniformly orange-coloured; the walking legs are dark green with a few scattered, white tubercles; the anterior part of the carapace is greenish, with scattered shades of green and white posteriorly (MATHER & BENNETT, 1993).

Photos:

Calcinus californiensis in an aquarium (top; photo: Scott W. Michael), and *C. elegans* at Kimberley, Western Australia (bottom; photo: C. Bryce).

- *Calcinus laevimanus* occurs widely throughout the Indo-Pacific. This species is easy to keep in an aquarium. The lower half of the eye stalks is blue, the upper half is orange; eyes black and blue; both pairs of antennas with orange flagella; chelae with variable shades of white; chelipeds light brown with dark brown longitudinal stripes; movable digit (dactylus) of chelae is white.

- *Calcinus minutus* (not illustrated) is widely distributed throughout the Indo-Pacific. This hermit crabs lives among the branches of stony corals of genera *Acropora* and *Pocillopora*. The body is white; dactylus orange with black tips; eye stalks white to pale orange, and the eyes are black.

- *Calcinus tibicen* occurs in the Caribbean. An excellent aquarium inhabitant. Chelae and chelipeds orange, red, chestnut brown or dark reddish-brown, with a scattering of white dots and with white or yellow tips; the eye stalks and antennas are orange, antennas with white tips; eyes black.

Aquarium requirements: All species are excellent algae grazers, which are imported regularly by the aquarium trade. These hermit crabs feed mainly on short green algae; some species will also take macro-algae. They are among those aquarium inhabitants most useful for controlling the growth of filamentous algae. This, however, requires an appropriate number of hermit crabs, if algae control is to be effective (see page 291). *Calcinus* species in general do not have a long life span, and so it is quite normal to see an aquarium population becoming decimated due to natural attrition. It is important that sufficient numbers of empty mollusc shells of different sizes are available for "changes of accommodation" for these hermit crabs.

GA: +; SE: +; CO: +

Photos:
Two colour forms of *Calcinus laevimanus* (top and centre) and *C. tibicen* in an aquarium.

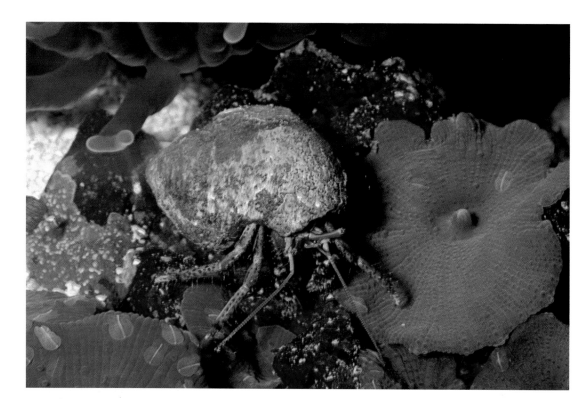

Clibanarius spp.
Equal-handed hermit crabs

Distribution: Indo-Pacific and Caribbean.
Size: Most species are of medium size, with a carapace length normally about 4 cm.
Reproduction: Details unknown.
Food: Most species feed principally on algae and uneaten food.
Description of genus: These hermit crabs occur in the intertidal zone and in shallow water just below, among rubble and corals, but also on soft bottom and often in mangrove areas; rarely found deeper than 10 m. VINE (1986) reports, that *Clibanarius longitarsus* is common in mangrove zones in the Red Sea, and he lists 5 species for this type of habitat. The chelae are of equal size (thus their common name Equal-handed hermit crabs) and are held in such a way, that the digits open horizontally in front of the body. Most species have a green or brown carapace, while the walking legs are green, covered by longitudinal stripes, which are often yellowish. The chelae are greenish

and often equipped with spines. There are externally visible, sexual differences. Species identification is often difficult because of unstable intra- and inter-specific colour variations (JONES & MORGAN, 1994).
Description of species:
- *Clibanarius corallinus* (not illustrated) often occurs together with *C. virescens*. The carapace of *C. corallinus* is reddish brown with three conspicuous lighter, longitudinal stripes; chelae reddish-brown with yellow or white tubercles; the eye stalks are reddish brown, with orange along the sides.
- *Clibanarius taeniatus* (not illustrated) lives in coastal habitats along eastern Australia, but it is rarely found on the Great Barrier Reef. Carapace, eye stalks, chelae and pereiopods with conspicuous greenish brown and creamy yellow stripes; the eyes are whitish (MATHER & BENNETT, 1993).

Photos:
Clibanarius tricolor in an aquarium.

- *Clibanarius tricolor* is endemic to the Caribbean, where it can occur in large aggregations on sandy- or rocky substrate. The chelipeds are blue with red or orange red cross bands; the chelae are black with orange-coloured markings. This species is frequently imported and it has proven to be an excellent algae grazer, and will including (some) red slimy algae (Cyanobacteria) in its diet.

- *Clibanarius virescens* (not illustrated) is common in the Indo-West-Pacific, where it often lives in the proximity of rocky shores. The base colouration varies from yellow, olive green and green blue to blue or brown; the eye stalks are olive-coloured or dark brown with a narrow white ring; the chelae are olive-coloured or brown with white tubercles; chelae digits white with black tips; walking legs olive-coloured or dark brown.

Aquarium requirements: Our own aquarium experiences have revealed that Clibanarius species are peaceful and extraordinarily resistant hermit crabs, which are almost continuous algae grazers. Therefore, they are ideal aquarium inhabitants for controlling the growth of filamentous algae. We have noticed that these crabs sometimes congregate in small groups and then suddenly remain motionless, as if they were having an after-lunch sleep! After a certain period of time the group "awakes" and resumes its grazing activities.

GA: +; SE: +; CO: +

Photos:
Top: *Clibanarius* sp. "KA6-CRU-30" in an aquarium.
Photo: Scott W. Michael
Below left: *Clibanarius* sp. "KA6-CRU-31" in an aquarium.
Below right: *Clibanarius* sp. "KA6-CRU-32" in an aquarium.

Dardanus guttatus
Spotted hermit crab

Distribution: Indo-Pacific: from East- and South Africa to Indonesia and Australia; absent in the Red Sea.
Size: Carapace length about 8 cm.
Reproduction: Details unknown.
Food: Feeds on many different types of food, including dead organisms, small invertebrates, such as molluscs and worms, possibly also on algae. Will readily accept most substitute food.
Description: Normally lives in mollusc shells with a narrow opening, such as those of cone shells (genus *Conus*, family Conidae). The carapace is purple red with many bronze-coloured or white spots, and dark green-blue markings anteriorly. The eye stalks are purple pink with a narrow, white ring directly under the black eyes; both pairs of antennas are purple pink with transparent, light brown flagella; the walking legs and chelae are purple red with small white spots. Walking legs with large dark green-blue pat-

ches. Body and legs often covered with purple red setae with white tips (MATHER & BENNETT, 1993).
Aquarium requirements: Occasionally available in the aquarium trade, but it is basically unsuited for a coral reef aquarium, since it is an aggressive predator of smaller organisms. Yet, in a special aquarium or in a fish aquarium with large, robust fishes it makes an excellent and hardy aquarium inhabitant.

GA: +; SE: +; CO: -

Photo:
Dardanus guttatus at Madang, Papua-New Guinea.
Photo: L. Newman and A. Flowers

Dardanus lagopodes

Distribution: Widely distributed throughout the Indo-Pacific, including the Red Sea.

Size: Carapace length about 6 cm.

Reproduction: Details unknown.

Food: This species feeds principally on algae and uneaten food, but will also take small invertebrates, such as molluscs and worms. Under aquarium conditions it will readily accept most substitute food.

Description: Can be found in various habitats, and it is one of the most common hermit crabs on Indo-Pacific coral reefs. This species tends to share its mollusc shell with the shrimp *Aretopsis amabilis* of family Alpheidae (VINE, 1986). It normally occupies mollusc shells with a wide opening, as those of snails of genera *Tectus* and *Lambis*, but it can also move into shells with narrower openings, as those of cone- and conch shells of genera *Conus* and *Strombus*. There are two colour forms: "black" and "red", which often occur together. The difference between these two forms exists in the colour of the anterior part of the carapace, which is red and mottled with white dots. In the "red" form it has a red

patch, in the "black" form it has a black patch. The eye stalks are pinkish grey with a yellow ring directly below the black eyes. Both pairs of antennas have yellow-orange or pale green flagella. The chelae are covered with setae and tubercles, and scattered over them are red, brown-orange and white dots. The chelae also have a large purplish red patch on the carpus; their tips are white. The walking legs are mottled red-brown with pale violet dots. The body is covered with setae (MATHER & BENNETT, 1993).

Aquarium requirements: Appears relatively often in the aquarium trade. Rather peaceful and can indeed be kept together with other invertebrates; however, one has to keep in mind that this species may occasionally abuse smaller invertebrates. Basically hardy and easy to keep.

GA: +; **SE:** +; **CO:** +/-

Photo:
Dardanus lagopodes at Bintan Island, Indonesia.
Photo: C. Bryce

Dardanus megistos
Red hermit crab, White-spotted hermit crab

Distribution: Widely distributed throughout the Indo-Pacific.

Size: Carapace length up to 10 cm; total length occasionally up to 30 cm. Males are normally larger than females.

Reproduction: Details unknown.

Food: Carnivore; very aggressive predator. Utilise many different food sources, including molluscs, echinoderms and worms. Can easily be adapted to substitute food, such as raw clam meat and fresh or frozen fish.

Description: Occurs from the intertidal zone down to more than 100 m depth, in various habitats: on sandy bottom, among rocks, coral boulders as well as among corals. The larger specimens are normally found in deeper water, while the smaller ones inhabit reef flats. Occupies many different molluscs shells, often those of *Turbo* and *Strombus* snails. The larger crabs prefer Triton horns, *Charonia tritonis*. The left chelae is larger than the right one. Colour of carapace, antennas, chelae and walking legs is red, covered by numerous black-edged, white spots. Most white spots are co-vered by red setae; those on the carapace can have white tips. The eye stalks are red-orange and the eyes are greenish black.

Aquarium requirements: This species is often imported, but usually only as juveniles. One of the most commonly kept crustaceans since the early days of the marine aquarium hobby. Because of its highly predatory behaviour it is not suited for a community tank, but it makes an excellent inhabitant for a large aquarium and in the company of large fishes and some robust invertebrates, such as sea anemones and larger crustaceans. Basically, very hardy and easy to keep.

GA: +; SE: +; CO: -

Photo:
Dardanus megistos in an aquarium.

Dardanus pedunculatus
Anemone hermit crab

Distribution: Indo-Pacific, from East- and South Africa northward to Japan and Korea, as well as eastward to the Society Islands and to Hawaii.
Size: Total length up to 10 cm, but usually smaller.
Reproduction: Details known.
Food: Utilise a variety of food sources, including dead organisms, small invertebrates, such as molluscs and worms, and also probably algae.
Description: This hermit crab lives in shallow water areas of the reef flat, and down to a depth of about 40 m in various habitats, such as on sandy bottom, among rock- and coral boulders, as well as around corals. The mollusc shell is almost totally over-grown by the anemone *Calliactis polypus* (family Hormatiidae). This symbiosis provides the hermit crab with protection and camouflage, while the anemone is being transported "free of charge" to various locations, in order to feed. When changing shell, *Dardanus pedunculatus* simply transfers the anemones to its new accommodation. The closely related *Dardanus tinctor* oc-

curs in the Red Sea, and *D. deformis* is endemic to the Great Barrier Reef. Both species also carry anemones around on their shell. The chelae of all three species are spiny and covered with pale yellow setae; the left chelae is larger than the right one. The eyestalks are red with white stripes, and the eyes are green. Body colouration may be variable within the three species.

Aquarium requirements: Although *Dardanus pedunculatus* is common in its natural habitats, it is only ever occasionally imported. Because of its extremely predatory behaviour this species is not suited for a community tank, but it makes a good inhabitant for large tanks in the company of large fish and other robust invertebrates, such as sea anemones and larger crustaceans. Basically, very hardy and easy to keep.

GA: +; SE: +; CO: -

Photo:
Dardanus pedunculatus at Teluk Riung, Indonesia.
Photo: C. Bryce

Paguristes cadenati
Red-leg hermit crab, Scarlet hermit crab, Shiraz hermit crab

Distribution: Caribbean, including Florida and the Bahamas.

Size: Carapace length about 2 cm.
Reproduction: Details unknown.
Food: Feeds on algae and uneaten food.
Description: Generally solitary, but sometimes it occurs also in smaller aggregations on reefs, normally in deeper water. The walking legs, chelae and the carapace are deep red, sometimes with scattered white spots. The eyes stalks and antennas are pale orange, and the eyes are greenish.
Aquarium requirements: This is an excellent algae grazer and scavenger for a coral reef aquarium; however, to achieve efficient algae removal requires an appropriate number of these hermit crabs in the tank. We have never observed this species attacking other aquarium inhabitants. Yet, other species of the same genus are aggressive predators, but these are generally larger.

GA: +; **SE:** +; **CO:** +

Photos:
Paguristes cadenati in an aquarium (bottom photo: Scott W. Michael).

Petrochirus diogenes
American giant hermit crab

Distribution: Caribbean and western Atlantic.

Size: This is the largest Caribbean hermit crab, with a carapace length of 12 cm and a total length of 25 cm or more.

Reproduction: Details unknown.

Food: This is primarily a carnivore, which feeds on a variety of food sources, including dead organisms, small invertebrates, such as molluscs and worms, and probably also on algae. It accepts most substitute food, including raw clam- prawn- and fish meat, as well as food tablets.

Description: Lives on sandy bottom and is also common in seagrass beds close to coral reefs. The walking legs and chelae are grey to reddish brown, with as surface texture reminiscent of overlapping scales (HUMANN, 1993). The chelae are large, strong and nearly equal in size. The eye stalks are grey, the eyes are green or blue green. The antennas are marked with red and white bands. This species lives in large snail shells, such as those of *Strombus gigas*.

Aquarium requirements: Occasionally available in the aquarium trade, but usually as juveniles. Any one considering acquiring this species, needs to keep in mind that this is a very large hermit crab. Because of its predatory behaviour it is not suited for a community tank, but it is an excellent inhabitant for large aquaria and in the company of large fish and robust invertebrates, such as anemones and other large hermit crabs. Basically very hardy and easy to keep.

GA: +; **SE:** +; **CO:** -

Photo:
Petrochirus diogenes in an aquarium.

Photo: Scott W. Michael

Trizopagurus strigatus
Striped hermit crab

Distribution: Widely distributed throughout the Indo-Pacific, including the Red Sea.
Size: Carapace length 6 cm.
Reproduction: Details unknown.
Food: Feeds on a variety of food sources, including dead organisms, small invertebrates, such as molluscs and worms, and probably also on algae. Accepts most substitute food.
Description: This is a rare species, which lives normally under coral boulders along the reef flat. Adult specimens occupy shells of *Conus* snails, which have an opening well suited for the flattened body of this hermit crab (see photo). Juveniles also live in the shells of *Murex* and *Mitra* snails. The carapace is white, flat and wide. The eyestalks are red, and the eyes are orange. Both pairs of antennas are reddish and carry transparent flagella. The chelipeds are conspicuously banded in orange and red. The chelae digits are orange with black tips. The entire body is substantially flattened.

Aquarium requirements: Occasionally available in the aquarium trade, but usually as juveniles only. Any one considering acquiring this species, needs to keep in mind that this is a very large hermit crab. Because of its predatory behaviour it is not suited for a community tank, but it is an excellent inhabitant for large aquaria and in the company of large fish and robust invertebrates, such as sea anemones and other large hermit crabs. Basically very hardy and easy to keep.

GA: +; **SE:** +; **CO:** -

Photo:
Trizopagurus strigatus in an aquarium.

Photo: M. Chamberlain

Phimochirus operculatus
Polka-dotted hermit crab, Little big claw hermit crab

Distribution: Caribbean, including Florida and the Bahamas.
Size: Carapace length 2.5 cm.
Reproduction: Details unknown.
Food: Feeds on micro-algae and uneaten food.
Description: One of the most common hermit crabs on Caribbean coral reefs. The right chelae is chestnut brown with white spots; compared to the body size it is extraordinarily large; the movable digit (dactylus) is white. The left chelae and the walking legs are red to reddish brown. The eyestalks are white chestnut-brown bands, and the eyes are blue.
Aquarium requirements: This is the most aggressive species among the small, algae-eating hermit crabs, but it does not damage other invertebrates (SCHIEMER, 1994). It is aggressive in the sense that it intimidates other hermit crabs and steals their food. Basically, it is an excellent and very attractive algae grazer, which is ideally suited for a coral reef aquarium.

GA: +; **SE:** +; **CO:** +

Photos:
Phimochirus operculatus in an aquarium.

Coenobita perlata
Red land hermit crab

Distribution: Central Indo-Pacific; absent from the Australian mainland, but it occurs on the islands of the Great Barrier and those in the Coral Sea.

Size: Carapace length 9 cm.

Reproduction: The female has to return to the sea, in order to facilitate the release of the planktonic larvae hatching from its eggs. Once the larvae have developed into juvenile crabs, they move into a small, empty snail shell and migrate onto land.

Food: This hermit crab feeds on a wide range of food items, probably including some plant material.

Description: This species is similar to *Coenobita variabilis* (see fact sheet on page 309), however, it is larger and more attractively coloured. Large specimens are deep red, juveniles are paler and with red spots.

Aquarium requirements: A very interesting hermit crab for an aqua-terrarium or for a tidal aquarium with a beach area. Rather easy to keep; will accept most standard type of food; however, must be given ample hiding places, such as below roots or rocks. Can be kept together in a large group.

GA: +/-; **SE:** +/-; **SE:** +/-

Photos:
Coenobita perlata in its natural habitat on Flinders Cay, Coral Sea.

Coenobita variabilis
Variable land hermit crab

Distribution: Indo-Pacific.

Size: Carapace length 4 cm.

Reproduction: The female has to return to the sea, in order to facilitate the release of the planktonic larvae hatching from its eggs. Once the larvae have developed into juvenile crabs, they move into a small, empty snail shell and migrate onto land.

Food: This species is a nocturnal scavenger. It is specialised for feeding on decaying material, such as dead fish, washed up on land by the tides. Will also take household food wastes and even pet food (JONES & MORGAN, 1994).

Description: Occurs along most beaches and up to 100 m inland; very common in mangrove swamps. It is a nocturnal crab, which hides during the day. Carapace and chelae not heavily covered by spines; the eye stalks are laterally compressed; the body is cream-coloured or pale brown with a variable pattern of brown markings on carapace and walking legs; secondary sexual differences are not present (JONES & MORGAN, 1994).

Aquarium requirements: A very interesting hermit crab for an aqua-terrarium or for a tidal aquarium with a beach area. Rather easy to keep; will accept most standard type of food; however, must be given ample hiding places, such as below roots or rocks. Can be kept together in a large group.

GA: +/-; **SE:** +/-; **CO:** +/-

Photos:
Coenobita variabilis in its natural habitat in the Maldives.

Allogalathea elegans
Feather star squat lobster

Distribution: Widely distributed throughout the Indo-Pacific.
Size: Carapace length maximum 2 cm.
Reproduction: Details unknown.
Food: This squat lobster feed probably mainly on organic particles and tiny plankton, which is collected by a feather star (its commensal host). Under aquarium conditions it al-

legedly accepts food which has drifted to the bottom (BAENSCH & DEBELIUS, 1992).

Description: It lives as a commensal organism on feather stars, where it adapts its colouration to that of its (respective) host; however, the basic pattern is always the same: consisting of longitudinal stripes on carapace and walking legs. Yet, according to GOSLINER et al. (1996) there is one exception: specimens living on red feather stars are completely red. The chelae are always as long as the body. The rostrum is long, terminating in a point and covered with spines laterally. Females are larger than males.

Aquarium requirements: Little squat lobsters are often inadvertently imported together with feather stars, where they are frequently overlooked. Unfortunately, with our current (limited) knowledge and state of (aquarium) technology, feather stars do not survive for long in an aquarium, and therefore, they should not be imported. Although *Allogalathea elegans* is more resistant than its host, it does not survive without it.

GA: -; **SE:** +/-; **CO:** +/-

Photos:
Allogalathea elegans at Kimberley, Western Australia (top; photo: C. Bryce) and in Papua-New Guinea (bottom; photo: L. Newman and A. Flowers).

Squat lobster *Galathea* sp. "KA6-CRU-12" among the branches of a fire coral of the genus *Millepora*.

Photo: E. Svensen

Family Galatheidae

Squat lobsters of the family Galatheidae are rarely seen, but they are nevertheless very abundant on coral reefs. In fact, certain species occur continuously in quite large numbers, while others form huge aggregations during certain times of the year. Generally, they are small and inconspicuous. Thus, they are often overlooked by divers, unless they are specifically looking for them. The common name reflects that they bear some resemblance to small lobsters, but systematically squat lobsters are much closer to hermit crabs. The carapace is more or less oval, and the rostrum is sharp and pointed. Most species have long pincers, which are extended well in front of the animal. The abdomen is tugged under the carapace, so that the body appears to be very short. There are free-living species as well as spe-

Colour variety of feather star squat lobster, *Allogalathea elegans*, at Papua-New Guinea (two additional colour varieties on fact sheet on page 310).

Photo: L. Newman and A. Flowers

cies that live as commensals on corals, feather stars and certain other invertebrates. The principal genera of free-living squat lobsters on coral reefs are *Galathea* and *Munida*, which are also represented by species from the North Atlantic.

From among genus *Galathea*, the species, *G. humilis, G. magnifica* and *G. subsquamata* all live in association with corals, while *G.* *elegans, G. genkai* and the conspicuously-banded *Allogalathea elegans* (see fact sheet on page 310) lives on feather stars. The small species, *Lauriea siagiani* lives on the inside of sponges of genus *Xestospongia*.

Only little is known about the food and feeding habits of squat lobsters, but there is some reason to assume, that they feed on organic particles, including detritus and dead organisms, as well as tiny planktonic and benthic invertebrates.

Family Porcellanidae

Porcelain crabs (family Porcellanidae) are common in many coral reef habitats; however, much like the previously discussed squat lobsters, these crabs are rather shy and so they are often overlooked. They look very similar to true crabs, but systematically they are closer to hermit crabs. The last pair of pereiopods is much reduced; a character that clearly distinguishes them from true crabs. Also, they have much longer antennae than true crabs, and the third pair of maxillipeds is modified into large feathery brushes used for filter feeding. All species of porcelain crabs have very large and prominent pincers.

Although several porcelain crabs are occasionally available in the aquarium trade, only the anemone porcelain crabs *Petrolisthes maculatus* and *P. ohshimai* are regular inventory. Traditionally, these crabs have been placed in the genus *Neopetrolisthes*, however, it appears justified to give this merely subgeneric status. Both species live as commensals on sea anemones, or if such are unavailable, on other cnidarian animals, such as soft corals. They are easy to recognize by their white body, covered with reddish-brown spots and patches (for further information see fact sheet on pages 314-315).

Anemone porcelain crabs are very hardy aquarium inhabitants, but it is essential that they have a host animal. Without the protection of a host with its stinging cell-equipped tentacles, these crabs are rather vulnerable to attacks by predators.

In addition, the family Porcellanidae also contains other species of genera *Petrolisthes, Pachycheles, Pisidia, Polyonyx* and *Porcellana*, which are either free-living or occur as commensals on other invertebrates, such as sponges, soft corals, stony corals, sea feather, etc. HAIG (1965) reviews the

Porcellanella picta on a sea feather of the genus *Pteroeides* at Teluk Riung, Indonesia.   Photo: C. Bryce

Petrolisthes sp. "KA6-CRU-13" at One Tree Island, Great Barrier Reef.
Photo: L. Newman and A. Flowers

Unidentified porcelain crab "KA6-CRU-14" as a commensal on a soft coral of genus *Dendronephthya* in an aquarium.

porcelain crabs of Western Australia; WERDING (1983) the species of the Caribbean.

Family Albuneidae

This family, as well as family Hippidae (not discussed), contains the mole crabs. These crabs have generally a nearly cylindrical body shape, formed by a long carapace with the abdomen tucked under it. They are burrowing species, which spend most of the time covered in sand or sediment in search of food. They are able to swim backwards. When disturbed, they will very rapidly burrow into the substrate, using their feet, which are specially modified for digging.

Mole crabs live on open sandy beaches or in sand patches between coral boulders. Often only their eyes and antennae are visible, while the rest of the body is buried. Juveniles comb tiny organisms and organic particles out of the water with their feathery antennae. Adults are often scavengers, which feed on dead organisms and detritus.

Mole crabs are rarely seen, unless one specifically search for them, but divers have a chance to find some if they are looking hard enough. The principal genera in coral reef habitats are *Albunea* and *Ptychodera*. For unknown reasons, mole crabs do not seem to do well in coral reef aquarium.

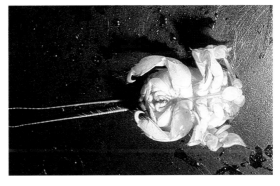

Dorsal (left) and ventral view (right) of the mole crab *Albunea gibbesi*, collected in Nassau, Bahamas.

Petrolisthes spp.
Porcelain crabs

Distribution: Widely distributed throughout the Indo-Pacific.

Size: Total carapace length 2.5 cm, but mostly smaller.

Reproduction: Details unknown.

Food: Filter feeder. The third pair of maxillipeds has become modified and is equipped with long, delicate setae which function as filters. These filters are dragged through the surrounding water in order to comb out microscopic particles. According to BARNES (1980), some species also scrape detritus off rocks.

Description of genus: A few authors place some of the species into genus *Neopetrolisthes*. The species best known to marine aquarists are those which live in association with anemones. There is also a very large number of free-living species. VINE (1986) lists 9 species for the Red Sea, with the most common one being *Petrolisthes leptocheles*. The chelipeds are large and flattened, the antennas are quite long, but not very hairy. The basic body colouration is generally transparent (like porcelain) but this varies among the species. For further information about genus and family, the reader's attention is direct to the relevant section in the following descriptive text, as well as to HAIG (1979), GORE & ABELE (1976), and WERDING (1983).

Description of species:

- *Petrolisthes alobatus* (not illustrated) occurs in the western Indo-Pacific, specifically at Mauritius and Madagascar. Lives in association with various sea anemones, often in pairs. Body, chelae and walking legs are white, mottled with a mixture of larger and smaller black dots, sometimes including diffuse, light brown patches; the bases of the walking legs are brown. Rarely available in the aquarium trade; hardy species.

- *Petrolisthes lamarckii* occurs widely in the Indo-Pacific among rock- and coral rubble. This species does not live in association with sea anemones. The body colours are rather dark, mottled with black and grey-bronze-coloured dots. Rarely ever imported, but easy to keep.

Photos:

Top: *Petrolisthes lamarckii* at One Tree Island, Great Barrier Reef.   Photo: L. Newman and A. Flowers

Centre: *Petrolisthes maculatus* in an aquarium.

Bottom: *Petrolisthes ohshimai* in an aquarium.

Photo: Scott W. Michael

- *Petrolisthes maculatus* is also widely distributed through-out the Indo-Pacific, and it is frequently imported. Lives associated with large sea anemones, usually as a pair. The body is white with many small reddish to reddish brown dots, which normally do not extend onto the digits of the chelae; intra-specific variations in colour pattern exist.
- *Petrolisthes ohshimai* occurs mainly in the central Indo-Pacific and lives in association with large sea anemones, usually as a pair. The body colour is white; scattered reddish-brown patterns on carapace, chelae and merus of the walking legs. Superimposed on these patterns are many large, deep red patches and dots. Easy to keep.

Aquarium requirements: *Petrolisthes maculatus* and *P. ohshimai* are the species most commonly imported. They are hardy and live for a long time, provided they are carefully acclimatised. We have kept a pair of *P. maculatus* successfully together with a sea anemone of genus *Phymanthus* for three years. In this period, the pair never left their host anemone. Specific food is not required, since there are normally sufficient food particles suspended in the water. Species, which do not live together with sea anemones, are only sporadically imported, but they are equally hardy. Normally the latter tend to hide under rocks and in crevices. Both types of porcelain crabs are best kept in a small special aquarium, where their behaviour can easily be observed close-up. In general, porcelain crabs moult rather frequently.

GA: +; SE: +; CO: +

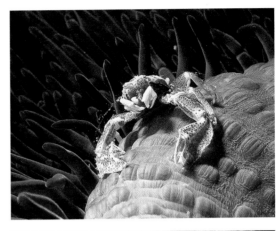

Photos:
Top: *Petrolisthes* sp. "KA6-CRU-33" at the Solomon Islands.   Photo: C. Bryce
Centre: *Petrolisthes* sp. "KA6-CRU-34" in an aquarium.
                         Photo: Scott W. Michael
Bottom: *Petrolisthes* sp. "KA6-CRU-35".
                    Photo: L. Newman and A. Flowers

In true crabs, the carapace is broad and the abdomen is reduced and small, firmly tugged under the cephalothorax. The first pair of pereiopods carries large, heavy pincers, the last (i.e. the fifth) pair is normally not much smaller than the others, but there are exceptions. The antennae are short and usually located in centrally between the eyes. In males, the first two pairs of pleopods are modified for sperm transfer. The first pair is cylindrical and the second pair acts as a piston inside the first. The abdomen in females is wider than in males. The eggs are attached to the pleopods of the female, and are carried under the curled-in abdomen.

The true crabs represent a rather species-diverse group, which is split up into five sections (see systematic overview below). These five sections encompass a total of at least 27 families, most of which are represented on coral reefs. In the material presented below we concentrate systematically on the sections, and include discussions on particular families. The section Cancridea is omitted here, because of little relevance to coral reef aquaristics.

Section Dromiacea

This section contains at least three families, of which family **Dromiidae** is the most important one from an aquarist's perspective. The species in this family are considered to be primitive crabs. They are commonly referred to as sponge crabs, because most carry live sponges on their carapace around with them, however, a few species prefer ascidians instead. These sponge- or sea squirt colonies are shaped in order to fit precisely on to the crab, so that its body is hidden.

The last two pairs of pereiopods carry pincers; they are smaller than the others and are curved upwards; a morphological characteristic uncommon in true crabs. The small pereiopods are used to grasp the sponge and hold on to it. The carapace in sponge crabs is normally about as wide as it is long, and armed with a variable number of spines along the sides. The dorsal surface is often covered by hair, which gives it a "fluffy" appearance; other than that, it is fairly smooth. The most common genera on coral reefs include *Cryptodromia, Dromidia* and *Petalomera* (see fact sheet on page 318). These crabs are occasionally imported, but they do not belong to the easy-to-keep crustaceans. Moreover, they represent a potential danger for other invertebrates.

Section Oxystomata

In the crabs of this section, the last pair of pereiopods is either

---

Systematic overview of the infraorder Brachyura

Section Dromiacea
　　　　Family Dromiidae
　　　　　　　　Cryptodromia, Dromia, Dromidia, Dromidiopsis, Petalomera
　　　　Family Latreilliidae *
　　　　　　　　Latreillia
　　　　Family Homolidae *
　　　　　　　　Homola, Homologenus, Paramola
Section Oxystomata
　　　　Family Dorippidae *
　　　　　　　　Ethusa, Ethusina, Medorippe
　　　　Family Raninidae *
　　　　　　　　Ranina
　　　　Family Leucosiidae – Pebble or nutcrabs
　　　　　　　　Arcania, Cryptocnemus, Ebalia, Ilia, Iphiculus, Ixa, Leucosia, Myra, Nucia, Nursia, Nursilia, Oreophorus, Pariphiculus, Philyra, Pseudophilura
　　　　Family Calappidae – Shame-faced crabs
　　　　　　　　Calappa, Cycloes, Matuta
Section Cancridea
　　　　Family Corystidae *
　　　　　　　　Corystes
　　　　Family Atelecyclidae *
　　　　　　　　Atelecyclus
　　　　Family Cancridae *
　　　　　　　　Cancer

The families marked with an asterisks * are not dealt with in this book.

Section Oxyrhyncha

    Family Majidae – Decorator- and spider crabs

        Acanthonyx, Achaeus, Aepinus, Anamathia, Camposcia, Chionoecetes, Cyclax, Cyphocarcinus, Dorhynchus, Entomonyx, Ergasticus, Eurynome, Herbstia, Hoplophrys, Huenia, Hyastenus, Inachoides, Inachus, Lambrachaeus, Leptomithrax, Macropodia, Maja, Maxioides, Menaethiops, Menaethius, Micippa, Micropisa, Mithraculus, Naxia, Oncinopus, Ophthalmus, Paranaxia, Perinia, Phalangipus, Pisa, Pseudomicippe, Rochinia, Schizophrys, Simocarcinus, Stenorhynchus, Stilbognathus, Tylocarcinus, Xenocarcinus

    Family Hymenosomatidae – Wrong spider crabs

        Amarinus, Elamena, Halicarcinus, Hymenosoma, Trigonoplax

    Family Parthenopidae

        Ceratocarcinus, Daldorfia, Eumedonus, Heterocrypta, Lambrus, Parthenope, Thyrolambrus

Section Brachygnatha

    Family Geryonidae *

        Chaecon, Geryon, Paragalene

    Family Portunidae – Swimming- and beach crabs

        Bathynectes, Callinectes, Caphyra, Carcinus, Carupa, Charybdis, Liocarcinus, Lissocarcinus, Lupocyclus, Necora, Nectocarcinus, Ovalipes, Podophthalmus, Polybius, Portumnus, Portunus, Scylla, Thalamita, Thalamitoides

    Family Goneplacidae *

        Carcinoplax, Eucrate, Georgeoplax, Goneplax, Litocheira, Machaerus, Notonyx, Paranotonyx, Typhlocarcinus, Xenophthalmoides

    Family Xanthidae – Black finger crabs

        Actaea, Atergatis, Atergatopsis, Banareia, Carpilius, Chlorodiella, Coralliope, Cycloxanthops, Cymo, Domecia, Dyspanopeus, Etisus, Euryozius, Euxanthus, Glyptoxanthus, Halimede, Hypocolpus, Lachnopodus, Leptodius, Liocarpilodes, Liomera, Lophozozymus, Lybia, Macromedaeus, Medaeus, Microcassiope, Monodaeus, Nanocassiope, Neoliomera, Neoxanthops, Panopeus, Paractaea, Phymodius, Pilodius, Platypodia, Platypodiella, Pseudoactumnus, Pseudocarcinus, Pseudoliomera, Rhithropanopeus, Xanthias, Xantho, Zosimus, Zozymodes

    Family Menippidae – Red-eye crabs

        Domezia, Ephixanthus, Eriphia, Globopilumnus, Hypothalassia, Lydia, Menippe, Ozius, Pseudozius, Schaerozius

    Family Trapeziidae – Coral crabs

        Trapezia, Tetralia

    Family Pilumnidae – Hairy crabs

        Actumnus, Eurycarcinus, Glabropilumnus, Heteropanope, Heteropilumnus, Parapilumnus, Pilumnoides, Pilumnopeus, Pilumnus, Planopilumnus

    Family Pinnotheridae *

        Duerckheimia, Ostracotheres, Pinnotheres, Neopinnotheres

    Family Palicidae *

        Palicus

    Family Grapsidae – Shore crabs

        Brachynotus, Cyclograpsus, Eriocheir, Euchirograpsus, Geograpsus, Grapsus, Helice, Helograpsus, Iliograpsus, Leptograpsodes, Leptograpsus, Metograpsus, Metopograpsus, Nanosesarma, Pachygrapsus, Paragrapsus, Percnon, Plagusia, Planes, Pseudograpsus, Sarmatium, Sesarma, Utica

    Family Mictyridae – Soldier crabs

        Mictyris

    Family Ocypodidae – Fiddler- and Ghost crabs

        Heloecius, Macrophthalmus, Ocypode, Paracleistosoma, Scopimera, Uca

    Family Sundathelphusidae – Fresh-water crabs *

    Family Cryptochiridae – Gall crabs

        Cryptochirus, Hapalocarcinus, Neotroglocarcinus, Troglocarcinus

Cryptodromia **spp.,** *Dromidia* **spp., and** *Petalomera* **spp.**

Distribution: Indo-Pacific and Caribbean.
Size: Maximum carapace length up to 8 cm, but most species remain smaller.
Reproduction: Details unknown.
Food: Most species feed on dead organisms, detritus and small invertebrates.
Description: These crabs occur in the intertidal zone and down to more than 200 m depth on sandy bottom, among rocks, corals and in algae cover. They are among the most primitive crabs. The last two pairs of walking legs are smaller than the others, and are equipped with claws used for grasping and holding sponges. The majority of species carry a sponge around on them for protection and camouflage. The carapace is usually exactly as wide as it is long, and has a variable number of spines along the sides. The dorsal region is soft and covered with fine hairs. Females are characterised by clearly distinctive longitudinal grooves along the underside of the thoracic armour.
Aquarium requirements: Sponge crabs are occasionally imported, and they are certainly an attraction in a coral reef aquarium. Unfortunately, their commensal sponges are often far more difficult to keep alive than the crabs. Therefore, it is advisable to keep sponge crabs in a special aquarium, where an ample supply of microscopically small food particles can be readily provided as food for the sponges.

GA: +/-; **SE:** +/-; **CO:** +/-

Photos:
Top: Unidentified sponge crab of family Dromiidae ("KA6-CRU-18"), hiding under *Caulerpa* algae, in an aquarium of Kölle Zoo, Stuttgart.
Bottom: *Petalomera* sp. "KA6-CRU-19" at Carter Reef near Kimberley, Western Australia.   Photo: C. Bryce

normally developed, or modified as in crabs of section Dromiacea. In contrast to the other true crabs, where the oral frame is rather square, it is triangular in the Oxystomata (*oxys*, Greek = pointed, and *stoma*, Greek = mouth). From among the four recognized families, we will only discuss Leucosiidae and Calappidae.

The pebble- or nut crabs of the family **Leucosiidae** are characterized by a globular carapace, which is slightly pointed anteriorly. The pincers are well-developed, but the legs are rather thin. Pebble crabs are found in shallow water among coral rubble, in the intertidal zone and subtidally down to a depth of 50 m. They are often found in large aggregations. It is thought that they are fairly common, but they are not often seen since they bury in substrate during the day. The different species display many different colour patterns. Many are brightly coloured, with conspicuous patterns. The carapace rarely reaches a width of more than 2.5 cm, so that in terms of size, these crabs could be excellent aquarium inhabitants. The diet is believed to consist mainly of detritus and other organic particles. The genera *Philyra* and *Leucosia* are the ones most likely to be found on coral reefs. There does, however, not seem to be any information about any imports of these crabs for the aquarium trade.

The shame-faced crabs of family **Calappidae** (also referred to as box- or sand crabs) are rather unusual, but very interesting crustaceans. The rather large pincers are laterally flattened and are being held close to the head, creating the impression as if these crabs are "ashamed". They live along beaches, in shallow as well as in deeper water. During the day they remain buried in sand, and become active only at night, to hunt for molluscs. They could be suitable aquarium animals, however, their predatory behaviour could pose a problem; if their preferred food is not available, they will "sample" alternatives, such as other invertebrates.

The pebble crab *Leucosia anatum* in the Philippines.   Photo: P. Schupp

Experiences have shown that they readily adapt to various substitute foods. The most important genus is *Calappa* (see fact sheet on page 320).

Section Oxyrhyncha

Typical for this section are the rather grotesque decorator- and spider crabs of the family Majidae, which contains many species of interest for coral reef aquaria. The two other families (i.e. Hymenosomatidae and Parthenopidae) are hardly significant for the aquarium hobby, but they still deserve a brief mentioning here.

The carapace of crabs in this section narrows anteriorly into a distinct rostrum (*oxy*, Greek = sharp, pointed and *rhynchos*, Greek = proboscis). Consequently, the body shape appears somewhat triangular. Long, slender walking legs make most species look like spiders. Many species are well camouflaged, since they carry algae, hydroids, sponges and other organisms attached to their carapace and legs. This habit is especially well developed in the family **Majidae**. Some

Unidentified decorator crab.   Photo: Scott W. Michael

Calappa spp.
Shame-faced crabs

Distribution: Circumtropical.

Size: Maximum carapace length between 3 and 8 cm, depending upon the species.

Reproduction: Details unknown.

Food: Many species feed at night on molluscs, which are opened or broken up by the powerful claws of these crabs. They quick learn to accept substitute food. KASTLE (1994) reports, that one species in his tank fed on gorgonian corals.

Description: These are nocturnal crabs, which hide during the day by burrowing into sandy bottom or by retreating into rocky crevices among corals. They occur in shallow water and down to a depth of at least 100 m. The carapace is equipped with wing-like extensions along the sides and at the posterior section, which partially cover the walking legs. The edges of these extensions often have spines. The top of the movable digit of the chelae is comb-like serrated (JONES & MORGAN, 1994). The basic colouration is normally brownish with darker markings, but this can vary within a species, as in *Calappa calappa*, which is one of the most common shame-faced crabs in the Indo-Pacific. This species can be white with red spots or of a uniform light brown colour.

Aquarium requirements: Shame-faced crabs are excellent inhabitants for a small sand zone aquarium, where their extraordinary behaviour is easy to observe. In a large community tank these crabs are rarely ever seen. Basically, they are hardy aquarium animals; however, sometimes they prey on corals and other invertebrates.

GA: +; **SE:** +; **CO:** +/-

Photos:

Top: *Calappa* sp. "KA6-CRU-20" in its typical beach habitat at the Maldives. One has to look closely to find these crabs.

Centre: *Calappa* cf. *japonica* at Guam.   Photo: P. Schupp

Bottom: Uniformly coloured form of *Calappa calappa* at Sulawesi.   Photo: Scott W. Michael

of the decorator crabs of this family occasionally appear in aquarium shops. *Camposcia retusa* is an example of these grotesque-appearing crabs (see fact sheet on page 323).

The only species of family Majidae regularly available in the aquarium trade is the Caribbean spider crab, *Stenorhynchus seticornis*. It is a rather small crab; the carapace, excluding the rostrum, reaches a length of only 2 cm. The total leg span in adult specimens can be between 5 and 10 cm. Without question, this is a beautiful crab and an interesting addition to the aquarium. In our experience, it can normally be kept without problems in most coral reef aquaria; it is, however, carnivorous and has a large variety of

Xenocarcinus depressus is an unusual spider crab of the family Majidae, which lives as a commensal on gorgonian coral, as seen here in Heron Island, Great Barrier Reef. Photo: L. Newman and A. Flowers

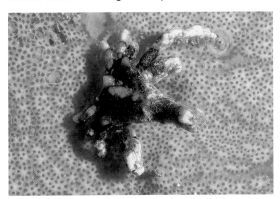 

Huenia cf. *heraldi* (left) and *H. brevifrons* of the family Majidae live in association with green algae, specifically with *Halimeda* species. They mimic the shape of the algae so well that they are perfectly camouflaged as long as they remain among them. These are small crabs with a maximum carapace size of about 3 cm. It is assumed, that they feed on microscopic algae and tiny invertebrates that live on them. There is no information available on their aquarium husbandry. Photos: L. Newman and A. Flowers

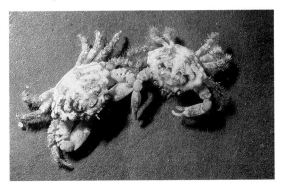 

Left: *Mithraculus coryphe* of the family Majidae was introduced into an aquarium as stowaways on live rock. This species can harm other invertebrates. Right: *Schizophrys* sp. "KA6-CRU-22", also belongs to the family Majidae, are commonly known as sea toads (photo: Dr. I. Illich).

We are always reluctant to refer to an animal as being ugly, however, with *Parthenope turriger* (seen here at Guam) we must agree with the words of JONES & MORGAN (1994): This animal is "rarely seen by most people ... but when once seen, however, it is not quickly forgotten".

Photos: P. Schupp

small invertebrates on its menu. Tubes worms in particular, appear to be at risk (see fact sheet on page 324).

Many other majid species can also be found on coral reefs. Sometimes, specimens are introduced into aquariums as "stowaways" on live rocks or corals. The majority is carnivorous or omnivorous, so that there is a risk that they may damage other animals in the same tank. The important genera are: *Achaeus, Camposcia,*

Trigonoplax sp. "KA6-CRU-21" of the family Hymenosomatidae, at Heron Island, Great Barrier Reef.   Photo: L. Newman and A. Flowers

Cyclax, Eurynome, Huenia, Hyastenus, Leptomithrax, Menaethiops, Mithraculus, Naxia, Paranaxia, Schizophrys, Simocarcinus and *Xenocarcinus.* The world's largest crab - the deep-water Japanese giant spider crab, *Macrocheira kaempferi,* belongs to the family Majidae. GRIFFIN (1966) provides an overview of the family Majidae in Australian waters.

The false spider crabs of family **Hymenosomatidae** do not look as

grotesque and they do not decorate themselves with other organisms. With a carapace width of less than 2 cm they are rather small, and also rather inconspicuous. Often they occur in very large numbers, especially in protected sea grass beds. The false spider crabs that are most commonly found on coral reefs are the species of genus *Trigonoplax.* Typically they live under coral boulders on reef flats. As scavengers they do reasonably well in an aquarium, but they are rarely ever imported.

The crabs of family **Parthenopidae** once again look somewhat grotesque. They are rarely ever seen and they are also hardly of significance for the aquarium hobby, but the extreme looks makes them worth presenting. The carapace is triangular or pentagonal, covered with blunt spines or knobs. In most species it is less than 5 cm wide, but in a few species it can be up to 12 cm. The colours in most species are drab, frequently in shades of brown. Yet, the extraordinary shape of the carapace makes these crabs fascinating. The most important coral reef species belong to the genera *Daldorfia, Lambrus* and *Parthenope.* We are not aware that any of these have ever been imported for the aquarium trade; but we believe, that they would probably make rather hardy aquarium inhabitants.

Camposcia retusa
Decorator crab

Distribution: Indo-Pacific; known from South- and East Africa in the Indian Ocean, the western Pacific and northern Japan.

Size: Total carapace length 5 cm; legs longer; appears larger because of the "decoration".

Reproduction: Details unknown.

Food: Carnivore, which is likely to feed on all available food in an aquarium.

Description: The hairy carapace is triangular, tapering off in an anterior direction. This crab tends to decorate itself artfully with all sorts of plants and invertebrates, which gives it an ornamental and highly colourful appearance. Often very difficult to recognise. On a coral reef this species usually lives under coral rocks.

Aquarium requirements: This crab is occasionally imported; an "eye catcher" because of its ornamental "costume", however, it is a serious enemy of other invertebrates, such as a disc- and encrusting anemones, which are being used to decorate the carapace, however, they are also eaten. It is advisable to keep this crab in a special aquarium, but periodically suitable decorative material must be provided.

GA: +; SE: +; CO: -

Photos:
Caposcia retusa at Guam (top; photo: P. Schupp) and in Indonesia (bottom; photo: Scott W. Michael).

Stenorhynchus seticornis
Caribbean spider crab, Caribbean ghost crab

Distribution: Caribbean; from the Bahamas to Brazil. According to GONZALES (1995), reports on the occurrence of this species in the eastern Atlantic (Canary Island and Madeira) are based on misidentification of the related *Stenorhynchus lanceolatus*.

Size: Carapace length 2 cm, rostrum as long or longer than the body. Total length, including the legs, usually from 5 to 10 cm.

Reproduction: Details unknown.

Food: Carnivore. BAENSCH & DEBELIUS (1992) report an observation, where this species pierced an *Apogon maculatus* with its sharp rostrum.

Description: This species lives in various habitats. The legs are very long and spider-like. The carapace is elongated and pointed; the spiny rostrum is long and sharp. The chelae of the first of walking legs are only small, but still quite powerful. The body and the thin legs are striped in white, brown and bronze colour; the tips of the chelae digits are blue.

Aquarium requirements: A hardy and quite suitable aquarium inhabitant, but tends to pick on other invertebrates, such as corals, encrusting anemones and tube worms. Easy to catch in an aquarium, in the event it causes too much damage. It is advisable to keep this crab in a special aquarium, e.g. in a tank solely for Caribbean animals.

GA: +; **SE:** +; **CO:** +/-

Photos:
Stenorhynchus seticornis in an aquarium (top and centre; centre photo: Scott W. Michael) and at the U.S. Virgin Islands (bottom; photo: Scott W. Michael).

Swimming crabs of the family Portunidae can be recognised by their paddle-shaped last pair of pereiopods, an adaptation for swimming. Here a mating pair of an unidentified species.   Photo: Scott W. Michael

Section Brachygnatha

The section Brachygnatha contains the majority of true crabs, as well most of those species which are of significance from an aquarists's perspective. The body is round, oval in cross-section or square; the carapace does not narrow anteriorly. This section encompasses at least 15 families, containing many interesting coral reef species suitable for aquarium keeping. Below we will discuss only the most important families.

The swimmer crabs of the family **Portunidae** are conspicuous animals along the reef flat. Most can instantly be recognised by their broadly flattened, paddle-shaped last pair of pereiopods, which are adapted for swimming. Many are aggressive and voracious predators and scavengers, which can be difficult to keep in most aquaria. Small fish as well

Scylla serrata (here at Exmouth Gulf, Western Australia) is a robust, large swimming crab, which may reach a carapace width of up to 20 cm, and a maximum weight of up to 1 kg.   Photo: C. Bryce

Lissocarcinus species are beautifully coloured swimming crabs, which live in association with sea anemones, soft corals, sea cucumbers and various other invertebrates. Top left: *L. laevis* in an aquarium (photo: Scott W. Michael). Top right: *L.* cf. *laevis* at Monte Bellos Island, Western Australia (photo: C. Bryce). Below: *L. orbicularis* at Papua-New Guinea (left photo: L. Newman and A. Flowers) and at Indonesia (right photo: J. Cairns-Michael).

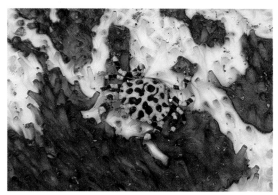

as many invertebrates are likely to become their victims. *Thalamita*- and *Portunus* species are particularly abundant in reef habitats. *Thalamita* species are also marginally suitable for general aquarium keeping (see fact sheet on page 327).

Most swimmer crabs grow to substantial sizes and are valued for human consumption; *Scylla serrata* is a good example of that. A few smaller swimmer crabs live as commensals on other invertebrates, such as *Lissocarcinus orbicularis* on sea cucumbers and

L. laevis on sea anemones. Both of these are relatively easy to keep, provided suitable hosts are available. With maximum sizes around 3 cm, they are also reasonably safe for general aquarium keeping. *Caphyra rotundifrons* is found on turtle weed

Charybdis cf. *hawaiiensis* (left; photo: M. Cufer) and *Portunus granulatus* (right).

Thalamita sp.
Swimming crabs

Distribution: Widely distributed throughout the Indo-Pacific.

Size: Some species can reach a carapace length of 10 cm, but most remain smaller.

Reproduction: Details unknown.

Food: These crabs feed on small invertebrates and fishes. Will accept substitute food.

Description: Swimming crabs occur principally in the intertidal zone, but also on soft- as well as on rocky and rubble bottom, and in seagrass beds. The carapace has normally five teeth on each side, which is a characteristic of the entire family. The fifth pair of walking legs is paddle-shaped (flattened) and is used for swimming (JONES & MORGAN, 1994). Colouration is rather variable from one species to the next, and can be in shades of blue, green or brown, often in mottled patterns. In males, the chelae are larger and the abdomen smaller, than in females.

Aquarium requirements: Often introduced into an aquarium together with live rocks (remember: these crabs feed on invertebrates!). Basically very hardy, but because of their predatory behaviour, they are not suitable for a community aquarium. They should only be kept in a dedicated aquarium, which has been set up specifically for other predatory invertebrates and large fish.

GA: +; **SE:** +; **CO:** -

Photos:
Right: *Thalamita* sp. "KA6-CRU-23" in Indonesia.
                              Photo: Scott W. Michael
Bottom: Two different viewing angles of *Thalamita danae* at Stradbroke Island, Queensland, Australia.
                         Photo: L. Newman and A. Flowers

(*Chlorodesmis*; see Volume 1, page 292).

The members of the family **Xanthidae** are the dominating crabs on the reef flat. They are commonly referred to as black-finger crabs, since the pincer digits usually have a deep, dark colouration. An alternatively name sometimes used is "stone crabs". In most species, the carapace is anteriorly wider than posteriorly. There is a large number of species belonging to at least 44 genera, and so species identification can often be rather difficult.

Many black-finger crabs are accidentally introduced into aquaria as "stowaways" on live rocks, in which case they may provide the aquarist with pleasure as well as displeasure, since their behaviour and food preferences are highly variable. The majority of these crabs are peaceful herbivores, scavengers and detritus feeders or grazers of tiny invertebrates, but there are also highly predatory species. At night we have watched small xanthid crabs emerge from their hiding places, searching for food among coral colonies. In order to detect undesirable black-finger crabs in an aquarium, one should search the tank at night with a flash light. This way one find out where the crabs are hiding and can then remove them together with the respective live rock. Otherwise, it is nearly impossible to remove such a crab alive from its hiding place. One possibility may be to kill it with a pointed object. **Please note:** This should not be read as a recommendation for uncritical removal of all crabs in live rock! In fact, our experience has shown that the majority are peaceful, and often extremely interesting and beautiful animals. For instance, we have found many *Cymo* spp. in our aquaria, which turned out to be excellent aquarium inhabitants (see fact sheet on page 330). *Liomera-* and *Neoliomera* species may be either peaceful or predatory, so careful observation of the actual specimen is required. Do not declare war towards the crabs, unless you are certain that there is a culprit present!

Although xanthids usually get into an aquarium as "stowaways" together with live rocks, some species are specifically imported. Yet, the only species, of which it can be said that it is frequently available, is the small *Lybia tesselata*. This species carries small sea anemones around on its pincers, acquiring a defence weapon as well as efficient tool for picking up small food particles (see fact sheet on page 332).

The most important genera of the family Xanthidae are *Actaea, Atergatis* (see fact sheet on page 329), *Cymo, Etisus, Liomera, Lybia, Neoliomera, Xanthias* and *Zosimus* (see fact sheet on page 333).

Black-finger crabs of the family Xanthidae: *Carpilius convexus* (left; photo: E. Svensen) and *Etisus splendidus* (right).

Unidentified black-finger crab, which has shown to cause damage in an aquarium (left; photo: Scott W. Michael) and *Xanthias punctatus* at Heron Island, Great Barrier Reef (right; photo: L. Newman and A. Flowers).

Atergatis floridus
Shawl crab

Distribution: Widely distributed throughout the Indo-Pacific.
Size: Can reach a carapace length of up to 12 cm.
Reproduction: Details unknown.
Food: Feeds on various invertebrates, probably including molluscs in particular.
Description: This crab lives on rocky substrates and on coral reefs, from shallow water down to about 50 m depth. The carapace is elongated oval and relatively smooth; edges not serrated. The chelae are large and powerful. The basic colouration is brown-greenish covered with pale, cream-coloured or yellow patches. Males and females look alike, however, the male has larger chelae. It is very toxic to humans (like *Zosimus aeneus*; see fact sheet on page 333) when eaten.
Aquarium requirements: Because of its size and food preferences, this crab is not suited for a community aquarium, but it can be kept in large fish aquarium.

GA: +/-; SE: +; CO: -

Photos:
Atergatis floridus at One Tree Island, Great Barrier Reef (top; photo: L. Newman and A. Flowers) and at Kimberley, Western Australia (bottom; photo: C. Bryce).

***Cymo* spp.**
Hairy coral crabs

Distribution: Circumtropical.
Size: Maximum carapace diameter 3 cm.
Reproduction: Details unknown.
Food: Herbivores or grazers. These crabs live in association with stony corals, especially those of genera *Acropora* and *Pocillopora*. They lodge themselves with special hooked claws in the corallites of coral. With brushes at the tips of their legs they scrape back and forth between the tentacles of the coral polyps. Coral mucus and other particles, which adhere to the brushes are combed out with a special appendage and are eaten. Even though some of the host's tissue is either damaged or eaten, respectively, strict territorial boundaries guaranty that there is only a scattered crab population, which assures that a host colony is not overcrowded (by crabs) and this then avoids excessive damage to the host (ZANN, 1980).
Description: The carapace is always roundish or oval-shaped, and only marginally wider than it is long; the edges are convex and equipped with soft teeth. One of the claws

is larger than the other. In males, both claws are larger than those of females. The walking legs have a granular appearance, and they are – like the body – more or less heavily covered with hair (JONES & MORGAN, 1994). The basic colouration is brown or brownish green. The carapace is often overgrown with algae, which assures good camouflage. These crabs are often difficult to find.
Aquarium requirements: Hairy crabs are often introduced into an aquarium inadvertently together with corals. These crabs should not be removed, since they do not damage their host, and they are totally dependent upon it for their survival. Excellent inhabitants in tanks with branched stony corals. Basically, they are hardy and easy to keep.

GA: +; **SE:** +; **CO:** +

Photo:
Cymo sp., "KA6–CRU-24", introduced into an aquarium together with a coral colony.

Liomera spp. and Neoliomera spp.

Distribution: Widely distributed throughout the Indo-Pacific.

Size: Most species reach a carapace width of less than 3 cm, however, in some the carapace may be up to 7 cm wide.

Reproduction: Details unknown.

Food: These crabs feed on detritus and other organic particles, as well as on various small invertebrates.

Description: Live in association with rocks, corals or coral rubble. The carapace is oval-shaped and normally it is wider than it is long. The teeth on the carapace are only weakly developed. Chelae of equal size (JONES & MORGAN, 1994). Colouration highly variable. Many species are bright red, purple or red and white. Both genera look very similar; in *Liomera* species the various zones of the carapace are distinctly defined, while those in *Neoliomera* species are confluent.

Aquarium requirements: Sometimes introduced into an aquarium together with live rocks or corals. Can be predators, but not all are. It is important to observe whether other aquarium inhabitants are being damaged, and which ones.

GA: +/-; **SE:** +; **CO:** +/-

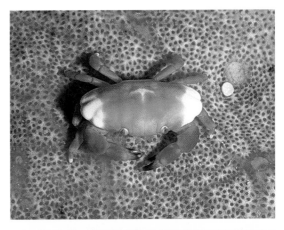

Photos:
Liomera cinctimana at Heron Island, Great Barrier Reef (top) and *Liomera* sp. "KA6-CRU-25" at One-Tree Island, Great Barrier Reef (centre), as well as *Neoliomera insularis* (bottom). Photos: L. Newman and A. Flowers

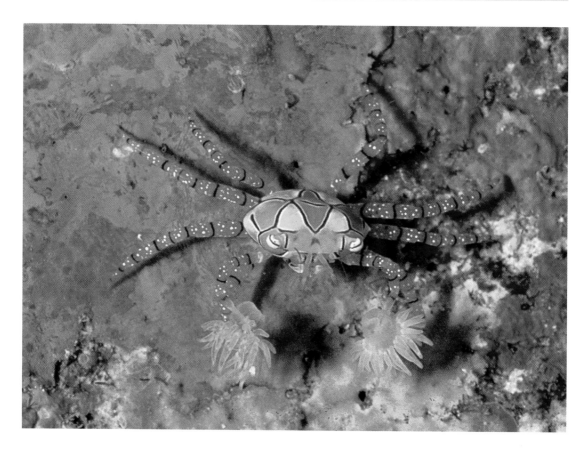

Lybia tesselata
Boxer crab

Distribution: Indo-Pacific; from the Red Sea and East Africa to Japan, possibly even to Hawaii.
Size: Maximum carapace diameter 1.5 cm.
Reproduction: Details unknown.
Food: Feeds principally on detritus.
Description: Occurs in the intertidal zone of coral reefs. This crab carries tiny sea anemones (*Triactis producta*) on its slender, narrow and modified digits of the chelae. The anemones are used as defence as well as a brush for collecting food, by dragging them through detritus. Particles attached to the anemones are then eaten by the crab. The carapace is always hexagonal and is marked by dark lines, which create the impression as if it is divided into polygons. The legs feature conspicuous bands (JONES & MORGAN, 1994).

Aquarium requirements: This species is imported only occasionally. It should be kept in a special aquarium, so that the symbiosis with anemones can be observed more closely. In a large tank this crab is rarely ever seen.

GA: +; **SE:** +/-; **CO:** +

Photo:
Lybia tesselata at Madang, Papua-New Guinea.
Photo: L. Newman and A. Flowers

Zosimus aeneus
Devil crab, Toxic reef crab

Distribution: Central Indo-Pacific; specific location details not available, but very common on shallow water reefs in northern Australia.

Size: Can reach a carapace diameter of at least 10 cm.

Reproduction: Details unknown.

Food: It is assumed that this crab feeds primarily on clams and single-shelled molluscs (snails), but probably also on other invertebrates.

Description: Deep grooves divide the carapace into zones. There are four teeth on each side, of which the last one is more pointed than the others. The walking legs and the first digit of the chelipeds have clearly visible combs. The chelae are large and strong (JONES & MORGAN, 1994). The basic colours are variable, but there are always distinct, red spots. Eating this crab is fatal for humans! Half a gram of chelae muscle can contain sufficient toxin to kill a person! It is assumed that this venom is a saxitoxin, which is produced by dinoflagellates, and is accumulated in the flesh of the crab through the food chain via plankton-feeding molluscs (MARSH & SLACK-SMITH, 1986). Not dangerous to humans unless it is eaten.

Aquarium requirements: This crab is rarely ever imported, but it does appear sporadically in the aquarium trade, or possibly get into an aquarium as a "stowaway" on live rocks. Because of its size and food preferences it is not a suitable species for a community tank, but can readily be kept in a large fish aquarium.

GA: +/-; **SE:** +; **CO:** -

Photos:
Three different colour forms of *Zosimus aeneus*: on the Great Barrier Reef (top; photo: L. Newman and A. Flowers), in the Cocos Islands in the Indian Ocean (centre; photo: C. Bryce), and in Guam (bottom; photo: P. Schupp).

Typical shore- or rock crab of the family Grapsidae in the Maldives.

The red-eye crabs of the family **Menippidae** look very similar to xanthids, and many authors also include them in the family Xanthidae. However, the males of menippid crabs have seven abdominal segments, while there are only five segments in xanthid males. The information provided above about family Xanthidae, does otherwise generally apply to family Menippidae as well. *Eriphia* spp. (see fact sheet on page 335) have often been introduced into aquaria with live rocks. These crabs are, unfortunately, among the most predatory and aggressive of all, and an aquarist must be very cautious, if he discovers such a crab in his aquarium.

The true coral crabs of the genera *Trapezia* and *Tetralia* have been removed from the family Xanthidae, and placed in their own family **Trapeziidae**. They are easy to identify by the shape of their carapace and the length of the pincers. The carapace if flattened, pentagonal and has its largest width anteriorly. One or both pincers are much larger than the walking legs. The common name "coral crabs" refers to their asso-

ciation as commensals on branched stony corals of the genera *Pocillopora* and *Acropora*. If a natural host is available to them in the aquarium, these crabs thrive, are hardy and highly desirable aquarium inhabitants (see fact sheet on pages 336-337).

Hairy crabs of the family **Pilumnidae** occur frequently in coral reefs, in terms of species numbers as well as in population sizes. Yet, they are only insufficiently known and their systematics is complicated. They are virtually never specifically imported, but do often arrive as stowaways on live rocks and corals. We believe that *Pilumnus* (see fact sheet on page 338) is the most widely occurring genus, however, a few other genera have also been described. Our experiences with these crabs are mixed. Some species are obvious predators while others appear to be perfectly peaceful towards other aquarium inhabitants. Careful observation, like we suggested for Xanthidae, is necessary in order to decide on what to do with a particular specimen. Once again, we strongly object to unnecces-

ary removals of animals that perhaps are highly compatible with the other aquarium inhabitants; besides being both very interesting and attractive animals.

The shore- or rock crabs of the family **Grapsidae** are common inhabitants of the intertidal zone of coral reefs all over the world. They have a typically flattened, square-like shape. The legs are modified for climbing and running across rocks, sand and mud. They are "experts" at that, since they can move very fast. Some species are equally well adapted for life in and out of water, and do, in essence, lead a more or less amphibian way of life.

None of the grapsid crabs are frequently for sale in the aquarium trade, however, intermittently *Grapsus* spp. from the Indo-Pacific and *Percnon gibbesi* from the Caribbean are available. Although they are not particularly well suited for a standard aquarium, they are interesting specimens for an aqua-terrarium or a coral reef profile aquarium (see fact sheet on pages 340).

Eriphia spp.
Red-eye crabs

Distribution: Widely distributed throughout the Indo-Pacific. More specific details are not known.
Size: Maximum carapace diameter 6 cm.
Reproduction: Details unknown.
Food: These crabs feed on various small invertebrates.
Description: *Eriphia* crabs occur in the intertidal zone or in the adjacent shallow water area. Nocturnal; during the day they hide under rocks, coral rubble or in crevices and caves, where they firmly lodge themselves, so that they can not be removed without damaging them. The carapace edges appear to be rounded off when viewed from above, but there are a few teeth located along the edges, which decrease in size posteriorly. The carapace has a granulated surface; the claws are large and smooth; the walking legs are equipped with brushes made up of dark brown or brown-green hairs. Vivid red eyes are located on top of white eyestalks (JONES & MORGAN, 1994).
Aquarium requirements: These are highly predatory crabs, not suited for a community aquarium, but they can be kept in a large fish aquarium, or in an aquarium with large, tough invertebrates, such as anemones.

GA: +/-; **SE:** +; **CO:** -

Photos:
Top: *Eriphia sebana* at Fiji.
Centre: Egg-carrying female of *Eriphia sebana* on the Great Barrier Reef.   Photo: L. Newman and A. Flowers
Bottom: This *Eriphia verrucosa* specimen was introduced into the aquarium attached to live rocks.

Trapezia spp. and *Tetralia* spp.
Coral crabs

Distribution: Circumtropical, widely distributed.

Size: Most species have a carapace diameter of less than 2 cm; only a few are larger.

Reproduction: Details unknown.

Food: These crabs are herbivores, which lodge themselves among the corallites of their host coral, very much like *Cymo* spp. (see fact sheet on page 330).

Description: In general, *Trapezia* spp. live in pairs on stony corals of genus *Pocillopora*, while *Tetralia* spp. are normally found (also in pairs) on stony corals of genus *Acropora*. The carapace is trapeze-shaped (= trapezoid); the chelipeds are enlarged. Formerly, these crabs were included in the family of round crabs (Xanthidae), since they also have five abdominal segments. The genera *Trapezia* and *Tetralia* are clearly distinctive: *Trapezia* species have four wide lobes at the anterior part of the carapace, while these are hardly discernable in *Tetralia*. Instead, in the latter, the anterior margin of the carapace is covered with many tiny teeth. Two species common throughout the Indo-Pacific are *Trapezia ferruginea* and *T. wardi*.

Aquarium requirements: Often introduced into an aquarium attached to branched, stony corals, from which they should not be removed. Many aquarists believe that the crabs damage the corals, but this is definitely NOT the case. Why should they cause serious damage to their hosts, when they are totally dependent upon them for their own survival? Very well-suited and hardy inhabitants for an aquarium with branching stony corals, and for a community aquarium.

GA: +; **SE:** +; **CO:** +

Photos left:
Typical colony of trapezoid coral crabs, probably *Trapezia ferruginea* on a *Pocillopora* stony coral in Indonesia (top) and *T. ferruginea* in an aquarium (bottom).

Photos right:
Trapezia wardi (top) in an aquarium. *Trapezia lutea* (bottom left), as well as *Tetralia nigrolineata* (bottom right), which had been imported attached to corals.

Pilumnus spp.
Hairy crabs

Distribution: Widely distributed throughout the Indo-Pacific; details unknown.
Size: Some species reach a carapace width of 5 cm, but most remain smaller, with a carapace width of about 3 cm.
Reproduction: Details unknown.
Food: These crabs use a broad spectrum of food items.
Description: *Pilumnus* crabs live in many different habitats, including muddy or sandy bottom, on rocks, in mangrove regions and on coral reefs. The carapace has normally a sharp marginal serration, however, this is covered over by short or long hairs. Most species have drab brown colours. The hairs are covered over by algae and detritus for camouflage purposes. Males and females look rather similar, but males have slightly larger chelipeds (JONES & MORGAN, 1994). In Australia, the species *Pilumnus pulcher* and *P. vespertilio* are rather common. *P. pulcher* is covered with thin, stiff brown bristles, while *P. vespertilio* has long, soft (flat-lying) hairs, which give this crab the appearance of a wool mop.
Aquarium requirements: These crabs are often introduced into aquaria together with corals and live rocks (see Volume 1, page 184), whereby *Pilumnus vespertilio* is probably the most frequently occurring hairy crab. Many aquarists are familiar with this "monster", which is normally seen only at night. Sometimes, these crabs can inflict serious damage upon other invertebrates, yet, under different conditions they may not be predatory at all. In fact, we have observed how some of these crabs were feeding on corals and other invertebrates. Yet, other specimens in other aquaria, have not harmed any other aquarium inhabitants for years. May be such difference in behaviour among specimens of the same species are due to individual food preferences in the sea. If a hairy crab is to be removed from an aquarium, this should be done at night and with the aid of forceps. Alternately, the live rock or other decorative item used by the crab as its hiding place, can be taken out of the aquarium.

GA: +; **SE:** +; **CO:** +/-

Photo:
Pilumnus sp. "KA6-CRU-26", in an aquarium, partially hiding in cave.

Left: The mangrove crab, *Neosarmatium meinerti,* is one of the crabs responsible for the many crab burrows in mangrove forest of the Indo-Pacific. It is a highly aggressive crab, which feeds on plant- and animal material (photo: C. Bryce). Right: A typical shore crab of the family Grapsidae at Belau (photo: Dr. I. Illich).

Grapsidae - Shore Crabs

Grapsus **spp.**
Rock runners, Spray crabs, Swift-footed crabs

Distribution: Widely distributed throughout the Indo-Pacific.

Size: Carapace width maximally 6 cm.

Reproduction: Details unknown.

Food: Principal food item is algae, and, if need be, also detritus, as well as smaller invertebrates.

Description: These crabs are well adapted for a terrestrial life in the intertidal zone and in mangrove areas, where they sometimes occur in large numbers. When disturbed, they rapidly flee, to hide in crevices and caves. The anterior margin of the carapace is less than half as wide as its maximum width. The carapace edges are convex. The upper segment of the third maxilliped is longer than it is wide. With a well-developed toothed or spinous expansion on the end of the merus of the claw (JONES & MORGAN, 1994). Colouration is highly variable, even within a species. In most instances the carapace and the walking legs are red, red brown or dark olive-green, sometimes almost black with lighter-coloured patches and spots. Males have larger claws than females. *Grapsus albolineatus* and *G. tenuicrustatus* are two common species over the entire range of this genus, while *G. granulosus* – according to VINE (1986) – is possibly endemic to the Red Sea.

Aquarium requirements: Shore crabs are suitable for an intertidal zone aquarium, for a marine aqua-terrarium or for a mangrove aquarium. We believe, that these crabs do well in such special aquarium, where they should be easy to keep. Definitely not suited for the typical coral reef aquarium.

GA: +/-; **SE:** 0; **CO:** +/-

Photo:
Grapsus albolineatus in the Maldives.

Percnon gibbesi
Urchin crab, Nimble spray crab

Distribution: Widespread in the Caribbean; from North Carolina to Brazil. In the eastern Atlantic; from the Azores and Canary Isles to the Cape of Good Hope, South Africa. Also occurs in the eastern Pacific from Sea of Cortez to Chile, at Clipperton and Galapagos.

Size: Carapace with rarely exceeds 3 cm.

Reproduction: Details unknown.

Food: Feeds by grazing algae off rocks.

Description: Occurs on coral reefs and in rocky shore areas in the region of the high water mark. Often hides under sea urchins of genus *Diadema*. The carapace is strongly flattened, disk-like and dark brown to olive, with an iridescent green line along the anterior edge. The walking legs are brown, with golden yellow bands. The claws of the male are substantially larger than those of the female. The association between crab and sea urchin is only lose; both animals can be found without the other being present. Presumably, the crab merely uses the sea urchin for protection against predators, while the sea urchin does not derive any benefit from this association.

Aquarium requirements: Less inclined to venture on to land than *Grapsus* species (see fact sheet on page 339); consequently, it is also more suitable for a coral reef aquarium; however, it is not one of the hardiest crabs. It seems to do better in an aquarium with a strong current and wave action. Although it feeds primarily by grazing algae off rocks, it can not be trusted altogether in respect to smaller invertebrates.

GA: +; **SE:** +/-; **CO:** +/-

Photos:
Percnon gibbesi in an aquarium at Kölle Zoo (top) and in the Caribbean (bottom; photo: Scott W. Michael).

Male fiddler crab, *Uca* sp. "KA6-CRU-27" in a brackish water aquarium. One of the pincers is so large that the animal can almost totally hide behind it. Photo: U. Werner

Soldier crabs is the common name of the members of the family **Mictyridae**. The name has probably been derived from the fact that they tend to "march" across tide flats in literal mass manoeuvres, when the tide is out. An alternate explanation is that their blue or blue-grey colouration is reminiscent of a soldier's uniform. All soldier crabs belong to the genus *Mictyris*. They live in estuaries or muddy, sandy areas in bays and river deltas. They are not suited for a "normal" coral reef aquarium, but they would make interesting inhabitants for an aqua-terrarium or for a reef profile aquarium with a large beach zone (see fact sheets on pages 342-343).

The fiddler- and ghost crabs of the family **Ocypodidae** are conspicuous crustaceans along sandy beaches, mud flats as well as in mangrove forests. Several species occur on inner reef flats or along beaches, where they are more or less dependent on entering dry land.

Species of interest for the aquarium hobby include those with an amphibian mode of life, such as *Ocypode* and *Uca* (see fact sheets on page 344). Although they are not suited for a standard coral reef aquarium, they have interesting potential for the specifically set-up aqua-terrarium with tidal simulation.

In the small family **Cryptochiridae**, we find the gall crabs that live as obligatory commensals of stony corals. They stimulate the corals to form galls, in which the female lives. These tiny crabs are often overlooked on a reef, but they are easy to find if one knows what to look for and scrutinise the coral branches carefully. There are no reports about aquarium observations on these crabs, but probably they would make suitable aquarium inhabitants. *Hapalocarcinus marsupialis* (see fact sheet on page 345) is the most common and widespread species of the family.

Male *Ocypode saratan* on a beach in the Maldives.

Mictyris sp.
Soldier crabs

Distribution: Central Indo-Pacific.

Size: Carapace diameter to about 3 cm.

Reproduction: Migrates to the water in order to lay the eggs in the sand just below the low water mark.

Food: These crab emerge from their burrows in the sediment at low tide to feed on detritus left behind by the receding water.

Description: Soldier crabs live in muddy areas of the intertidal zone and bury themselves – in a corkscrew-like fashion – when they are being disturbed or when the water rises during the incoming tide. The body is always (almost) spherical. The walking legs are positioned under the body, so that they lift off the sediment. The third maxilliped is very long and wide. Hardly any (external) sexual differences (JONES & MORGAN, 1994). *Mictyris longicarpus* and *M. platycheles* are two common soldier crabs in Australia. Their carapace is usually bright blue or blue green, becoming paler towards the edge. The legs are pale yellowish.

Aquarium requirements: These fascinating crabs must be given a special aquarium, where a muddy intertidal zone is being simulated, may be even with some mangroves. Such a tank can be used to keep a large group of soldier crabs. They can not and must not be kept in an ordinary coral reef aquarium.

GA: +, SE: +/-; CO: 0

Photos:

Mictyris longicarpus at the Philippines (top; photo: P. Schupp), and *M. platycheles* at Stradbroke Island, Queensland, Australia (centre and bottom; photos: L. Newman and A. Flowers).

Ocypode spp.
Ghost crabs

Distribution: Widely distributed throughout the Indo-Pacific.

Size: Carapace width normally less than 5 cm.

Reproduction: In some species, the males build "sand castles" up to 15 cm tall, in the proximity of the burrows, in order to impress females. Then they gesticulate with their large, orange-yellow claws, to attract females into their burrow.

Food: These crabs utilise a broad spectrum of food items. They will readily accept substitute food in a marine aqua-terrarium.

Description: Live in burrows along beaches, from where they usually emerge at night. If an observer is patient and remains very still, they sometimes come out of their burrows even during the day. The body is rather square. The eyes are located on long stalks. Some species have stilettos on top of their eyes, but these are absent in others. Colouration of the different species is highly variable. Most species have strong claws, where one is larger than the other. Body and claws of males are normally larger than those of females.

Aquarium requirements: Ghost crabs are suitable for an intertidal zone aquarium, for a marine aqua-terrarium or for a mangrove aquarium. We believe they will do well in such special aquarium, where they should be easy to keep. They are totally unsuitable for the traditional coral reef aquarium.

GA: +/-; **SE:** 0; **CO:** +/-

Photos:
Ocypode sp. "KA6-CRU-28" at Cook Island (top), as well as *O. ceratophthalma* in Dampier Archipelago, Indian Ocean (centre; photo: C. Bryce) and in the Philippines (bottom; photo: P. Schupp).

***Uca* spp.**
Fiddler crabs

Distribution: Widely occurring in tropical regions; sometimes also in subtropical regions.

Size: Carapace width 3.5 cm.

Reproduction: No details available from the natural habitat of these crabs. WERNER (1998) reports, that observed matings in his aquarium lasted from a few minutes and up to half an hour. Male and female were positioned abdomen against abdomen, held on to each other, touching each other. The male knocked repeatedly on the back of the female with its very large claw. Later on the female carried the eggs, and when the larvae hatched the female would rinse them off into the water by forceful whipping motions of its tail section. Rearing the larvae was not successful.

Food: Omnivores; detritus feeders.

Description: These crabs live in the intertidal zone over muddy to slightly sandy substrate, in protected bays, stream- and river estuaries. Tall bodies with a carapace which is slightly wider than it is long. In males, one of the claws is enormously enlarged. Carapace and walking legs are very brightly coloured. Each species has its own, extraordinary colour pattern. The male waves its large claw in a rhythmic pattern, to attract a female during courtship, as well as during competitive fighting with other males. While waving its claw, the male can change colour, and in sexually active females the colours can similarly change. In females both claws are small. Females are more plainly coloured than males. These crabs are common in many tropical and subtropical regions. Australia alone has 16 different species.

Aquarium requirements: Fiddler crabs are suitable for an intertidal aquarium, for a marine aqua-terrarium or for a mangrove aquarium. They must never be kept in any type coral reef aquarium.

GA: +/-; **SE:** +; **CO:** +/-

Photos:
Top: *Uca flammula* at Kimberley, Western Australia.
Photo: C. Bryce
Centre: *Uca* sp. "KA6-CRU-29" at the Philippines.
Photo: P. Schupp
Bottom: *Uca* sp. "KA6-CRU-27" in an aqua-terrarium, viewed from above. The differential claw sizes are clearly visible, as well as the size relationship of the large claw to the body.
Photo: U. Werner

Hapalocarcinus marsupialis
Common coral gall crab

Distribution: Indo-Pacific, including the Red Sea.
Size: Female with a carapace length of about 6 mm; males only to 2 mm.
Behaviour, food and reproduction: This crabs lives symbiotically with stony corals of genera *Pocillopora, Stylophora* and *Seriatopora*. A young female settles on a coral branch and starts to create water currents with its setae-equipped claws, to filter out food particles. This action irritates the coral, and it reacts by developing a spherical-shaped tissue outgrowth – a so-called "gall" – which eventually encloses the female crab. Only a small opening remains, for the female to "swirl" water in order to obtain food. With increasing growth, the female steadily fills out the gall, and then starts to re-direct the swirling activities in such a way that above the old gall a new, larger one is being formed. The male, which always remains in the vicinity, but outside the gall occupied by a female (and where it can normally be readily seen), moves into the gall only to mate with the female and then leaves again, to resume its permanent life outside the gall. The female, enclosed for the remainder of its life, carries the eggs and broods them inside the gall (ZANN, 1980).
Description: The carapace is rather narrow and elongated, with smooth edges, and the chelipeds are slightly larger than the walking legs. Colouration is pale brown, silvery or cream-coloured (JONES & MORGAN, 1994).
Aquarium requirements: Without doubt, it would be extremely interesting to observe the symbiosis between the gall crab and its coral host in detail in a small, special aquarium. We have seen galls on branches of imported *Pocillopora* colonies, but as for yet there are no reports on aquarium observations of the crabs themselves. Nevertheless, we believe that this species has already occurred in aqua-

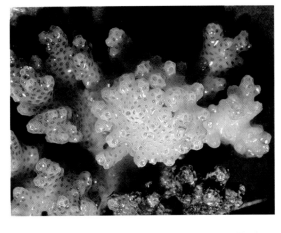

ria, without having been discovered or noticed. Furthermore, we are also certain, that it is rather easy to keep a male and a female in an aquarium for an extended period of time. We would like to ask aquarists to look out for corals with gall crabs, in the aquarium trade. For further information about this symbiotic relationship the reader's attention is drawn to BRUCE (1976).

GA: 0; **SE:** 0; **CO:** 0

Photos:
Top: Gall on a *Seriatopora* stony coral.
Bottom: Female *Hapalocarcinus marsupialis* in an opened gall (left) and a close-up view of an exposed female (right).

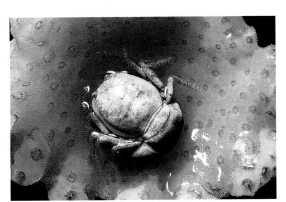

This order is a large assemblage of crustaceans, with nine suborders. It encompasses nearly 40 % of all crustacean animals, but, as the majority are quite small and inconspicuous, they are normally not discussed in aquarium books. That is clearly unfortunate, since many species are very common on coral reefs, and quite many do also reach home aquaria regularly, particularly as stowaways on live rocks. The peracaridan fauna on coral reefs is very diverse, but many species have so far not yet been described scientifically. The most abundant groups are the suborders Amphipoda and Isopoda, followed by suborders Tanaidacea, Cumacea and Mysidacea. All of these are very common among coral rocks, rubble and various sediments.

A characteristic feature of the order Peracarida is the presence of a ventral brood sac (marsupium) in females. The marsupium is formed by large, plate-shaped extensions of certain basal thoracic segments (coxae). In primitive peracaridans, the thorax is covered by a carapace, but in the suborders Isopoda and Amphipoda the carapace is substantially reduced or lacking altogether. Beyond that, the primitive mode of feeding among peracaridan crustaceans is maxillary filter feeding (indirect food intake), as can be seen, for instance, in many species of the suborders Mysidacea

and Tanaidacea. Yet, in more advanced peracaridans the tendency is towards direct food intake via the mouth.

Below we will briefly describe the suborders Isopoda, Tanaidacea, Amphipoda and Mysidacea, together with some comments about their relative importance in the coral reef biotope and as aquarium animals.

Suborder Isopoda
Sea Lice, Pill Bugs

With more than 4,000 described species in approximately 700 genera, the sea lice and pill bugs of suborder Isopoda represent a very large group of crustaceans. Most species are marine, but there are also a few freshwater forms and some live even in moist terrestrial habitats. The most conspicuous characteristic of isopods is the strongly dorso-ventrally compressed body. The head is normally shield-shaped and fused with one or two of the subsequent thoracic segments. A carapace is not present. The eyes are not movable, the antennae are uniramous and the pereiopods are connected to the body with a basal segment (coxa). The anterior body region has seven pairs

of similar-looking appendages, thus the name "Isopoda" (*isos*, Greek = similar, alike and *pous*, genetive *podos*, Greek = foot). Isopods have separate sexes.

Most marine isopods grow to a length of 5 to 15 mm, however, there are also a few giant deep-sea species, such as *Bathynomus giganteus*, which grows to a length of more than 40 cm with a width of 15 cm. Fundamentally, the isopods display a greater morphological diversity than any other crustacean group. Nearly every sample taken from coral rubble, sand, algae or other reef substrates contains many isopods. In addition, some species live as parasites on fishes as well as on other crustaceans. The free-living species are mainly detritus feeders.

There are not very many reports about isopods in aquaria. Our experiences show, though, that this must be due to the fact, they have not been specifically looked for, because they are present in aquaria (!). Unquestionably, they represent a significant component of the micro- and macro fauna.

Suborder Tanaidacea

The crustaceans in this suborder used to be included in the suborder Isopoda, with which they have many similarities. The body is more or less cylindrical, and a carapace covers the two anterior thoracic segments. The first pair of pereiopods carries pincers. The eyes are located either lobes, or in some species they are absent. The inner surface of the carapace functions as a gill. A current for food intake (posterior towards anterior) is created by the maxillipeds and the second and third pair of thoracic appendages. The second maxilla filters out some food particles, however,

Unidentified isopod of the suborder Isopoda at One Tree Island, Great Barrier Reef.   Photo: L. Newman and A. Flowers.

in most species large food particles are combed out of the water with the brushing setae of the maxillipeds. The diet is also supplemented by raptorial feeding. A few species are hermaphrodites, however, the eggs are brooded the same way as in the other peracaridans.

The suborder Tanaidacea is the least known suborder of the Peracarida. So far, world-wide, about 600 species in 100 genera have been described. They are very small crustaceans with an average adult length of only 1 to 2 mm, only a few of the larger ones reach sizes of up to 20 mm. The majority are bottom dwellers in the littoral region, where they burrow into mud, constructing tubes, or live in small caves or crevices in rocks. In a coral reef aquarium, they can often be found among algae and in sediments.

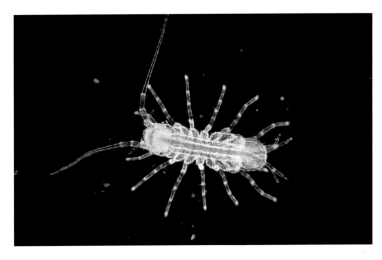

Species of Tanaidacea.   Photo: R. Brons

Beach flea of the infraorder Gammaridea at One Tree Island, Great Barrier Reef.
Photo: L. Newmann and A. Flowers

Suborder Amphipoda
Beach Fleas, Whale Lice, Skeleton Shrimps

Amphipods inhabit nearly all marine and freshwater habitats. In general, they are very small; most species remain smaller than 5 mm, and only a few deep sea species reach a length of 10 cm (MARSHALL, 1979). This suborder has the largest number of species within the order Peracarida. There are about 6,000 species in approximately 1,100 genera (MATHER & BENNETT, 1993), which are placed in four infraorders: Gammaridea, Hyperiidea, Caprellidea and Ingolfiellidea. Only the first three of these are represented on coral reef.

The basic body structure of amphipods is rather similar to that of isopods. Typically, they have immobile eyes, but there are also a few blind species. A carapace is not present, although the first and sometimes also the second thoracic segment is fused to the head. Moreover, the abdomen is normally not distinctly off-set from the thorax, neither in size nor in shape. In contrast to the Isopoda, the body of amphipods is laterally depressed, which gives these crustaceans a shrimp-like appearance.

Most of the amphipods are detritus feeders or scavengers, a few groups are filter feeders, and very few are algae grazers. Although many amphipods compliment their diet by catching small animals, outright predatory behaviour is not common. In spite of

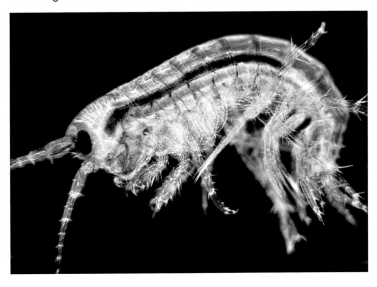

Beach flea of the infraorder Gammaridea from an aquarium.
Photo: R. Brons

elongated body and small eyes. The thorax takes up the main part of the body, since the substantially reduced abdominal segments have become highly reduced and are fused with each other.

Although amphipods are abundant in coral reef habitats, there are only few, widely scattered reports of their occurrence in aquaria. Yet, on many occasions we have shown that they are indeed present in aquaria. Species identification of amphipods is a cumbersome task, and requires special knowledge as well as particular skills in microscopic dissection. Therefore, the amphipods shown here are placed mostly into the respective infraorders only.

Beach flea of the infraorder Gammaridea (left) and skeleton shrimp of the infraorder Caprellidea (right). Photos: R. Brons

that, there are some remarkable examples of predatory behaviour among pelagic species of infraorder Hyperiidea and Caprellidea. Parasitism is rare among amphipods, but a few species live as ectoparasites on fishes.

Gammaridea is the most dominant infraorder within the Amphipoda. It contains about 5,700 species, and yet in spite of such a large number of species, the overall appearance of them is rather uniform. They look like beach-sea fleas or freshwater scuds, as we known them from our coasts or from freshwater creeks and streams.

The infraorder Hyperiidea contains only pelagic, open ocean forms, which are not commonly encountered close to coastlines. Many species are associated with sea jellies and siphonophores; some feed off their hosts. Although hyperiideans are basically of the same appearance as amphipods, they are often more spherical. Many species have very large eyes that are joined to each other and cover most of the head.

Members of the infraorder Caprellidea, which are known under the rather appropriate common name "skeleton shrimps", have an

Suborder Mysidacea
Mysiids

Mysiids look little shrimp, and since they posses a ventral marsupium, they are also sometimes referred to as "opossum shrimps". The majority of the more than 800 species grows to a length of merely 0.3 to 2.5 cm. But again, there are some deep sea species, which become literal giants, with total lengths in excess of 35 cm!

Mysiids have a prominent ca-

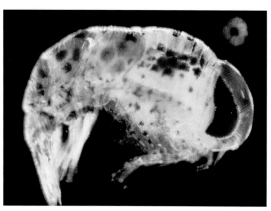

Left: Beach flea of the infraorder Hyperiidea from Heron Reef, Great Barrier Reef (photo: L. Newman and A. Flowers). Right: Mysiid in an aquarium at the "Great Barrier Reef Aquarium", Townsville, Australia.

Many of the tropical and subtropical beach fleas (infraorder Gammaridea) are very beautifully coloured, but very few can match these juveniles (above) and adults (below), photographed at Ulladulla, New South Wales, Australia. As far as we know, this species has not yet been described.

Photos: K. Bates

rapace, stalked eyes and a very elongated abdomen with a shrimp-like tail fan. Along coral reefs they are often found in depressions in dense schools, but they are also common in nocturnal plankton. A few live in association with other invertebrates, including corals and certain hermit crabs. The schooling species represent an important component in the diet of many fish species. The mysiids themselves are primarily filter feeders.

We have no personal experience keeping tropical mysiids in aquaria. Yet experiences gathered at the "Great Barrier Reef Aquarium" in Townsville, Australia, indicates that mysiids are reasonably hardy aquarium animals.

Chapter 7:

A Presentation of some selected Aquaria

When we, for the first time in 1985, got the opportunity to visit marine enthusiasts in Germany, we found that the practice of keeping coral reef aquaria with a wealth of live invertebrates already was well established in that country. For us Scandinavians, this was a true novelty. In Scandinavia, as in most parts of the world at that time, the marine aquarists still played around with the "dead-coral-skeleton-tanks". The large majority of aquarists kept practically nothing but fishes; most invertebrates were generally considered far too difficult to keep alive for more than a few months or a year at the best.

We already knew that the quality standard in German marine aquarium keeping was high. Our early correspondence with Mr. Peter Wilkens and other German

Top: Advances in the marine aquarium hobby are strongly dependent upon experienced aquarists; but they too are still continuously learning a great deal about aquatic biology from their aquaria. Here aquarists (from left to right: Tony Vargas, Terry Siegel, Dough Robins and Gregory Schiemer, the owner of this tank) appeared to have discovered something in the aquarium, which has caught their attention.

Left: The greatest strength of a coral reef aquarium is probably its ability to attract and impress. We are certain that this special lesson at the "Dallas World Aquarium" – where a diver conducts a fish feeding session in a reef aquarium – will long live the memory of these children. The children of Dallas, the Capital of the State of Texas, live a long way from the nearest seashore. Possibly, some of them may have never even seen a live fish before. The reef aquarium brings nature close to them; it teaches them a lot about life in the sea and it instils in them respect for all life.

aquarists, as well as our studies of German aquarists' magazines, left little doubt in that regard. However, we were nevertheless struck by surprise when we dis- covered how incredibly magnificent the German reef tanks of 1985 really were! Aquaria such as those kept by Johannes Birkholz in Linz, or by Rudi Krause, Die- trich Stüber and Erhard Ewald – at that time the leading members of "Verein für Meeresaquaristik Berlin 1969 e.V." – were quite frankly extremely impressive!

When we found German marine aquaria like these back in the middle eighties, we immediately realised the huge potential for keeping and growing live corals in aquaria, thereby creating a completely new world of coral reef aquarium keeping.

Aquarium of Johannes Birkholz, Linz am Rhein, Germany

Aquarium of Rudi Krause, Berlin, Germany

Aquarium of Dietrich Stüber (left) and of Erhard Ewald (right), both Berlin, Germany

Here we found a completely new world of aquarium keeping, right in front of our eyes. What we had dreamt about, but never thought possible, was already a reality!

Today, several countries have reached "German standard" in our hobby. The marine aquaria in North America have evolved rapidly and beautifully, and in the short span of a decade the most incredible results have been achieved. In Europe, successful, fascinating coral reef tanks can be found in practically every single country. The aquaria we kept 20-30 years ago do not even bear the slightest resemblance to what we commonly see today. The development has been, and still is, remarkable (FOSSÀ, 1995 & 1996; NILSEN, 2000b).

Let us hope the development will continue and that the reef aquarium hobby will prosper for many years to come. One basic point remains our conclusion from personal experience and contact with other aquarists world-wide. In order for an aquarist to be successful in reef aquarium keeping, there is nothing more important than the exchange of experience and ideas with other aquarists, combined with the study of relevant literature on aquarium keeping and biology. Even if reading books and journals may seems dry and boring to many aquarists, such literature provides the most important fundamentals for understanding this hobby and - most important - for developing it further yet! Especially for a beginner, who is setting up the first tank, it should be self-evident that he or she must have read at least one (but preferentially several) of the more comprehensive and detailed publications about marine aquarium keeping.

An aquarists should feel obligated to pass on his knowledge and experiences to others, as a means of contributing to the advancement of the coral reef aquarium hobby. As far as possible, we should all attend aquarium congresses and seminars, not only as observers, but as active participants whenever that is possible. We should all publish our experiences and observations in aquarium journals, from the glossy international ones to the small photocopied club newsletters. Furthermore, aquarium societies are an excellent forum for discussions. It may be tempting to fall down on the conclusion that "I had to manage on my own; therefore let everyone else do his or her own trials and errors as well". But no, no aquarist live in a vacuum; - like us, you too have drawn on the knowledge pool and experiences from thousands of aquarists who have chosen to share their knowledge through the years. Let us all do what we can to continue that chain.

Perhaps the most noble aim should be to make the coral reef aquarium a positive event for all those who are not aquarists, i. e. for the general public. That means, for those who do not know what the coral reef aquarium hobby is, or possibly even for those who have heard of it, but who loudly and vocally point to the negative aspects of the animal trade and aquarium hobby, in respect to nature conservation and the protection of animals.

The coral reef aquarium must yet become an even better source of knowledge for all those, who do not have the opportunity to actually visit a coral reef and who are not familiar with the beautiful fauna and flora of a reef. The coral reef aquarium must contribute to a live encounter with nature and become a source of inspiration for aquarists, as well as for the lay community.

In the following, we want to emphasize quite unequivocally that our hobby is internationally successful. All over the world, we have found really beautiful and fascinating coral reef aquaria. Some of the most interesting of these are presented in text and photos on the following pages. These are not all "huge, expensive, or perfect tanks", but vary in size and construction as well as in quality (quality lies also, to some extent at least, in the eyes of the beholder). We have selected aquaria with the desire to show different approaches to the use of decorations and animal population. All together, the chosen tanks are definite proof that the modern coral reef aquarium hobby has reached a level, unimaginable only 20 years ago. With the impressive successes achieved in such a short period of time, the expectation appears justified, that we can look forward to further significant achievements in understanding the biology and aquarium technology; but may be not within such a short time span as before. Under no circumstances is there any room for (a possible world-wide) complacency among aquarists, with a feeling that all that is needed to sustain our hobby has already been achieved.

It must be remembered, that there are still many problems to be solved, not only with respect to species which are still "difficult" or "impossible" to keep, but also in terms of further improvements of the technology needed for keeping those species better and more effectively that are already being maintained in our tanks. We also need further improvements in home aquarium breeding activities, as well as in the commercial reproduction of species currently under our care. Beyond that, it would be desirable to see more habitat-correct, natural-looking and correctly functioning aquaria. In essence then, a successful start does not mean at all, that the continued development of the coral reef aquarium hobby is assured and does not need to be pursued further.

Explanatory notes for the Fact Sheets to follow:

Tank dimensions are given as L (= length) x W (= width) x H (= height) cm

Carbonate hardness is generally reported in German °dKH, ppm CaCo₃ or meq/l. For the conversion of °dKH to CaCo₃ multiply by 17.9 to meq/l divide by 2.8

General view

Dimensions (L x W x H): 120 x 61 x 61 cm, for a total volume of 447 l.

As of June 1997 in operation for: Four years and six months.

Water management: Home-built protein skimmer (app. 75 cm high), operated with an "EHEIM 1060". The protein skimmer is located in a filter chamber below the tank; a pump "OTTO 200" returns the water from the filter chamber to the aquarium. Water circulation within the aquarium achieved by means of two circulating pumps: "PH 850" and "AQUACLEAR 201", which are connected to a wave automatic, which changes the direction of the current in the aquarium every 30 seconds. Two pumps of type "PRO-JECT 1501" create continuous water movement behind the decoration. 6.5 l of "Kalkwasser" (see vol. 1, page 229) are added daily via a continuous trickle method.

Lighting: One HQI lamp 400 W Tungsram MH 6,500 K, with a lighting period of 10 h/d, in combination with four fluorescent lamps TL03 "actinic blue" each 40 W, with an illumination period of 12 h/d.

Water parameters: pH 8.1-8.5; temperature 25-27 °Cel-sius; salinity 35 ‰; NO₃ none detectable.

Decoration: 70 kg live rocks; 5 cm bottom substrate consisting of very fine-grained sand.

Cnidarians: 18 species of stony corals, including *Euphyllia* sp., *Acropora* spp., *Pocillopora damicornis, Lobophyllia* sp. and *Fungia* sp. In addition, there are various soft corals, including *Sarcophyton* sp., *Sinularia* sp., *Anthelia* sp., as well as three zoanthid anemone and seven disk anemone species and a large symbiosis anemone, probably *Entacmaea quadricolor*.

Fishes: Only four small fishes, including *Amphiprion* sp.

Other organisms: Juvenile *Tridacna* sp., one sea cucumber, *Holuthuria* sp., and a few algae-eating snails. In addition, there are also calcareous algae of genus *Halimeda*.

Special features: A reliable observation has revealed that the stony coral *Pocillopora damicornis* has sexually reproduced in the aquarium, i. e. it was certainly not polyp separation, as can often be observed in this species under aquarium conditions. The fact, that a large symbiosis ane-

Right section of the aquarium with a bubble anemone, *Entacmaea quadricolor* (left), and a close-up photo of a stony coral from the genus *Lobophyllia* (right).

mone thrives in an aquarium with such good stony coral development, could also be considered as a special feature.

Owner's comment: "I love everything that has to do with coral reefs, and in general I have a passion for life in the sea."

Middle section of the aquarium.

Four photos: N. Cope

Dimensions (L x W x H): 180 x 120 x 80 cm, for a total volume of 1,728 l.

As of July 1997, in operation for: Two years and three months.

Water management: Protein skimmer, followed by a trickle filter; bottom is siphoned regularly. Calcium hydroxide solution is trickle continuously into the tank (10 l per day).

Lighting: Three HQI lamps each 400 W/D with an illumination period of 7 h/d, and six fluorescent lamps each 58 W/67 with an illumination period of 11 h/d.

Water parameters: pH 8.0-8.4; temperature 22-30 °Celsius; salinity app. 35 ‰, Ca^{2+} 400-420 mg/l; NO_3^- less than 10.0 mg/l.

Decoration: Solid calcareous rocks with large holes (in Germany named "Lochgestein") as base decoration and 30 kg live rocks.

Cnidarians: Stony corals, holaxonian corals (mainly from the Caribbean) and soft corals, as well as disk and zoanthid anemones.

Fishes: 30 fishes.

Special features: Shape and structure of the decoration, but especially the large diversity of organisms kept, especially the branching gorgonians.

Owner's comment: "I have had already many hobbies, but none has kept me in its spell for so long as the aquarium hobby, in which I have been involved for 38 years, and seven of these years by keeping coral reef aquaria."

Right: In plan, this tank is almost square, and can be viewed from two sides.

View from one side into the aquarium.

Above: Close-up photo of an *Acropora* sp.

Close-up photos of *Pavona cactus*.   Four photos: T. Luther

General view.

Middle section

Close-up photos of *Acropora* sp.

Dimensions (L x W x H): 142 x 62 x 70 cm, for a volume of 616 l, in addition a sump with a volume of about 135 l.

As of June 1997, in operation for: Two years and two months.

Water management: The main filter consists of a home-built, external protein skimmer, which is operated by an "EHEIM 1030" circulation pump and a "WISA 300" air pump. In addition, there is mechanical filtration via wool cartridges with a "TURBELLE 4002" (4,000 l/h), and with an additional two "TURBELLE 4002" without filter cartridges. The total circulation varies from 4,000 to 12,000 l/h (controlled by a time switch). Calcium supplement via two systems; one home-built reactor, were "Kalkwasser" is blended with osmosis water and mixed by magnetic stirrers, and one calcium reactor made after the "Löbbecke calcium reactor" (see vol. 1, page 233) system. In the latter a small flow of water runs through a container filled with coral gravel in which the pH is lowered to 6.5 by using CO_2. This dissolves the gravel and enriches the water, which returns to the aquarium, with calcium and bicarbonates. With both systems, the calcium level in the aquarium is being held stable. In addition, there are weekly supplements of potassium iodide, strontium chloride and 25 ml trace element solution ("SPURAL").

Lighting: Three HQI lamps each 250 W Osram HQI-TS/D 6,500 K and two fluorescent lamps each 40 W Philips TL 03 "actinic blue".

Water parameters: pH 7.8-8.7; temperature 24-38 °Celsius; salinity app. 33 ‰; °dKH 4-6; Ca^{2+} 420 mg/l; NO_3^- none detectable; PO_4 1.0 mg/l.

Decoration: 100 kg live rocks imported from Singapore. To create a tall decoration, the rocks were mounted on PVC pipes.

Cnidarians: In total about 60 colonies of stony corals, including 15 *Acropora* spp., two *Euphyllia ancora*, *Euphyllia glabrescens*, two *Physogyra lichtensteini*, *Catalaphyllia jardinei*, *Lobophyllia corymbosa*, *Trachyphyllia geoffroyi*, *Plerogyra sinuosa*, six colonies from family Faviidae, *Caulastrea furcata*, one *Blastomussa* sp., two *Hydnophora* sp., and *Turbinaria peltata*, as well as one unknown stony coral and a few smaller coral fragments. In terms of soft corals, mainly *Sinularia* and *Cladiella* species.

Fishes: 10 fishes, including *Zebrasoma flavescens*, *Z. scopas*, *Z. desjardinii*, *Acanthurus leucosternon*, one pair of *Synchiropus splendidus* and one *Centropyge flavicauda*.

Other organisms: Among others, ten brittle stars of different species, a blue sea star, *Linckia laevigata*, various shrimps, such as *Stenopus hispidus*, *Lysmata amboinensis* and *Lysmata debelius*, and coral crabs, which were introduced with an *Acropora* colony. Finally, two *Tridacna maxima* and one *T. derasa*.

Prawn goby, *Cryptocentrus leptocephalus*, among disk- and zoanthid anemones.   Four photos: T. Slettengen

Special features: Coral growth is excellent; the *Acropora* colonies have reached a substantial size. The *Sinularia* colonies are large and are growing so well, that they have to be frequently thinned out.

Owner's comment: "I have been an aquarists since the age of seven, and in the course of time have gone through various stages; from guppies to discus and Lake Malawi cichlids to the marine aquarium, where I had an anemone aquarium first, and later on a fish aquarium for marine angelfish. My current coral reef aquarium is so far the highlight of a fantastic hobby."

General view.

Photosynthesising gorgonians corals from the Caribbean.
Two photos: K. Bieder

Dimensions (L x W x H): 180 x 70 x 70 cm, for a total volume of 882 l.

As of July 1997 in operation for: Seven years.

Water management: Home-built protein skimmer with a height of 160 cm and a diameter of 15 cm, operated by a "WISA 300" air pump and with a water flow of 200 l/h; in addition, there is a mechanical filter with a capacity of about 1,500 l/h. Water movement in the aquarium is about 1,200 l/h. Calcium supplements are done by adding app. 5 l "Kalkwasser" per day. About 40 l of water are changed every third week.

Lighting: Six fluorescent lamps, three of these are 58 W Osram 12 (white) and the other three are 58 W Osram 67 (blue): lighting is controlled by five time switches; the average illumination period is app. 9 h/d.

Water parameters: pH 8.2-8.3; temperature 25-26 °Celsius; salinity about 29 ‰; °dKH 6-7; Ca^{2+} about 440-460 mg/l; NO_3^- 0-5 mg/l.

Decoration: Mainly solid calcareous rocks with large holes (in Germany named "Lochgestein"), as well as 30-40 kg live rocks; bottom substrate consisting of about a 6-7 cm layer of crushed coral.

Cnidarians: About 40-45 different colonies, mainly octocorals. Only a few stony corals.

Fishes: Only three fishes, one *Apogon* sp., one *Gramma loreto*, and one angelfish.

Other organisms: One sea urchin of genus *Diadema*; about ten large, blue hermit crabs, five brittle stars and various shrimps and snails.

Special features: Soft corals are growing very well, so that cuttings can be taken frequently.

Owner's comment: "I have been an aquarist since the age of 6, and observing the organisms in my aquarium is of paramount importance to me. The life in an aquarium means more to me than all technological innovations."

Dimensions (L x W x H): 305 x 244 x 122 cm, for a total volume of 9,079 l, whereby the actual water volume is only about 6,500 l, because of an open space above the water surface. In addition, there is a sump containing about 1,500 l.

As of July 1997, in operation for: One year, but most material transferred from another three year old aquarium.

Water management: Protein skimmer with a diameter of 18 cm and a height of 180 cm, installed on the outside of the aquarium, with a water flow rate of 5,400 l/h. At night about 50 l "Kalkwasser" are added, which corresponds to the daily evaporation of water in the aquarium. "Kalkwasser" is added via a 55-litre calcium reactor, which uses app. 400 g Ca(OH)$_2$ per week. Water movement in the aquarium is achieved via an air induction aggregate, which consists of 2 x 8 sections 3"- PVC pipes with a $^1/_2$" PVC pipe for air injection from an HK compressor. Current flow is controlled by means of electrically operated ball valves in a "left-both-right-left-both right" cycle, which changes every three hours. This simulates the differences of tidal flow twice a day. The water volume moved is 2,200 l/min which is equal to 135,000 l/h or 12 times the aquarium volumes per hour.

Lighting: Six HQI lamps; 2 x 400 W "Iwaiski" 6,500 K mounted above the front of the aquarium, and 4 x 400 "Iwaiski" 6,500 K all installed inside a reflector, which can be moved on a track along the back part of the aquarium. Fluorescent tubes and moonlight: 1 x 40 W TL03 "actinic blue", 1 x 25 W blue incandescent lamp and 4 x 40 W moonlight, computer-controlled, which simulate the lunar cycle over the Great Barrier Reef. The illumination period with the HQI lamps varies depending upon the season and is maximally 14 h/d.

Water parameters: pH 8.4; temperature 26 °Celsius; salinity app. 35 ‰; Ca^{2+} 440 mg/l; NO$_3$ 0 mg/l; PO$_4$ 0 mg/l;

Decoration: 500 kg live rocks from Florida, most in the 10-40 kg range.

Cnidarians: *Pavona cactus, Acropora microphthalma, A. grandis, A. nana* (?), Stüber's *Acropora, Acropora pulchra, A. formosa, Acropora* sp., *Stylophora pistillata, Montipora* sp., *Porites* sp., *Catalaphyllia jardinei, Euphyllia glabrescens,* several gorgonians corals from the Caribbean, *Millepora* sp., several zoanthid- and disk anemones, as well as stoloniferans (star polyps).

Fishes: Seven *Paracanthurus hepatus*, six *Zebrasoma flavescens*, one *Z. veliferum*, two *Naso lituratus*, two *Acanthurus pyroferus*, two *Amphiprion melanotus* (?), two *Centropyge loriculus*, one *C. bispinosus*, two *Valenciennea puellaris*, one *Malacanthus brevirostris*, two *Pterapogon kauderni*, about twelve *Chromis viridis*, three *Chromis* sp.

Other organisms: A few cleaner shrimps, *Stenopus hispidus* and some sea urchins.

Special features: Virtually all stony corals where grown from coral fragments, provide by other aquarists. Many came from the Waikiki Aquarium, Honolulu, Hawaii.

Owner's comment: "It is a long way from St. Louis to the nearest coral reef."

General view.

These newly introduced fragments of an *Acropora* sp. are starting to grow.　　　　　Two photos: K. Carpenter

General view.

Dimensions (L x W x H): 80 x 40 x 40 cm, for a volume of 130 l, plus a sump below the aquarium containing 50 l, so that the total volume is 180 l.

As of April 1997, in operation for: Two years and five months.

Water management: Surface overflow drain with mechanical filtration. The water flows into a darkened chamber in the sump, which contains live rocks. A "TUNZE" rotation skimmer is driven by a "Turbelle 2002" pump giving 2,200 l/h. A level sensor controls the refilling of about 2 l "Kalkwasser" per 24 h, via a calcium reactor. A separate pump with a capacity of 1,200 l/h, circulates the water between the aquarium and the sump.

Lighting: Six fluorescent lamps; 3 x 18 W Sylvania "Aquastar" 10,000 K, 1 x 18 W Osram "blue", 1 x 18 W Osram "biolux", and 1 x 20 W Philips TL03 "actinic blue".

Water parameters: pH 7.5-8.2: temperature 24-29 °Celsius; °dKH app. 7; salinity app. 32 ‰; Ca²⁺ 520 mg/l; NO₃ approximately 3.0 mg/l.

Decoration: 27 kg live rocks.

Cnidarians: 21 colonies; six soft corals and 15 stony corals, and among others a colony of an *Acropora* species (possibly *A. latistella*), which probably originated from the aquarium of D. Stüber, Berlin; there are also *Euphyllia* sp., *Trachyphyllia geoffroyi, Favia* sp., *Catalaphyllia jardinei, Sarcophyton* sp., *Sinularia* spp., *Pachyclavularia violacea* and one large *Rhodactis* sp.

Fishes: One *Zebrasoma xanthurus* and one *Amphiprion clarkii*, as well as three *Pomacentrus caeruleus*.

Other organisms: One giant clam, *Tridacna derasa*.

Special features: The aquarium accommodates a colony of *Euphyllia glabrescens*, which originates from a colony that seven years ago grew out of live rock in the aquarium to Mrs. and Mr. Enger in Oslo (shown in volume 1, page 177). Beyond that and most important, the aquarium is a beautiful example of what can be successfully achieved with a small tank, which is illuminated by fluorescent lamps only.

Owner's comment: "I firmly believe an aquarium should be decorative. Beyond that, I find keeping stony corals very interesting. It is for me quite a challenge to get them to grow and reproduce. Generally, it is very satisfying to maintain a closed system, which does not need to be replenished frequently with new organisms. The coral reef aquarium has also given me a new circle of friends, which is very important to me."

This *Euphyllia glabrescens* colony developed from a fragment, which was introduced into the aquarium attached to a live rock (see vol. 1, page 177)

View from above on to *Acropora latistella* and *Pachyclavularia violacea*, which have both grown to reach the surface.

General view.

Dimensions (L x W x H): 240 x 100 x 80 cm, for a volume of 1,920 l.

As of August 1997, in operation for: Six years.

Water management: Injector protein skimmer with a flow rate of 2,400 l/h and an air capacity of 1,500 l/h.

Lighting: Two HQI lamps each 1000 W/D with an illumination period of 7 h/d, and six blue fluorescent lamps each 36 W.

Water parameters: pH 7.85-8.40; temperature 23-28 °Celsius; °dKH 6-8; salinity 35 ‰; NO_3 shown not to be present.

Acropora sp.

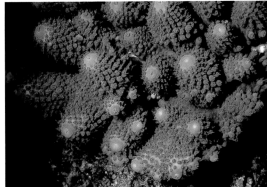

Acropora sp. (left) and *Platygyra daedalea* (right).

Acropora sp.

Decoration: 5 kg live rocks.

Cnidarians: About 80 stony corals and 40 soft corals, and in addition colonies that have grown from off springs from parent colonies in the aquarium.

Fishes: 70 fishes.

Other organisms: Four *Tridacna maxima*, two *T. squamosa*, two *T. crocea*, one *T. gigas*, various sponges and a diverse growth of animals that has developed from live rocks and from the base of corals.

Special features: In addition to this aquarium, there are also three rearing tanks; one 200 x 100 x 30 cm and two each 150 x 80 x 50 cm.

Owner's comment: "The involvement with the coral reef aquarium is very enjoyable. Moreover, I am actively engaged in breeding stony- and soft corals."

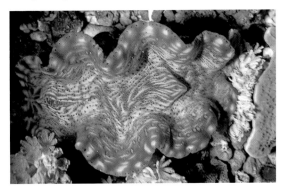

Tridacna derasa

Acropora sp.

Pachyseris sp.

Seven photos: T. Luther

Dimensions (L x W x H): 183 x 51 x 51 cm, for a volume of 476 l.

As of July 1997, in operation for: Three years and six months.

Water management: Protein skimmer "Red Sea Berlin", operated by an "EHEIM 1060"; in addition, the water is filtered over activated carbon using a "FLUVAL 303" filter unit. The water overflows to a sump below the aquarium, which houses the technical equipment. From there the water is pumped into a wave tank with a volume of 20 l and installed about 2.4 m above floor level. The content of the wave tank empties into the aquarium at a rate of once per minute. This creates an effective and presumably biologically important wave action in the aquarium, which is drained of a corresponding volume of water every 55 seconds. Three litres of "Kalkwasser" are added per day via a float valve.

Lighting: Two HQI lamps: 1 x 250 W GE 6,000 K, 1 x 250 W "aqualine" 10,000 K both with an illumination period of 10 h/d; four fluorescent lamps each 40 W TL03 "actinic blue" with an illumination period of 12 h/d.

General view.

Water parameters: pH 7.8-8.4; temperature 26 °Celsius; °dKH 8; Ca^{2+} 350 mg/l; NO_3^- and PO_4 none detectable.

Left section.

Cnidarians: 21 stony coral colonies, among others *Acropora* spp., *Pocillopora damicornis*, *Turbinaria* sp., *Lobophyllia* sp., *Porites* sp. and *Favia* sp.(?); soft corals: only *Sarcophyton* sp.; also four disk anemones.

Fishes: Eleven fishes, among others *Zebrasoma flavescens*, *Paracanthurus hepatus*, *Valenciennea strigata*, two *Gobiodon* sp. and *Chelmon marginalis*.

Other organisms: Giant clams *Tridacna* sp. and calcareous "Christmas Tree" tube worms of genus *Spirobranchus*, which are associated with a *Porites* colony. In addition, there are several algae-eating snails and blue sea stars, *Linckia laevigata*.

Owner's comment: "The organisms of the sea, especially those of coral reefs are so remarkable and so unique compared to the many terrestrial organisms, that I simply had to have a coral reef aquarium in my home, in order to satisfy my curiosity."

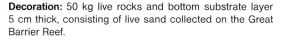

Three photos: N. Cope

Decoration: 50 kg live rocks and bottom substrate layer 5 cm thick, consisting of live sand collected on the Great Barrier Reef.

Middle section.

General view.

Middle section.

Close-up photo of *Montipora* sp.
Three photos: F. van Langenhoven

Dimensions (L x W x H): 80 x 30 x 39 cm, for a volume of 94 l.

As of July 1997, in operation for: Three years.

Water management: Undergravel filter mounted below- and working through a layer of live sand. In addition, a denitrifying filter with a very slow flow-rate, only one or two drops of water per second. There is no skimmer. A simple tidal system direct the discharge from the denitrification filter into a chamber, which – when full – overflows into the aquarium. This causes the water level to drop twice a day by 5 to 10 cm. "Kalkwasser" is not added and there is neither a calcium reactor nor is calcium added to the system in any other way. There are no water changes. The internal water movement is 2 x 500 l/h.

Lighting: Five fluorescent tubes: 1 x 20 W "Aqua Glow", 1 x 20 W "Marin Glo", 2 x 18 W "Aquarelle" and 1 x 20 W "Triton"; with an illumination period of 14 h/d.

Water parameters: pH 7.8-8.2; temperature 25-27 °Celsius; salinity app. 31 ‰; Ca^{2+} 440-480 mg/l; NO_3 app. 5 mg/l; NO_3^- from the denitrifying filter about 0 mg/l; PO_4 app. 0 mg/l.

Decoration: 25 kg live rocks.

Cnidarians: 24 coral colonies, many from cuttings or fragments received from other aquarists, among others *Acropora* sp., *Montipora* spp., *Favia* sp., *Sinularia dura*, *Protopalythoa* sp. "KA4-ZOA-07". A dark zone in the aquarium accommodates non-photosynthesising cnidarians, such as *Dendronephthya* sp. and *Tubastraea* sp., as well as sponges.

Fishes: Three fishes, a pair of *Pseudochromis fridmani* and one *Doryrhamphus excisus excisus*, which was bred by the tank's owner.

Other organisms: Four shrimps, including a symbiotic shrimp, *Turbo* and other snails, colonies of *Homotrema rubrum* (three colour forms), at least four sponge species, many marine worms (including *Phyllochaetopterus* sp.) and sipunculids, brittle stars, tunicates and one *Tridacna* sp. Many different algae, among others *Ventricaria* sp., *Bryopsis, Caulerpa* spp., *Halimeda* sp., *Dictyota* sp., *Halymenia* sp., *Ochtodes* sp., *Amphiroa* sp., and many species of red calcareous algae.

Special features: This aquarium also functions as a breeding tank, where the owner has previously bred *Hippocampus reidi* and more recently *Doryrhamphus excisus excisus*; currently he is attempting to breed *Pseudochromis fridmani*.

Owner's comment: "Being interested in the sea is my motivation for being involved with coral reef aquaria."

Dimensions (L x W x H): 57 x 57 x 57 cm and a filter chamber 60 x 32 x 32 cm, for a total water volume of 247 l.

As of May 1997, in operation for: Seven years.

Water management: One "TUNZE protein skimmer 230/2U" and 250 g activated carbon in the sump, where it is replaced every month. Calcium supplements by means of a home-built "Löbbecke calcium reactor". Cooling unit type "Teco Teclima RA 200" with "EHEIM1048" pump. "TUNZE Osmosis unit 3150". Circulating pumps ("TUNZE 2002") controlled by "TUNZE-Intervallautomatik" (= automatic interval timer) 7082. One "EHEIM 1250" (app. 500 l/h) pumps the water between aquarium and filter chamber.

Lighting: 1 x 250 Watt HQI "aquasunlight" 10,000 K from "aqualine" installed in an Osram NAQI-TS 250 W fitting, which is suspended 14 cm above the water surface, with an illumination period of 10 h/d; the bulb is replaced every 6 months. In addition, 1 x Philips TLDK 30 W/03 "supra actinic fluorescent" installed inside an aluminium reflector; with an illumination period of 12 h/d; the light-tube is replaced every four months.

Water parameters: pH in the morning 7.8, evening 8.2; 10 °dKH; Mg^{2+} 1212 ± 25 mg/l; Ca^{2+} 420 mg/l; Sr^{2+} app. 10 mg; NH_4^+ 0.02 ± 0.01 mg/l; NO_3 less than 0.05 mg/l; nitrite less than 0.025 mg/l; PO_4 less than 0.025 mg/l; SiO_2 0.15 ± 0.05 mg/l; NO_3-N less than 0.2 mg/l; $I+IO_3$ 0.07 ± 0.02 mg/l; Fe (total) less than 0.005 mg/l; salinity 31.5 ‰.

Decoration: 30 kg live rocks, half of them from the Caribbean and the other half from Indonesia. The decoration is nearly totally surrounded by sandy bottom.

Cnidarians: Three *Acropora* species, *Montipora digitata, M. incrassata, Pocillopora damicornis, Stylophora pistillata, Pavona cactus, P. decussata, Turbinaria partula, T. reniformis, Porites porites, Porites* sp. (possibly *divaricata*), *P. lobata, Caulastrea furcata, Favia* sp. *Colpophyllia natans, Diploria* sp., *Pectinia paeonia, Merulina ampliata, Hydnophora rigida, Trachyphyllia geoffroyi, Fungia* sp., *Tubipora musica, Millepora alcicornis, Millepora* sp., *Protopalythoa* sp., *Ricordea yuma*.

Fishes: *Ctenochaetus hawaiiensis, Zebrasoma flavescens, Calloplesiops altivelis* (juvenile), *Synchiropus splendidus, Gobiodon okinawae* (pair), *Ptereleotris heteroptera* (female).

Other organisms: *Stenopus hispidus* (pair) and unidentified coral crabs.

Special features: Many brittle stars, sea stars, snails and hermit crabs as natural cleaning organisms. The sump or filter chamber is run by the "Jaubert-System" (see vol. 1, page 256) and has a 1.5 cm space with confined water below a 5-9 cm thick layer of coral sand (grain size 2-4 mm).

Owner's comment: "I keep a coral reef aquarium, because I find coral reefs fascinating. My aim is to understand the fundamental functions, as well as those processes, which facilitate the (dynamic) equilibrium in various sections of a (coral) reef. The coral reef is a fantastic ecological and educational example. In France I actively contribute to this field with advisory services, lectures and articles in relevant journals."

General view of aquarium and support components.
Photo: S. Fournier

Dimensions (L x W x H): 150 x 50 x 60 cm, for a volume of 450 l, in addition a reservoir with 250 l, making up a total volume of 700 l.

As of June 1997, in operation for: One year.

Water management: One "ATK" protein skimmer with a flow rate of 1,200 l/h, and a height of 150 cm. Calcium additions via a "Löbbecke calcium reactor" and the adding of CO_2. This reactor is filled with a mixture of calcareous material and crushed coral; the pH is lowered to 6.2 in the reactor; the water flow rate is one drop per second. "Kalk-

wasser" is not used. Iodine, strontium, trace elements and the vitamin solution "Marinvit" are added. There is a 10 % water change once a month. The water movement inside the tank is provided by three circulating pumps of type "Turbelle 4002" (4000 l/h), and one "Turbelle 2002" (2000 l/h), both coupled to an automatic pulsating device.

Lighting: Two HQI lamps each 250 W "aquasunlight" 10,000 K with an illumination period of 8.5 h/d, and four fluorescent lamps: two x 65 W Osram 65 and 2 x 140 TL03 "actinic blue" with an illumination period of 13 h/d.

Water parameters: pH 8.3; temperature 25 °Celsius; salinity 31 ‰; 7 °dKH; Ca^{2+} 420-450; NO_3 app. 0 mg/l; PO_4 app. 0 mg/l.

Decoration: 300 kg live rocks.

Cnidarians: About 60 colonies: *Acropora* spp., several species of family Faviidae, *Trachyphyllia geoffroyi*, *Plerogyra sinuosa*, soft corals of genera *Sarcophyton*, *Lobophyton* and *Sinularia* (with a group of large colonies of *Sinularia dura*), among others. Several colonies of disk- and zoanthid anemones.

Fishes: 18 Fishes: *Zebrasoma flavescens*, two *Gramma loreto*, five *Pterapogon kauderni*, *Sphaeramia nematoptera*, three *Chromis* sp., *Assessor flavissimus*, *Liopropoma rubra*, *Calloplesiops altivelis*, two *Amphiprion* sp., *Doryrhamphus janssii*.

Other organisms: Giant clams of genus *Tridacna*.

Special features: Many corals came originally from coral fragments transferred from other aquaria. Since a calcium reactor has been installed, growth of stony corals is excellent.

Owner's comment: "I am interested in the biology of aquarium organisms, and I am particularly intrigued to find that corals and other invertebrates are growing well and reproduce in a coral reef aquarium. The latter affords aquarists the opportunity to exchange surplus specimens among each other, which is of paramount importance for the diversity of a coral reef aquarium."

General view.

Left region of the aquarium.
Two photos: F. van Langenhoven

General view.

Dimensions (L x W x H): 200 x 100 x 70 cm, for a volume of 1,400 l.

As of June 1997, in operation for: Two years.

Water management: A home-built protein skimmer, 150 cm high, counter-flow principle; filter chamber with live sand; wave generator, which produces 1-2 waves per minute. Evaporated water is replaced with "Kalkwasser". Also small quantities of iodine and strontium are added daily.

Lighting: 12 x 40 W light-tubes, 6 "tri phosphorus" 6,500 K "88CRI" and six fluorescent lamps TL03 "actinic blue". All lamps with an illumination period of 10 h/d.

Water parameters: pH 8.4; temperature 25-5 °Celsius; salinity 34 ‰; °dKH 6-8; Ca^{2+} 400 mg/l; PO_4 1.0 mg/l; NO_3 less than 5 mg/l.

Decoration: About 30 % of the tank decoration consists of live rocks from Queensland and Western Australia. The importation of live rocks into Australia from other parts of the world is prohibited.

Cnidarians: 30 stony coral colonies, mostly *Acropora* spp., as well as seven different soft corals and zoanthid anemones. The high temperature on only a few days of the year, has caused some of the *Acropora* to bleach and die.

Fishes: 15-20 fishes of different species, without any one of them being dominant.

Other organisms: Various burrowing organisms, which contribute to the cleanliness and oxygenation of the bottom substrate, among others, two different sea cucumber species and snails of genus *Trochus*.

Special features: Most of the *Acropora* species have nicely fluorescing colouration.

Owner's comment: "This aquarium is maintained on the operating principle of Underwater World, whereby all aquarium animals are being returned to the reef after a certain period of time on display. During the time the animals are in the aquarium, I hope that they contribute to generating respect and enthusiasm for the coral reef fauna among our visitors."

Right section.

Two photos: N. Cope

General view.

This large *Acropora* colony (possibly *A. latistella*) spawned in August 1997.

Dimensions (L x W x H): 120 x 52 x 50 cm, for a volume of 312 l.

As of July 1997, in operation for: One year and two months.

Water management: Combination of protein skimmer and the "Jaubert-System" (see vol. 1, page 256). The bottom consists of 2.5 cm high water subspace and above it a 6-7 cm thick layer of coral sand (1-3 mm grain size) both are separated from each other by nylon mesh. The coral sand is quickly inhabited by organisms introduced together with live rocks. The protein skimmer is home-built. It has a water flow rate of about 400 l/h and requires 600 l/h of air. The internal circulation is about 2,400 l/h with changing flow directions. The calcium level is being maintained by three different methods: freshly generated "Kalkwasser" is added, and the "Jaubert-System" also supplies some of the calcium requirements. These systems, either alone or jointly cannot maintain the required calcium concentration, so that the level drops quickly to 300 mg/l. For that reason an additional calcium reactor is required, where calcium carbonate is being dissolved with CO_2. This then assures that the calcium level is maintained at 420 mg/l. Strontium is added once a week, with 20 ml of a 10 % Strontiumchloride solution. Iodine is supplemented as Lugol's solution with 1 ml per week. There are also irregular supplements of trace elements.

Lighting: Only fluorescent lamps: combination of 4 x 40 W Philips TL03 "actinic-blue" and 4 x 36 W Philips TDL. The actinic-blue lamps are on for 11-12 h/d, the day light lamps for 5 h/d.

Water parameters: pH 8.0-8.4; temperature 26 °Celsius; salinity 35 ‰; °dKH 10-14; Ca^{2+} 400-420 mg/l; PO_4 0-0.01 mg/l; NO_3 none detectable.

Decoration: 40 kg live rocks arranged in such a way that the aquarium can be viewed from two sides.

Cnidarians: Two large *Acropora* colonies and their respective progeny-colonies are dominating; in addition, there are the following stony corals: one *Euphyllia ancora*, one *Plerogyra sinuosa*, one *Plerogyra* sp., one *Cynarina lacrymalis*, one *Caulastrea furcata*, one *Favia* sp., one *Fungia* sp., one *Polyphyllia talpina*, two *Porites* sp., two *Trachyphyllia geoffroyi*, one *Turbinaria peltata* and one *Turbinaria patula*. Other cnidarians: several disk- and zoanthid anemones, soft corals of genera *Sarcophyton, Sinularia, Xenia* and *Anthelia*, as well one Gorgonian.

Fishes: Two *Synchiropus splendidus*, one *Nemateleotris magnifica*, three *Chrysiptera hemicyanea*, which spawn regularly, and one *Zebrasoma flavescens*.

Other organisms: Two *Tridacna crocea*, which spawn twice a year; one *Stenopus hispidus* and two *Lysmata amboinensis*, which also spawn regularly; two brittle stars of genus *Ophiotrix* and app. 15 snails of genus *Astraea*. There is also ample growth of calcareous algae (genus *Halimeda*), which have to be harvested regularly.

Special features: The largest *Acropora* colony has grown from 7 x 7 cm to 35 x 35 x 20 cm. On August 28, 1997 it released many small, 1 mm "egg-sperm-bundles". Also, one *Tridacna crocea* has spawned three-times; sperm cells have been released twice, and eggs cells the last time in September 1997. In addition, many other organisms also spawn regularly. After a period of 12 months, the *Goniopora* colonies do not show signs of any deficiencies.

Owner's comment: "The beauty of a coral reef, together with the fact that we can duplicate a small section of this diverse ecosystem in our aquarium, is my motivation for being involved in keeping a coral reef aquarium."

This female giant clam, *Tridacna crocea* released eggs in September 1997.　　　　　**Three photos: M. Haaga**

General view.

Dimensions (L x W x H): 200 x 76 x 70 cm, for a volume of 1,064 l.
As of July 1997, in operation for: Seven years.
Water management: Protein skimmer; filter tank with live rocks and crushed coral; "Kalkwasser" supplement drop-by-drop, from a reservoir.

Lighting: Two HQI lamps each 250 W/D 10,000 K and three fluorescent lamps "actinic blue".
Water parameters: pH 8.2; temperature 26 °Celsius; °dKH 7-8; salinity app. 35 ‰; NO_3 below 30-40 mg/l.
Decoration: Live rocks only.
Cnidarians: 70 stony corals, seven soft corals, four gorgonians, a big anemone probably *Heteractis* sp.
Fishes: 20 fishes.
Special features: Shape and structure of decoration, but specifically the large diversity of corals kept.
Owner's comment: "I have a coral reef aquarium out of love for nature."

Psammocora contigua.

Acropora sp.

Trachyphyllia geoffroyi.

Acropora sp.

Right section of the aquarium.

Six photos: T. Luther

Dimensions (L x W x H): 220 x 100 x 75 cm, for a volume of 1,650 l, plus a sump with app. 350 l; also, a smaller tank of 250 l is linked to the main aquarium. This tank is used for growing new coral colonies from fragments. The total volume of the system is 2,250 l.

As of July 1997, in operation for: Three years and six months.

Water management: "H+S" protein skimmer, which operates with an air-flow of 1,100 l/h. The internal circulation of 16,000 l/h is made by four circulating pumps, each with a capacity of 4,000 l/h. In addition, an "ATK" pump creates a flow of water from the sump to the aquarium and back of 5,500 l/h. Calcium supplements occurs via calcium reactor, which (depending on the season) refills evaporated water with 10-25 l "Kalkwasser" a day. Beyond that, there are also two "Löbbecke calcium reactors" in operation.

One of these reactors returns two drops of water per seconds and uses 1-2 CO_2 bubbles per second (°dKH 50 in the returned water); the other reactor returns 4-5 drops per second and uses 3-4 CO_2 bubbles per second (°dKH 45 in the returned water). Iodine, strontium and many trace elements are also supplemented; every eighth to tenth day about 10 % of the water is replaced.

Lighting: Two HQI lamps each 400 W with an illumination period of 8 h/d, and eight fluorescent lamps: 7 x 58 W Osram 67 and 1 x 58 W Osram 11, with an illumination period of 12 h/d.

Water parameters: pH 8.2-8.4; temperature 25-29 °Celsius; salinity 33 ‰; °dKH 11; Ca^{2+} 450 mg/l; NO_3 24 mg/l; PO_4 less than 0.1 mg/l.

Decoration: 120 kg live rocks and 350 kg calcareous rocks from "Cora Pet".

General view.

Left section and ...   ...right section.

Close-up photo of a magnificently-coloured *Acropora* sp.

Four photos: K. Ilmberger

Cnidarians: Stony corals: 22 *Acropora* spp., five *Pocillopora* spp., three *Seriatopora*: spp., tree *Stylophora* spp., eight *Montipora* spp., *Astreopora* sp., five *Porites* spp., *Goniopora* sp., two *Pavona* sp., two *Pachyseris* sp., seven *Fungia* sp., *Herpolitha* sp., *Hydnophora*, two *Pectinia* sp., two *Blastomussa* sp., two *Lobophyllia* sp., *Merulina* sp., *Caulastrea* sp., *Tubipora* sp., two *Favia* sp., *Goniastrea* sp., two *Trachyphyllia geoffroyi*, two *Euphyllia* sp., two *Plerogyra* sp., six *Turbinaria* sp. and *Psammocora* sp. There are also 20 small stony coral fragments. Octocorals: three *Xenia* sp., *Anthelia* sp., *Nephthea* sp., three *Sarcophyton* sp., two *Parerythropodium* sp., four *Sinularia* sp., *Cladiella* sp., *Heliopora coerulea* and unidentified gorgonians. Others: *Millepora* sp. And about 15 disk anemones.

Fishes: 45 fishes: 14 *Pseudanthias* spp., two *Pterapogon kauderni*, *Doryrhamphus jansii*, *Pseudochromis springeri*, *P. fridmani*, *Assessor flavissimus*, two *A. macneillii*, *Callople-* siops altivelis, *Chelmon rostratus*, six *Chromis scotti*, *Neocirrhites armatus*, *Halichoeres chrysus*, *Pseudocheilinus hexataenia*, *Cirrhilabrus dejongi*, *Atrosalarias fuscus*, *Synchiropus picturatus*, *Amblygobius rainfordi*, two *Nemateleotris decora*, *Gobiodon atrangutatus*, *Paracanthurus hepatus*, *Ctenochaetus hawaiiensis*, *Zebrasoma flavescens*, *Z. xanthurus* and *Lo vulpinus*.

Other organisms: Ten brittle stars, five shrimps and ten giant clams of genus *Tridacna*.

Special features: Excellent coral growth, typically about 2 cm/month. The soft corals are nine to ten years old (transferred from a previous tank), and the *Tridacna* clams have been kept for five years.

Owner's comment: "I started out ten years ago with a marine aquarium, since my wife was fascinated with magnificently coloured fish. Nowadays, keeping and breeding corals is my passion."

General view.

Dimensions (L x W x H): 160 x 90 x 55 cm, for a volume of 792 l, plus an additional filter volume of 140 l, making up a total volume of 932 l.

In operation for: Eight years.

Water management: Biological filtration with a filter chamber of 140 l, which contains 35 kg live rocks. The water flow rate is 2,000 l/h. In addition, there is a protein skimmer with a flow rate of 2,400 l/h. The internal water movement in the aquarium is about 6,500 l/h (distributed over five circulating pumps). The weekly water change is 70 l.

A smaller section of the aquarium as it looked many years before the photo at the top of this page was taken.
Two photos: J. Harbers

Lighting: Five fluorescent lamps: 3 x 58 W Osram 11 "daylight" and 2 x Philips TL03 "actinic blue", with an illumination period of 14 h/d.

Water parameters: pH 8.2; salinity app. 33 ‰; 7 °dKH 7: Ca^{2+} 425 mg/l; NO_3 and PO_4 none detectable.

Decoration: 180 kg live rocks.

Cnidarians: *Plerogyra sinuosa*, *Acropora* spp., *Catalaphyllia jardinei*, *Galaxea* sp., *Hydnophora* sp. and *Sarcophyton* sp., among others.

Fishes: Two *Calloplesiops altivelis* (pair), five *Pterapogon kauderni* and three *Centropyge acanthops*.

Special features: The pair of comets, *Calloplesiops altivelis* is more than 20 years old; also, the aquarium shows a good balance between corals, fishes and algae.

Owner's comment: "The aquarium hobby is just magic and the aquarium is full of colour and life. One of my personal aims is to breed and rear some of the fishes in my aquarium. Moreover, the aquarium brings me into contact with other aquarium enthusiasts, that is, the social element of our hobby is also important."

Dimensions (L x W x H): 240 x 70 x 70 cm, for a volume of 1,680 l; sump volume 110 l, making up a total volume of 1,790 l.

As of July 1997, in operation for: Seven years.

Water management: Protein skimmer "Sander III P" mounted outside the aquarium, and a "UPSCALE NF-400 Electron" NO_3 reducing filter; water flow through the protein skimmer 1,800 l/h and through the NO_3 filter 900 l/h. Calcium supplement via calcium reactor with a continuous CO_2 adding. "Kalkwasser" and trace elements are not added, however, there is a monthly water change of 25 l, mainly in order to replenish trace elements. Evaporative loss is made up daily with 8.3 l freshwater. Ozone is added via an automatic ozone generator "Sander"; on the average 2.5 mg/h for app. 10 minutes per week.

Lighting: Two HQI lamps each 250 W TS/D 6,500 K and a fluorescent lamp 36 W Osram 11 "daylight".

Water parameters: pH 8.1; temperature 24 °Celsius; salinity 31 ‰; °dKH 6.5-7.0; Ca^{2+} 290 mg/l; NO_3 about 40 mg/l; redox potential 310-350 mV.

Decoration: 700 kg porous calcareous rocks ("faxekalk" - fossilised reef rock as found in many areas of Scandinavia, especially in Denmark and Southern Sweden) glued together with polyester resin into 15 sections. In addition, there are 100 kg of live rocks imported from Indonesia.

Cnidarians: 15 soft coral colonies; *Cladiella* sp., *Sarcophyton* sp., *Sinularia* sp.; various stony corals, among others, *Acropora* sp., *Herpolitha limax* and *Trachyphyllia geoffroyi*, among others, as well as twelve colonies of disk- and zoanthid anemones.

Sinularia sp.

Fishes: Six *Zebrasoma flavescens*, one *Acanthurus achilles*, one *Zebrasoma scopas*, one *Centropyge loriculus*, one *C. bispinosus*, one *Gramma loreto* and ten blue *Abudefduf* sp.

Other organisms: 50 snails of genus *Astraea*, three brittle stars, one unidentified sponge, one Harlequin shrimp, *Hymenocera picta*, and several stands of an unidentified, red macro-algae.

Owner's comment: "The coral reef aquarium is a hobby that conveys knowledge from many areas, such a biology, physiology, chemistry and the effects and influence of light in the aquatic environment. And, of course, we must not forget the contacts to other aquarists."

General view.

Two photos: T. Kjellberg

Dimensions (L x W x H): 300 x 200 x 90 cm, for a volume of 5,400 l.

As of May 1997, in operation for: Five years.

Water management: Protein skimmer "Knop Mega 300", with a diameter of 30 cm and a height of 160 cm. Additionally, there is the frequent use of activated carbon. No mechanical filtration. Calcium supplement via a "Knop-Kalkreaktor", filled with 50 kg "Knop Korallith", supplied with CO_2. The internal water movement is facilitated by circulating pumps 4 x 2,200 l/h. 30 % of the bottom substrate is cleaned two- or three times a year.

General view.

Attractive soft coral growth.

Close-up photo of calcareous algae, which have encrusted most of the decoration.

Lighting: Two HQI lamps Osram T 1000 W 6,500 K with an illumination period of 8 h/d, as well as ten fluorescent lamps Philips TLD 18 each 36 W with an illumination period of 14 h/d.

Water parameters: pH 8.1-8.3; temperature 23-30 °Celsius; salinity app. 30 ‰; °dKH 9; Ca^{2+} 400 mg/l; NO_3 5 mg/l; PO_4 0.025 mg/l.

Decoration: Initially, only with 25 million year-old calcareous rocks (some contained fossilised bivalve molluscs), and no live rocks. This did not work well since the ammonium concentration increased and the fishes were severely infested with parasites. The problem was solved (after one year of operation) by adding crushed *Acropora* coral.

Cnidarians: 20 different genera of stony corals; *Acropora microphthalma* and *A. formosa, Merulina* sp., *Cynarina lacrymalis, Pectinia* sp., *Herpolitha limax, Fungia* sp., *Pavona* sp., among others, and a few unidentified species. Soft corals: including *Sinularia* cf.*mollis, S. dura, Sinularia* sp., *Lobophytum* sp., *Sarcophyton* sp. and *Heliopora* sp. In addition, there are also some tube corals of genus *Clavularia*. The small hydroid *Myrionema* sp. develop quickly in nuisance proportions.

Fishes: Relative to the tank volume there are only a few fishes. Some *Chromis* sp. (*C. viridis* or *C. caeruleus*), some *Acanthurus* spp., two *Zebrasoma flavescens*, two *Naso vlamingi* and a few damselfishes.

Other organisms: The photo-synthesising ear sponge, *Collospongia auris* (see chapter 2, page 59), has produced many colonies, of which some have reached a diameter of 80 cm. This sponge can (according to KNOP, personal com-

munication) damage stony corals, by attacking the tissue chemically (without coming into direct contact with the coral), and then by eventually settling on the coral skeleton.

Special features: The various invertebrates are growing and developing unimpeded. The intent is primarily to "establish a reef". It is not important which corals are growing, but instead that corals are growing.

Owner's comment: "The answer to the question as to why I maintain a coral reef aquarium is very simple: I love the aquarium hobby."

Four Photos: D. Knop

Partial view of the right section.

Left and ...   **... right section.**

Partial view of the right section.

Dimensions (L x W x H): 3120 x 110 x 80 cm, for a volume of 2,700 l; in addition, there is the volume of the filter chamber.

As of May 1997, in operation for: Four years and six months.

Water management: Via a surface overflow along one side of the tank, the water flows to a protein skimmer and from here to a biological dry/wet filter mounted below the aquarium, before it is pumped back into the aquarium. The water flow rate in the protein skimmer is app. 1,500 l/h and that of the dry/wet filter is 4,000 l/h. The dry filter has a thin layer of filter wool with coral sand, while the wet filter contains crushed live rocks (fragment size 10 - 15 mm). The water is filtered over activated carbon. The water movement in the aquarium is facilitated by internal circulating pumps: four "Turbelle 4004" (each 4,000 l/h) and two "SACCEM" with 3,500 l/h each.

Lighting: Three HQI lamps each 250 W 6,500 K with an illumination period of 7 h/d, as well as four fluorescent lamps each 58 W Philips TL54 and six fluorescent lamps each 58 W Osram 64, which are wired in such away that always two fluorescent lamps gradually increase the illumination level, until the HQI lamps are turned on; turning off the lighting is in reverse sequence, after the main lights are off. The entire illumination period is from 11:30 h to 24.00 h.

Water parameters: pH 8.30; temperature 25 °Celsius; °dKH 5-6.

Decoration: Combination of dead coral skeletons on the bottom and live rocks placed on top.

Cnidarians: At least 50-60 colonies of different species, many of them are quite large. Soft coral dominate in the aquarium, including many magnificent colonies of genera *Sarcophyton, Sinularia* and *Nephthea.* In addition, there are also many encrusting- and disk anemones, as well as tube corals, but also magnificent, individual stony corals.

Fishes: The fish fauna is diverse and consists of 40-50 small fishes, among others a school of *Pseudanthias squamipinnis*, which is being fed regularly; there are also ten *Sphaeramia nematoptera* and one *Centropyge bispinosus*, which only occasionally picks on corals.

Other organisms: Many macro-algae, including strong growth of *Lobophora* sp. and magnificent colonies of *Halimeda* sp.; also shrimps of genera *Stenopus* and *Lysmata.*

Special features: Some of the soft coral colonies are and have grown to a substantial size, extending up to the surface. The aquarium contains a rare combination of thriving cnidarians, many fishes and interesting algae growth. All components of the aquarium have been home-built.

Owner's comment: "Because of the fact that I have built the entire aquarium unit from scratch and now, that I can see that all has evolved into a living system, gives me great pleasure."

Sinularia **sp. and green calcareous algae of genus** *Halimeda*, **which have grown up to the surface in the centre section of the tank.**

Close-up photo of a fully expanded *Cynarina lacrymalis.*

General view.

Dimensions (L x W x H): 150 x 75 x 60 cm, for a volume of 675 l.

As of June 1997, in operation for: Two years.

Water management: Combination of a "Red Sea Berlin" protein skimmer and "Jaubert System" (see Volume 1, page 256). Daily addition of 4-5 l "Kalkwasser" via a level compensating valve; Iodine is also being added.

Lighting: Two HQI lamps: 2 x 150 W "aqualine" 10,000 K and two fluorescent lamps: 1 x 40 W Philips TL03 and 1 x 40 W Sylvania "Grow Lux", with an illumination period of 10 h/d.

Water parameters: pH 8.2-8.4; temperature 25 °Celsius; salinity 34 ‰; °dKH 8: Ca^{2+} 450-500 mg/l; NO_3 10 mg/l; PO_4 0.5 mg/l.

Decoration: Live rocks take up half of the aquarium volume.

Cnidarians: 15 coral colonies, including *Acropora* sp., *Catalaphyllia jardinei*, *Heliofungia actiniformis*, several species from family Faviidae and *Lobophyllia* sp. Beyond that, several zoanthid anemones, including *Palythoa tuberculata*, and also soft corals of genera *Sinularia* and *Sarcophyton*, as well as the symbiosis anemone *Entacmaea quadricolor*.

Fishes: Twelve fishes, including *Zebrasoma flavescens*, *Amphiprion* spp., *Chromis* sp., *Abudefduf* sp., *Centropyge bicolor* and *Chaetodon auriga*.

Other organisms: *Tridacna* sp. and one cleaner shrimp, *Stenopus hispidus*.

Special features: The stony coral *Catalaphyllia jardinei* is

showing very strong growth, and has increased its size with 70-80 mm in height, within the period of one year. The symbiosis anemone *Entacmaea quadricolor* has proven to be very hardy, and has twice survived damages caused by the suction at the circulating pump.

Owner's comment: "I am fascinated by life in the sea, and I have always enjoyed keeping fish in an aquarium, especially tropical marine species. I also like to experiment with the aim of finding yet better living conditions for aquarium inhabitants."

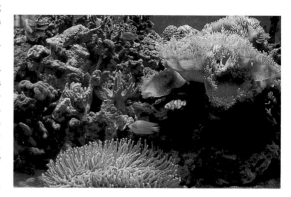

Partial view of the right section.   Two photos: N. Cope

Dimensions: Pentagonal aquarium, front panel 60 cm long and 50 cm high, volume 100 l, plus a filter volume of also 100 l.

As of July 1997, in operation for: Three years.

Water management: A protein skimmer mounted inside the filter chamber with a flow rate of app. 1,500 l/h. The water flows out of the tank via a surface overflow, to the filter chamber, where a pump (1,500 l/h) returns the water to the aquarium. The filter chamber is darkened and contains 20 kg live rocks. There is a weekly water change of about 1% of the entire system, and iodine and strontium are also added. Calcium supplements via a calcium reactor, which contains shell grit and crushed corals and is supplied with CO_2, so that the pH is lowered to 6.6. The remainder of the evaporated volume is replaced daily with unfiltered freshwater and with "Kalkwasser".

Lighting: One HQI lamp 70 W Osram TS/D 6,500 K with an illumination period of 12 h/d, and one fluorescent lamp 18 W Philips TL03 "actinic blue" with an illumination period of 14 h/d.

Water parameters: pH 8.5; temperature 25 °Celsius; salinity 31 ‰; °dKH 7-8; Ca^{2+} 390 mg/l; NO_3^- 5 mg/l; PO_4 0.2 mg/l.

Decoration: Live rocks: 25 kg in the aquarium and 20 kg in the filter chamber.

Cnidarians: 20 colonies: a mixture of *Sarcophyton* sp. and *Sinularia*, including *S. dura*, *Acropora* sp., tube corals, disk- and zoanthid anemones, as well as one sand anemone of genus *Phymanthus*.

Fishes: Five *Zebrasoma flavescens*, seven *Amphiprion ocellaris*, one *Synchiropus* sp., and one *Centropyge bicolor*.

Other organisms: Various shrimps, including *Lysmata amboinensis*, several brittle stars and many hermit crabs. There are also green calcareous algae of genus *Halimeda*. The filter chamber contains a population of red calcareous tube worms and tunicates, which live attached to live rocks.

Special features: Small volume and particular design.

Owner's comment: "The coral reef aquarium is a hobby, which always reveals new wonders and surprises to the aquarist."

Partial view.   Two photos: T. Ländström

Close-up photo of (probably) *Anthelia* polyps.

General view.

Dimensions (L x W x H): 240 x 65 x 80 cm, for a volume of 1,248 l; together with a filter volume of 1,250 l, the entire system contains app. 2,500 l.
As of June 1997, in operation for: Five years.

Filter technology: The water is filtered over two home-made protein skimmers, which are operated with "EHEIM 1060" (2,140 l/h). In addition, the water passes over 150 kg live rocks in a dark filter chamber. The filter system is pla-

Bottom row: A reef column is densely overgrown with stony corals of genus *Acropora* (left). View from above on to the same reef column (right).

ced in a filter-room in the basement directly below the aquarium. There is daily supplement of 15 l "Kalkwasser".

Lighting: 2 x 500 W 20,000 K "Radium blue" (in Osram fittings) and 3 x 150 W 10,000 K Arcadia; also 4 x 40 W Philips TL03 "actinic blue" (Aqua Coral). Illumination period app. 12 h/d.

Water parameters: pH 8.45; °dKH 8-9; temperature 25-26 °Celsius; salinity 35 ‰; Ca^{2+} app. 400 mg/l; PO_4 app. 0 mg/l; NO_3 app. 0 mg/l.

Decoration: App. 400 kg live rocks, attached to PVC pipes.

Cnidarians: 75 stony coral colonies, of genera *Acropora, Montipora, Pocillopora, Euphyllia, Blastomussa, Cynarina, Plerogyra, Lobophyllia, Fungia, Favia, Favites, Heliofungia, Galaxea* and *Turbinaria.* Among soft corals, genera *Sinularia* and *Cladiella* are dominating, whereby the latter is currently in the process of becoming established in a decorative manner on the back wall of the aquarium.

Fishes: About 30 fishes, including twelve *Zebrasoma flavescens,* two *Zebrasoma xanthurus,* two *Paracanthurus hepatus,* one *Acanthurus leucosternon,* one *Ctenochaetus striatus,* three *Pterapogon kauderni,* two *Gramma loreto,* two *Pseudochromis flavivertex,* one *Pseudochromis springeri,* one *Centropyge loriculus* (neither one of the two pygmy angelfish has so far caused any serious damage to corals), one *Neocirrhites armatus.*

Other organisms: Many detritus feeding and algae-grazing organisms, including snails of genus *Turbo,* 50 brittle stars of various genera, 30 hermit crabs of genus *Calcinus* and sea cucumbers. The aquarium also contains giant clams of genus *Tridacna,* pistol shrimps of genus *Alpheus* with live in association with *Cryptocentrus* sp., and shrimps of genera *Lysmata* and *Stenopus.*

Special features: The aquarium contains a good mixture of stony- and soft corals. Many corals have grown to a substantial size. The most conspicuous coral is a red colony of genus *Montipora,* which is growing rapidly and is unusually colourful. Some of the *Acropora* colonies have grown right up to the surface directly under the HQI lamps, where they have developed a beautiful, fluorescing colouration. Snails of genus *Turbo* have reproduced several times; the fishes spawn regularly. The filter chamber contains one *Larabicus quadrilineatus* from the Red Sea, which is a cleaner as a juvenile, but as an adult will feed exclusively on corals. A mass spawning of corals, snails and sea cucumbers took place in December 1997 (see NILSEN, 1998).

Owner's comment: "My interest in nature generally and in life in the sea in particular, are my motivation to be involved with coral reef aquaria."

This *Centropyge loriculus* specimen has not yet damaged any of the corals.

This *Montipora* sp. is hardy and thrives in an aquarium.

Brilliant red hawkfish, *Neocirrhites armatus.*

Dimensions (L x W x H): 220 x 90 x 80 cm, for a volume of 1,584 l.

As of July 1997, in operation for: Seven months.

Water management: Airlift operated protein skimmer with a diameter of 10 cm and a height of 100 cm; calcium reactor and additional kalkwasser supplement.

Lighting: Two HQI lamps each 400 W 10,000 K and four Osram fluorescent lamps each 58 W L67.

Decoration: Principally special ceramics for coral reef aquaria (from "Korallenwelt" company) and 12 kg live rocks.

Cnidarians: 80 stony- and soft corals, of which 80 % are progeny from other aquaria.

Fishes: 40 fishes.

General view.

Successful recreation of reef column made of ceramics.

Acropora sp.

Cespitularia sp.

Special features: This tank serves as an experimental aquarium. Initially it contained only a few live rocks, but since then it functions as an "artificial live reef", because the majority of organisms have been captive-bred. It is maintained only with minimal technical support.

Owner's comment: "We would like to try to maintain the reef aquarium hobby with a high degree of self-sufficiency, in order to be largely independent in respect to fit-out and animal acquisition from imports. In the meantime, the aquarium has numerous maternal colonies of mainly coloured corals, which – among other things – form the basic breeding stock for the breeding program of the "Korallenwelt" Company. All these animals are already captive-bred progeny. Moreover, all product developments are tested and regularly used in this aquarium."

Six photos: T. Luther

Newly positioned fragment of an *Acropora* sp.

Stereonephthya sp. (?)

Middle section.

Dimensions (L x W x H): 160 x 80 x 65 cm, for a volume of 832 l, with another 120 l for the filter chamber, making up a total volume of 952 l.

As of July 1997, in operation for: One year and six months.

Water management: The aquarium is operated with a protein skimmer mounted outside of the aquarium and having a water flow rate of 2,000 l/h, and an air rate of 1,000 l/h. Periodically the water is filtered over activated carbon. When new fishes are introduced a small dose of UV light is used, in order to kill parasites, which may be present. There are also additions of small amounts of iodine and trace elements. Calcium supplement is done with a "Löbbecke calcium reactor" in combination with the adding of 4-7 l "Kalkwasser" daily, which is dispensed automatically, depending upon the volume of evaporated water. The internal water movement is about 10,000 l/h, controlled by an automatic pulse regulator.

Lighting: Two HQI lamps each 250 W 10,000 K "aqualine", and a fluorescent lamp 40 W Philips TL03 "actinic blue"; illumination period 12 h/d.

Water parameters: pH 8.2-8.45; temperature 25-28 °Celsius; salinity app. 30 ‰; °dKH 9-11; Ca^{2+} 500-550 mg/l; NO_3 2 mg/l; PO_4 0.1 mg/l.

Decoration: 40 kg live rocks, introduced into the aquarium four weeks after the aquarium had been filled with water.

Cnidarians: 15-20 colonies of hermatypic corals, including *Acropora* sp., *Pocillopora damicornis, Seriatopora hystrix, Heliofungia actiniformis* (many juvenile polyps), *Polyphyllia talpina, Trachyphyllia geoffroyi*, brain coral of family Faviidae and many small new fragments of stony corals, provided by other aquarist. Among soft corals, there is a large stand of *Xenia* sp., which is growing well, and several *Sarcophyton* sp. Then there are photo-synthesising scleraxonians from the Caribbean, one symbiosis anemone of genus *Heteractis* or *Macrodactyla*, colonies of star polyps (order Stolonifera) and several colonies of disk- and zoanthid anemones.

Fishes: 25 fishes: one *Zebrasoma flavescens*, one *Z. scopas*, two *Lo vulpinus* (which do not feed on algae, but will prey on zoanthid anemones and xeniids), one *Chelmon rostratus*, three *Pterapogon kauderni*, ten *Chromis* sp., one *Pseudochromis* sp., one *Amblyeleotris guttata*, two *Nemateleotris decora*, two *Amphiprion* sp., one *Pholidichthys leucotaenia*, one *Pseudocheilinus hexataenia* and one *Synchiropus picturatus*.

Other organisms: Some echinoderms (sea stars and sea urchins), *Tridacna* spp., snails of genus *Nerita* and the shrimp *Lysmata amboinensis*.

Special features: Reproduction through planula larvae stage by *Heliofungia actiniformis, Pocillopora damicornis* and *Xenia* has been observed. Currently, the aquarium accommodates a great many juvenile polyps of *H. actiniformis*, which have developed from planula larvae. *H. actiniformis* is known to be a free spawner as well as a brooder (see vol. 2, chapter 2). It is therefore conceivable, that primary polyps developed following sexual reproduction. As far as we know, asexual formation of planula larvae, which has been observed in some other stony corals (again see vol. 2), has not been reported from *Heliofungia*. Further-

Details from the middle section.

more, the stony corals and calcareous algae are showing excellent growth.

Owner's comment: "The coral reef aquarium gives me the opportunity, to study the fascinating coral reef organisms and the diversity of this ecosystem, close-up in my living room. This fauna is fantastic and mystic, and every time I look into my aquarium I discover something new."

Left: Close-up photo of a newly settled anthocaulus of *Heliofungia actiniformis*. **Right:** This *Xenia* sp. is growing extraordinary good in the aquarium.

Four photos: M. Megerle

Entire facility.

Dimensions (L x W x H): 160 x 70 x 65 cm, for a volume of 728 l, in addition a reservoir with 280 l, making up a total volume of 1008 l.

As of June 1997, in operation for: One year and four months.

Water management: Two home-built, counter-flow protein skimmers with an air consumption of 950 l/h. The reservoir has an 8-9 cm thick bottom layer with a 2.5 cm thick sub-layer as a type of "Jaubert-System". No mechanical filtration. A "TUNZE 7640" P-Wave generator provides water movement. The water is pumped from the reservoir to the aquarium with an "IWAKI" MD70R, with a capacity of 6,000 l/h. A home-built calcium reactor filled with calcium carbonate or PO_4-free aragonite, assure an adequate calcium supply. A "TUNZE 3150U Osmotic Regulation Set" replaces evaporated water, as required, with "Kalkwasser" (average 5 l/d). Weekly addition of 15 ml, 10 % strontium chloride solution and 3 ml, 5 % potassium iodide solution.

Every sixth to eighth week 40 l of aquarium water are exchanged, and mud at the bottom of the reservoir is siphoned off at the same time.

Lighting: Two HQI lamps à 150 W HQI "aqualine" 10,000 K with an illumination period of 13 h/d, and one fluorescent lamp 140 W Philips T L03 "supra-actinic H. O." used as twilight illumination.

Water parameters: pH 7.8-8.2; temperature 22-26 °Celsius; salinity app. 33 ‰; °dKH 8; Ca^{2+} 420 mg/l; NO_3 less than 10 mg/l; PO_4 less than 0.5 mg/l.

Decoration: 170 kg live rocks from the Caribbean Sea, bottom substrate made from coral sand with variable grain size.

Cnidarians: Among others, *Acropora*, *Montipora* spp., *Pocillopora damicornis*, *Stylophora pistillata*, *Pavona decussata*, *Turbinaria peltata*, *T. reiniformis*, *Porites lobata*, *Caulastrea furcata*, *Favia* sp., *Colpophyllia natans*, *Pectinia* *paeonia, Pectinia lactuca, Merulina ampliata, Galaxea fascicularis, Plerogyra sinuosa, Physogyra* sp., *Protopalythoa* sp., several star polyps, *Pachyclavularia violacea, Sarcophyton* sp., *Sinularia* sp.

Fishes: *Amphiprion ocellaris, Pterapogon kauderni, Pseudocheilinus hexataenia, Synchiropus splendidus, Chromis* sp., *Chelmon rostratus* and *Paracanthurus hepatus*.

Other organisms: Many unidentified coral crabs and 50 hermit crabs from the Caribbean.

Owner's comment: "Aquarium biology and technology are closely related and permit me to discover constantly new aspects in the coral reef aquarium. I enjoy looking at the aquarium, where I discover new organisms every day. The coral reef aquarium is a convincing ecological tool, and it makes me proud to be able to duplicate a part of the fantastic world of coral reefs in my own living room. Currently I would like to simplify the system and increase the number of hermatypic stony corals."

Acropora microphthalma.

Acropora sp.

Pectinia lactuca.   **Four photos: S. Fournier**

Left and ...   ... right section.

Dimensions (L x W x H): Aquarium 160 x 65 x 65 cm and a filter chamber 120 x 50 x 50 cm, for a total volume of 976 l.

Period of operation when photos, shown here, were taken: Two years and two months

Filtration technology: Two "TUNZE 240" protein skimmers. Continuous addition of "Kalkwasser" to replace evaporative loss. About 600 g $Ca(OH)_2$ is used every month. There is also a periodic supplement of "C-Balance" in order to replenish trace elements, as well as calcium ions.

Lighting: Three HQI lamps each 150 W (BLV) 10,000 K with an illumination period of 9 h/d; two fluorescent lamps (VHO) 40 W "actinic-blue" with an illumination period of 11 h/d.

Water parameters: pH 8.15-8.40 (controlled by CO_2-injection); temperature 24-26.5 °Celsius; salinity 32 ‰; Ca^{2+} 390-420 mg/l; NO_3 and PO_4 none detectable.

Decoration: 100 kg live rocks, as well as 25 kg layer of *Halimeda* fragments on a perforated plate.

Cnidarians: Stony corals are dominating with 18 *Acropora* spp., apart from *Montipora* sp., *Plerogyra sinuosa*, *Cynarina lacrymalis*, *Nemenzophyllia turbida*, *Hydnophora* sp., *Caulastrea* sp., *Fungia* sp., *Pavona cactus*, *Porites* sp., and *Euphyllia ancora*. Soft corals maintained include *Sarcophyton* spp., and *Xenia* sp., as well as the tube coral *Tubipora musica* and gorgonians, and also many disk- and some zoanthid anemones.

Fishes: About 15 fishes, including *Zebrasoma desjardinii*, *Acanthurus japonicus*, *Acanthurus lineatus*, three *Pseudanthias dispar*, three *Amphiprion ocellaris*, *Synchiropus* sp., and *Paracheilinus hexataenia*.

Other organisms: Three variable giant clams, *Tridacna maxima*, one scaley giant clam, *T. squamosa*, one giant clam,

Middle section.

Close-up photos of lower zones in the middle section.

T. gigas, one smooth giant clam, *T. derasa* and one boring giant clam, *T. crocea.*

Special features: The growth of *Acropora* spp. is particularly strong. When the pH was adjusted to a maximum of 8.4 by adding CO_2, the alkalinity and other parameters have become more stable.

Owner's comment: "I want to learn as much as possible from a coral reef aquarium. Nothing is a better teacher for that, than a well-functioning aquarium, where the organisms are growing and are generally thriving."

Five photos: A. Povoa

General view.

Dimensions (L x W x H): 192 x 92 x 95 cm, for a volume of 1,678 l, plus an additional 60 l for a reservoir mounted along the one side of the aquarium.

As of August 1997, in operation for: Seven years.

Water management: A home-built protein skimmer is installed outside the aquarium; water flow rate 2,000 l/h by the use of an "EHEIM 1060", sufficient air supply by the use of a "WISA 1000" air pump. On three or four days of the month there is additional filtration over app. 100 g activated carbon. The internal water movement is very good due to a "Marlow 550 W" water pump (originally designed for pools) with a capacity of 12,000 l/h. In addition, three "Turbelle 4002" pumps are used with a capacity of 4,000 l/h each. "Kalkwasser" is supplied by a calcium reactor, where 100 g $Ca(OH)_2$ is stirred with magnetic mixer for 2 x 15 min/d. The calcium hydroxide content of the reactor is replaced once a week. Evaporative loss is about 7 l/d, which is all replaced with "Kalkwasser". Only natural seawater is used. There are occasional supplements of "CombiSan" (trace element mixture), strontium and iodine.

Lighting: One HQI lamp 1,000 W Radium 20,000 K and three fluorescent lamps each 40 W Philips TL03 "actinic-blue"; with an illumination period of 12 h/d respectively.

Water parameters: pH 8.2-8.5; temperature 26-30 °Celsius; salinity app. 33 ‰; °dKH 5; Ca^{2+} 450 mg/l; NO_3^- and PO_4 none detectable.

Decoration: 140 kg live rocks from Indonesia. The decoration is partially mounted on PVC pipes, so that there is a reef slope on the left side of the aquarium and a level plateau with a cantilevered section on the right side. A crevice was created in the centre of the aquarium (details about this decorative layout: see Volume 1, pages 114-115). The bottom substrate consists of coral sand.

Cnidarians: Among others, there are *Acropora* spp. (including *A. latistella*, *A. microphthalma* and *A. formosa*), *Astreopora* (from the Maldives), *Montipora* spp. (including *Montipora digitata* from the Waikiki Aquarium, Honolulu, Hawaii), *Pocillopora damicornis*, *Porites* spp. (probably including *P.*

rus and one other species from the Maldives, as well as several colonies, which have grown on live rocks). *Caulastrea furcata* (from the Waikiki Aquarium, Honolulu, Hawaii), *Montastrea curta, Favia* sp., *Polyphyllia talpina, Fungia* sp., *Turbinaria* spp. (from Suva Reef, Fiji Islands), *Euphyllia glabrescens* as well as several colonies of disk- and zoanthid anemones and some unidentified, smaller corals.

Fishes: *Acanthurus leucosternon, Ctenochaetus strigosus,* one pair of *Centropyge argi*, several *Assessor flavissimus,* two *A. macneillii*, two *Amphiprion ocellaris, Chrysiptera* sp., and *Pseudochromis flavivertex.*

Other organisms: A large population of tube worms, *Bispira viola.* In addition, there are two *Tridacna derasa*, which have grown from 4 cm to 50 cm within four years, and two *Tridacna maxima.*

Special features: The decorative design of the aquarium should be pointed out in particular, as well as the fact that many of the colonies have been collected (under official permit) in the Fiji- and Maldive Islands.

Owner's comment: "I have always admired the wonders of creation. When I saw a well-established coral reef aquarium in 1989, I simply had to have such an aquarium. Since then the aquarium has become my passion. Beyond that, it is very interesting to become acquainted, close up, with this tropical life. The coral reef aquarium is an excellent teaching aid in every respect, and at the same time one also gains an insight in to the biochemical processes which maintain a coral reef."

Dense growth of *Acropora* sp., extending close to the surface on the right.

The left section of the tank has coral growth from the bottom to the surface.

Section in plan view (photo from above the tank).

Dimensions (L x W x H): 165 x 65 x 65 cm, for a volume of 697 l.
As of August 1997, in operation for: Eleven years.
Water management: Filtration with "EHEIM" canister filter, filled with 250 g carbon and coarse crushed coral, used as pre-filter for protein skimmer. A "Löbbecke calcium reactor"

Red form of *Seriatopora hystrix*.

refills evaporated water automatically through a calcium hydroxide reservoir.
Lighting: Two HQI lamps each 250 W 10,000 K and two blue fluorescent tubes.
Water parameters: pH 7.8-8.2; temperature 22-29 °Celsius; °dKH 8; salinity app. 30 ‰; Ca^{2+} 380 mg/l; NO$_3$ 0-0.5 mg/l.
Decoration: Foundation structure made of calcareous rocks from Altmühltal (a creek valley in Germany); no live rocks.
Cnidarians: 150 stony- and soft corals, including rearing tank for small coral fragments.
Fishes: 14 fishes.
Other organisms: Giant clams and diverse secondary growth.
Special features: Extraordinary diversity and excellent growth of coloured stony corals, as well as soft- and leather corals.
Owner's comment: "I maintain a coral reef aquarium, in order to be able to experience daily the fascination emanating from it."

Pocillopora damicornis.

Trachyphyllia geoffroyi.

Left section of the aquarium.

Five photos: T. Luther

General view.

Dimensions (L x W x H): 160 x 55 x 55 cm, for a volume (including filter chamber) of 550 l.

As of April 1997, in operation for: Nine years and six months.

Water management: 2 x 75 mm "Bioquatic M75" protein skimmers installed on the outside of the aquarium, in combination with periodic, sparing use of activated carbon. "Kalkwasser" is automatically used for replacing evaporative loss (4-5 l/d). The pH is regulated through automatic CO_2 supply.

Lighting: One HQI lamp 250 W 6,000 K with an illumination period of 12h/d; two fluorescent lamps each 36 W Philips TL03 "actinic blue" with an illumination period of 12.5 h/d.

Water parameters: pH 8.2; temperature 26 °Celsius; salinity app. 31 ‰; °dKH 5.0; Ca^{2+} 400 mg/l; NO_3 app. 0 mg/l; PO_4 0.2 mg/l.

Decoration: App. 65 kg live rocks of Indonesian origin.

Cnidarians: About 45 coral colonies, half of these are soft corals and other cnidarians, and the remaining half consists of stony corals. Many stony corals have been raised from fragments provided by other aquarists.

Fishes: Ten fishes, including *Acanthurus sohal* and the lemon coral goby *Gobiodon citrinus*.

Other organisms: Several algae-eating hermit crabs, which have been collected by K. Olsen in Thailand.

Special features: The oldest stony coral is *Psammocora contigua*, which is nine years old and grew up from a live rock, immediately after the aquarium had been set up (see photo vol. 1, page 177). Also, a *Seriatopora hystrix* was collected as a small fragment at Zanzibar, East Africa; it subsequently developed into a medium-size colony. A three year old colony of *Euphyllia divisa* has recently produced 30 daughter colonies along its calcareous skeleton, following damage to the maternal polyp which, has since regenerated. The small daughter colonies have now grown together side-by-side.

Owner's comment: "With corals to look after, my life has a new meaning. Apart from that, I am generally interested in studying all life forms. The coral reef aquarium is an excellent opportunity to study the animal life of a coral reef close-up."

Cynarina lacrymalis (?) grows well on the bottom, under subdued lighting.

This *Acanthurus sohal* is doing very well in this aquarium.

A narrow reef passage was created on the left side of the aquarium.

Psammocora contigua colony, which has grown from live rocks.

General view.

Left section.

Dimensions (L x W x H): 124 x 62 x 62 cm, for a volume of 476 l.

As of July 1997, in operation for: Two years.

Water management: Protein skimmer outside the aquarium; evaporated water is replaced with "Kalkwasser" through an automatic level control; additional use of a calcium reactor.

Lighting: Three HQI lamps: 1 x 500 W 20,000 K and 2 x 150 W 10,000 K, as well as six fluorescent lamps each 40 W Philips TL03 "actinic blue".

Water parameters: pH 8.1-8.3: temperature 24-26 °Celsius, maintained with a cooling unit; °dKH 7-8; salinity app. 31 ‰; Ca^{2+} 400 mg/l; NO_3 app. 0 mg/l; PO_4 app. 0 mg/l; Mg^{2+} 1,100 mg/l.

Decoration: Live rocks; dead coral branches attached with underwater adhesive.

Cnidarians: Stony corals: *Stylophora pistillata, Pocillopora verrucosa, P. damicornis, Seriatopora hystrix* (pink coloured form), *Montipora digitata, Acropora* spp., *Goniopora* sp., *Porites antennuata* (yellow form), *Pavona cactus, Fungia fungites, Lobophyllia* sp., *Symphyllia* sp., *Favia* sp., *Euphyllia ancora, E. glabrescens, Turbinaria* sp., *Tubastraea* sp., *Blastomussa wellsi, Cynarina lacrymalis, Hydnophora grandis, H. rigida, Nemenzophyllia turbida, Caulastrea furcata, Cyphastrea microphthalma, Trachyphyllia geoffroyi.* Octocorals: *Heliopora coerulea*, photo-synthesising gorgonians from the Caribbean and star polyps. Various zoanthid- and disk anemones, as well as a nine year old anemone, *Heteractis crispa.*

Fishes: A nine year old pair of *Amphiprion percula*, one *Chromis xanthurus*, one *Gramma loreto*, one pair of *Synchiropus splendidus*, one *Zebrasoma flavescens*, one pair *Gobiodon citrinus* and a *Macropharyngodon ornatus.*

Other organisms: Two *Tridacna derasa*, one *T. crocea* and one *T. maxima.*

Special features: Successful co-existence of a host-sea anemone together with corals.

Owner's comment: "I grew up in Africa and I have always had a fish aquarium. Ten years ago I had the opportunity to visit a reef and there experienced this incredibly beautiful sight – something which I am now trying to recreate in my living room."

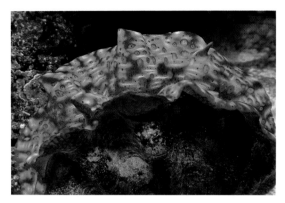

Smooth giant clam,*Tridacna derasa.*

Fungia fungites with tentacles expanded.

Pocillopora damicornis.

Five photos: QuArt IMAGES/Proietti

General view.

Dimensions (L x W x H): 133 x 51 x 46 cm, for a volume of 312 l, and in addition, a small filter chamber.

As of October 1996, in operation for: Four years and six months.

Water management: There are two "TUNZE" rotation protein skimmers, installed in a filter chamber below the aquarium. In addition, two nylon bags with 450 g activated carbon (Hydrocarbon 2 GAZ) suspended in the filter chamber. The carbon is replaced every sixth month. Internal water movement with two "TUNZE 2002" (2,000 l/h), which are coupled to a "TUNZE" power timers. Cooling unit present. An "Iwaki" 40 RLXT with a capacity of 2,250 l/h pumps the water from the filter chamber via the cooling unit ("Universal Marine HK") to the aquarium, from where it returns, via a surface skimmer, to the filter chamber. In addition, there is a continuous water exchange between aquarium and filter chamber through an "EHEIM 1250". This pump is connected to a battery, which is activated automatically in case of a power failure (a necessity in Miami, where there are frequent tropical cyclones). The evaporated water (app. 5 l/d) is automatically replaced (via an "IKS LP 130 Vario") with "Kalkwasser", which is made with freshwater, generated by an osmosis unit. Beyond that, a few times during the week "TLF C-Balance" is also added in order to optimize carbonate concentration and buffering capacity. There is also a weekly supplement of 30 ml "CombiSan" (trace element mixture).

Lighting: Three HQI lamps each 150 W "Giesemann System 260" (burner: "TS Aqua" 6,800 K) with an illumination period of 10 h/d. Two fluorescent lamps each 60 W Philips TL03 "actinic blue" with an illumination period of 12 h/d.

Water parameters: pH 7.8-8.4: temperature 24-25 °Celsius (regulated via cooling unit); salinity app. 30 ‰; °dKH 8-10; Ca^{2+} 425-450 mg/l; NO_3^- and PO_4 none detectable.

Decoration: Mixture of live rocks from the Gulf of Mexico and from Indonesia for a total of 50 kg. The live rocks are glued together with an underwater epoxy adhesive from

"AquaStik". Half of the bottom is covered with coral sand and the other half with live rock fragments.

Cnidarians: Stony corals: *Acropora* spp, including Stüber's *Acropora* and a growing fragment from Waikiki Aquarium (Honolulu, Hawaii), *Blastomussa merleti, B. wellsi, Lobophyllia* sp., *Montipora* sp., *Duncanopsammia axifuga, Herpolitha* sp., *Fungia* sp., *Diaseris* sp. (from the Galápagos Islands, fragment provided by Dr. P. Glynn, Miami), *Cycloseris* sp., *Pavona* sp., *Leptoseris* sp., *Madracis* sp., *Meandrina* sp., *Siderastrea* sp., *Hydnophora* sp., *Eusmilia* sp., *Diploria* sp., *Cataliaphyllia jardinei, Cynarina* sp., *Pocillopora* sp., *Psammocora* sp., *Plerogyra sinuosa, Caulastrea furcata* (probably a growing fragment from Waikiki Aquarium) and *Tubastraea* sp. Octocorals: *Sarcophyton* sp., *Sinularia* sp., *Nephthea* sp., *Erythropodium* sp., *Scleronephthya* sp., *Pachyclavularia violacea, Clavularia* spp., *Gorgonia ventalina, Chironephthya* sp. Zoanthid anemones: several colonies of *Palythoa* sp., *Protopalythoa* as well as *Zoanthus* sp. Also several colonies of disk anemones of genera *Discosoma* and *Rhodactis*.

Fishes: Twelve fishes: including *Zebrasoma* spp., *Neocirrhites armatus*, a pair of *Amphiprion percula, Pterapogon kauderni, Pseudochromis fridmani, Oxymonacanthus longirostris* (we have personally observed this specimen to feed on flake food), two males of *Geniacanthus bellus* and one *Pygoplites diacanthus* from the Red Sea, which is fed daily with dry food, and occasionally it is given Mysis and frozen Artemia.

Other organisms: Various macro-organisms on live rocks, together with variable growth of sponges and turf algae.

Special features: The flourishing growth is extraordinary, in view of the combination of cnidarian animals kept together. Rarely have we seen such an aquarium, where the animals have been so well-established! One *Tubastraea* sp. is more than three years old, and is attached to a side wall with underwater epoxy adhesive.. One of the *Gorgonia ventalina* in the tank was washed up by a cyclone on a beach in Miami. The most significant special feature though is probably a colony of *Chironephthya* sp., which has been kept for more than 4 months and is still flourishing.

Owner's comment: "I was born in Miami and I have spent a lot of time on the beach. I have been snorkelling and scuba-diving in the Miami (Florida) Keys, in Cuba and the Bahamas. That inspired me to set up my coral reef aquarium during the mid-1980's."

Flourishing growth of the red algae *Peysonellia* sp. among corals.

This *Oxymonacanthus longirostris* accepts dry food, which is uncommon for this species.

The stony coral *Duncanopsammia axifuga* is very rarely seen in an aquarium.

View into one of the aquarium segments.

Anemone with fully expanded tentacles.

Both of these photos illustrate the effective reef structure.

Dimensions (L x W x H): The aquarium is built U-shaped, in the living room, and can be viewed from three sides. It consists of three rectangular segments: 300 x 90 cm, 110 x 100 cm and 53 x 65 cm with a height of 100 cm each, which makes for a total volume of 4,000 l. A reservoir with a volume of 2,000 l is located underneath the aquarium. A set of steps is erected between the segments, so that the aquarium can also be viewed from above.

As of October 1997 in operation for: Two years.

Water management: Two "Deltex" protein skimmers with a flow rate of 5,000 l/h each; a UV lamp with a water flow of 2,000 l/h. Every week 800 l of water are replaced, with seawater made up from "Reef Crystals", supplied by "Aquarium Systems". There is no biological filter, but the reservoir contains some live rocks. Calcium reactor with CO_2 and additional replacement of evaporated water with "Kalkwasser" via a dosing system.

Lighting: 10 HQI lamps: 5 x 400 W 20,000 K "Radium Blue", 4 x 400 W 5,300 K and 1 x 250 W 6,500 K, with an illumination period of 10 h/d. Fluorescent lamps over the reservoir with an illumination period of 12 h/d.

Water parameters: pH 8.1-8.4: temperature 24.2-24.6 °Celsius regulated with a cooling units; salinity 33 ‰; °dKH 11.2; Ca^{2+} 420-450; NO_3 25 mg/l; PO_4 app. 0 mg/l; Mg^{2+} 1,100 mg/l.

Decoration: 1,250 kg "toother rocks" (which are fossil reef rocks found in many areas in northern Europe). There are no live rocks (except in the reservoir). Corals and rocks have been joined together with the underwater adhesive "Defcon".

Cnidarians: Stony corals: including *Pocillopora verrucosa, P. damicornis, Seriatopora hystrix, Montipora* spp., *Acropora* spp., *Porites* spp., *Pavona cactus, Fungia* sp., *Cycloseris cyclolites, Scolymia* spp., *Symphyllia* spp., *Euphyllia ancora, E. glabrescens, Catalaphyllia jardinei, Turbinaria reniformis, Turbinaria* sp. In addition, there are many photo-synthesising gorgonians from the Caribbean, many soft corals, as well as disk- and zoanthid anemones.

Fishes: 56 fishes, including eight *Pseudanthias* sp., various tangs, one *Synchiropus* sp., one *Gramma loreto*, one *Pseudochromis fridmani*, a number of clown fish and gobies, among others.

Other organisms: About 500 hermit crabs, two *Stenopus hispidus*, two *Lysmata debelius*, one pair *Hymenocera picta*, which is flourishing, 40-50 large snails (*Turbo* sp.), thousands of other, smaller snails and a few sea stars. Five months ago a small octopus, *Octopus* sp., was introduced, and has since grown to 40 cm. It is fed daily with shrimps, and occasionally it also catches the odd fish. It has eliminated a nuisance population of predatory crabs.

Special features: The unusual structure of the aquarium and the combination of corals together with other invertebrates and fishes.

Owner's comment: "I like the technical challenge provided by a coral reef aquarium. Beyond that, I enjoy immensely the underwater garden in my living room."

A multitude of different organisms flourishes on this reef wall. **Five photos: Miss C. Saxby**

General view.

Dimensions (L x W x H): 150 x 50 x 60 cm, for a volume of 450 l.

As of July 1997, in operation for: Fourteen years.

Water management: Protein skimmer with 10 cm diameter and a height of 110 cm installed outside the aquarium and operated with an air pump "WISA 300" and with a water

Flourishing growth of soft corals and zoanthid anemones.
Two photos: P. G. Rohleder

flow of 350 l/h. The entire internal circulation is about 3,500 l/h. Neither biological- nor carbon filtration; however, every ten weeks ozone is added for ten hours at 10 mg/h. In addition, a water change of 10 l/week is made. Calcium supplement is done by adding 1 l of freshly mixed "Kalkwasser" every morning. There is also an irregular supplement of "Marinvit" solution, strontium and iodine.

Lighting: Seven fluorescent lamps: 4 x 36 W Osram Lumilux 11, 3 x 36 W Osram 67 (blue). The illumination period is 12 h/d.

Water parameters: pH 7.9-8.2; temperature 23-28 °Celsius; salinity app. 34 ‰; °dKH 6; Ca^{2+} app. 450 mg/l; NO_3^- 5 mg/l; PO_4 app. 0.5 mg/l.

Decoration: App. 150 kg live rocks and some German "tuffa rocks", as well as some other large rocks, covered with encrusting- disk anemones, which also came from the sea, but as live rocks. During the period of operation, the bottom substrate has occasionally been renewed.

Cnidarians: Mainly octocorals with references to volume 2: *Capnella imbricata, Sarcophyton* spp., *Cladiella* sp. "KA4-ALC-45", *Cladiella* sp. "KA4-ALC-54", *Sinularia dura, S. brassica, Sinularia* sp. "KA4-ALC-46", *Sinularia* sp., *Sinularia* sp. "KA4-ALC-47", *Alcyonium* sp. "KA4-ALC-57", *Erythropodium caribaeorum, Eunicea* sp. "KA4-HOL-14" (?), *Pseudoplexaura* sp. "KA4-HOL-13", and the blue coral, *Heliopora coerulea*.

Fishes: Only five fishes; one *Zebrasoma flavescens*, two *Gramma loreto*, one *Serranus tigrinus* and one *Oxycirrhites typus*.

Other organisms: One variable giant clam,*Tridacna maxima*, has been kept for 13 years and continues to flourish. In addition, large colonies of *Zoanthus* sp. "KA-ZOA-24", which need to be harvested regularly.

Special features: The age of the aquarium as such, is already extraordinary. For six years there have been significant problems with slimy red algae. Illuminating the aquarium for six weeks exclusively with blue fluorescent lamps solved this problem. To this day, the aquarium is sensitive to large water changes, which leads directly to a massive growth of diatoms and filamentous green algae.

Owner's comment: "The coral reef environment interests and fascinates me. My three coral reef aquaria afford me the opportunity, to study the organisms more closely and in detail. Moreover, I am actively involved in SMAC (Siegerländer Meerwasser-Aquarien-Club), which gives me with a lot of stimuli for my hobby."

Dimensions (L x W x H): 110 x 70 x 60 cm, for a volume of app. 400 l; acrylic (12 mm) with two "cut off" corners; drain channel centrally located, sound-proofed with fill/packing material and filter mats.

As of July 1997, in operation for: One year and three months.

Water management: Filter chamber "AquaCare Basic 1000" with air-driven, internal protein skimmer "Aquaflotor 90i/500", additional chamber where the water parameters are measured, trickle filter filled with "AquaCare" plastic trickle filter medium, use of activated carbon, if required (app. 1 l for three days). Internal water movement with two pumps ("Fischer TKP 2000") with suction strainers; two circulating pumps "EHEIM 1060". Turbo-calcium reactor of the type "AquaCare". Water treatment is also done by the use of a reverse osmosis unit ("AquaCare Professional 500") and "AquaCare" sea salt. Supplements of 16 trace elements. Control and operation of the entire system with "AquaCare" digital master (control) equipment. Partial water change of 5%. POD_4 is kept to a maximum of 1 mg/l by the use of "AquaCare PO_4-minus".

Lighting: One HQI lamp 400 W "Aquastar", Breßlein Company (E40 with screw fitting) with an illumination period of 4 h/d; four fluorescent lamps with electronic ballasts and Breßlein Reflectors: 2 x 30 W Lumilux 21 with an illumination period of 7 h/d, and 2 x 30 W Lumilux 67 with an illumination period of 10 h/d; one incandescent lamp 20 W as moon light.

Water parameters: pH 8.0-8.3; temperature 25-25.5 °Celsius (cooling by means of ventilator); °dKH app. 8; salinity 35 ‰; redox potential (measuring circuit voltage) 250-300 mV; Ca^{2+} 400-450 mg/l; ammonium / ammonia none detectable; PO_4 less than 1,0 mg/l.

Decoration: App. 150 kg live rocks.

Cnidarians: White xeniids, one *Sarcophyton* sp., three *Sarcophyton* cf. *ehrenbergi*, two *Lobophyton* sp., one *Sinularia brassica*, one *Galaxea* sp., one *Pocillopora* sp., one *Lobophyllia* sp., one red *Euphyllia* sp., two *Plerogyra* sp., one *Catalaphyllia jardinei* as well as scleraxonian and holaxonian corals, zoanthid- and disk anemones.

Fishes: One *Gramma loreto*, five *Chromis viridis*, three *Chrysiptera parasema*, one *Cryptocentrus leptocephalus*, one *Amblygobius phalaena*, one *Zebrasoma flavescens* one *Z. veliferum,* and one *Acanthurus* cf. *nigrofuscus*; feeding once a day (except Sundays) with sufficient Artemia and micro-algae.

Other organisms: Two white-banded cleaner shrimps, *Lysmata amboinensis.*

Special features: The aquarium is used principally for laboratory tests by the "AquaCare Company".

General view.

Central section.　　Two photos: B. Sellner and B. Ramsch

General view.

Dimensions (L x W x H): 130 x 50 x 70 cm, for a total volume of 455 l; in addition, there is a filter volume of 45 l.
As of May 1997, in operation for: Four years.
Water management: Combination of protein skimmer and biological filtration. The biological filter has a volume of 120l and is totally submerged. Daily addition of 1 l of "Kalkwasser". A water change of 50 l is done every other week.
Lighting: Five fluorescent lamps: 3 x 36 W Osram 11 (daylight), and 2 x 36 W "blue moon", with an illumination period of 14.5 h/d.
Water parameters: pH 8.3; temperature 26 °Celsius; salinity 31 ‰; °dKH 6; Ca^{2+} 400 mg/l; NO_3 and PO_4 none detectable.
Decoration: 120 kg live rocks.
Cnidarians: Soft corals of genera: *Cladiella, Sarcophyton* and *Sinularia*, a large colony of *Sinularia dura*, among others. Also, attractive colonies of star polyps, possibly *Clavularia* sp. In terms of stony corals: some large *Euphyllia* sp.

Partial view, which illustrates that soft corals, other cnidarians and fish can be readily kept together and flourish in the same tank.

Fishes: One pair *Calloplesiops altivelis*, one *Centropyge acanthops*, one *Gramma loreto* and one specimen of the extremely rare *Centropyge aurantius*.

Other organisms: *Lysmata debelius* and *Tridacna*, one large colony of the photo-synthesising blue ear sponge, *Collospongia auris*. In addition, a large stand of *Caulerpa* sp., and many turf algae, which normally remain rather short in a coral reef aquarium, however, in this aquarium they have developed into a sizeable plant as macro-algae on a live rock.

Special features: This aquarium shows a very interesting development of macro-algae in combination with colonies of octocorals, and it can serve as an example that extensive algae growth can also make for a beautiful aquarium. The outstanding feature, however, is probably the *Centropyge aurantius*, which occurs on the Great Barrier Reef and eastward to Samoa.

Owner's comment: "Keeping a coral reef aquarium is a fantastic hobby."

Centropyge aurantius.　　　　Photo: F. Schaap

This section of the aquarium also shows a considerable diversity of reef organisms. The pair of comets, *Calloplesiops altivelis*, in this aquarium is thriving particularly well.

Dimensions (L x W x H): 183 x 61 x 64 cm, for a volume of 714 l.

As of October 1996 in operation for: Seven years.

Water management: Protein skimmer of Type DDS 800 from "Reef Enterprises" with a flow rate of 4,700 l/h ("IWAKI 70 RL" pump). 300 g activated carbon is replaced every sixth week. There is a daily addition of about 17 l "Kalk-wasser", to replace evaporated water, 75% of that volume during the night so that the pH remains stable within a 24 hour period. Water required for make-up and water change is mixed from osmosis-generated freshwater.

Lighting: Three HQI lamps each 175 W 6,500 K of type "Coralife"; two fluorescent lamps each 160 W URI 03 "actinic blue".

Water parameters: pH 8.3–8.4; temperature 25 °Celsius; salinity app. 33 ‰; °dKH 8.4; Ca^{2+} 450 mg/l; NO$_3$ 0.03 mg/l; PO$_4$ 0.01 mg/l.

Decoration: App. 110 kg live rocks from different geographical regions: Hawaii, Marshal Islands and Fiji Islands, Indonesia and the Caribbean.

Cnidarians: Principally *Acropora*, more than 50 colonies.

Fishes: 25 fishes, including a seven year old *Gramma loreto* and *Pseudocheilinus hexataenia*.

Other organisms: The aquarium also accommodates seven giant clams (*Tridacna*), many crustaceans, including

View into the middle section with its attractive ...

The attractive anemone *Epicystis crucifer*.

Another partial section with ...

... reef structure and flourishing growth.

more than 500 hermit crabs and many molluscs, including 300 algae-eating snails. Most of the hermit crabs have been collected by the owner himself, in the Caribbean and along the Pacific coat of Mexico; the most common species are *Calcinus tibicen, Pagurus cadenati* and *P. tricolor*. Most of the snails belong to the genera *Astraea* and *Turbo*.

Special features: A large colony of Stüber's *Acropora*, which originated from the parent colony in the aquarium of Dietrich Stüber, Berlin. Fragments of this coral were taken to United States by Julian Sprung, and its "progeny" are now in many American coral reef aquaria. The colony depicted here has been in the aquarium for 18 months, and it represents the third generation of Stüber's *Acropora* in the USA. In addition, the aquarium accommodates six year old colonies of *Acropora aculeus* and *A. hyacinthus*, as well as a boring giant clam, *Tridacna crocea*, which is more than seven years old.

Owner's comment: "My aquarium lets me forget the stress of daily life. Every day the coral reef aquarium reveals something special or new mysteries to my family and me. Moreover, I have made many new friends through the coral reef aquarium."

... attractive coral reef growth.

Soft coral of genus *Paralemnalia*.

Julian Sprung looks at his "pocket-size aquarium" with obvious satisfaction.

This *Pocillopora damicornis* originated from a planula larva, which has attached itself to the front glass, close to the surface.

Dimensions (L x W x H): 61 x 30 x 30 cm, for a volume of 55 l, plus 20 l for a reservoir underneath the aquarium. Moreover, for a year now, this aquarium has been connected up to another aquarium, using the "Jaubert-System".

As of October 1996, in operation for: Eight years and six months.

Water management: The water flows from the aquarium, via a surface runoff, into a container with three submersible pumps, two of which pump the water back into the aquarium and the third pumps water to the other aquarium. For the last five years a "TUNZE" protein skimmer has been installed in the reservoir; however, with a failure of the pump operating the protein skimmer, it has been turned off for the last few months. At night "Kalkwasser" is added to replace evaporated water. There have been no water changes for the last three years, however, occasionally some natural sea water is being added, in order to maintain the salinity of the system. More frequently "CombiSan"(trace element solution) is being added, and the fishes are fed daily.

Lighting: Two HQI lamps: 1 x 175 W "coralife" 20,000 K, and 1 x 150 W "aqualine" 10,000 K.

Water parameters: pH 8.1-8.3; temperature 25-27 °Celsius; salinity app. 33 ‰; NO_3 less than 1.0 mg/l; Ca^{2+} 450 mg/l.

Decoration: 2-3 kg live rocks and at least the same amount of corals. Moreover, the bottom is covered with a 2 cm thick layer of fine-grained coral sand. In addition, the reservoir chamber contains individual corals and live rocks, while the inter-connected "Jaubert-System" contains about 25 kg of coral sand.

Cnidarians: Stony corals: *Acropora* sp. (A.cf.*formosa*) and *A. latistella* (provided by D. Stüber, Berlin), *A. microphthalma* and *Acropora* sp. (provided by Waikiki Aquarium), *Acropora* sp.,*Pocillopora damicornis* (provided by D. Stüber), *Seriatopora hystrix, Psammocora contigua, Siderastrea radicans, Duncanopsammia axifuga, Cycloseris* sp., *Fungia* sp., *Pavona cactus, Pavona decussata, Pavona* sp., *Turbinaria peltata, Trachyphyllia geoffroyi, Blastomussa wellsi, Goniopora* spp., *Alveopora gigas, Cynarina lacrymalis, Cataphyllia jardinei* (provided by Storace), *Montastrea cavernosa, Caulastrea furcata* (provided by the Waikiki Aquarium), *Caulastrea curvata, Favias* sp., *Goniastrea palauensis, Tubastrea* sp. from the Fiji Islands. Octocorals: *Xenia* spp., *Clavularia* sp., *Alcyonium* spp., *Sinularia dura, Sinularia* cf. *notanda, Paralemnalia* sp. (provided by P. Findeisen and H. Schmidt), *Capnella* sp. (provided by A.J. Nilsen), *Tubipora musica, Heliopora coerulea.* Others: one white disk anemone with bulbous tentacle tips, which was collected at the Fiji Islands, by Tony Nahacky.

Fishes: Three *Amphiprion percula* and *Pseudochromis fridmani.*

Other organisms: Mysis shrimps, many sponges, two transparent tunicates (which have lived and reproduced in the aquarium for years), many algae, including *Coelothrix* sp., and *Ochtodes* sp. and also several colour forms of *Dictyota*. Also, one 'bonsai' form of mangrove, which blossomed for several months in 1996, although it was only three years old.

Special features: The small size of the aquarium relative to the incredible diversity, which has existed for many years now is indeed unique. Moreover, the combination of seed plants (mangrove), algae and corals is something very special. This aquarium demonstrates graphically, how a small and relatively economical aquarium system can be extremely multi-faceted and biologically very interesting. The majority of corals have been placed in this tank as "cuttings"; some have developed from planula larvae.

Owner's comment: "It is extremely satisfying to see how care and diligent control of growth can induce the animals to create a decorative entity. It goes without saying, that I am also interested in the biology, taxonomy as well as in the ecology of animals and plants. It is also a large challenge, to establish a small, stable system, with minimal maintenance requirements – and after all it is scientifically interesting to note, that the diversity as such is clearly important for stability of the system."

View on to the water surface.

Both of these photos illustrate the dense and flourishing growth of a large number of cnidarian animals, which seems hardly possible for such a small aquarium.

Very colourful corals characterize this aquarium.

Dimensions (L x W x H): 152 x 66 x 61, for a volume of 612 l.
When the photos were taken, in operation for: Two years.
Water management: A 212 cm tall "Venturi" protein skimmer installed outside the aquarium. 25-50 % of the water evaporated daily is replaced with "kalkwasser". The calcium carbonate concentration is frequently raised with calcium chloride additions.

Lighting: HQI lamps: 2 x 400 W "Radium blue" 20,000 K and 3 x 175 W 10,000 K "Coralife", with an illumination period of 11-13h/d.

Water parameters: pH 8.20-8.45; temperature 26.5 °Celsius; °dKH 10; salinity app. 32 ‰; NO_3 1-3 mg/l; Ca^{2+} 375 mg/l.

Decoration: Live rocks from the Fiji Islands.

Cnidarians: Large number of hermatypic stony corals, principally from genera *Acropora, Montipora, Pocillopora, Stylopora* and *Porites*.

Fishes: Many large surgeon fishes and tangs, including *Zebrasoma flavescens* and *Z. veliferum*.

Other organisms: Many sponge colonies have become established and are flourishing in shaded parts of the aquarium.

Special features: This aquarium can almost be described as a pure stony coral aquarium.

Owner's comment: "My principal aim with the coral reef aquarium is to learn as much as possible about reef-building corals."

Middle section.   **Two photos: S. Tyree**

General view.

Dimensions (L x W x H): 160 x 80 x 55 cm, for a volume of 704 l.

As of May 1997, in operation for: Eight years.

Water management: Combination of protein skimming and biological filtration. The biological filter, which has a volume of 120 l, is totally submerged. Addition of app. 1 l "Kalkwasser" per day. 50 l of the water is changed every second week.

Lighting: Six fluorescent lamps: 4 x 58 W Osram 11 (daylight), 2 x 58 W "blue moon", with an illumination period of app.14 h/d.

Water parameters: pH 8.0; temperature 25 °Celsius; salinity 30 ‰; Ca^{2+} 374 mg/l; NO_3 25 mg/l; PO_4 0.5 mg/l.

Decoration: 40 kg porous rocks and 90 kg live rocks.

Cnidarians: Soft corals of genera *Sinularia* (including *S. dura*), *Sarcophyton* and *Litophyton* (?). Also, a large colony *Pseudoplexaura* sp. and the stony corals *Catalaphyllia jardinei* and *Caulastrea furcata*, apart from some specimens of disk anemones.

Fishes: Two *Calloplesiops altivelis*, five *Pterapogon kauderni*, one *Centropyge bispinosus*, one *Zebrasoma flavescens* and two blue *Abudefduf* sp.

Other organisms: Diverse algae growth, including a large stand of *Caulerpa* sp., and attractive colonies of red algae, probably *Halymenia*.

Special features: Significant growth of macro-algae in combination with soft corals. The high levels of NO_3 and PO_4 are probably the main reason for the strong algae growth and for the unsatisfactory development of stony corals.

Owner's comment: "The colours of the coral reef aquarium are gorgeous, and this aspect of the hobby alone is fantastic."

Macro-algae, possibly *Halymenia*, grow well in this aquarium.

Left section of the sparsely decorated aquarium.

Two photos: J. H. Vikjord

Xeniids and disk anemones are growing together, closely side-by-side.

Dimensions (L x W x H): 150 x 60 x 60 cm, for a volume of 540 l; plus a filter chamber of 60 l, making up a total volume of 600 l.

As of September 1997, in operation for: One year and six months.

Water management: Protein skimmer "STK Junior", operated by an "EHEIM 1060", installed in a reservoir below the aquarium. The internal circulation in the aquarium is 4,000 l/h with four circulating pumps of 1,000 l/h each. Water exchange between aquarium and filter chamber is at a rate of 1,000 l/h. "Kalkwasser" made from calcium hydroxide and freshwater from as reverse osmosis unit, is added drop-by-drop, in order to replace evaporated water. Additional supplement of strontium.

Lighting: Two HQI lamps each 250 W TS 6,500 K and one fluorescent lamp 40 W "actinic blue", each with an illumination period of 11 h/d.

Water parameters: pH 8.3; temperature 28 °Celsius; salinity app. 31 ‰; Ca^{2+} 465 mg/l.

Decoration: 60 kg live rocks.

Cnidarians: Xeniids, disk- and zoanthid anemones.

Fishes: *Zebrasoma flavescens, Synchiropus* sp., *Chrysiptera* sp., *Abudefduf* sp., *Neocirrhites* sp., among others.

Other organisms: Hermit crabs, some crabs, which have been introduced into the aquarium together with live rocks, as well as a few sea urchins.

Owner's comment: "I am fascinated by life in the sea and would like to study it close-up. I also dive. The coral reef aquarium brings a familiar and beautiful environment into my living room."

Dimensions (L x W x H): 125 x 90 x 72 cm, for a volume of 810 l, plus a reservoir of 120 l, making up a total volume of 930 l.

As of June 1997, in operation for: One year and two months.

Water management: Three protein skimmers: one of them a home-built, counter-current skimmer and two "TUNZE 230" protein skimmers. An "EHEIM 1060" (2,200 l/h) pumps the water from the reservoir back to the aquarium, and the internal circulation is being maintained by two "Turbelle 4002" (4000 l/h). A "Jaubert-System" (see vol. 1, page 256) is also used, but there is no mechanical filtration. Calcium supplement from a calcium reactor, which is filled with coral sand and with CO_2 added. Water replacement with a "TUNZE 3150" osmotic regulation set. Weekly addition of 20 ml of a 10 % strontium chloride solution, and 5 ml of a 5 % potassium iodide solution. Occasional water changes with natural seawater from the Mediterranean Sea.

Lighting: Four HQI lamps: 2 x 250 W "aqualine" 10,000 K, and 2 x 150 W "aqualine" 10,000 K, with an illumination period of 9.5 h/d. "Actinic-blue" fluorescent lamps, which are turned on in the morning and in the evening, for 2 hours each.

Water parameters: pH 7.75-8.2: temperature 25 °Celsius; salinity 35 ‰; °dKH 8; Ca^{2+} 460 mg/l; NO_3^- less than 0.2 mg/l; PO_4 less than 0.2 mg/l.

Decoration: Live rocks, with 60 % from the Mediterranean Sea, 30 % from Mauritius, the rest of unknown origin. Bottom layer 6 cm thick in the aquarium, and 12 cm in the lower reservoir ("Jaubert-System"). Decorative design to simulate a "patch reef"; one in the centre of the aquarium, and another along the back wall.

Cnidarians: Stony corals: *Acropora* spp., *Montipora* spp., *Galaxea fascicularis*, *Goniopora* sp., *Favia* sp., *Turbinaria peltata*, *Stylophora pistillata*, *Pocillopora damicornis*, *Seriatopora hystrix*, *Porites* sp. Octocorals: *Xenia* sp., *Pachyclavularia violacea*, *Sarcophyton* sp., *Sinularia* sp. Others: *Discosoma* sp., *Protopalythoa* sp., *Millepora* sp.

Fishes: *Zebrasoma veliferum*, *Chelmon rostratus*, *Synchiropus picturatus*, two *Gobiodon* sp., two *Nemateleotris magnifica*, *Pseudocheilinus hexataenia*, five *Chromis viridis*, *Pseudanthias* sp., and two *Eleotris* sp.

Other organisms: Giant clams of genus *Tridacna* and *Hippopus*. Also, many algae and detritus feeders, such as snails, hermit crabs, brittle stars and sea stars.

Special features: The simultaneous operation of two different filtration systems.

Owner's comment: "I discovered coral reefs while diving off Martinique and immediately decided to set up my own coral reef at home. My first attempt was with the "Jaubert-System", but I soon discovered that this does not function well without a protein skimmer. Because of effective protein skimming my corals are now growing very well, and are reproducing with new colonies from fragments. Apart from the exchange of runners with other aquarists, it is also important that aquarists swap their experiences. In this respect, aquarium clubs are particularly important."

General view.

Seriatopora hystrix.　　　　　　　**Two photos: N. Leclercq**

Entire facility.

Dimensions (L x W x H): 180 x 85 x 60 cm, for a volume of 918 l.

As of July 1997, in operation for: Three years.

Water management: A "Sander" protein skimmer operated with ozone; mechanical filter; filtration over 500 g activated carbon for four days, every four to five week; calcium reactor with CO_2, filled to one-fifth of it's volume with calcium granulate.

Lighting: Two HQI lamps each 400 W 20,000 K and two fluorescent lamp: 1 x 18 W TLD 18 and 1 x 18 W Osram 11 with Norka-Reflector.

Water parameters: pH 7.9-8.3; temperature 26 °Celsius; °dKH app. 8; salinity 33 ‰; Ca^{2+} 400-450 mg/l; NO_3 30-40 mg/l.

Decoration: One-fifth dead reef rocks, the remainder consists of "tufa rocks"; loose reef structure with caves, arches and columns.

Cnidarians: App. 85 corals (mainly stony corals), and 50 anthocauli from a *Fungia* sp., bred by the owner; also some disk anemones.

Fishes: 22 fishes.

Other organisms: Crustaceans, brittle stars, sea urchins and snails.

Special features: Successful duplication of reef structure and harmonious compatibility of many organisms. During the last two years 150 anthocauli of a *Fungia* sp. have been produced, and many of these have been passed on to other aquarists.

Owner's comment: "Unfortunately, I did not have any pets as a child. With the coral reef aquarium may dream has now come true."

Effective reef structure in the centre.

Some of the 150 *Fungia* specimens ...

A yellow tang, *Zebrasoma flavescens*, and a jack-knife fish, *Equetus lanceolatus*, encounter each other over disk anemones on the bottom.

... bred by A. Zöllner over two years.

Right section.

Five photos: A. Zöllner

Dimensions (L x W x H): 160 x 50 x 40 cm, for a volume of 320 l.

As of July 1999, in operation for: Five years.

Water management: One protein skimmer with a height of 120 cm and a diameter of 10 cm, operated by a "RENA 30 l" (app. 500 l/h). Water flow through the protein skimmer is secured with a "FLUVAL 203" (420 l/h), which also serves a mechanical pre-filter. In addition, two "Aqua Clear 801" (together 1,500 l/h) are used as internal circulation pumps, as well as a "FLUVAL 2" (360 l/h) for creating a surface movement of the water. 3 l of "Kalkwasser" (made from tap water) are added daily, and 15 % of the aquarium water is replaced every three weeks with fresh seawater (made from tap water).

Lighting: Five fluorescent lamps: 2 x 58 W Osram Lumilux 11, 1 x 58 W Osram Lumilux 67 (blue) and 2 x 38 W Philips 18 (blue), with an illumination period of 12 h/d.

Water parameters: pH 8.2; temperature 25 °Celsius; salinity app. 33 ‰; °dKH 7; Ca^{2+} app. 400 mg/l.

Decoration: 30 kg porous rocks and 10 kg live rocks; 25 kg coral fragments as bottom substrate.

Cnidarians: Principally octocorals, including four *Sarcophyton* spp., eleven *Sinularia* spp., one *Litophyton arboreum* (?), five *Xenia* sp., three *Xenia umbellata*, six colonies of brown star polyps and four colonies of green star polyps of an unidentified species, and various fragments of disk anemones.

Fishes: One *Zebrasoma flavescens*, one *Paracanthurus hepatus* and a pair of *Amphiprion frenatus*.

Other organisms: One *Tridacna* sp., and eight small hermit crabs, twelve snails, two brittle stars, one cleaner shrimp, *Stenopus hispidus*, and one sea urchin.

Special features: All corals are growing and reproducing rather quickly. This aquarium has already produced many cuttings for other aquarists; in fact, 80 % of the coral population in the aquarium originated from cuttings form the tanks of other aquarists.

Owner's comment: "I am specifically interested in marine organisms, whereby the coral reef aquarium affords me the opportunity, to study them close up. After eight years as a freshwater aquarist, I started with a marine aquarium. However, the first aquarium with fishes and some soft corals was not a total success. My luck improved when I joined the SMAC (Siegerländer Meerwasser-Aquarien-Club). Since then I have had good results with the care and fragmentation of soft corals."

General view.   Photo: A. Wegner

Appendix

Geological Time Scale

Geological time	Million years ago	Main evolutionary events
	4800-4500	Formation of the solar system
ARCHEAN	4000	The first life on earth appears
	3800	Oldest known mountains
	3600	Oldest known organisms, cyanobacteria and skeletal metazoans
	2800	Photosynthetic bacteria develop
PROTEROZOIC	2500	Oxygen is released from the first photosynthetic bacteria
	2000	Ozone builds up in the Earth's atmosphere
	1500	The first Eucaryote cells are formed
	1400	The first plants with mitochondria and plastids appear
	700	The first multi cellular organisms
VENDIAN	565-543	Vendian fauna, e.g. from Ediacara
CAMBRIUM	543-505	The formation of many invertebrate phyla ("The Cambrian Explosion"); algae were the dominant plants.
ORDOVICIAN	505-438	The first fishes
SILURIAN	438-408	The first land plants
DEVONIAN	408-360	The first tetrapods
CARBONIFEROUS	360-286	The first reptiles
PERMIAN	286-245	Many life forms become extinct, e.g. the Trilobites
TRIASSIC	245-208	The first dinosaurs and the first mammals appear
JURASSIC	208-144	The dinosaurs are dominating, the first birds appear
CRETACEOUS	144-65	The dinosaurs become extinct
PALEOCENE	65-57	The modern invertebrate groups appear. Photosymbiotic Scleractinian corals appear. Many smaller and moderately sized mammals develop.
EOCENE	57-34	Many of today's orders of mammals, like true primates appear. Many groups become extinct towards the end of the period.
OLIGOCENE	34-23	The world becomes cooler and many groups become extinct. The first monkeys appear.
MILOCENE	23-5	The first Hominids appear
PLIOCENE	5-1,8	Many of the early mammals become extinct. *Australopithecus* and *Homo habilis* appear and become extinct.
HOLOCENE	1,8-present	*Homo erectus* appears and becomes extinct. *Homo sapiens* appears and starts dominating the world.

Overview over Kingdom Animalia
(Based on various sources)

Phylum	Common name	MCRA Volume no.
Placozoa		3
Porifera	Sponges	3
Mesozoa		-
Monoblastoidea		-
Cnidaria	Jellyfish, Corals, Anemones, etc.	2
Ctenophora	Comb Jellies	3
Platyhelminthes	Flat Worms	3
Gnathostomulida	Jaw Worms	3
Nemertea	Ribbon Worms	3
Nematoda	Round Worms	3
Nematomorpha	Horsehair Worms or Hair Worms	-
Gastrotricha		3
Rotifera	Rotifers	3
Acanthocephala		-
Kamptozoa		-
Kinorhyncha	Mud Dragons	3
Priapulida	Proboscis Worms	3
Loricifera	Girdle Wearers	3
Annelida	Segmented Worms	3
Echiurida	Sausage Worms	3
Sipunculida	Peanut Worms	3
Pogonophora		3
Cycliophora		3
Vestimentifera		-
Arthropoda	Joint-Footed Animals	3
Onychophora		-
Tardigrada	Water Bears	3
Pentastomida		-
Mollusca	Molluscs	4
Brachiopoda	Lamp Shells	3
Bryozoa	Moss Animals	3
Phoronida		3
Chaetognatha	Arrow Worms	3
Echinodermata	Echinoderms	4
Hemichordata	Acorn Worms	3
Chordata	Sea Squirts and Vertebrates	4

Scientists frequently have different opinions on the hierarchical division of the animal kingdom, on how the various phyla should be defined and how they relate to each other. We have tried to use a practicable system, which should be neither too conservative nor too radical, but rather reflect a generally acceptable average.

Commensal Pontoniin shrimps and their hosts

Based on BRUCE (1976b; 1977; 1981), and various other sources

Whenever three or more species of a single genus are known to serve as hosts,
we have listed these by the genetic name, as "spp.", only

Shrimp	Host group	Host(s)
Allopontontonia iaini	Sea Urchins	*Salmacis sphaeroides*
Anapontonia denticauda	Stony Corals	*Galaxea fascicularis*
Anchistioides compressus	Sponges	*Haliclona* spp.; *Caminus* spp.
— *willey*	Sponges	
Anchistus custoides	Bivalves	*Atrina vexillum*
— *demani*	Bivalves	*Tridacna* sp.
Cavicheles kempi	Stony Corals	*Acropora* sp.
Conchodytes meleagrinae	Bivalves	*Pinctada margaritifera*
— *tridacnae*	Bivalves	*Tridacna* sp.
Coralliocaris brevirostris	Stony Corals	*Acropora* spp.
— *graminea*	Stony Corals	*Pocillopora danae; P. elongata; Seriatopora hystrix; Stylophora erythraea; Acropora* spp.
— *nudirostris*	Stony Corals	*Acropora* spp.
— *pavonae*	Stony Corals	*Pavona divaricata; P. minor*
— *superba*	Stony Corals	*Pocillopora danae; Acropora* spp.
— *venusta*	Stony Corals	*Acropora* spp.
— *viridis*	Stony Corals	*Acropora* spp.
Dasella herdmaniae	Ascidians	*Herdmania momus*
Dasycaris ceratops	Sea Pens	*Pteroeides bankanense*
— *zanzibarica*	Black Corals	*Cirripathes* spp.
Fennera chacei	Stony Corals	*Pocillopora verrucosa; P. eydouxi*
Hamodactylus aqabai	Octocorals	*Nephthea* spp.; *Lithophyton* sp.
— *broschmai*	Octocorals	*Subergorgia reticulata; Melithea ocracea*
— *noumeae*	Octocorals	*Euplexora flava; Subergorgia reticulata; Pseudapterogorgia pinnata*
Hamopontonia corallicola	Stony Corals	*Fungia actiniformis; Goniopora* spp.
Harpiliopsis depressus	Stony Corals; Hydroids	*Pocillopora* spp.; *Seriatopora angulata; S. hystrix; Stylophora mordax; S. pistillata; Acropora* sp.; *Porites* sp.; *Millepora* sp.
— *spinigera*	Stony Corals	*Pocillopora eydouxi; P. verrucosa; Stylophora* spp.; *Seriatopora hystrix*
— *beaupresii*	Stony Corals	*Pocillopora* spp.; *Seriatopora hystrix; Stylophora* spp.; *Acropora variabilis*
Ischnopontonia lophos	Stony Corals	*Galaxea fascicularis*
Jocaste japonica	Stony Corals	*Pocillopora damicornis; Acropora* spp.
— *lucina*	Stony Corals	*Pocillopora verrucosa; Stylophora* sp.; *Acropora* spp.; *Porites* sp.
Metapontonia fungiacola	Stony Corals	*Fungia* spp.; *Halomitra* sp.; *Hydnophora microconus; Goniastrea pectinata*
Onycocaris amakusensis	Sponges	*Callyspongia* sp.
Palaemonella pottsi	Feather Stars	*Comanthus parvicirrus; Comanthina schlegeli*

Continuation of the list		
Paranchistus pycnodontae	Bivalves	*Onuxodon parvibrachium*
Parapontonia nudirostris	Feather Stars	*Himerometra robustipinna; Pontiometra andersoni*
Paratypton siebenrocki	Stony Corals	*Acropora* spp.
Periclimenaeus arabicus	Sponges	*Callyspongia* spp.; *Acarnus* spp.
— *ardeae*	Sponges	*Jaspis stellata; Asteropus simplex*
— *bidentatus*	Sponges	*Arenochalina flamulata; Spongionella* sp.
— *diplosomatis*	Ascidians	*Diplosoma rayneri*
— *djiboutensis*	Sponges	*Spongia officinalis*
— *gorgonidarum*	Sponges	*Siphonochalina* sp.; *Callyspongia* sp.
— *hecate*	Ascidians	*Diplosoma* sp.; *Didemnum* sp.
— *odontodactylus*	Sponges	*Ircinia fasciculata*
— *ornatus*	Sponges	*Jaspis stellifera*
— *rhodope*	Sponges	*Haliclona* spp.
— *tridentatus*	Ascidians	*Diplosoma* sp.
— *tuamotae*	Sponges	*Acarnus ternatus*
Periclimenes affinis	Feather Stars	*Comathula cratera; Comanthina schlegeli*
— *amboinensis*	Feather Stars	*Comantheria briareus; Comaster bennetti*
— *amymone*	Stony Corals	*Pocillopora damicornis; Stylophora mordax; S. pistillata; Seriatopora hystrix; Acropora* spp.
— *anthophilus*	Anemones	*Condylactis gigantea*
— *attenuatus*	Feather Stars	
— *brevicarpalis*	Anemones	*Stichodactyla* spp.; *Cryptodendrum adhaesivum*
— *brocketti*	Feather Stars	*Comanthina schlegeli*
— *brocki*	Sea Urchins	
— *carinidactylus*	Feather Stars	
— *ceratophthalmus*	Feather Stars	*Himerometra robustipinna*
— *colemani*	Sea Urchins	*Asthenosoma intermedium*
— *commensalis*	Feather Stars	*Comanthus parvicirrus; Comanthina schlegeli; Comaster multifidus*
— *consobrinus*	Stony Corals	*Pocillopora hemprichi; P. damicornis; Seriatopora* sp.
— *cornutus*	Feather Stars	*Himerometra robustipinna*
— *cristimanus*	Sea Urchins	*Echinothrix calamaris; Diadema* spp.
— *difficilis*	Stony Corals	*Porites nigrescens*
— *diversipes*	Stony Corals	*Psammocora togianensis; Pocillopora damicornis; Stylophora erythraea; Seriatopora* sp.; *Acropora tenuis; Acropora variabilis; Montipora circumvallata; M. prolifera; Pavona danai; Porites* spp.; *Galaxea clavus*
— *galene*	Hydroids	*Lytocarpus philippinus; Aglaophenia* sp.
— *gonioporae*	Stony Corals	*Goniopora* spp.; *Lobophyllia* sp.; *Galaxea fascicularis*
— *gorgonicola*	Gorgonians	

– granulimanus	Hydroids	*Lytocarpus philippinus*
– hertwigi	Sea Urchins	
– hirsutus	Sea Urchins	
– holthuisi	Anemones; Jellyfish; Stony Corals	*Dofleini* sp.; *Cassiopea* sp.; *Fungia actiniformis*; *Heliofungoa actiniformis*; *Cataliaphyllia jardinei*; *Goniopora* sp.; *Plerogyra sinuosa*
– hongkongensis	Sea Cucumbers	
– imperator	Nudibranchs; Sea Cucumbers; Fetaher Stars	*Hexabranchus sanguineus*; *Pleurobranchus forskali*; *Stichopus* spp.; *Bohadschia* spp.; *Synapta* spp.
– incertus	Sponges	*Arenochalina flammula*; *Leucetta microraphis*
– inornatus	Anemones	*Radianthus* spp.
– investigatoris	Octocorals	
– kempi	Octocorals	*Lemnalia peristyla*; *Sarcophyton* spp.: *Microspicularia* spp.
– kororensis	Stony Corals	*Fungia actiniformes*
– lanipes	Serpent Stars	*Euryale aspera*
– latipollex	Octocorals	
– lutescens	Stony Corals	*Seriatopora hystrix*; *Acropora* spp.
– madreporae	Stony Corals	*Pocillopora damicornis*; *P. verrucosa*; *Seriatopora hystrix*; *Stylophora mordax*; *S. pistillata*; *Acropora* spp.; *Turbinaria* sp.; *Montipora* sp.
– mahei	Stony Corals	*Pocillopora elongata*; *Seriatopora hystrix*; *Acropora corymbosa*
– magnificus	Stony Corals; Anemones	*Cataliaphyllia jardinei*; *Dofleinia armata*
– niladensis	Octocorals; Hydroids	*Lytocarpus philippinus*
– novaecaledonia	Feather Stars	
– noverca	Sea Stars	
– obscurus	Sponges	
– ornatellus	Anemones	
– ornatus	Anemones	*Radianthus* spp.; *Parasicyonis* spp.
– parasiticus	Sea Stars	
– pedersoni	Anemones	*Bartholomea* spp.; *Lebrunia danae*; *Condylactis gigantea*
– perlucidus	Octocorals	
– psamathae	Octocorals; Hydroids	*Lytocarpus philippinus*
– rathbunae	Anemones	*Stichodactyla helianthus*
– rex	Sea Cucumbers	
– setoensis	Octocorals	
– sinensis	Octocorals	
– soror	Sea Stars	*Acanthaster planci*; *Culcita novaeguineae*; *Echineaster luzonicus*; *Halityle regularis*
– tenuis	Feather Stars	*Himerometra magnipinna*; *Heterometra carinata*
– toloensis	Hydroids	*Lytocarpus philippinus*

Continuation of the list

— *yucatanicus*	Anemones	*Bartholomea* spp.; *Lebrunia danae*; *Condylactis gigantea*
— *zanzibaricus*	Sea Urchins	
Philarius gerlachei	Stony Corals	*Acropora* spp.
— *imperialis*	Stony Corals	*Acropora* spp.
— *lifuensis*	Stony Corals	*Acropora* sp.
Platycaris latirostris	Stony Corals	*Galaxea fascicularis*
Pliopontonia furtiva	Zoanthids; Corallimorpharians	*Rhodactis rhodostoma*
Pontonia katoi	Ascidians	*Polycarpa* spp.; *Cynthia* spp.
— *okai*	Ascidians	*Ascidia* sp.
Pontonides maldivensis	Stony Corals	*Tubastraea micrantha*
— *unciger*	Stony Corals; Black Corals	*Dendrophyllia ijimae; Cirripathes anguinis*
Pontoniopsis comanthi	Feather Stars	*Comatula pectinata; Comatula purpurea*
Stegopontonia commensalis	Sea Urchins	*Diadema setosum*
Typton australis	Sponges	
— *bawii*	Sponges	*Iotrochota baculifera*
— *dentatus*	Sponges	*Reniera* sp.
— *wasini*	Sponges	*Dysidea* sp.
Vir orientalis	Stony Corals	*Pocillopora damicornis; P. verucosa; Stylophora erythraea; S. pistillata; Acropora* spp.
Zenopontonia noverca	Sea Stars	*Pentaceraster* spp.; *Culcita* spp.; *Protoreaster* spp.; *Halityle* spp.

The Encyclopaedia

on

The Modern Coral Reef Aquarium
in five volumes

by
Svein A. Fosså and Alf Jacob Nilsen

Volume 1:
Biological and technical basics – Algae

ISBN 3-928819-29-1

Volumes 4 and **5** in preparation

Volume 2:
Cnidarians (Hydroids, Jellyfish, Pipe Corals, Soft Corals, Gorgonians, Anemones, Stony-Corals etc.)

ISBN 3-928819-23-2

List of References

AHYONG, S. (1997): Phylogenetic analysis of the stomatopoda (Malacostraca). *Jour. Crust. Biol.* **17** (4): 695-715.

ALLDREDGE, A. L. (1972): Abandoned larvacean houses: A unique food source in the pelagic environment. *Science* **177**: 885-887.

ALLEN, G. R. & R. STEENE (1994): *Indo-Pacific Coral Reef Field Guide.* Tropical Reef Research, Singapore.

ANSARI, Z. A. & B. S. INGOLE (1983): Meiofauna from some sandy beaches of Andaman Islands. *Indian J. Mar. Sci.* **12**: 245-246.

ANKEN, R. H. & T. KAPPEL (1992): Ein Stamm, eine Art. Trichoplax adhaerens. *das Aquarium* **26** (6): 27-28.

APELT, G. (1969): Die Symbiose zwischen dem acoelen Turbellar Convoluta convoluta und Diatomen Gattung Licmophora. *Mar. Biol.* **3**: 165-187.

ARCHER, M, S. J. HAND & H. GODTHELP (1991): *Riversleigh.* Reed Books, Kew, Victoria, Australia.

AUGENER, H. (1922): Litorale Polychaeten von Juan Fernandez. In C. SKOTTSBERG (ed.): *The Natural history of Juan Fernandez and Eastern island 3*: 161-218, 1 pl.

AUGENER, H. (1927): Bijdragen tot de Kennis der Fauna van Curaçao. Resultaten eener Reis van Dr. C. J. Van der Horst in 1920. Polychaeten von Curaçao. *K. zoolog. henootschap "Natura artis magistra"* **25**: 39-82.

AX, P. (1963): Relationship and phylogeny of the Turbellaria. In DOUGHERTY (ed.): *The lower Metazoa*: 191-224. University of California Press, USA.

BAENSCH, H. A & H. DEBELIUS (1992): *Meerwasser Atlas*, Band 1. Mergus Verlag, Melle.

BAILEY-BROCK, J. H. (1985): Polychaetes from Fijian Coral Reefs. *Pac. Sci.* **39** (2): 195-220.

BANNER, D. M. & A. H. BANNER (1975): The Alpheid Shrimp of Australia, Part 2: The Genus Synalpheus. *Rec. Aust. Mus.* **29** (12): 267-389.

BANNER, D. M. & A. H. BANNER (1982): The Alpheid Shrimp of Australia, Part 3: The Remaining Alpheids, Principally the Genus Alpheus, and the Family Ogyridae. *Rec. Aust. Mus.* **34** (1): 1-357.

BARNES, R. D. (1964): Tube-building and Feeding in the Chaetopterid Polychaet, Spiochaetopterus oculatus. *Biol. Bull.* **127** (3):397-412.

BARNES, R. D. (1965): Tube-building and feeding in chaetopterid polychaetes. *Biol. Bull. Mar. Biol. Lab.* **127**: 397-412.

BARNES, R. D. (1980): *Invertebrate Zoology.* Saunders College, Philadelphia.

BASSLEER, G. (1996): *Diseases in Marine Aquarium Fish: Causes, Symptoms, Treatment.* Bassleer Biofish, Westmeerbeek, Belgium

BEN-ELIAHU, M. N. & J. DAFNI (1979): A new reef-building Serpulid Genus and Species from the Gulf of Elat and the Red Sea, with notes on other Gregarious Tubeworms from Israeli Waters. *Israel Journal of Zoology* **28**: 199-208.

BERGER, W. H. (1978): Deep-sea carbonate: Pteropod distribution and aragonite compensation depth. *Deep-Sea Research* **25**: 447-452.

BENHAM, W. B. (1927): Polychaeta. *British Antartic TERRA NOVA Expedition. 1910. Nat. Hist. Rep. Zool.* **7**: 47-182, 6 pls.

BERGQUIST, P. R. (1978): *Sponges.* Hutchinson, London.

BERGQUIST, P. R. (1980): A revision of the supraspecific classification of the orders Dictyoceratida, Dendroceratida, and Verongida (class Demospongiae). *New Zealand Journ. Zool.* **7**: 443-503.

BERGQUIST, P. R. (1995): Dictyoceratida, Dendroceratida and Verongida from the new Caledonia Lagoon (Porifera: Demospongiae). *Mem. Queensland Mus.* **38** (1): 1-51.

BERGQUIST, P. R., R. C. CAMBLE & M. R. KERMAN (1990): Scalarane sesterterpenes from Collospongia auris, a new thorectid sponge. *Biochem. System. Ecology* **18** (5): 349-357.

BETZER, P. H., R.H. BYRNE, J. G. ACKER, C. S. LEWIS, R. R. JOLLEY & R. A. FEELY (1984): The oceanic carbonate system: A reassessment of biogenic controls. *Science* **226**: 1074-1077.

BHAUD, M. (1998): Variability of segment number and regeneration in Spiochaetopterus solitarius. Comparison with S. costarum (Polychaeta : Chaetopteridae). *J. Mar. Biol. Ass. U.K.* **78**: 1127-1141.

BHAUD, M., M. C. LASTRA & M. E. PETERSEN (1994): Redescription of piochaetopterus solitarius (Rioa, 1917), with notes on tube structure and comments on the generic status (Polychaeta: Chaetopteridae). *Ophelia* **40**: 115-133.

BLAKE, J. A. (1996a): Family Spionidae Grube, 1850, including a review of the genera and species from California and a revision of the genus Polydora Bosc, 1802. In J. A. BLAKE, B. HILBIG & P. H. SCOTT (eds.): *The Annelida Part 3. Polychaeta: Orbiniidae to Cossuridae. Taxonomic Atlas of the Benthic Fauna of the Santa Maria Basin and Western Santa Barbara Channel*, Vol. 6: 81-223. Santa Barbara Museum of Natural History, Santa Barbara, California.

BLAKE, J. A. (1996b): Family Cirratulidae Ryckholdt, 1851. In J. A. BLAKE, B. HILBIG & P. H. SCOTT (eds.): *The Annelida Part 3. Polychaeta: Orbiniidae to Cossuridae. Taxonomic Atlas of the Benthic Fauna of the Santa Maria Basin and Western Santa Barbara Channel*, Vol. 6: 263-384. Santa Barbara Museum of Natural History, Santa Barbara, California.

BOADEN, P. J. (1975): Anaerobiosis, meiofauna and early metozoan evolution. *Zoologia Scripta* **4**: 21-24.

BOWMAN, T. E. & L. G. ABELE (1982): Classification of the Recent Crustacea, the Systematics, the Fossil Record and Biogeography. In ABELE, L. G.: *The Biology of Crustacea*, Vol. 1. Academic Press, New York.

BRIGGS, D. E. G. (1979): Anomalocaris, the largest known Cambrian arthropod. *Paleontology* **22**: 631-634.

BRIGGS, D. E. G., D. H. ERWIN & F. J. COLLIER (1994): *The Fossils of the Burgess Shale.* Smithsonian Institution Press, Washington and London.

BRUCE, A. J. (1975): Coral reef shrimps and their colour patterns. *Endeavour* **34** (121): 23-27.

BRUCE, A. J. (1976a): Coral Reef Caridea and „Commensalism". *Micronesica* **12** (1): 83-98.

BRUCE, A. J. (1976b): Shrimps and Prawns of Coral Reefs, with special reference to commensalism. In: *Biology and Geology of Coral Reefs* Vol. III. Academic Press, New York.

BRUCE, A. J. (1977): The Hosts of the Coral-Associated Indo-West-Pacific Pontoniine Shrimps. *Atoll Res. Bull.* **205**: 1-19.

BRUCE, A. J. (1980): Pontoniine shrimps from the Great Astrolabe Reef, Fiji. *Pacific Science* **34** (4): 389-400.

BRUCE, A. J. (1981): Pontoniine Shrimps of Heron Island. *Atoll Reas. Bull.* **245**: 1-33.

BRUCE, A. J. (1983): The Pontoniine shrimp fauna of Australia. *Mem. Aust. Mus.* **18**: 195-218.

BRUCE, A. J. (1989): A report on some coral reef shrimps from the Philippine Islands. *Asian Mar. Biol.* (6): 173-192.

BRUSCA & BRUSCA (1990): *Invertebrates.* Sinauer Associates, Sunderland, Massachusetts.

CALDWELL, R. L. & H. DINGLE (1975a): Stomatopods. *Scient. Am.* **234**: 80-89.

CALDWELL, R. L. & H. DINGLE (1975b): Ecology and Evolution of Agonistic Behavior in Stomatopods. *Naturwissenschaften* **62**: 214-222.

CANNON, L. R. G. (1986): *Turbellaria of the World. A guide to Families and Genera.* Queensland Museum, South Brisbane, QLD., Australia.

CASTER. K. E. (1994): Edicarian fossils. *Science* **223**: 1129-1130.

CLOUD, P. & M. F. GLASSNER (1982): The Ediacarian Period and System: metazoa inherit the Earth. *Science* **271**: 783-792.

COLEMAN, N. (1987): *Australia Sea Life south of 30° S.* Doubleday Australia Pty Limited, Sydney, Australia.

COLIN, P. I. (1978): *Caribbean reef invertebrates and plants.* TFH Publ. Inc, Neptun, N. J., USA.

COLIN, P. L. & C. ARNESON (1995): *Tropical Pacific Invertebrates.* Coral Reef Press, California.

COULL, B. C. (1970): Shallow water meiobenthos of the Bermuda platform. *Oecologica* **4**: 325-357.

CRANE, J. (1975): *Fiddler crabs of the world. Ocypodidae: Genus Uca.* Princeton University Press, Princeton, New Jersey, USA.

CROZIER, W. J. (1917): On the pigmentation of a polyclad. *Proc. Am. Acad. Arts Sci.* **52**: 723-730.

DABER, R. & J. HELMS (1985): *Fossils; the oldes treasures that ever lived.* TFH Publ. Inc., Neptun, N. J., USA.

DAVIDSON, A. (1977): *Seafood of South-East Asia.* Federal Publications, Singapore.

DAVIDSON, A. (1981): *Mediterranean Seafood,* 2nd ed. Penguin Cookery Library, Penguin Books Ltd, Harmondsworth, Middlesex.

DARWIN, C. (1859): *On the origin of species by means of natural selection, or the preservation of favoured races in the struggle for life.* John Murray, London.

DARWIN, C. (1968): *The Origin of Species,* 1. edition. Penguine Books Ltd., Harmondsworth, Middlesex, UK.

DARWIN, C. (1979): *The Illustrated Origin of Species.* Abridged and Introduced by Richard E. leakey. Faber and Faber, London, UK.

DARWIN, C. (1980): *The Voyage of the Beagle* (1st edition 1906). J. M. Dent & Sons, Ltd., London, UK.

DAWKINS, R. (1981): The Selfish Gene. Granada Publishing, London, U.K.

DAY, J.H. (1967): *A monograph on the Polychaeta of South Africa. Part 2. Sedentaria.* British Mus. (Nat. Hist.), London: 459-878.

DEBELIUS, H. (1983): *Gepanzerte Meeresritter.* Kernen Verlag, Essen, Germany.

DEEVY, G. B. & A. L. BROOKS (1977): Copepods of the Sargasso Sea off Bermuda: Species composition, and vertical and seasonal distribution between the surface and 2.000 m. *Bull. Mar. Sci.* **27** (2): 256-291.

DELBEEEK, J. C. & J. SRUNG (1994): *The Reef Aquarium,* vol. 1. Ricordea Publishing, Miami, USA.

DENDEY, A. (1889): Report on a second collection of sponges from the Gulf of Manaar. *Annls. Mag. Nat. Hist.* **6** (3): 73-99.

DENDEY, A. (1922): Report on the Sigmatotetraxonida collected by H.M.S. «Sealark» in the Indian Ocean. *Transl. Linnean Soc. London* **18**: 1-164.

DEVANEY, D. M. & L. G. ELDREDGE (1977): *Reef and Shore Fauna of Hawaii.* Bernice P. Bishop Museum Special Publication **64** (1). Bishop Museum Press, Honolulu, Hawaii, USA.

DÖRJES, J. (1968): Die Acoela (Turbellaria) der deutschen Nordseeküste und ein neues System der Ordnung. *Zeitschr. Zoolog. Syst. Evolutionsforschung* **6**: 56-452.

DOUGHERTY, E. C. (1963): *The Lower Metazoa - Comparative Biology and Phylogeny.* University of California Press, Berkeley, USA.

DÜRBAUM, J. (1997): Copepoden - ein ideales Fischfutter. *DATZ* **50** (11): 726-729.

DWORSCHAK, P. C. & W. HÖDL (1994): Zur Biologie von Maulwurfskrebsen. In KOLAR, E. & K. KOLAR: *Internationales Symposion für Vivaristik 1994,* Dokumentation: 19-25.

EIBYE-JACOBSON, D. & C. NIELSEN (1997): Point of view. The rearticulation of annelids. Zoologica Scripta **25**: 275-282.

EHLERS, E. (1901): Die Polychaeten des magellanischen und chillenischen Strandes. Ein faunistische Versuch. Festschrift zur Feier 150-Jahrigen Bestehens des könglichen Gesellschaft de Wissenschaften zu Göttingen. *Abh. Math.-Phys. Berlin,* Wiedmannsche Buchhandlung: 1-232.

EHLERS, E. (1907): Neuseeländdische Anneliden II. *Abh. K. Ges. wiss Göttingen (Math.-Phys. Kl.), n. F.* **5** (4):1-31.

EHLERS, U. (1985): The basic organisation of the Platyhelminthes. *Hydrobiologia* **305**: 21-26.

EMIG, C. C. (1977): The systematics and evolution of the Phylum Phoronida. *Zeitschr. Zool. Syst. Evolutionsforschung* **12** (2): 128-151.

ERHARD, H. & H. MOOSLEITNER (1995): *Meerwasser Atlas,* Band 2 & 3. Mergus Verlag, Melle, Germany.

FAUBEL, A. (1983): The Polycladida, Turbellaria. Proposal and establishment of a new system. Part I. The Acotylea. *Mtlg. Hamburg. Zool. Mus.* **80**: 17-121.

FAUBEL, A. (1984): The Polycladida, Turbellaria. Proposal and establishment of a new system. Part II. The Cotylea. Mtlg. Hamburg. Zool. Mus. **81**: 189-259.

FAUCHALD, K. (1977): The Polychaete Worms. Definitions and Keys to the Orders, Families and Genera. *Nat. Hist. Mus. Los Angeles County, Science Series* **28**:1-190.

FAUCHALD, K. (1992a): A review of the genus Eunice (Polychaeta: Eunicidae) based upon type material. *Smithson. Contrib. Zool.* **523**: 1-422.

FAUCHALD, K. (1992b): Review of the types of Palola (Eunicidae: Polychaeta). *J. Nat. Hist.* **26**: 1177-1225.

FAUCHAULD, K. & P.A. JUMARS (1979): The diet of worms: a study of polychaet feeding guilds. *Oceanogr. Mar. Biol., Ann. Rev.* **17**:193-284.

FAUCHALD, K. & G. ROUSE (1997): Polychaete systematics: Past and present. Zoologica Scripta **26**: 71-138.

FENTON, T. D. & M. A. FENTON (1989): *The Fossil Book; A Record of Prehistoric Life.* Doubleday, N.Y., USA.

FIEGE, D., & H. A. TEN HOVE (1999): Redescription of Spirobranchus gaymardi (Quatrefages, 1866). *Zool. J. Linn. Soc.* **126**: 355-364.

FORTEY, P. L. (red.) (1991): *The evolving Biosfere. Chance, Change & Challenge.* BMNH & Cambridge University Press, London. U.K.

FOSSÀ, S. A. (1995): Schritte der Zukunft - zu einer naturnahen Korallenriff-Aquaristik. In *3. Internationales Meerwasser-Symposium* VDA, ZZF & Tierpark Bochum, Lünen, germany: 25-31.

FOSSÀ, S. A. (1996): Korallenriff-Aquaristik: Vergangenheit - Gegenwart - Zukunft. In E. KOLAR & K. KOLAR (eds.): *Internationales Symposion für Vivaristik - 1995 Dokumentation,* Wiener Volksbildungswerk, Verband für Freizeit und Kultur, Vienna: 13-18

FOSSÀ, S. A. & A. J. NILSEN (1996a): *Korallenriff-Aquarium,* Band 5. Birgit Schmettkamp Verlag, Bornheim, Germany.

FOSSÀ, S. A & A. J. NILSEN (1996b): *The Modern Coral Reef Aquarium,* vol. 1. Birgit Schmettkamp Verlag, Bornheim, Germany.

FOSSÀ, S.A & A. J. NILSEN (1998a): *The Modern Coral Reef Aquarium,* vol. 2. Birgit Schmettkamp Verlag, Bornheim, Germany.

FOSSÀ, S. A. & A. J. NILSEN (1998b): *Korallenriff-Aquarium,* Band 6. Birgit Schmettkamp Verlag, Bornheim, Germany.

FRANK, U. & H. A. TEN HOVE (1992): In Vitro Exposure of Spirobranchus giganteus and S. tetraceros (Polychaeta, Serpulidae) to various turbidities; Branchial Morphologies and expression of Filtering Strategies. *Oebalia,* vol. XVIII, N.S.: 45-52.

FRICKHINGER, K. A. (1991): *Fossilien Atlas.* Mergus Verlag, Melle, Germany.

FUNCH, P. & R. M. KRISTENSEN (1995): Cycliophora is a new phylum with affinities to Entoprocta and Ectoprocta. *Nature* **378** (6558): 711-714.

GAILL, F. & S. HUNT (1988): Tubes. *Microfauna Mar.* **4**: 61-70.

GELLINGER-TUNZE, B. (1995): Beobachtungen bei der Nachzucht der Blutstriemen-Putzergarnele. *das Aquarium* **29** (8): 32-33.

GEORGE, D. & J. GEORGE (1979): *Marine life.* Harrap, London, UK.

GIBBS, P. E. (1971): The Polychaet fauna of the Solomon Islands. *Bull. British Mus. (Nat. Hist.), Zool.* **21** (5):101-111.

GIBSON, R. (1973): A New Littoral Hoplonemertean (Divanella evelinae, Gen. Et Sp. Nov.) from the Coast of Brazil. *Bull. Mar. Sci.* **23** (4): 793-810.

GIBSON, R. (1974a): Two species of Baseodiscus (Heteronemertea) from Jidda in the Red Sea. *Zool. Anz.* **192**: 255-270.

GIBSON, R. (1974b): Occurrence of the Heteronemertean Gorgonorhynchus bermudensis Wheeler, 1940, in Floridan Waters. *Bull. Mar. Sci.* **24** (3):473-492.

GIBSON, R. (1979a): Nemerteans of the Great Barrier Reef 1. Anopla Palaeonemertea. *Zool. J. Linnean Soc.* **65** (4): 305-337.

GIBSON, R. (1979b): Nemerteans of the Great Barrier Reef 2. Anopla Heteronemertea (Baseodiscidae). *Zool. J. Linnean Soc.* **66**: 137-160.

GIBSON, R. (1981a): Nemerteans of the Great Barrier Reef 3. Anopla Heteronemertea (Lineidae). *Zool. J. Linnean Soc.* **71**: 171-235.

GIBSON, R. (1981b): Nemerteans of the Great Barrier Reef 3. Anopla Heteronemertea (Valenciniidae). *Zool. J. Linnean Soc.* **72**: 165-174.

GIBSON, R. (1982): Nemerteans of the Great Barrier Reef 5. Enopla Hoplonemertea (Monostilifera). *Zool. J. Linnean Soc.* **75**: 269-296.

GIBSON, R. (1983): Nemerteans of the Great Barrier Reef 6. Enopla Hoplonemertea (Polystilifera: Reptantia). *Zool. J. Linnean Soc.* **78**: 73-104.

GIBSON, R. (1986): The Macrobenthic Nemertean Fauna of Hong Kong. *Proc. Second Intern. Mar. Biol. Workshop: The Marine Flora and Fauna of Hong Kong and Southern China*, Hong Kong. (Ed. B. Morton). Hong Kong University Press: 33-212.

GIBSON, R. (1990): The macrobenthic nemertean fauna of the Albany region, western Australia. In WELLS, F. E., I. D. WALKER, H. KIRKMAN & R. LETHBRIDGE: *Proc. Thrid Intern. Mar. Biol. Workshop: The Marine Flora and Fauna of Albany, Western Australia*. Western Australian Museum, Perth. Vol. 1: 89-194.

GIBSON, R. (1993): Phylum Nemertea - Ribbon Worms. In P. MATHER & I. BENNETT (eds.): *A Coral Reef Handbook*, 3rd. Edition: 84-87, Surrey Beatty & Sons, Chipping Norton (Australian Coral Reef Society).

GIBSON, R. (1995): Nemertean genera and species of the world: an annotated checklist of original names and description citations, synonyms, current taxonomy status, habitats and recorded zoogeographic distribution. *J. Nat. Hist.* **29**: 271-562.

GIBSON, R. & P. SUNDBERG (1992): Three New Nemerteans from Hong Kong. In B. MORTON (ed.): *The Marine Flora and Fauna of Hong Kong and Southern China III*. Proceedings of the Fourth International Marine Biological Workshop: The Marine Flora and Fauna of Hong Kong and Southern China, Hong Kong: 97-129. Hong Kong University Press

GIBSON, R., J. MOORE & F. B. CRANDALL (1982): A new semi-terrestrial nemertean from California. *J. Zool. Lond.* **196**: 463-474.

GOLDSCHMIDT, T. (1996): *Darwin's Dreampond*. MIT Press, Cambridge, Mass., USA.

GONZÁLEZ, J. A. (1995): *Crustáceos Decápodos de las Islas Canarias*. Publicaciones Turquesa, Santa Cruz de Tenerife.

GORE, R. (1993): The Cambrian Period - Explosion of Life. *National Geographic*, October 1993: 120-136.

GORE, R. H. & L. G. ABELE (1976): Shallow Water Porcelain Crabs from the Pacific Coast of Panama and Adjacent Caribbean Waters (Crustacea: Anomura: Porcellanidae). *Smiths. Contr. Zool.* **237**: 1-30.

GOSLINER, T. M., D. W. BEHRENS & G. C. WILLIAMS (1996): *Coral Reef Animals of the Indo-Pacific*. Sea Challengers, Monterey, California, USA.

GOULD, S. J. (1980): *Ever since Darwin*. Penguin Books Ltd., Harmondsworth, Middlesex, UK.

GOULD, S. J. (1991): *Wonderful Life: The Burgess Shale and the Nature of History*. W.W. Norton, N.Y., USA.

GOULD, S. J. (ed.) (1993): *The book of Life*. Ebury Hutchingson, London, UK.

GRASSLE, J. F. & J. P. GRASSLE (1974): Opportunistic life histories and geneetic systems in marine bentic polychaets. *J. Mar. Res.* **32** (2): 253-284.

GRASSLE, J. P. & J. F. GRASSLE (1976): Sibling species in the marine pollution indicator Capitella (Polychaeta). *Science* **192**: 567-569.

GRAY, J. E. (1870): Notes on the arrangements of sponges, with descriptions of some new genera. *Proc. Zool. Soc. London* **1867**: 492-558.

GRAVIER, C. (1906): Contribution à l'étude des annélides polychètes de la Mer rouge. *Nouv. Arch. Mus. d'Hist. nat., Paris, Serie 4* **8**: 123-236, pls 1-8.

GRAVIER, C. (1908): *Ibid.* **10**: 67-168.

GRELL, K. G. (1971): Trichoplax adhaerens F.S. Schulze und die Entstehung der Metazoen. *Naturw. Rundsch.* **42**: 160-161.

GRELL, K. G. (1972): Eibildung und Furchung von Trichoplax adhaerens F.S. Schulze. *Z. Morph. Tiere* **73**:297-314.

GRELL, K. G. & M. BENWITZ (1971): Die Ultrastruktur von Trichoplax adhaerens F.S. Schulze. *Cytobiologie* **4**: 216-240.

GRIFFIN, D. J. G. (1966): A review of the Australian Majid Spider Crabs (Crustacea, Brachyura). *Austr. Zoologist* **13** (3): 259-298.

GROSS, G. (1995): Ein Räuber im Riffaquarium. *das Aquarium* **29** (10): 27.

GRUBE, A. E. (1862): Mittheilungen über die Serpulen, mit besonderer Berücksichtigung ihrer Deckel. *Jahresb. Abh. Schles. Ges. Breslau* **39**: 53-69, 5 figs.

GRUBE, A. E. (1863): Beschreibung neuer oder wenig bekannter Anneliden. *Arch. Naturgeschichte, Berlin* **29**: 37-69.

GRUBE, A. E. (1878): Annulata Semperiana. beitrage zur Kenntniss der Annelidenfauna der Philippinen nach von Herrn Prof. Semper mitgebrachten Sammlungen. *Mem. l'Acad. Imp. Sc. St Petersburg, VII Serie* **25**: 1-300.

GUZMÁN, H. M., V. L. OBANDO & J. CORTÉS (1987): Meiofaunba associated with a Pacific Coral Reef in Costa Rica. *Coral Reefs* **6** (2):107-112.

HAIG, J. (1965): The Porcellanidae (Crustacea, Anomura) of Western Australia with Descriptions of Four New Australian Species. *J. Roy. Soc. West. Aust.* **48** (4): 97-118.

HAIG, J. (1979): Expedition Rumphius II (1975), Crustaces Parasites, Commensaux, etc. (Th. Monod et R. Steene. ed.) V. Porcellanidae (Crustacea, Decapoda, Anomura). *Bull. Mus. Nat. d'Hist. Nat., Paris 4-ère series*, 1, 1979, section 1, no. 1: 119-136.

HAMMER, W. M., L. P. MADIN, A. L. AALLDREDGE, R. W. GILMER & P. P. HAMMER (1975): Underwater observations of gelatinous zooplankton: Sampling problems, feeding biology and behaviour. *Limn. Oceanogr.* **20**: 907-917.

HANLEY, R. (1986): Co-operative effort in a new species of tube-dwelling Worm, Eunice metatropos (Polychaeta:Eunicidae). *The Beagle* **3** (1): 215-221.

HARDING, G. C. H. (1974): The food of deep-sea copepods. *J. Mar. Biol. Assoc. UK.* **54** (1): 141-155.

HARTMANN, W. D. (1982): Porifera. In S. P. PARKER (ed.): *Synopsis and Classification of Living Organisms*: 640-666. McGrawe-Hill, New York, USA.

HAY, M. E., J. R. PAWLIK, J. EMMET DUFFY & W. FENICAL (1989): Seaweed-herbivore-predator interactions: host-plant specialization reduces predation on small herbivores. *Oecologia* **81**: 418-427.

HAYWARD, P. J. & J. S. RYLAND (1996): *Handbook of the Marine Fauna of North-West Europe*. Oxford University Press, Oxford, UK.

HAYWARD, P., T. NELSON-SMITH & C. SHIELDS (1996): *Collins Pocket Guide. Sea Shore of Britain and Northern Europe*. Harper Collins Publishers, London, UK.

HENTSCHEL (1913): Kiesel und Hornschwämme der Aru und Kei-Inseln. *Senkenberg. Naturf. Gesellsch.* **34**: 295-448.

HIGGINS, R. P. & R. M. KRISTENSEN (1986): New Loricifera from southeastern Unated States coastal waters. *Smiths. Contr. Zool.* **438**: 1-70.

HILBIG, B. (1995): Family Dorvilleidae Chamberlin, 1919. 341-364 in J. A. BLAKE, B. HILBIG & P. H. SCOTT (eds.): *The Annelida Part 2. Polychaeta: Phyllodocida (Syllidae and scale-bearing families), Amphinomida, and Eunicida. Taxonomic Atlas of the Benthic Fauna of the Santa Maria Basin and Western Santa Barbara Channel*, Vol. 5: 341-364. Santa Barbara Museum of Natural History, Santa Barbara, California.

HOFF, F. H. & T. W. SNELL (1989): *Plankton culture manual. 2.* edition. Florida Aqua Farms, Florida, USA.

HOLTHUIS, L. B. (1955): The Recent Genera of Caridean and Stenopodidean Shrimps (Class Crustacea, Order Decapoda, Supersection Natantia) with Keys for their Determination. *Zool. Verhanded, Leiden* **26**: 3-153.

HOLTHUIS, L. B. (1980): FAO Species Catalogue, Vol. 1; Shrimps and Prawns of the World, An Annotated Catalogue of Species of Interest to Fisheries. *FAO Fisheries Synopses 125*, Vol. 1: 1-261.

HOLTHUIS, L. B. (1991): FAO Species Catalogue, Vol. 13; Marine Lobsters of the World, An Annotated and Illustrated Catalogue of Species of Interest to Fisheries Known to Date. *FAO Fisheries Synopses 125*, Vol. 13: 1-261.

HOLTHUIS, L. B. (1993): *The recent genera of the Caridean and Stenopodidean shrimps (Crustacea, Decapoda): with an appendixon the order Amphionidacea*. In C. H. J. M. FRANSEN & C. VAN ACHTERBERG (eds.), Nationaal Natuurhistorisch Museum, Leiden.

HOOPER, J. N. A. (1986): Revision of the marine sponge genus Axos Gray (Demospongiae : Axinellida) from North-West Australia. *The Beagle 3* (1): 167-189.

HORSTMANN, T. & J. VENZLAFF (1996): Neues zur Haltung von Landeinsiedlerkrebsen. *DATZ 49* (1): 32-34.

HOVE, H. A., TEN (1988): Bloemen in zee. *Dieren 4*: 116-121.

HOVE, H. A. TEN (1994): Serpulidae (Annelida:Polychaeta) from the Seychelles and Amirante Islands. In: Oceanic reefs of the Seychelles. *Cruise reports Neth. Indian Ocean Program, II* (ed. J. VAN DER LAND), Nat. Nat. Mus. Leiden: 107-116, 1 table.

HOVE, H. A. TEN & P. VAN DEN HURK (1993): A review of Recent and fossile serpulid «reefs»; actuopalaeontology and the «Upper Malm» serpulid limestones in NW Germany. *Geologie en Mijnbouw 72*: 23-67.

HUMANN, P. (1994): *Reef Creatures*, 4. edition. New World Publications, Inc., Florida, USA.

HUTCHINGS, P. & C. GLASBY (1988): The Amphitritinae (Polychaeta: Terebellidae) from Australia. *Rec. Aust. Mus. 40*: 1-60.

HUTCHINGS, P. & C. J. GLASBY (1995): Description of the widely reported terebellid polychaetes Loimia medusa (Savigny) and Amphitrite rubra (Risso). *Mtlg. Hamb. Zool. Mus. Inst. 92*: 149-154.

IMAJIMA, M., & H. A. TEN HOVE (1984): Serpulinae (Annelida, Polychaeta) from the Truk Islands, Ponape and Majuro Atoll, with some other new Indo-Pacific ecords. *Proc. Jap. Soc. syst. Zool. 27*: 35-66, 6 figs, 4 maps, 1 tab.

INGLE, R. (1997): *Crayfish, Lobsters and Crabs of Europe*. Chapmann & Hall, London, UK.

IWATA, F. (1954): Some nemerteans from the coasts of the Kii Peninsula. *Publ. Seto Mar. Biol. Lab. 4*: 33-42.

JAUBERT, J. (1989): An integrated nitrifying-denitrifying biological system capable of purifying sea water in a closed circuit aquarium. *Bull. Inst. Oceanogr., Monaco*, no spécial 5: 101-106

JÄGERSTEIN, G. (1955): On the early phylogeny of the Metazoa. *Zool. Bidr. Uppsala 30* :321-354.

JENNINGS, K. A. & L. J. NEWMAN (1996a): Four new stylochid flatworms (Platyhelminthes, Polycladida) associated with commercial oysters from Moreton Bay, southeast Queensland, Australia. *Raffl. Bull. Zool. 44* (2): 493-508.

JENNINGS, K. A. & L. J. NEWMAN (1996b): Two new stylochid flatworms (Platyhelminthes, Polycladida) from the Great Barrier Reef, Australia. *Raffl. Bull. Zool. 44*: 135-142.

JOHANSON, D. & M. EDEY (1981): *Lucy*. Simon & Schuster, N.Y., USA.

JUMARS, P. A. (1974): A generic revision of the Dorvilleidae (Polychaeta) with six new species from the deep North Pacific. *J. Linn. Soc. London, Zool. 54*:101-135.

JONES, D. & G. MORGAN (1994): *A Field Guide to the Crustaceans of Australian Waters*. Reed, Chatswood, NSW, Australien.

JUAN, A. S. (1998): The Lurker's Guide to Stomatopods. *http://www.blueboard.com/mantis/* (1998, September).

KASTL, J. (1994): Überraschungen aus lebende Steinen. *das Aquarium 28* (3): 25.

KENSLEY, B. & M. SCHOTTE (1989): *Guide to the marine isopod crustaceans of the Caribbean*. Smithsonian Institution Press, Washington D.C., USA.

KERSTITCH, A. (1989): *Sea of Cortez Marine Invertebrates - A Guide for the Pacific Coast, Mexico to Equator*. Sea Challengers, Monterey, California, USA.

KING, P. E. (1974): *British Sea Spiders*. Academic Press, London and New York, USA.

KIRKPATRIC, R. (1900): On the marine fauna of Christmas Island (Indian Ocean). IV. On the sponges of Christmas Island. *Proc. Zool. Soc. London 1*: 127-141.

KNIGHT-JONES, P. (1994): Two new species of Megalomma (Sabellidae) from Sinai and New Zealand with redescription of some types and a new genus. Fifth International Polychaet Conference at Qindaq, China. REISH & PEI-YUAN QIAN (eds.). *Bull. Mar. Sci. 60* (2): 313-323.

KNIGHT-JONES, P. & T. H. PERKINS (1998): A revision of Sabella, Bispira and Stylomma (Polychaeta:Sabellidae). *Zool. J. Linnean Soc. 123*: 385-467.

KNIGHT-JONES, P., E. W. KNIGHT-JONES & Z. ERGEN (1991): Sabelliform polychaets, mostly from Turkey's Aegan coast. *J. Nat. Hist. 25*: 837-858.

KRAUL, S. & A. NELSON (1986): The Life Cycle of the Harlequin Shrimp. *Freshw. Mar. Aq. Mag. 9* (9): 28-30.

KRISTENSEN, R. M (1983): Loricifera, a new phylum with ashelminthes characters from the meiobenthos. *Zool. Syst. Evolutf. 21*: 163-180.

KRISTENSEN, R. M. (1984): On the biology of Wingstrandarctus corallinus nov. gen. et. spec., with notes on the symbiotic bacteria in the subfamily Florarctinae (Arthrotardigrada). *Vitensk. Meddr. Dansk naturh. Foren. 145*: 201-218.

KRISTENSEN, R. M. (1989): . Bjørnedyr er sjove dyr. *Dyr i Natur og Museum* (1): 2-6.

KRISTENSEN, R. M. & R. P. HIGGINS (1989): Marine Tardigrada from the Southeastern United States Coastal Waters, I. Paradoxipus orzeliscoides n.gen., n. sp. (Arthrotardigrada: Halechiniscidae).*Trans. Am. Microsc. Soc. 108* (3): 262-282.

KRISTENSEN, R. M. & A. NØRREVANG (1978): On the Fine Structure of Valvognathia pogonostoma gen et. sp.n. (Gnathostomulida, Onychognathidae) with Special Reference to the Jaw Apparatus. *Biologica Scripta 7*: 179-186.

KRISTENSEN, R. M. & Y. SHIRAYAMA (1988): Pliciloricus hadalis (Pliloricidac) a new loriciferan species collected from the Izu-Ogasawara Trench, Western Pacific. *Zool Sci. 5*: 875-881.

KRISTENSEN, R. M. & W. STERRER (1986): In STERRER, W. (ed.) *Marine Fauna and Flora of Bermuda*: 265-268.

KUDENOV, J. D. (1995): Family Amphinomidae Lamarck, 1818. In J. A. BLAKE, B. HILBIG & P. H. SCOTT (eds.): The Annelida Part 2. Polychaeta: Phyllodocida (Syllidae and scale-bearing families), Amphinomida, and Eunicida. *Taxonomic Atlas of the Benthic Fauna of the Santa Maria Basin and Western Santa Barbara Channel*, Vol. 5: 207-215. Santa Barbara Museum of Natural History, Santa Barbara, California, USA.

KUDENOV, J. D. & L. H. HARRIS (1995): Family Syllidae Grube, 1850. In J. A. BLAKE, B. HILBIG & P. H. SCOTT (eds.): The Annelida Part 2. Polychaeta: Phyllodocida (Syllidae and scale-bearing families), Amphinomida, and Eunicida. *Taxonomic Atlas of the Benthic Fauna of the Santa Maria Basin and Western Santa Barbara Channel*, Vol. 5: 1-97. Santa Barbara Museum of Natural History, Santa Barbara, California, USA.

LADILAW, F. F. (1902): The marine Turbellaria, with an account of the anatomy of some of the species. In: *The Fauna and Geography of the Maldive and Laccadive Archipelago*. I (3): 282-313.

LAMM, D. R. (1988): Culturing copepods: A food for marine fish larvae. *Freshw. Mar. Aq. Mag. 11* (10): 98-99, 102-104, 110.

LAMPRELL, K. & T. WHITEHEAD (1992): *Bivalves of Australia*, Vol. 1, Crawford House Press; Bathurst, NSW, Australia.

LANDMAN, N. H., J. K. COCHRAN, D. M. RYE, K. TANABE & J. M. ARNOLD (1994): Early life history of evidence from isotopic analyses of aquarium-reared specimens. *Paleobiology 20* (1):40-51.

LANZAVECCHIA, G., R. VALVASSORI & M. D. CANDIO CARNEVALI (eds.) (1995): *Body cavities: function and phylogeny. Selected Symposia and Monographs*, U.Z.I., 8, Mucchi Modene, Italy.

LAVENS, P. & P. SORGELOS (eds.) (1996): Manual on the production and use of live food for aquaculture. *FAO Fisheries Technical Paper*. No. 361. FAO, Rom, Italy.

LAUBENFELS, M. W. DE (1954): The Sponges of the West central Pacific. *Oregon State Monographs 7*: 4-306.

LEVETZOV, K. G. (1943): Zur Biologie und Verdauungsphysiologie der Polycladen Turbellarien. *Zoo. Anz. 141*: 189-196.

LEVI, C. (1973): Systématique de la classe des demospongiaria (Démosponges). In P. BRIEN, C. LEVI, M. SARA, O. TUZET & J. VACELET (eds.): *Traité de Zoologie. Anatomie, Systématique, Biologie. III. Spongiaries*: 577-631. Masson et Cie, Paris, France.

LEVINE, D. M. & O. J. BLANCHARD, Jr. (1980): Acclimation of two shrimps of the genus Periclimenes to sea anemones. *Bull. Mar. Sci. 30* (2): 460-466.

LIMBAUGH, C., H. PEDERSON & F. A. CHACE, Jr. (1961): Shrimps that clean fishes. *Bull. Mar. Sci. Gulf Carib.* (11): 237-257.

LING, S.-W. (1977): *Aquaculture in Southeast Asia - A Historical Overview.* Washington Sea Grant Publication. University of Washington Press, Seattle, USA.

LITVAITIS, M. K. & K. RHODE (1999): A molecular test of platyhelminth phylogeny: inferences from partial 28S rDNA sequences. *Invertebrate Biology* 118 (1): 42-56.

LITTLEWOOD, D. T. J., K. RHODE & K. A. CLOUGH (1999): The interrelationships of all major groups of Platyhelminthes: phylogenetic evidence from morphology and molecules. *Biol. J. Linnean Soc.* 66: 75-114.

MACGNITIE, G. E. (1939): The method of feeding of Chaetopterus. *Bio. Bull.* 77: 115-118.

MADDOCKS, R. R. (1987): An ostracode commensal of an ophiuroid and other new species of Pontocypria (Pontocopida: Cypridacea). *Jour. Crust. Biol.* (7): 727-737.

MANNING, R. B. (1980): The superfamilies, families, and genera of recent stomatopod Crustacea, with diagnosis of six new families. *Biol. Soc. Washington* 93 (2): 362-372.

MANNING, R. B. (1995): Stomatopod Crustacea of Vietnam. *Crustacean Research*, special issue No. 4, Carcinological Society of Japan.

MANTON, S. M. (1977): *The Arthropoda: Habits, Functional Morphology and Evolution.* Oxford University Press, London, UK.

MARENZELLER, E. VON (1884): Sudjapanische Anneliden II. *Akad. Wiss. Wien. Denkschr.* 49:197-224.

MARGULIS, L. & K. V. SCHWARTZ (1998): *Five Kingdoms: An Illustrated Guide to the Phyla of Life on Earth*, 3rd ed. W. H. Freeman & Co.

MARSDEN, J. R. (1962): A Coral-eating Polychaete. *Nature* 193 (4815): 598.

MARSH, L. & S. SLACK-SMITH (1986): *Sea Stingers.* Western Australian Museum, Perth, Australia.

MARSHALL, N. B. (1979): *Developments in Deep-Sea Biology.* Blandford Press, Poole, Dorset.

MARTIN, N. & M. ANCTIL (1984): Luminescence control in the tubeworm Chaetopterus variopedatus: role of nerve cord and photogenic gland. *Biol. Bull. Mar. Biol. Labor.* 166: 583-593.

MATHER, P. & I. BENNETT (1993): *A Coral Reef Handbook*, 3. edition. Surrey Beatty & Sons Pty. Ltd., Chipping Norton, NSW, Australia.

McHUGH, D. (1997): Molecular evidence that echiurans and pogonophorans are derived annelids. *Proc. Nat. Acad. Sci.* 94: 8006-8009.

McLAUGHKIN, P. A. (1980): *Comparative Morphology of Recent Crustacea.* Freeman & Co., San Francisco, USA.

McLAUGHLIN, P. A. & R. LEMAITRE (1993): A review of the hermit crab genus Paguritta (Decapoda: Anomura: Paguridae) with descriptions of three new species. *Raffles Bull. Zool.* 41 (1): 1-29.

McMENAMIN, M. A. S. (1998): *The Garden of Edicara.* Columbia University Press, N.Y., USA.

MEBS, D. (1989): *Gifte im Riff.* Wissenschaftliche Verlagsgesellschaft mbH, Stuttgart, germany.

MEBS, D. (1992): *Gifttiere.* Wissenschaftliche Verlagsgesellschaft mbH, Stuttgart, Germany.

MELHORN, B., H. MELHORN & G. SCHMAL (1992): *Gesundheit für Zierfische - Parasiten erkennen und bekämpfen.* Springer-Verlag, Berlin, Germany.

MEINKOTH, N. A. (1994): *National Audubon Society Field Guide to North American Seashore Creatures*, 7th printing. Alfred A. Knopf, Inc., New York, USA.

MICHIELS, N. K. & L. J. NEWMAN (1998): Sex and violence in hermaphrodites. *Nature* 391: 647.

MIKKELSEN, T. (1982): *Eventyret om Dolkhalerne.* Forlaget Rhodos, Danmark.

MONTICELLI, F. S. (1897): Treptoplax reptans. *Mtlg. zool. Stat. Naepel* 12: 444-462.

MOORE, R. C.(1969): *Treatise on Invertebrate Paleontology. Pt. R. Arthropoda 4.* Vol. 1 & 2. Geological Society of America and Univ. of Kansas Press, USA.

MORGAN, G. J. (1987): Hermit Crabs (Decapoda: Anomura:Coenobitidae, Diogenidae, Paguridae) of Darwin and Port Essington, Northern Australia. *Beagle* 4 (1): 165-186.

NESIS, K. N. (1987): *Cephalopods of the World.* TFH Publications, Inc., Neptun, N. J., USA.

NEWMAN, L. J. & C. ANDERSON (1997): A new polyclad flatworm from the Maldives. *J. South Asian Nat. His.* 2: 237-245.

NEWMAN, L. J. & L. R. G. CANNON (1994a): Biodiversity of Tropical Polyclad flatworms from the Great Barrier Reef, Australia. *Mem. Queensland Mus.* 36 (1): 159-163.

NEWMAN, L. J. & L. R. G. CANNON (1994b): Pseudoceros and Pseudobiceros (Platyhelminthes, Polycladida, Pseudocerotidae) from eastern Australia and Papua New Guinea. *Mem. Queensland Mus.* 37 (1): 205-266.

NEWMAN, L. J. & L. R. G. CANNON (1995): The importance of the fixation of colour, pattern and form in tropical Pseudocerotidae (Platyhelminthes, Polycladida). *Hydrobiologia* 305: 141-143.

NEWMAN, L. J. & L. R. G. CANNON (1996a): New pseudocerotid genera (Platyhelminthes, Polycladida) from Australasian coral reefs. *J. Nat. Hist.* 30: 1425-1441.

NEWMAN, L. J. & L. R. G. CANNON (1996b): Bulaceros, new genus and Tytthosoceros, new genus (Platyhelminthes, Polycladida, Pseudocerotidae) from the Great Barrier Reef, Australia and eastern Papua New Guinea. *Raffles Bull. Zool.* 44: 479-492.

NEWMAN, L. J. & L. R.G. CANNON (1997): Nine new Pseudoceros (Platyhelminthes, Polycladida, Pseudocerotidae) from the Indo-Pacific. *Raffles Bull. Zool.* 45: 341-368.

NEWMAN, L. J. & L. R. G. CANNON (1998): Pseudoceros (Platyhelminthes, Polycladida) from the Indo-Pacific with twelve new species from Australia and Papua New Guinea. *Raffles Bull. Zool.* 46: 293-323.

NEWMAN, L. J, L. R. G. CANNON & H. GOVAN (1993): Stylochus (Imogene) matatasi n. sp. (Platyhelminthes, Polycladida): Pest of culture giant clams and pearl oysters from Solomon Islands. *Hydrobiologia* 257: 185-189.

NEWMAN, L. J., L. R. G. CANNON & D. J. BRUNCKHORST (1994): A new polyclad flatworm which mimics a phyllidiid nudibranch. *Zool. J. Linnean Soc.* 110: 19-25.

NICOL, E. A. T. (1931): The feeding mechanism, formation of the tube, and physiology of digestion in Sabella pavonina. *Trans. Royal Soc. Edinburg* 56 (1930): 537-598, 2 pls.

NIELSEN, C. (1997): *Animal Evolution: Interrelationships of the Living Phyla.* Oxford University Press, UK.

NIELSEN, C. (1998): Sequences lead to tree of worms. *Nature* 392 (5):25-26.

NILSEN, A. J. (1988): Ein Juvel im Meerwasser-Aquarium, Thor amboinensis. *das Aquarium* 22 (7): 419-420.

NILSEN, A. J. (1996): Palola siciliensis - Ein schönes Monster im Korallenriff-Aquarium. *das Aquarium* 30 (4): 27-28.

NILSEN, A. J. (1998): Mass Coral Spawning in a Captive Reef Tank. *Aquarium Frontiers Online Magazine* (http://www.aquariumfrontiers.com), Januar 1998 issue.

NILSEN, A. J. (1999): A small experimental Aquarium. *Marine Fish & Reef* 1 (1): 102-120.

NILSEN, A. J. (2000a): Worms in the reef aquarium. *Marine Fish and Reef* 2 (2): 104-120.

NILSEN, A. J. (2000b): From Tropical Graveyard to Biological Wonders. *Aquarium Fish Magazine.* 12 (1): 31-41.

NISHI, E. (1996): Dense aggregation of Chaetopterus longipes Crossland, 1904 (Chaetopteridae, Polychaeta) in coral reefs at Okinawa, Japan. *Nat. Hist. Res.* 4: 41-47.

NISHI, E. & Y. ARAI (1996): Chaetopterid polychaetes from Okinawa Island, Japan, with notes on the feeding behaviour of Spiochaetopterus costarum costarum. *Publ. Seto. Mar. Biol. Lab.* 37 (3/4): 51-56.

NISHI, E. & M. NISHIHIRA (1996): Age-estimation of the Christmas Tree Worm Spirobranchus giganteus (Polychaeta, Serpulidae) Living Buried in the Coral Skeleton from the Coral-growth Band of the Host Coral. *Fisheries Science* 62 (3): 400-403.

OKUNO, J. (1994): Rhynchocinetes concolor, a new species (Caridea: Rhynchocinetidae) from the Indo-West Pacific. *Proc. Jap. Soc. Syst. Zool.* (52): 65-74.

OKUNO, J. & M. TAKEDA (1992): Distinction between Two Hinge-beak Shrimps, Rhynchocinetes durbanensis Gordon and R. uritai Kubo (Family Rhynchocinetidae). *Rev. fr. Aquariol.* 19 (3): 85-90.

PARKE & I. MANTON (1967): The specific identity of the algal symbiont of Convoluta roscoffensis. *J. Mar. Biol. Assn.U.K.* 47: 445-464.

PERKINS, T. H. (1984): Revision of Demonax Kinberg, Hypsicomus Grube, and Notaulax Tauber, with a review of Megalomma Johansson from Florida (Polychaeta: Sabellidae). *Proc. Biol. Soc. Washington* **97**: 285-368.

PERKINS, T. H. (1991): Calcisabella piloseta, a new geneus and species of Sabellinae (Polychaeta; Sabellidae). *Bull. Mar. Sci.* **48** (2): 261-267.

PERKINS, T. H. & P. KNIGHT-JONES (1991): Towards a revision of the genera Sabella and Bispira (Polychaeta: Sabellidae). In M. E. PETERSEN & J. B. KIRKEGAARD (eds.): *Systematics, Biology and Morphology of World Polychaeta. Ophelia Supplement 5*: 698.

PETERSEN, M. E. (1984a): Chaetopterus variopedatus (Renier) (Annelida: Polychaeta: Chaetopteridae): a species complex. What species are being used at MBL? *Biol. Bull. Mar. Biol. Lab. Woods Hole* **167**: 513.

PETERSEN, M. E. (1984b): Chaetopterus variopedatus (Annelida: Polychaeta): another victim of the «characteristic species disease». *Amer. Zool.* **24** (3): 62A.

PETERSEN, M. E. (1991): A review of asexual reproduction in the Cirratulidae (Annelida: Polychaeta), with redescription of Cirratulus gayheadius (Hartman, 1965), new combination, and emendation or reinstatement of some cirratulid genera. *Bull. Mar. Sci.* **48**: 592.

PETERSEN, M. E. (1994): Hermaphroditic cirratulids (Annelida, Polychaeta) from Danish waters, with notes on early development, description of a new species of Aphelochaeta Blake and review of hermaphroditism among the Cirratulidae. In J. C. DAUVIN, L. LAUBIER & D. REISH (eds.): Actes de la 4ème Conférence internationale des Polychètes. *Mem. Mus. Nat. Hist. Nat.* **162** (Zool.): 634.

PETERSEN, M. E. (1997): Contribution to a revision of Chaetopterus cuvier (sic, error for Cuvier) (Polychaeta: Chaetopteridae): Redescription of C. appendiculatus Grube and C. cautus Marenzeller, with comments on some other species. *Bull. Mar. Sci.* **60**: 619-620.

PETERSEN, M. E. (1999): Reproduction and development in Cirratulidae (Annelida: Polychaeta). *Hydrobiologia*.

PETERSEN, M. E. & J. B. KIRKEGAARD (1991): Systematics, Biology and Morphology of World Polychaeta. *Proc. 2nd Intern. Polychaete Conf., Copenhagen 1986. Ophelia Supplement 5.*

PETERSEN, M. E. & T. A. BRITAYEV (1997): A new genus and species of polynoid scaleworm commensal with Chaetopterus appendiculatus Grube from the Banda Sea (Annelida: Polychaeta), with a review of commensals of Chaetopteridae. *Bull. Mar. Sci.* **60**: 261-276.

PETIBONE, M. H. (1982): Annelida. Pp. 1-43 in S. P. Parker (ed.): *Synopsis and Classification of Living Organisms*, Vol. 2. McGraw-Hill Book Co., Inc., New York, St. Louis, etc., USA.

PFUGFELDER, O. VON (1933): Landpolychäten aus Niederländisch-Indien. *Zool. Anz., Leipzig* **105** (3/4): 65-76.

PINTAK, T. (2000): Anmutige Helfer ohne Gnadenbrot? *Der Meerwasser Aquarianer.* **4** (1): 4-8.

PLEIJEL, F. (1991): Phylogeny and classification of the Phyllodocidae (Polychaeta). *Zool. Scr.* **20**: 225-261.

PLEIJEL, F. (1998): Phylogeny and classification of Hesionidae (Polychaeta). *Zool. Scr.* **27**: 89-163.

POTTS, F. A. (1914): Polychaets from the N.E. Pacific: The Chaetopteridae, with an account of the phenomenon of asexual reproduction in Phyllochaetopterus and the description of two new species of Chaetopteridae from the Atlantic. *Proc. Zool. Soc, London, 1914*: 955-994, pls. 1-6.

PRUDHOE, S. (1985): Polyclad Turbellaria. British Museum (Natural History), Oxford University Press, U.K.

RANDALL, J. E. & W. D. HARTMAN (1968): Spongefeeding fishes of the West Indies. *Mar. Biol.* **1**: 216.

RAO, G. C. & A. MISRA (1983): Meiofauna from Lakshadweep, Indian Ocean. *Cah. Biol. Mar.* **24**: 51-68.

RILEY, C. M. (1994): Captive spawning and Raring of the Peppermint Shrimp (Lysmata wurdemanni). *Sea Scope* **11** (4): summer 1994.

REISINGER, E. & S. KELBETZ (1964): Feinbau und Entlandungs-mechanismus der Rhabditen. *Z. Wiss. Mikroskopie und mikr. Technik* **65** (8): 472-508.

RENAUD-MORNANT, J. , P. SERÈNE & C. BOSSY (1971): Macrobetnhos and meiobenthos from the closed lagoon of a Polynesian Atoll, Maturei Vavao (Tuamotu). *Biotropica* **3**: 36-55.

RIEGER, R. M., S. TYLER, J. P. S. SMITH & G. E. RIEGER (1991): Platrylhelminthes: Turbellaria. In F. W. HARRISON & B. J. BOGITSH (eds.): *Microscopic anatomy of invertebrates. Vol. 3: Platyhelminthes and Nemertinea*: 7-140. Wiley-Liss, New York, USA.

ROUSE, G. (1997): Rearticulating with extra assumptions: A response to Eibye-Jacobsen and Nielsen. *Zool. Scr.* **24**: 61-66.

ROUSE, G. & K. FAUCHALD (1995): The articulation of annelids. *Zool. Scr.* **24**: 269-301.

ROUSE, G. & K. FAUCHALD (1997): Cladistics and polychaetes. *Zool. Scr.* **26**: 139-204.

RUETZLER, K. & K. P. SMITH (1992): Guide to Western Atlantic species of Cinachyrella (Porifera: Tetillidae). *Proc. Biol. Soc. Washington* **105** (1): 148-164.

RUFF, R. E. (1995): Family Polynoidae Malmgren, 1867. In J. A. BLAKE, B. HILBIG & P. H. Scott (eds.): The Annelida Part 2. Polychaeta: Phyllodocida (Syllidae and scale-bearing families), Amphinomida, and Eunicida. *Taxonomic Atlas of the Benthic Fauna of the Santa Maria Basin and Western Santa Barbara Channel, Vol. 5*: 105-166. Santa Barbara Museum of Natural History, Santa Barbara, California, USA.

RUIZ-TRILLO, I., M. RIUTORT, D. T. J. LITTLEWOOD, E. A. HERNIOU & J. BAGUNA (1999): Acoel flatworms: earliest extant bilaterian metazoans, not members of Platyhelminthes. *Science* **283**: 1919-1923.

RUPPERT, E. E. & R. D. BARNES (1994): *Invertebrate Zoology*, 6th Edition. Saunders College Publishing, Harcourt Brace Publishers, Philadelphia-New York-London, USA-UK.

RUSSO, R. (1994): *Hawaiian Reefs*. Wavecrest Publications, San Leandro, California, USA.

RUTHMANN, A. & U. TERWELP (1979): Disaggregation and reaggregation of cells of the primitive metazoan Trichoplax adhaerens. *Differentiation* **13**: 815-198.

SALVAT, B. & J. RENAULD-MORNANT (1969): Etude écologique du macrobenthos et du meiobenthos d'un fond sableux du Lagon de Mururuoa (Tuamotu-Polynesi). *Cha Pac* **13**: 159-179.

SAVIGNY, J. C. (1820): System des Annelides, principalement de celles des cotes de l'Egypte et de la Syrie. *Description de l'Egypte, Historie Naturelle. Vol. III, Pt 1*. Paris: Imp. Roy: 1-128.

SCHIEMER, G. (1994): Hermit Crabs in the Reef Aquarium. *Aquarium Frontiers*, summer 1994: 4-5, 10-11.

SCHMIDT, O. (1862): *Die Spongien des Adriatischen Meeres*. Engelmann, Leipzig, Germany.

SCHRAMM, F. R. (1986): *Crustacea*. Oxford University Press, Oxford, UK.

SCHULZE, F. E. (1883): Trichoplax adhaerens, nov. gen., nov. spec. *Zool. Anz.* **132** (6): 92-97.

SCHUHMACHER, H. (1982): *Korallenriffe*. BLV Verlagsgesellschaft, München, Germany.

SCHÖNE, H. (1995): Die Aufzucht von Garnelenlarven in Mikroaquarien. *das Aquarium* **29** (8): 34-38.

SEILACHER, A. (1992): Vendobionta and Psammocorallia: lost constructions of Precambrian evolution. *J. Geol. Soc., London* **149**: 607-613.

SEMB-JOHANSON, A. (ed.) (1988): *Verdens Dyr, Virvelløse Dyr II*. Cappelens Forlag, Norway.

SMITH, D. C. & A. E. DOUGLAS (1987): *The Biology of Symbiosis*. Edward Arnold, London, UK.

SOEST, R. W. M. VAN & J. VERSEVELDT (1987): Unique symbiotic octocoral-sponge association from Komodo. *Indo-Malayan Zoology* **4**: 27-32.

SOLLAS, I. (1902): On the sponges collected during the Skeat expedition in the Malay peninsula (1899-1900). *Proc. Zool. Soc. London* **2**: 210-221.

SOROKIN, Y. I. (1995): *Coral Reef Ecology* (2nd. printing). Springer Verlag, Berlin, Germany.

STANLEY, G. D. & W. STÜRMER (1989): A new fossil ctenophore discovered by X-rays. *Nature* **327**: 61-63.

STODDART, J. (1989): Fatal Attraction. *Landscope* **4** (4): 14-20.

STRATHMANN, R. R, R. A. CAMERON & M. F. STRATHMANN (1984): Spirobranchus giganteus (Pallas) breaks a rule for suspension-feeders. *J. Exp. Mar. Biol. Ecol.* **79**: 245-249.

SUNSBERG, P. & R. GIBSON (1995): The nemerteans (Nemertea) of Rottnest Island, Western Australia. *Zool. Scr.* **24** (2): 101-141.

TESCH, J. J. (1950): The Gymnosomata. II. *Dana Report* **36**: 1-55.

TRENCH, R. K. & H. WINSOR (1987): Symbiosis with Dinoflagellatess in Two Pelagic Flatworms, Amphiscolops sp. and Haplodiscus sp. *Symbiosis* **3**: 1-22.

TRENCH. R. K., D. S. WETHEY & J. W. PORTER (1981): Some observations on the symbiosis with zooxanthellae among Tridacnidae (Mollusca: Bivalvia). *Biol. Bull.* **161**: 180-198.

UCHIDA, H. (1978): Serpulid tube worms (Polychaeta, Sedentaria) from Japan with the systematic review of the group. *Bull. Mar. Park Res. Stak.* **2**: 98 pp., 6 figs., 19 pls.

VINE, P. (1986): *Red Sea Invertebrates*. Immel Publ., London, UK.

VERON, J. E. N. (1995): *Corals in Space and Time. The Biogeography and Evolution in Scleractinia*. Comstock/Cornell, London, U.K.

WALKER, A. & P. SHIPMAN (1996): *The Wisdom of the Bones*. Alfred A. Knopf, N.Y., USA.

WALKER, C. & D. WARD (1992): *Fossils*. Dorling Kindersley Inc., N.Y., USA.

WALLACE, R. A., J. L. KING & G. P. SANDERS (1986): *Biology the Science of Life*. Scott, Forseman and Company, London, U.K.

WALLS, J. G. (1982): *Encyclopedia of Marine Invertebrates*. TFH Publications, Inc., Neptune, N. J., USA.

WARNER, G. F. (1977): *The Biology of Crabs*. Van Nostrand Reinhold Company, New York, USA.

WENDELL, K. P. (1966): Decapod Crustacea Commensal with Queensland Branching Corals. *Crustaceana* **10** (3): 271-295.

WERDING, B. (1983): Der Petrolisthes galathinus-Artenkomplex im karibischen Raum mit Beschreibung von P. caribensis n. sp. und P. columbiensis n. sp. *Senckenbergiana Biol.* **63** (5/6): 407-418.

WERNER, U. (1998): Krabben – Teil 1: Allgemeines zur Anotomie und Biologie sowie Arten für das Süßwasser-Aquarium. *das Aquarium* **32** (10): 24-28.

WESTHEIDE, W. & E. RIEGER (eds.) (1996): *Spezielle Zoologie. Teil 1: Einzeller und Wirbellose Tiere*. Gustav Fischer, Stuttgart-Jena-New York, USA.

WILEY, E. O. (1981): *Phylogenetics - the theory and practics of phylogenetics systematics*. John Wiley & sons Inc., N.Y., USA.

WILEY, E. O. & BROOKS, D. R. (1982): Victims of history - a nonequilibirium approach to evolution. *Syst. Zool.* **31** (1): 1-24.

WILKINSON, C. R. (1983a): Net Primary Production in Coral Reef Sponges. *Science* **219**: 410-412.

WILKINSON, C. R. (1983b): Interocean Differences in size and Nutrition of Coral reef Sponge Populations. *Science* **236**: 1654-1657.

WILKINSON, C. R. (1984): Immunological evidence for precambrian origin of bacterial symbiosis in marine sponges. *Proc. R. Soc. London* **220**: 509.

WILKINSON, C. R. (1987a): Interocean Differences in Size and Nutrition of Coral Reef Sponges Populations. *Science* **236**: 1654-1657.

WILKINSON, C. R. (1987b): Productivity and abundannce of large sponge populations on Flinders Reef flats, Coral Sea. *Coral Reefs* **5** (4): 183-188.

WILKINSON, C. R. & A. C. CHESHIRE (1989): Patterns in the distribution of sponge populations across the central Great Barrier Reef. *Coral Reefs* **8** (3): 127-134.

WILKINSON, C. R. & E. EVANS (1989): Sponge distribution across Davis Reef, Great Barrier Reef, relative to location, depth, and water movement. *Coral Reefs* **8** (1): 1-8.

WILLIAMS, A. B. (1984): *Shrimps, lobsters, and crabs of the Atlantic coast of the eastern United States, Maine to Florida*. Smithsonian Institution Press, Washington D.C., USA

WINSOR, L. (1988): A new acoel (Convolutidae) from the north Queensland coast, Australia. In AX, EHLERS & SOPOTT-EHLERS (eds.): *Progress in Zoology Free-living and Symbiotic Plathelminthes*. Gustav Frischer Verlag, Stuttgart/New York, Germany/USA.

WINSOR, L. (1990): Marine Turbellaria (Acoela) from north Queensland. *Mem. Queensland Mus.* **28** (2): 785-800.

WIRTZ, P. (1996): Putzergarnelen. Lysmata grabhami und Lysmata amboinensis sin Simultanhermaphroditen. *das Aquarium* **30** (6): 27-31.

WOLFRUM, A. (1993): Nachwuchs von der Weißband-Putzergarnele im heimischen Korallenriff-Aquarium. *das Aquarium* **27** (10): 23-25.

WOLFRUM, A. (1996): Langzeitkultur von Artemien. *das Aquarium* **30** (6): 37-39.

ZANN, L. P. (1980): *Living together in the Sea*. TFH Publications Inc. Ltd., Neptune, N. J., USA.

Palinurellus wieneckii, a beautiful animal for small aquaria.

Index

All scientific genera and species names are printed in *italics*. Page numbers printed in **bold** types refer to illustrations and/or major discussions of the topic. The letter 'S' behind a page number indicates that the page in question contains a summary (fact page) on the taxon in question. See page 13 for an explanation of the summary codes.